CU00657592

W. C. Kerr

Report of the Geological Survey of North Carolina

Vol. I

W. C. Kerr

Report of the Geological Survey of North Carolina

Vol. I

Reprint of the original, first published in 1875.

1st Edition 2024 | ISBN: 978-3-38538-498-9

Verlag (Publisher): Outlook Verlag GmbH, Zeilweg 44, 60439 Frankfurt, Deutschland
Vertretungsberechtigt (Authorized to represent): E. Roepke, Zeilweg 44, 60439 Frankfurt, Deutschland
Druck (Print): Books on Demand GmbH, In de Tarpen 42, 22848 Norderstedt, Deutschland

OFFICE STATE GEOLOGIST,
RALEIGH, Oct. 1, 1875.

To his Excellency, CURTIS H. BROGDEN,
Governor of North Carolina:

SIR: I have the honor to submit the following Report of the Geological Survey of North Carolina.

Your obedient servant,
W. C. KERR.
State Geologist.

REPORT

OF THE

GEOLOGICAL SURVEY

OF

NORTH CAROLINA.

VOLUME I.

PHYSICAL GEOGRAPHY, RESUME', ECONOMICAL GEOLOGY.

W. C. KERR.

1875.

BY AUTHORITY OF THE GENERAL ASSEMBLY.

RALEIGH:
JOSIAH TURNER, STATE PRINTER AND BINDER.
1875.

CONTENTS.

CHAPTER I.

CHAPTER II.

CHAPTER III.

CHAPTER IV.

CHAPTER V.

PREFACE.

HISTORICAL SKETCH.

It is noteworthy that the first geological survey by public authority in America was made by the state of North Carolina. The first suggestion of such survey was made by Prof. Olmsted, of the State University, in 1821, in a letter to the Board of Public Improvements. Judge Murphy, however, on the part of the said Board, had observed in their official report for 1819, that in executing the surveys which they were required to have made, in the prosecution of various schemes of internal improvement, they had "attempted to render the surveys subservient to the interests of science by collecting information of the geology and mineralogy of the state," but they had failed.

The suggestion was renewed by Prof. Olmsted a year or two later, with the proposal to spend his vacations in geological excursions, and he asked "merely such an appropriation as would defray the expenses of the undertaking." The result was the passage of an act of Assembly in 1823, authorizing the Board of Agriculture to have such survey made, and appropriating for the purpose the sum of $250 a year for four years. The appropriation was afterwards renewed for two years.

The survey thus ordered was partly executed by Prof. Olmsted, and after his removal to Yale College, was continued by Dr. Mitchell. The published results consist of two reports of Prof. Olmsted, issued in 1824 and 1825, and a third on the Mineralogy of the state by his assistant, C. F. Rothe, of Saxony, and two reports, (1826 and 1827,) by Dr. Mitchell. A geological map of the eastern half of the state was also prepared by the former, but was never published, and has disappeared.

The above geological reports are the first of the kind ever made in this country. They are of course very brief, amounting in all to not more than 250 pages, and from the necessity of the case, they relate exclusively to the middle and eastern regions of the state, chiefly the latter.

Dr. Mitchell continued his explorations during his vacations, on his own private account, and gave a summary of the result in a text book for his classes, published in 1842, with a small geological map of the state, the only one hitherto published.

The work was resumed, under the existing law on the subject, by Dr. E. Emmons, who received the appointment of State Geologist in 1852. He retained the office, nominally at least, until his death in 1863, but the actual work of the survey seems to have closed in 1860, the geologist having been called to other duties by the exigencies of the war. Dr. E. Emmons Jun. was appointed Assistant Geologist. Dr. E. has given the results of his work in five reports. The first, issued in 1852 relates to the agriculture of the eastern counties, and the coal of Chatham and Rockingham; it contains 181 pages. The second report of 351 pages, issued in 1856, is the largest of the series, and relates chiefly to the geology, and particularly to the mines, of the "midland counties." It contains also some additional matter on the coal fields. The report for 1858 (314 pages), contains a general treatise on agriculture, and about one-third of it is devoted to the paleontology of the state. Two short reports appeared in 1860, one a continuation of the subject of agriculture, of 112 pages; the other, (95 pages), a special report on the Swamp Lands belonging to the Literary Board. A report on the "Woody Plants" of the state, prepared by Dr. M. A. Curtis, at the request of Dr. Emmons, was also published; and a "Catalogue" of the plants of the state, by the same author, failing of publication at that time, has been issued since the war. Dr. Emmons also prepared a draught of a geological map, which however was never published: and, at his death, there seems to have remained a considerable additional amount of material, (manuscript and notes, as indicated in some official correspondence), which has never seen the light.

Dr. Curtis also prepared a partial report on the zoology of the state, which the legislature declined to publish; and he left in manuscript an extensive work on the flowerless plants of the state. This eminent botanist has given us not only the results of his own labors and explorations, extending over a large part of a lifetime, and covering almost the whole territory of the state, but has collected, embodied and preserved the results of the scattered and fragmentary work of other, preceding and cotemporary laborers in the same field, both foreign and native; among the latter of whom are worthy of especial mention, Croom of Newbern, Dr. McCree of Wilmington, Dr. Mitchell of Chapel Hill, Dr. C. L. Hunter of Lincoln, and Dr. Schweinitz of Salem. Dr. Curtis also collected an extensive herbarium, containing labelled specimens of all the plants of the state. This collection he hoped to see placed at the University for permanent preservation and reference, as containing the types of all the species then known to exist in the state. One half of it has however already left our borders having been purchased by Dr. Gray for Harvard University; and the other half, the flowering plants, will probably find its way also to some foreign collection. By way of illustrating the appreciation of such collections elsewhere, I quote from a letter of Dr. Gray, seconding an effort which I have several times made to have this herbarium purchased by the state: "For your state it is invaluable, being the exponent and authority, or authentic record of Dr. Curtis' naming of the trees, shrubs, &c., in his Report,—a standard which all who follow in the study, and all who are, or in the future may be interested popularly in your vegetable productions, will need to consult. Wherefore in the interest of the science which I cultivate, I beg you to have that herbarium purchased and preserved as a part of the collections which illustrate your State Survey. It would be injudicious on your part to let it go out of the State, which it very soon will, if not now secured." And Prof. Agassiz writes, "Allow me to add my earnest recommendation to that of Dr. Gray. As Director of a Museum, I have had every day opportunities of testing the great value of original collections representing the intellectual work of careful investigators, and no one has done so much to make known the plants of your state as Dr. Curtis; so much so that his herbarium forms in reality part of the history of the progress of civilization in North Carolina. On that account it should be preserved in your state as a precious monument of the past, and as a basis for future advancement. I trust you may find no difficulties in securing it." It was unfortunate that any part of such a collection, impossible to be replaced as it is, and increasing in interest and value as the plants described disappear with the destruction of our forests and the introduction of exotic species, should have been allowed to leave the state, but the remainder, like the sibylline books, is all the more important to be retained. And as the state will do nothing in the matter, it remains with the friends of Dr. C., and of science, and of the University, and of North Carolina, to take such action as they shall think worthy of themselves and of these high interests.

The work of the survey remained suspended from the date of Dr. Emmons' death until the latter part of the year 1866, when the present incumbent resumed operations under commission of Gov. Worth. Two small annual reports have since been published, one in 1867, the other in 1869. The present report was offered to the Legislature in 1870, but no appropriation was made for its publication; and at last, it is published, under a permissive resolution, out of the working fund of the survey, the public printer being allowed to set it up in the intervals of other work, on the Laws, Documents and Supreme Court Reports, &c., so that it has been on the stocks more than three years; and it bears too many and too obvious evidences of the mode and conditions of its getting up. Materials for a second volume are in hand, and will be put to press during the next year.

A valuable paper on the minerals of the State, was also prepared by Dr. Genth, in 1871, after a full examination of the collections in the museum and a visit to many of the most important mineral localities. Other brief reports have been submitted from time to time, on matters of special and immediate interest, as the pamphlets on the resources of the State, one in English and one in German, prepared for the Vienna Exposition.

PROGRESSIVE THEORETICAL VIEW.

The following scheme exhibits the progress of theoretical notions which have obtained at different times with regard to the classification of the formations,—the age and horizon of the rocks in the State.

MITCHELL. 1842.	EMMONS. 1856.	PRESENT. 1875.
Tertiary.	Ter. { Postpliocene. Pliocene. Miocene. Eocene.*	Quaternary. Miocene. } Ter. Eocene.
Secondary.	{ Cretaceous. Triassic. Permian.	Cretaceous. Triassic.
Transition.	Taconic.	{ Silurian ? Huronian.
Primitive.	{ Gneiss. Granite. Syenite.	Laurentian.

*Also partly Quaternary, and partly Cretaceous.

OBJECTS OF THE SURVEY.

The purpose of the Legislature in establishing a geological survey could not be better expressed than in the message of Gov. Graham, in 1846 :—" I trust no consideration will induce a longer delay in directing an Agricultural, Geological and Mineralogical Survey of the State. Three-fourths of our sister states have now in progress, or have finished like examinations of their territories. And in every instance, it is believed that they have not only added to the treasures of science, but have been attended with important and useful discoveries. Many valuable minerals are already known to exist in various sections of the state; and a further exploration cannot fail to bring to light other resources, and greatly favor the pursuits of Mining and Manufacturing; while a minute examination of our soils by persons uniting science and practical skill in agriculture, will be productive of improvement in that useful branch of industry." The importance of such a survey had been previously often urged by the leading minds of the state; notably, by Judge Murphy, Gov. Dudley and Gov. Morehead, the latter declaring his conviction that "The same amount of money could not be so usefully applied in any other way as in procuring these surveys." Similar views held by the statesmen of the previous generation had led to the former Survey, already described, which has given North Carolina the enviable position of the pioneer in a work which is now urged forward among all the enlightened nations of the world, as the highest and most immediate and indispensible means of industrial progress, and has become an index and measure of civilization. And it is worth a digression to note here, that however backward our state may be in some things, there have always been among us at least a few sagacious statesmen and patriots that kept in the very van of the world's progress, and pointed the way even to the leadership of that progress on our continent; but they lacked support,—they were ahead of their time. Witness, besides the first establishment of a geological survey, the erection at Chapel Hill of the first Astronomical Observatory in America, the foundations of which still remain, and the intelligent and urgent advocacy by Dr. Caldwell (see "Carlton Letters"), and the energetic attempt by Judge Murphy and others towards the execution, of schemes of internal improvement which were equal in conception and superior in practicability, to that of Clinton, which has given to New York the commercial and financial leadership of the continent, or that of Washington (the Chesapeake & Ohio Canal), which would have transferred that leadership to the mouth of the James—, schemes which, had they been carried out, would at least have made North Carolina the "Empire State" of the South.

The objects of the Survey are expressed with some particularity in the authorizing act of 1872. It is as follows:

1. The Governor shall appoint a suitable person to conduct under the supervision of himself and the Literary Board, a Geological, Mineralogical, Botanical and Agricultural Survey of the State.

2. The person appointed shall examine and survey each and every county of the State, and ascertain the different geological formation of each county and section of the state; the nature and character of its soils, and the best mode of improving the same; the nature and kind of its productions and their relative position and values; its facilities for manufactories; the extent and value of its water power; the character and value of its timber, and all other facts connected with its Geology, Mineralogy, Botany and Agriculture, which may tend to a full development of the resources of the state; and such person is authorized to employ as many proper agents and assistants, to be approved by the Governor, as may be necessary to enable him speedily and successively to accomplish the objects committed to his charge; and he shall from time to time communicate to the Governor, to be by him communicated to the Legislature, a report or reports in writing, setting forth fully the results of his Survey; which reports shall be published under the supervision of the Governor and Board of Literature.

3. The expenditures incurred by said Survey shall not exceed five thousand dollars per annum, to be paid by the Public Treasurer, upon the warrant of the Governor, out of any moneys in the Treasury not otherwise appropriated.

4. The person making such survey shall deliver lectures upon the subjects committed to his charge, in the villages through which he may pass: Provided, that he shall not thereby delay his other duties.

The scope of the Survey, it is obvious from the law, is very wide; it plainly includes in its purview whatever relates to the material development and progress of the state.

PROGRESS AND CONDITION OF THE WORK.

As will be seen from the report, much attention has been given to Agriculture. A laboratory was opened and furnished several years ago, and several chemists have been at work, one at least, for a considerable part of the time, and a large number of minerals, marls, soils &c. analyzed. And under an act of Assembly passed two years since, the inspection and analyses of commercial fertilizers was added to the labors of the office; but this work makes no show in the report. As a knowledge of the leading features of climate is essential to intelligent agriculture, and is required by the intelligent immigrant, observatories have been established and furnished, and observations procured at more than two dozen stations, distributed over the entire territory of the state, with a view to the discovery of the controlling elements of the regional and local climates, and some of the results are presented in this volume, both because they are valuable in themselves, (although the observations in many cases cover a period of only two or three years), and because they show the object and utility of such observations as no mere statement could do, and so, may promote the continuance of them at certain stations and their establishment at others, where it has not been possible to find, or to excite, interest enough for that purpose hitherto.

Much labor has also been expended in working out the topography, and in correcting the geography of many sections of the state, both because these are matters connected very directly with the development of our system of internal improvements, and because the existing maps of the state are, in some parts, so grossly inaccurate as to render their reconstruction absolutely necessary to any intelligible location or successful prosecution or presentation of geological work. A large amount of material is in hand, in the form of field notes, of a primary triangulation of the western half of the state, and also of copies, which have been collected from all quarters, of old surveys,—of railroads, turnpikes, canals and rivers, which remain to be worked up for presentation in another volume. The triangulation will be ultimately connected with that of the Coast Survey, and of the river surveys made by the U. S. Engineer Corps, of which copies have been procured by courtesy of Prof. Hilgard and of Gen. Humphreys.

Special attention has been given also to the subject of the state's resources in iron ores and the existing facilities for their reduction, and maps and sections are given of some of the more important ore beds, &c. The subject is by no means exhaustively treated, as there are many ore deposits of which only the locality is known; and doubtless many more which are yet to be discovered.

The department of Mineralogy has been very fully worked up by Dr. Genth, by means of the large amount of material in the State Museum, and his own private collection, which is very rich in North Carolina species, and Dr. G. also visited with me many of the more important mines and mineral localities, from the Cape Fear to the Nolechucky—from Buckhorn to Cranberry. The results of his studies are given in Appendix C. A more popular presentation of the subject by him, in its economical aspects, was published in a separate paper three years ago.

The subject of Lithology has not been reached for special or minute study until the present year, and the results can only be presented at a later date. This is unfortunate, as there are many points of great interest which only such minute and thorough study of the lithological characters, the composition and structure of the rock masses, can satisfactorily determine. This is especially true of the older crystalline formations, which are so extensively developed in this state. The most obscure of all the tracts of these rocks is that which was denominated the *Salisbury* and *Greensboro Granite* by Dr. Emmons; yet, as circumstances have necessitated the giving of an almost exclusively practical direction to the work of the Survey hitherto, except so far as volunteer work is concerned, this interesting series of rocks has passed without even a complete or systematic reconnoissance.

This belt of rocks appeared to be sufficiently distinct in some of its obvious characteristics from both the Huronian and Laurentian, to justify its separation from both (partially); and the general outlines given by Dr. Emmons have been preserved, as they were confirmed by my own observations, made in a number of incidental cross-sections. And in the chapter of Outlines, besides some observations of my predecessors, its salient features are briefly sketched. But Prof. Julien, of Columbia College, is now at work upon the series, and it is hoped that his study of them from the point of view of lithology, will throw important light on their geological relations hitherto set down conjectually.

The Surface Geology of the state has been studied with much care and in considerable detail, but for want of funds for illustration, the discussion of the subject was restricted to the narrowest limits, as it would not be practicable to convey an adequate impression of it without diagrams. It is hoped that this difficulty may be removed in the publication of the next volume.

And, *in general*, this volume may be considered, in part, as a sort of resume' of the whole subject of the geology of the state, as far as worked out, the labors of my predecessors being freely used and embodied with my own; and this course seemed the more needful, as the former reports of the Survey are out of print, and, from the smallness of the editions printed, are little accessible. (And among those who have contributed to the general store of information on the subject of the mineralogy of the state, besides such as have been officially connected with the Survey at various times, there are several gentlemen whose names deserve special mention, particularly Gen. Clingman, who has kindly contributed much valuable information on the discovery and localities of minerals, acknowledged in Dr. Genth's Appendix,—and Dr. C. L. Hunter, of Lincoln county, who has made some interesting discoveries of minerals in his region, and who also kindly placed his information at the service of the Survey).

USES OF THE SURVEY.

The benefits of a geological survey have come to be recognized in all civilized communities. They are two-fold, positive and negative. In this state they are seen in the discovery and development of mineral wealth,—coal, iron, copper, &c., in preventing or diminishing wasteful and ill-advised and ruinous enterprises. Several single mines,—of copper, of iron and of coal, whose development is due to the operations of the Survey have brought into the state an amount of capital many times greater than the whole cost of the work. More than a million dollars, for example, has been invested in four or five such mines within the last three or four years, and only a beginning has been made. And I make no doubt that in the repression and prevention of mistaken adventures, the pecuniary value of the work has been still more important. And many who live in the eastern section of the state will readily understand that the most important function of the Survey is found in the direction of agriculture:—the saving to the farmers of that section in one year in the matter of commercial fertilizers alone is counted by hundreds of thousands; without mentioning the direct benefits, from the analysis of marls, peats, &c., and the extension and direction of their use. And the educational value of the work is greater than can easily be stated; and the influence on immigration and the general influx of business, capital, and the better class of population is far greater and wider and subtler than is commonly imagined.

SURVEYS OF OTHER STATES.

For the information of those who think the work expensive, the following facts are given by way of showing the comparative cost of similar work in some of the other States.

The great surveys of New York, Massachusetts and Pennsylvania, with their magnificent folios of reports, are matters of world-wide note. The latter state has just entered on a new survey with an annual appropriation of $35,000, and has a corps of twenty geologists at work, under the directorship of Dr. J. P. Lesley, one of the ten geologists of the former survey. The state of Ohio expends about $20,000 per annum on her survey, and has eight or ten assistants, under Dr. J. S. Newberry as Chief. And in addition, the cost of publishing the first volume of the report was $82,000, and an appropriation of $60,000 was made to cover the expense of publishing the second volume. The cost of the entire work, in about four and a half years, was $256.000.

The state of Michigan appropriated $20,000 for the publication of a single report, embracing a few counties,—the iron and copper region bordering Lake Superior.

The California survey, under Prof. Whitney, was conducted on a like liberal scale. The following is a copy of the appropriating clause of the law for a portion cf the time:

"The following sums of money are hereby appropriated out of any money in the State Treasury, not otherwise appropriated, for the prosecution of a geological survey of the state, for the sixteenth and seventeenth fiscal years: For salary of State Geologist, nine thousand dollars, to be drawn monthly on the last day of each month; for the salary of two Assistants, $6,600, to be drawn in the same manner as the salary of the State Geologist; for publication of two volumes of reports, six thousand dollars; for office-rent, and expenses of survey in mining district, and experiments on ores, and all incidental expenses of work, ten thousand dollars, to be drawn, one half each fiscal year."

The State of Missouri appropriates $20,000 per annum for work, and $9,000 for publicalion of the report of one year's operations.

Georgia has started with an appropriation of $13,000, and employs a corps of eight geologists, chemists, &c.

Kentucky expends about $20,000 per annum for the work of her survey.

New Jersey, with a territory about one seventh of the size of North Carolina, and with railroad communication to nearly every county, (so that the whole State can be traversed in a few days,) expends $5,000 per annum, and $6,000 for printing a report, of a single volume.

In North Carolina $5,000 covers all expenses,—salaries, Museum rent, field work, laboratory, &c., *and publication*, in large part.

ASSISTANTS.

Prof. T. A. Conrad and Prof. E. D. Cope, whose papers are given in the Appendix, have kindly given their help without remuneration. They have made two visits each to the State, in order to work up the material collected in the Museum, and have also spent some months in the field. Rev. C. J. Curtis and Capt. W. Cain, of Hillsboro', rendered me important aid in the topographical work, giving two seasons each. The last named gentleman has also given much assistance in the office work, as Civil Engineer,—in making maps and sections and reducing the barometrical and astronomical observations. Dr. F. A. Genth has worked up the Mineralogy, furnishing two valuable papers on the subject as above stated, one of them given in the Appendix. Mr. G. B. Hanna has done most of the chemical work of the Survey, analyzing a great number of marls, soils, minerals, mineral waters, &c. He labored more than a year in the laboratory of the Survey, and has since given us the intervals of his work in the Government Assay Office. To his faithful and accurate labors this volume owes much of whatever interest or value it may have. Prof. E. H. Bogardus, of the New Jersey Survey, has also made a considerable number of the soil and marl analyses, which appear in this report. Rev. C. D. Smith has prepared, under the auspices of the Survey, two papers on the geology of some of the western counties. They will be found in the Appendix. Mr. W. D. Cooke, Mr. George Jordan and Mrs. C. P. Spencer have given much valuable help in the office, in the making of maps and diagrams and computations, and in arranging, labelling and cataloguing the cabinets. And in the meteorology I have had the volunteer assistance of more than a score of public spirited citizens, in all parts of the State; through their intelligent and patriotic co-operation I am enabled to present some interesting and valuable facts concerning the climatology of the State. The following persons have given their aid in this direction:

Mr. J. M. Woodhouse, Currituck county.
Mr. R. N. Hines, Edenton.
Dr. Richard Berry, Newbern.
Dr. Charles Duffy, Jr., Newbern.
Mr. James Rumley, Beaufort.
Rev. Daniel Morrell, Wilmington.
Rev. J. M. Sherwood, Fayetteville.
Mr. J. M. Sherwood, Jr., Fayetteville.
Mr. R. H. Austin, Tarboro'.
Mr. T. A. Clark, Weldon.
Mr. W. H. Murdock, Raleigh.
Mr. P. A. Wiley, Raleigh.
Dr. W. R. Hicks, Oxford.
Mrs. C. P. Spencer, Chapel Hill.
Mr. S. A. Howard, Greensboro.
Mr. G. B. Hanna, Charlotte.
Dr. T. A. Allison, Statesville.
Dr. John A. Allison, Statesville.
Dr. R. L. Beall, Lenoir.
Mr. R. S. Gilmer, Mt. Airy.
Dr. W. B. Council, Boone.
Mr. J. S. Hill, Boone.
Mr. J. H. Greene, Bakersville.

Dr. J. T. E. Hardy, Asheville.
Dr. J. G. Hardy, Asheville.
Dr. E. J. Aston, Asheville.
Mrs. D. D. Davies, Jackson Co.
Mrs. Albert Siler, Macon Co.
Prof. Wm. Beal, Murphy.
Mr. J. N. Smith, Scotland Neck.
Dr. Charles Jas. O'Hagan, Greenville.

Several of these have recently commenced their observations, some of them in place of others who have discontinued, and some in new localities. The results of their labors will come into the next volume.

And in addition, I take occasion here to acknowledge the hospitality, the courtesy, the intelligent interest, and the invaluable assistance in various ways, rendered by a large number of public-spirited citizens in every part of the state, while prosecuting the work in their vicinity.

And in fine, as to the short-comings of this report, (and I am but too conscious that they are many and not small), I will simply say that the work of the Survey, in all its stages, to and through the tedious and wearisome process of publication of this volume, has been prosecuted under untoward conditions, discouragements, disheartening obstructions and depreciations which have far more than countervailed the interest and pleasure of the work itself, (great as these are), and have rendered it a burden almost beyond endurance, so that it would have been thrown off long ago, but that I was under the necessity of giving to the public the results of labor already performed, and even of completing certain departments of the work partly executed. Another volume shall contain the remainder of the results of the field notes already in hand and of such additional work as is absolutely necessary to complete those parts of the survey which are too far advanced to be given up without serious loss, and then I have neither patriotism nor devotion to science enough to continue a labor, sufficiently onerous in itself, which, in addition, must be conducted under conditions which seem so incurably malign.

INTRODUCTION.

CHAPTER I.

GEOGRAPHICAL.

Situation.—The State of North Carolina is situated on the Atlantic slope of the Appalachian mountains, in the middle latitude of the United States, half way between Lake Erie, (the boundary of Canada,) and the Gulf of Mexico, being included (nearly) between the parallels 34° and 36½° north latitude, and between the meridians 75½° and 84½° west longitude, and extending from the sea coast to the crest of the Smoky mountains, which is the highest portion of the Appalachian range.

Area, &c.—The extreme length of the State from east to west is 485 miles, and the greatest breadth 188 miles, and its area 50,700 square miles; which is a little more than that of New York, almost exactly that of England, and just one fortieth of that of all the (37) States, (nearly the average size, therefore), and one seventieth of the area of the United States and Territories, and one-thousandth part of the land surface of the globe.

Sub-Divisions.—The State is divided into 93 counties, the average area of a county being between 500 and 600 square miles, or about 23 miles square.

Boundaries.—The State is usually described as bounded on the north by the parallel of 36° 30′ which divides it from Virginia; on the south by a line running north-west from Goat Island, on the coast, (latitude 33° 56′), to the parallel of 35° and then along that parallel to Tennessee; and on the west by the Smoky mountains. These are the limits claimed by the State itself in the Revised Statutes. In fact, the matter is not nearly so simple. It is highly probable that the only portion of the State boundary which is known, or ascertainable with any thing like accuracy, is the eastern or oceanic, and a small part of the western. A few thousand miles of territory, more or less, seems to have been a matter of so small moment to the forefathers of the Commonwealth for the last hundred years, that no care has been taken to secure the location of lines even approximately accordant with the boundaries claimed; or indeed the *location*, in any proper sense, of any boundaries at all, where nature has not taken the trouble to fix them for us beyond a peradventure.

The first and only serious attempt to ascertain the northern boundary was that made in 1728, by Col. Wm. Byrd and others, commissioners on the part of the two colonies, acting under royal authority. From the account given by Byrd of this undertaking, it appears that they started from a point on the coast whose position they determined by observation to be in 36° 31'., north latitude, and ran due west, (correcting for the variation of the compass), to Nottoway river, where they made an offset of a half mile, to the mouth of that stream, again running west. The line was run and marked 242 miles from the coast, to a point in Stokes county, on the upper waters of the Dan river, (on Peter's creek), the North Carolina Commissioners accompanying the party only about two-thirds of the distance. Beyond this point, the line was carried some 90 miles by another joint commission of the two colonies in 1749; this survey terminating at Steep Rock creek, on the east of Stone mountain, and near the present north-west corner of the State, estimated to be 329 miles from the coast. In 1779 the line was taken up again at a point on Steep Rock creek, determined by observation to be on the parallel of 36° 30'., (the marks of the previous survey having disappeared entirely,) and carried west to, and beyond Bristol, Tennessee. This last is known as the Walker line, from one of the commissioners of Virginia.

These lines were run and the latitude observations taken with very imperfect instruments, and the variation of the compass was little understood; so that it was not possible to trace a parallel of latitude. The line besides was only marked on the trees and soon disappeared, and as the settlements were very scattered, the location soon became matter of vague tradition and presently of contention and litigation, so that in 1858, at the instance of Virginia, commissioners were appointed to re-locate the line from the end of the Byrd survey, westward; but for some reason they did not act. In 1870, commissioners were again appointed by Virginia, and similar action asked on the part of this State; and the proposition was renewed in 1871, but ineffectually, as before. In all these numerous attempts to establish the line of division between the two Colonies and States, the intention and the specific instructions have been to ascertain and mark, as the boundary of the two States, *the parallel of* 36° 30'. The maps published towards the end of last century by Jefferson and others give that parallel as the line; and the Bill of Rights of North Carolina claims that "all the territory lying between the line above described, (the line between North and South Carolina), and the southern line of the State of Virginia, which begins on the sea shore in 36° 30' north latitude, and from thence runs west, agreeably to the charter of King Charles, are the right and property of this State."

But it appears from the operations of the United States Coast Survey, at both ends of the line, that the point of beginning on Currituck Inlet, instead being, as so constantly assumed, in latitude 36° 30′ or as determined by the surveyors in 1728, 36° 31′ is 36° 33′ 15″ and the western end, (of "the Walker line" of 1779, at Bristol, Tenn.), 36° 34′ 25.5″. It is stated in Byrd's Journal that the variation of the compass was ascertained to be a little less than 3° W. (The magnetic chart of the United States Coast Survey would make it *E*.) And no account is given of any subsequent correction; and if none was made, at the end of the line surveyed by him, the course would have been in error by nearly 3°, as the amount of the variation in this State changes a little more than 1° for every hundred miles of easting or westing. So that the northern boundary of the State as run, is not only not the parallel of 36° 30′ but is far from coincident with any parallel of latitude, and must be a succession of curves, with their concavities northward, and connected at their ends by north and south offsets.

The southern boundary, between this State and South Carolina and Georgia, was first established by a joint colonial commission in 1735 to 1746. The commissioners run a line from Goat Island on the coast, (in latitude 33° 56′, as supposed), N. W. to the parallel of 35° according to their observations, and then due west to within a few miles of the Catawba river, and here, at the old Salisbury and Charleston road, turned north along that road to the southeast corner of the Catawba Indian Lands. This line, re-surveyed in 1764, was afterwards (in 1772,) continued along the eastern and northern boundaries of the Catawba lands to the point where the latter intersects the Catawba river, thence along and up that river to the mouth of the South Fork of the Catawba, and thence due west, as supposed, to a point near the Blue Ridge. This part of the line was re-surveyed and confirmed by commissioners under acts of Assembly of 1803, 4, 6, 13, 14 and 15, and continued west to and along the Saluda mountains and the Blue Ridge to the intersection of the "Cherokee boundary" of 1797, and thence in a direct line to the Chatooga river at its intersection with the parallel of 35°. From this point the line was run west to the Tennessee line, between this State and Georgia, in 1807, and confirmed and established by act of 1819.

The boundary between this State and Tennessee was run, according to the courses designated in the act of 1789, entitled "An act for the purpose of ceding to the United States certain western lands therein described," (the State of Tennessee), that is, along the crest of the Smoky mountains, from the Virginia line to the Cataluche river (in Haywood county), in 1799, under act of 1796. It was continued from this point to the

Georgia line in 1821. The commissioners who completed this line at the date last mentioned, instead of following their instructions, diverged from the crest of the Smoky (Unaka) mountains at the intersection of the Hiwassee turnpike, and run *due South* to the Georgia line, thereby losing for the State the valuable mining region since known as Ducktown.

And as to the Southern boundary, the point of beginning on Goat Island is in latitude 33° 51′ 37″ as shown by the Coast Survey, and instead of running from Goat Island Northwest to latitude of 35° and thence along that parallel, it appears from the South Carolina geographical State survey of 1821–'25, that the course from the starting point is north 47° 30′ west., and instead of pursuing the parallel of 35, it°, turns west about 10 miles south of that line, and then on approaching the Catawba river, turns northward pursuing a zig-zag line to the forks of the Catawba river, which is about 12 miles north of that parallel; and from this point to the mountains, the boundary line (of 1772) runs, not west, but N. 88° W., bringing its western end about 17 miles too far north, an reaching the (supposed) parallel of 35° at a distance of about 130 miles west of the Catawba river. The loss of territory to the State resulting from these singular deviations is probably between 500 and 1000 square miles. These lines having been marked only on the trees, (except at a few corners, or road crossings, where stones were set up), have been obliterated by time and are for the most part unascertainable, and often give rise to interminable litigation. The time seems to have come when the boundaries of the State should be ascertained with scientific exactness, and marked by some permanent indications.

Population Statistics.—The census reports of the United States show the population to have been, in 1870, 1,071,361. Of this number 678,670 are white, and 392,891 colored. The rate of increase of the population deduced from the data of former census reports, would give about 50,000 more than the above aggregate; this number may, therefore, be taken as the approximate loss of population attributable to the late war. The foreign population numbered, in 1870, only 3,029; about one-third of the number being from Germany, one-third from Great Britain and Ireland, and the remainder from the following counrties, the number contributed by each, varying from more to less in the order in which they are given, viz: British America, Switzerland, France, Sweden, West Indies, Italy, Holland, Austria, Portugal, Russia, Spain, Denmark, Poland, Belgium, Norway, Bohemia, China, Mexico and Hungary. The number of persons to a square mile is, in round numbers, 21. The corresponding number for Massachusetts, the most populous State, is 187;

the average for all the States is 19, and for the United States and Territories 11. The ratio for England was, in 1851, 332, and is now probably about 450; that for the entire globe about 23. The number of families in North Carolina is 205,970; which gives 5.20 persons to a family. The number of dwellings is 202,604; persons to a dwelling, 5.29. The corresponding figures for New York are 898,722-4.88, and 688,559-6.37.

Industries.—More than three-fourths of the population of the State are engaged in agriculture; one-seventh in professional and personal services; one-eighteenth in manufacturing, mining and mechanical operations, and one thirty-fifth in trade and transportation; or, to give the numbers more exactly,

Engaged in all classes of occupations,	351,299
" in agriculture,	269,238
" in professions, &c.,	51,290
" in manufactures, &c.,	20,592
" in trade, &c.,	10,179

Agriculture.—The total number of acres in the State is 32,450,560. Of these 19,835,410 are included in farms; 5,258,742 acres being under cultivation, and 14,576,668 unimproved.

The totol number of farms is 93,565; the average size, 212 acres.

The number of farms under 3 acres, is	293
" " " between 3 and 10 acres, is	6,744
" " " " 10 and 20 " is	14,257
" " " " 20 and 50 " is	35,280
" " " " 50 and 100 " is	22,167
" " " " 100 and 500 " is	13,819
" " " " 500 and 1000 " is	880
" " " over 1000 " is	116

It will be observed that nearly nine-tenths of them contain less than 100 acres.

The principal agricultural products are, in the order of their money value, as follows, viz:

Indian corn,	18,454,215 bushels.
Cotton,	144,935 bales.
Wheat,	2,859,879 bushels.
Oats,	3,220,105 "

Tobacco,		11,150,087	pounds.
Rice,		2,059,280	"
Potatoes (Sweet),		3,071,840	bushels.
Potatoes (Irish),		3,738,803	"
Peas, &c.,		532,799	"
Naval Stores,	(value)	2,338,309	dollars.
Orchard products,	"	394,749	"
Forest products,	"	1,089,115	"
Mining products,	"	638,302	"
Fisheries products,	"	265,839	"

To these add rye, barley, buckwheat, hay, wool, sorghum, maple sugar, honey, wine, cheese, butter, &c.

The total annual value of farm products is $57,849,940. It is apparent that the leading crops are the cereals; next to these in value, are the market crops, cotton and tobacco.

The production of all these crops, except cotton, has largely diminished since the war, that of Indian corn having fallen off nearly 12,000,000 bushels, wheat 2,000,000, tobacco more than 20,000,000 pounds, and rice more than 5,500,000. The production of the sweet potato has also been reduced to one half, and that of peas and beans to one-fourth of the quantities given for 1860.

Manufactures.—Agriculture being the leading occupation, as above stated, manufactures have always occupied a secondary and subordinate place. But the facilities for many branches of manufacture are unsurpassed. Among the advantages may be mentioned first, an unlimited water power; second, an abundance and wide distribution of fuel; third, a wide range and great abundance of raw materials at hand, as cotton, tobacco, lumber of all sorts, iron and other ores, and a great variety of farm products; fourth, abundance and *cheapness of labor;* fifth, facilities for producing everything required by a manufacturing population; and sixth, a favoring climate—no obstructive ice. And as a matter of fact, those few capitalists who have embarked in enterprises of this sort find them very profitable; as for example, the cotton manufacturer, whose profits often exceed 20 per cent.

The following list of manufactures will show that already some attention has been diverted from the production of cotton and tobacco to the more profitable business of converting these and other agricultural products into more valuable forms:

Materials.	*No. of Factories.*	*Annual Products.*
Cotton,	36	$1,345,052
Tobacco,	110	718,765
Turpentine,	147	2,338,309
Lumber,	533	2,107,314
Iron, Wool, Paper, Wood, Leather, &c.,		13,315,636
		$19,559,263

It will be observed, by comparing the products of the different States, that in one article, turpentine, (Naval Stores,) this State produces two-thirds of the total made in the United States.

An examination of the census tables will show the notable fact that almost every crop produced in the United States is found in one region or another of this State, so that the widest diversification of industries is practicable. Corn, cotton and tobacco, however, still occupy too much attention; fruits, grasses, stock and grapes (especially), far too little. Fruits thrive remarkably in all parts of the State, the apple especially in the West, attaining there a degree of perfection not surpassed on the continent. The best grasses (and clover) grow abundantly and almost spontaneously in the mountains, and with moderate culture in all parts of the State. The vine flourishes in every section, and several of the best known American grapes originated here, as the Catawba, Isabella, Lincoln and Scuppernong.

Commerce.—The number of persons engaged in trade of all kinds, as seen from the tables of occupations above, is remarkably small. There are consequently no large cities or controlling centres of trade, the exterior commerce being carried on directly from nearly all sections of the State with Norfolk, Baltimore and New York. The principal seaport, as well as the largest city, is Wilmington, near the mouth of the Cape Fear river. Its population is nearly 20,000, and the amount of its exports which are rapidly increasing, is now about $12,000,000 in value, chiefly in naval stores, lumber and cotton. Newbern, near the mouth of Neuse river, is the next in rank for size and commercial importance; population about 10,000. The non-commercial character and habits of the people are sufficiently illustrated by the fact that the best harbor on the coast, at Beaufort, is scarcely used at all.

CHAPTER II.

PHYSICAL GEOGRAPHY.

TOPOGRAPHICAL.

General Topographical Features.—The topography of North Carolina is anything but monotonous. In fact, there is the greatest variety of topographical features to be found anywhere within an equal area.

Its *land surface* is diversified by *mountains*, *plateaus*, *valleys*, *plains*, *bottoms*, *swamps*, *savannahs*, *islands* and *sand dunes*. Its *water surface* is made up of *springs*, *natural wells*, *ponds*, *lakes*, *creeks*, *rivers*, *bays* and *sounds*.

Mountains.—The great continental system of the Appalachian mountains, which forms the barrier of the Atlantic ocean near the eastern margin of the continent and extends a thousand miles, almost from the mouth of the St. Lawrence to the Gulf of Mexico, reaches its greatest elevations and develops its grandest features in this State. The system is represented here by two great parallel chains,—the Smoky Mountains and the Blue Ridge, with a network of heavy cross chains connecting them, and numerous spurs thrown off to the east and south, some of them as high as the parent chain, and some more than fifty miles long. There are also several other disconnected minor chains to the eastward, having the same general trend as the Appalachians and the sea-coast. These different systems will be best studied in connection with the special features of the several sections of the State to which they belong.

Plateaus.—Between the main chains of the Appalachians and their spurs and cross chains, are many comparatively level benches, or areas of table-land, or plateaus, some of them hundreds of square miles in extent, and 2,000 to 4,000 feet high. These all belong to the western division of the State, and will be described in that connection.

Valleys.—The cross chains and mountain spurs above mentioned are separated by deep valleys, which have been channelled out by the rivers which flow through them. And the great rivers which drain the middle and eastern sections of the State, have likewise carved out for themselves wide valleys, many of which embrace frequent and large tracts of nearly level territory, and extensive stretches of

Bottoms.—These level tracts are found along the margins of the streams of all sizes in all sections of the State, and constitute a very notable feature of its landscape, and also a very important element of its agricultural wealth.

Swamps.—These are mostly confined to the counties near the Atlantic border. They are so extensive and constitute so peculiar a characteristic of that region as to demand special study when we come to the description of that portion of our territory. In this section also are found

Savannahs.—These are simply small prairies. They will be described in connection with the special topography of the region.

Rivers—with their network of tributary *creeks and springs*, "which run among the hills," abound every where, while *natural wells*, ponds, lakes, bays and sounds are limited to the coast region.

Natural Divisions.—In a general view the State may be described as consisting of two parts; one, a rugged, mountainous plateau, of 2,000 to 4,000 feet elevation lying between two heavy chains of the Appalachians, the Smoky Mountains and the Blue Ridge; the second, a long slope extending from the eastern edge of this plateau to the Atlantic. But as this slope subdivides itself naturally into two parts, it is perhaps better to describe the whole as consisting of three co-ordinate divisions, viz: the plateau above mentioned, the middle region, or hill country, and the champaign or coast region; or, by their relative geographical position, *western, middle and eastern.*

The Eastern Division extends from the coast about 100 miles to the lower falls of the rivers, and constitutes nearly two-fifths of the area of the State. This region is for the most part nearly level, or very gently undulating, except along the river courses, on the upper reaches of which rise bluffs and small hills. Its slope seaward is between 1 and 2 feet to the mile, and it is occupied geologically by the (sensibly) horizontal strata of the Post Tertiary and Tertiary formations, which consist of uncompacted sands, clays, marls and gravels in various commixture, and is divided by the southeasterly course of four or five large rivers into as many parallel zones or broad flattish swells, which shed their drainage waters northeast and southeast, by a system of small tributaries, into the larger streams. As may be seen by reference to a map, the water-shed, or crest of these zones lies much nearer to their northeastern margin, dividing them into two very unequal slopes, or drainage areas.

In the beginning of my explorations in this region the question was often asked, by the more observing and intelligent citizens, why the bluffs and high banks are always found on the south side of the rivers, and the swamps and low flats on the north. I did not know, and indeed doubted the fact. But my attention being called to it, the observation was soon ascertained to be valid to a very remarkable extent. Another question was also frequently asked which presented a difficulty not obviously connected with the former, viz: why the marl beds, (Miocene shell beds), are found only *on the south side* of these large rivers. This observation was also very soon verified as to its general application. Pursuing the subject, it was soon noticed that, as a consequence of this topographical structure, the great roads as well as the towns and residences on these streams are located very generally on the same side, as may be seen by a glance at the map of the State. Another curious point may also be noted here. each of these rivers, between the point where it enters the champaign and its mouth, makes a gradual sweep towards the south, (some of them more than one); so that they consist of one or more curves, whose convexity is turned southward, presenting the appearance on the map of a succession of catenaries. A cross section of these interfluvial zones will present about the following appearance:

N.  S.

Ideal section across the Roanoke, Tar, Neuse and Cape Fear Rivers; d, Cretaceous; c, Eocene; b, Miocene; a, Quaternary.

In seeking an explanation of this peculiar topography, the theory of a gradual subsidence towards the south was first considered. The objections to it, however, were obvious and insuperable. Finding the same observation to hold for the corresponding region of South Carolina, I consulted the Geological Report of Prof. Tuomey. He had noted the facts and their persistence through more than one State, but had rested in the theory of an unequal subsidence. The sufficient objection to this explanation is that there is no evidence of such a subsidence, but much evidence that it could not have taken place without producing a very observable difference in the present horizon of the formations affected. And furthermore, the phenomenon is not confined to the superficial strata of the Quaternary or Tertiary formations. If the covering of these were removed, a section of the Cretaceous would present the same appearance. The cause, therefore, whatever it be, has acted over a very large territory, through a very long period. That cause is doubtless the rotation of the earth, co-acting with the force of the river currents. Without stopping to refer to familiar instances of the sensible operation of this cosmical force in modifying the motions of projectiles, it is sufficient to refer to the well-known law of motions, developed by Prof. W. Ferrel in the Mathematical Monthly, vol. i. p. 307, according to which, "In whatever direction a body moves on the surface of the earth, there is a force arising from the earth's rotation, which deflects it to the right, in the northern hemisphere, but to the left, in the southern."

To the obvious objection that the deflective force of the river current is too inconsiderable to produce such effects, the equally obvious answer is, that though the force be small, it has been active for a very long period; and moreover, it may be added, that, since these river valleys were doubtless scooped out mainly, (as is apparent even from the above section), during the Drift, or Ice Period, when the volume and velocity of their currents were immeasurably greater than now, the deflective force of these currents was far from infinitesimal in amount, or insensible in aggregate effect. These river valleys were excavated while the region was elevated more than one, (probably several) hundred feet above its present level, and afterwards silted up during the later ages of the Ice Period, when it was sunk to a depth of more than 400 feet lower than now, and then re-excavated as the continent rose the second time from the sea. At the close of the Tertiary, when the coast was elevated so as to bring this territory above the waters of the Atlantic, the surface was doubtless left comparatively level with a gentle slope seaward; and the rivers, in seeking their channels by the lines of quickest descent, may be supposed to have divided it into belts whose drainage surfaces, north and south, were about equal. But as their course was over the surface of uncompacted sands, clays, &c., these currents, by the incessant impact of their waters upon the right bank, would gradually, but more and more slowly, eat their way southward. Whenever an obstacle was encountered in this southward movement, in the form of resisting clays, compacted earths or projecting rocks, the course of the river above would be thrown into a curve with its convexity to the south.

It is obvious that, under similar conditions, these phenomena must be observable elsewhere, that is, in regions where wide level tracts of unconsolidated earths have been traversed for long periods by strong river currents, especially by the floods of Glacial and sub-Glacial times. And even in regions occupied by the older rocks, the effects of this force of the earth's rotation may manifest itself, for example, in latitudes where the decomposition of the rocks more than keeps pace with the abrasive and transporting power of the meteoric waters. The middle region of North Carolina furnishes an illustration. Observant farmers who have been long accustomed to haul their produce to South Carolina, across the course of the principal streams, have asked me why they had all the worst hills to ascend *going* to market, and only moderate acclivities *returning*. In this region the rocks are concealed by a thick covering of earth, 30 to 50 feet and more, (resulting from their decomposition in situ); so that the conditions being somewhat similar to those existing near the coast, the topography may be supposed to have been affected to some extent by the rotation.

The State of Nebraska presents conditions quite similar to those of eastern North Carolina, its surface being a very gentle slope of probably not more than a few feet to the mile, and its superficial geology being quite similar also, the whole area being occupied by the loess, or Quaternary sands, such as one sees on the upper Missouri every where. And in a recent description of the State in the New York *Tribune*, the fact is mentioned that the *tributaries of its streams are all on the north side.* And the same conditions are said to obtain in the plains of Siberia.

Springs, Natural Wells and Ponds.—The rocks of this State, so far as their structure and stratigraphy affect the drainage and subterraneous circulation of meteroric waters may, for the most part, be briefly described as stratified or foliated slates, schists and gneisses, which are inclined to the horizon generally at high angles, so that the rain waters readily penetrate to great depths and issue at the base of the hills and mountains in numerous and perennial springs.

A different state of things, however, obtains in the eastern section, where the strata belong, as just described, to the newer system of uncompacted and nearly horizontal strata. These accumulations, being generally permeable to water, may give rise to springs wherever they happen to be intersected by valleys or ravines. In the south-eastern section of the State, however, in the region between the lower waters of the Neuse and Cape Fear, these superficial and permeable rocks are underlaid by a harder stratum of limestone, which is sometimes a compact shell rock, as about Newbern and along Trent river; sometimes a coarse, friable chalk, as on North-East river, in Duplin, and upper Trent, in Jones, &c.; and again a hard semi-crystalline limestone, as about Richlands, in Onslow; at Rocky Point, New Hanover; and a few miles above Wilmington, on the North-East river. It is this stratum which controls the subterraneous circulation of the region, being penetrated only at a few points where its substance has been dissolved and carried away by the percolation of carbonated waters, so that the overlying clays or sands have fallen through, giving rise to the phenomena of natural wells, as the noted one near Magnolia, in Duplin, and to the Crane Ponds in Onslow, which are only larger natural wells, and also to frequent sounding subterranean cavities, as in Jones county, into which sometimes cattle disappear by breaking through the thin covering of superficial earth or sand. This peculiar structure also gives rise to bold springs like those in Onslow called the "Alum Springs," which issue from beneath the limestone crust with a force and volume sufficient to turn an ordinary mill wheel. The last named springs constitute the outlet for the system of small lakes above mentioned, (" Crane Ponds)," whose surface is unaffected by drouth or flood.

Lakes.—The only bodies of fresh water in the State which attain to the dignity of lakes are in the eastern section. They are 15 in number. The largest is Mattamuskeet, in Hyde county, which has an area of nearly 100 square miles. Its form is elliptical, and its dimensions 15 miles by 5 to 7. This and three others, Phelps Lake, Alligator L. and Pungo L., are situated in the great swamp between Albemarle and Pamplico sounds. Phelps Lake has about one-third of the area of Mattamuskeet, and the others are of much smaller dimensions. In the White Oak swamp of Jones and Carteret counties is a group of small oval lakes only a few miles apart and connected by canals partly natural and partly artificial. The largest of these, North West Lake, has an area of 10 to 12 miles. In the Green Swamp of Brunswick county, occurs another lake of the same form and character, 8 miles long by 5 wide. These lakes are all situated *in the highest part of the swamps* in which they are found, and have sandy bottoms, for the most part, and a depth of 4 or 5, to 8 or 10 feet, and occasionally more. There are five other small lakes in Bladen county, about half way between Wilmington and Fayetteville, between Cape Fear river and South river. Their average area is probably not more than 2 square miles. The aggregate lake surface of the State is more than 200 square miles.

Sounds and Bays.—Along the entire sea front of North Carolina, nearly 300 miles in length, there is a chain of sounds, for the most part very narrow and shallow, separated from the sea by a succession of long lineer islands called *the banks*, which are disconnected only by occasional narrow inlets.

The largest of these are Pamplico Sound and Albemarle Sound; the former about 75 miles long and 15 to 25 miles wide, having a curvature nearly parallel to the coast, and the latter having an east and west direction, a length of 50 miles, and a breadth of 5 to 15 miles. From the eastern end of the Albemarle the long, narrow arm, called *Currituck Sound*, extends north about 40 miles, to and across the Virginia border. Its breadth varies from 3 to 5 or 7 miles, but is interrupted by frequent islands and shoals. Albemarle and Pamplico are connected by Croatan Sound, about 4 miles wide and 10 miles long, and also by a narrower channel lying nearer the coast (Roanoke Sound), separated from the former by Roanoke Island. The continuity of the line of sounds is kept up to the southward of Pamplico by Bogue Sound, Stump Sound, &c.,

which vary in breadth from less than half a mile to 4 and 5 miles, to within a few miles of the mouth of the Cape Fear River, where occurs, in a narrow isthmus of sand, the only interruption of this inland water-way. Below the wide bay-like mouth of the last named river the chain is continued to and beyond the southern border of the State. The depth of the narrower sounds is frequently very small, only sufficient to float the smallest vessels at low tide, but that of the larger varies from a few feet to three and a half fathoms. From the larger sounds project many bay-like arms, commonly called rivers, because they serve as the mouths of streams; but they are true bays, having a breadth of 2 or 3 to 5 or 6 miles, and a depth about as great as the sounds to which they belong. The greatest of these bays is the widened expanse of Tar river, (Pamplico river), and of the Neuse below Newbern, both of which are 5 and 6 miles and upwards in breadth. But Bay river, Alligator, Pungo, Chowan, and all the larger rivers entering Albemarle from the north are of the same description.

The entire surface covered by these sounds and bays is not less than 3,300 square miles.

The sounds, bays and rivers are connected with the ocean by numerous *inlets*, and with one another and with Norfolk harbor, partly by natural and partly by artificial water ways, (Dismal Swamp Canal and Albemarle and Chesapeake canal and others), constituting, with the navigable stretches of rivers that penetrate inland about 100 miles, a connected net-work of more than 1,100 miles of water way, for steam and sail vessels, furnishing the best facilities for carrying the produce of nearly half the territory of the State, either to Norfolk, or directly into the great Atlantic highway of the world's commerce. And by two or three additional canals of a few miles length much might be added to the value of the above aggregate of navigable water ways, which is already greater than that of New York, with her grand system of expensive canals; and greater than that of any other State, except perhaps, Louisiana.

Islands.—The largest and most noted island in the State is the historical locality called *Roanoke Island*, situated in the straits which connect Albemarle and Pamlico Sounds. Its area is about 25 square miles. Cedar Island in the southern end of Pamlico is about as large, and there are numerous other small islands enclosed within the general boundaries of many of the sounds. *Smith's Island*, in the mouth of Cape Fear, is a wide, flattish, triangular area of about 15 square miles. *Currituck Island* has lost its insular character by the disappearance of Currituck Inlet, and now forms part of a very narrow peninsula about 75 miles long, with its isthmus near Norfolk, Va. *Goat Island* is the most southern point of the State, the N. W. & S. E. boundary line between this State and South Carolina terminating on it at a point marked by a "Cedar Post," whose position is in latitude 33° 51′ 37″, as elsewhere stated.

The chain of long linear sand islands called *The Banks*, which fringe the entire coast, constitutes a very remarkable feature of the region. Though composed of drifting sands, they form an impregnable barrier to the waves of the Atlantic. They are in fact *Sand Dunes* of various elevations, from a few feet above tide level, (in many cases broken over by storm tides), to 25 or 30 feet, and sometimes more, as in the Killdevil Hills along Currituck Sound. The breadth of these islands varies from a few rods to more than 2 miles. The largest of them and the widest, is known as Hatteras Island, the easternmost point of which is the well known Cape Hatteras. These islands are composed partly of flat marshes, and partly of swells and ridges of beach sand, which the wind has heaped in ridges, often far beyound the reach of the highest waves.

As the sand and comminuted shells are rolled back in waves from the beach by the winds, they are, in part, caught and fixed by straggling tufts of a coarse grass which has the power of continuous growth upwards with the rise of the knobs and ridges of sand, and in part, are carried over into the flats and marshes and the shallow sounds beyond which are thus gradually silting up. The banks are generally covered with low scrubby thickets of cedar, live oak, pine, yaupon, myrtle and a number of smaller shrubby growths.*

Swamps, Pocosins and Savannahs.—There is a large aggregate of territory (between 3,000 and 4,000 square miles), mostly in the counties bordering on the sea and the sounds known as Swamp Lands. They are locally designated "dismals" or "pocosins," of which the great Dismal Swamp on the borders of North Carolina and Virginia is a good type. They differ essentially in their characteristic features from an ordinary swamp. They are not alluvial tracts or subject to overflow. On the contrary they occur on the divides or watersheds between the rivers and sounds, and

---

*These islands are inhabited by a hardy race of people, called *Bankers*, who subsist by fishing and whaling, occasionally by wrecking, and by raising for market a small, wiry, tough-sinewed, splay-hoofed variety of horse, called the *bank pony*, or *marsh pony*, which subsists on the coarse salt grasses of the wide marshes which margin the sound. These animals receive no care, save at the annual "penning" frolic, when the banks and marshes are "driven," as in a deer hunt, and the horses collected in hundreds in order to be claimed and branded, or sold.

Whaling is carried on chiefly along the Shackleford Banks, between Cape Lookout and Fort Macon. The whales are taken in April and May, some times 5 or 6 in the course of one or two weeks. They are the common right whales, 40 to 60 feet long; and a single animal frequently yields, in oil and bone, $1200 to $1500. On one occasion, two sperm whales were taken, one of which measured 62 feet in length.

are frequently elevated many feet above the adjacent streams, of which they are the sources. Some of them are in large part mere peat swamps or bogs; being characterised by the occurrence of an accumulation of decayed and decaying vegetation, from 1 or 2 to 10 feet deep and upwards, which, with the growing plants act as a sponge, arresting or retarding the escape of the rain water, whether by evaporation or efflux. The prominent ingredients are peat and fine sand in various proportions, and when of any agricultural value at all, there are also small proportions of clay, iron, lime and alkalies. The vegetation varies with the character of the soil, and serves therefore, as an index of its fertility. The prevalent growth of the best swamp soils is black gum, poplar, cypress, ash and maple. As the soil becomes more peaty, the proportion of cypress increases. Where juniper abounds, peat is in excess and the soil of little value or none. On the best lands there is often besides, a rank growth of canes; but such a growth is also often found on soils too peaty to be of any value. Much of the poorest and most worthless tracts of swamp, which are covered with several feet of half decayed wood and other vegetable matter saturated with water, is occupied by a stunted and scattered growth of bay, swamp pine and other scrubby vegetation; or if the drainage be a little better, with a thickety growth of bays, gallberries and a few other shrubs, with an occasional pine and maple. Most of the large bodies of swamp contain lands belonging to all these descriptions, and enclose besides within their boundaries, knolls, hummocks, belts and ridges, like islands, of firm land, and some of them, large areas of barren sandy soil, covered with a tangle of brambles and tufts of sedge, and in the middle of several of them occur fresh water lakes of considerable extent. Many of the open, gladey portions are covered with cranberries.

The largest continuous area of swamp lies between Albemarle and Pamplico sounds, and is called the *Hyde County Swamp.* It occupies a considerable part of the territory of five counties, and an area of nearly 3,000 square miles.

Large tracts of the better description of these lands, have been drained and subdued, and are among the finest farming lands in the State. The largest body of these lies along the rim of Matamuskeet Lake, which is raised four to six feet above the water in the lake (and sound.) From this marginal ridge the surface gradually descends in every direction, often reaching a level but two or three above tide at the distance of a few miles from the lake. These lands are drained by cutting ditches through the loose black soil down to water level, which is so near the surface that they never suffer from drouth, and the crops are independent of the rain fall. The north-eastern portion of this swamp is low and marshy and some of it subject to overflow by the highest storm-tides. No part of this immense tract is more than 15 feet above sea level. The highest part is the region about Pungo Lake.

Some 35 years ago the State undertook to drain that part of the tract between Pungo Lake, Pungo River and Mattamuskeet Lake, and expended nearly $200,000 in the effort, but without bringing much additional land into cultivation or into market. Most of that part of the swamp is too peaty to be of any value agriculturally.

About the same time a canal was cut by the State connecting Mattamuskeet Lake with Pamplico Sound, with the expectation of exposing an immense area of fertile soil, by reducing the level of the lake to that of the sound. The surface of the lake was lowered about four feet, and a large tract around the margin of the lake exposed, but it was found to be nothing but a white beach of fine sea-sand.

Above 100 square miles of the great *Dismal Swamp* lies within this State. Much of it is a peat bog, and a very large portion is covered with a stunted growth of shrubs and dwarfed trees,—pine, bay, gallberry, myrtle, &c., the soil consisting of a mixture of vegetable matter but little decayed, and fine sand. There are, however, occasional belts and patches of excellent soil, indicated by a heavy growth of gum, and poplar, &c. There are some considerable settlements, and many fine farms have been hewn out of the midst of the Dismal, which are very productive in corn, wheat and stock.

A third considerable body of swamp land, called *Bay River Swamp*, is situated between Pamplico and Neuse rivers, adjacent to Pamplico Sound. Its area is 30 or 40 square miles. It contains large bodies of the best qualities of swamp soil, which, when drained, as are several large tracts on and near Bay River and South Creek, produce large crops of corn, wheat and cotton.

Dover Swamp, in Craven county, between the Neuse and Trent rivers, has an area of about 150 square miles, and an elevation, (at least in its central parts), of more than 60 feet above the sea. Most of it belongs to the inferior grade of swamp lands, and is gladey and infertile. South-west of Pamplico Sound there is a long stretch of swamp extending westward a distance of more than 50 miles, and having a breadth of 5 to 15 miles. It is interrupted, however, by projecting sinuses of firm land at a number of points, so as in fact to sub-divide it into at least two (nearly equal) parts, the eastern, an oval peninsula, of about 150 square miles, called the *Open Ground Prairie;* and the western, under the name of the *White Oak Swamp*. The latter encloses five lakes in its higher and interior portions, from which issue numerous streams, north, east and south.

Both these sub-divisions are fringed in part by an irregular border of fertile, heavily timbered and cane-brake land, while the interior is generally sandy or gladey, and of little value. Considerable tracts, however, even of these less valuable parts, are covered with an indigenous growth of cranberries.

Holly Shelter and Angola Bay, in Onslow, Duplin and New Hanover counties, are swamps of the same general character as the last mentioned, but have a larger proportion of barren soil covered with brambles, gallberries, bay and stunted pines. Their area is about 150 square miles. The drainage is westward, chiefly by way of Holly Shelter Creek which separates them, into North East River. On the margins of these swamps are some fine heavily timbered white oak flats. South of the Cape Fear river is

Green Swamp, mostly in Brunswick county, but partly also in Coumbus; it is nearly circular in form, and has an area of more than 250 square miles. It contains vast quantities of cypress and juniper, which have for many years yielded a large product of shingle and bucket timber for the northern market. The timber tracts are separated by long, flattish ridges or hummocks of firm soil, which are available for roads and habitations, and are found even in the most interior parts of the swamp. The timbered tracts near the margins are often covered with a dense growth of reeds. One of these is crossed for a distance of nearly two miles by the Wilmington & Manchester Railroad. There is a large amount of fine agricultural land in the timbered and canebrake tracts, but very little of it has been reclaimed, although readily drainable, as the elevation above sea level is above 40 feet. This swamp encloses one of the largest lakes in the State, (Waccamaw), already described, through which and the river of the same name issuing from it, about half of the swamp is drained in a southeasterly direction, the remainder sending its waters mostly into the Cape Fear, but partly also eastward into the narrow sound which here belts the coast.

There are several other swamps of small size around this larger one and disconnected from it, as *Beaverdam* on the southwest; *Caw Caw*, south; and *White Marsh*, and *Brown Marsh* northwest, the latter being drained through the southern edge of Green Swamp by way of Waccamaw Lake and Waccamaw River. The area of these two almost contiguous tracts is, together, about 50 square miles.

Big Swamp, in Robeson and Bladen counties, about 20 miles long and 1 to 3 miles wide, is drained by Lumber River. It is, for the most part, covered with reeds and a heavy growth of cypress, ash, maple and gum, and has a black, rich, peaty soil of great depth. There are other less considerable swamps, as Flower's Swamp, lower down on Lumber River, and Horse Swamp on Cape Fear River; and others on South River and its tributaries; Coneto Swamp in the eastern part of Edgecombe; the swamps between Chockowinity Creek and Blount's Creek, Jackson Swamp, Pantego &c., in Beaufort; and Bear Swamp in Chowan, some of them 10 to 20 miles and more in area.

The most productive farms in the State have been reclaimed from the borders of many of these swamps, and they are comparable to the most fertile and inexhaustible soils in the world, constant cultivation for more than 100 years, without manure, having shown no sensible effect on their fertility. The words *pocosin* and *dismal*, so common in the coast region, are local synonyms for swamp.

Savannahs.—The term savannah is used to designate two very different classes of land, the one a gladey, peaty kind of swamp, the other a true *prairie*, a body of level, treeless, grass land. There are many tracts of the latter description in the counties near the coast. Probably the largest one is found in the eastern part of Beaufort county, called the Big Savannah near the mouth of Pungo river. Its extent is about 3,000 acres. Another nearly as large, is the well known Burgaw Savannah, on the railroad, 25 miles above Wilmington. The origin of the Savannahs is doubtless the same as that of the prairies of the West; the chief cause of them (here at least), is the want of drainage; and this is due partly to the level surface on which the water is held by the thick growth of grass, as by a sponge, and partly to a close, pasty, impervious soil.

THE MIDDLE DIVISION, or Hill Country, lying between the mountains on the west and the seaboard plain on the east, is not sharply defined on either hand, but is simply the term of transition from one to the other. It is, in form, a parallelogram, nearly included between the parallels of latitude 35° and 36½°, for a length of 200 miles; and its limiting lines, south-east and north-west, are about 150 miles long. It comprises nearly one half of the territory of the State. It rises, toward the northwest, not less than 4 feet to the mile, attaining an elevation of 1,000 to 1,500 feet at the foot of the Blue Ridge, and having an average elevation of about 650 feet. It is, however, traversed by a number of large rivers which have cut their channels 100 to 300 feet below the intervening ridges or divides, whose slopes are also channelled by the transverse courses of the smaller tributary streams, so that the whole surface is carved by their erosive action into an endless succession of hills and valleys.

On considering this region a little more narrowly, it is seen to separate itself into two regions, which may be described as the *middle region* proper and the *piedmont region*. The former is characterized by a long and broad ridge or swell of land which trends due east along the northern border of the State, preserving for more than 100 miles, an elevation of about 800 feet and upwards. It may in fact be regarded as a spur, or prolongation of the Pilot and Sauratown mountain range, carrying coastward almost the elevation of Surry county, (at the foot of the Blue Ridge), to the very borders of Granville, and making its last bold effort to assert and to emulate its origin in the high knobs and ridges about Roxboro, some of which exceed 1,000 feet in height, as Haga's mountain, &c.

In consequence of this structure the drainage along the northern border is *eastward*, the Dan River keeping this average course from the Blue Ridge, its channel being sometimes in this State and sometimes in Virginia, until it reaches the eastern champaign in Halifax county. A second consequence is, that the direction of the slope or greatest descent of this section is abnormal, the general course of the drainage waters being nearly due south, as is seen in the upper waters of the Tar, Neuse, Haw and Deep rivers, as well as several large tributaries of the Yadkin, all of which take their rise along the crest of this notable ridge. These streams, and also the lower portions of the Yadkin and Catawba, (which take the same course, after leaving the piedmont plateau), are separated by parallel ridges whose crests descend very gradually from the northern divide, several of the more western, preserving an elevation of nearly 600 feet almost to the southern border of the State. Near the middle of this region, in a northeast and southwest direction, that is, parallel to the Blue Ridge and the Atlantic coast, is a succession of elevated ridges and knobs, locally called mountains, which are visible one from another, and extend from the Uwharrie mountains in Montgomery county, to the heights about Roxboro, in Person, already mentioned; its course being marked in the intermediate counties, Randolph, Chatham, Alamance and Orange, by the conspicuous elevations known as the Pilot, Hickory, Cane Creek and Oconeechee mountains, whose heights are about 1,000 feet above sea level. These hard, slaty ridges are doubtless the remains of an ancient continuous mountain chain.

The Piedmont region, a submontane plateau, whose average elevation is about 1000 feet, is divided, as to its river systems, into three regions, drained respectively by the Broad, Catawba and Yadkin rivers; the slope of the first being towards the south, and of the others, a little east of north. These drainage surfaces are separated by two nearly parallel easterly chains of mountains, the South and the Brushy. The former is a spur of the Blue Ridge, and may be regarded as an eastern prologation of the Swannanoa range, in Buncombe. It is the divide between the upper

Catawba and Broad rivers, and attains a height of 3,500 to 4,000 feet in several points along its course of twelve or fifteen miles to the mouth of Crooked Creek, where it rises into a precipitous mural ledge, three or four miles in length and 3,300 feet in height.

From this point eastward for above twenty miles, it is a low straggling ridge, constituting the divide between the waters of the Catawba and Second Broad, scarcely reaching at any point an elevation of two thousand feet. But between the head waters of Silver Creek and First Broad it suddenly rises, in the South Mountains proper, to above 3,000 feet, which elevation it preserves with remarkable uniformity through the numerous peaks, as well along the massive spur, (Deal's Knob, &c.,) which it sends off northeastward between the waters of the Catawba and the South Fork, as throughout the main chain for a distance of fifteen miles to Ben's Knob; beyond which the chain is prolonged three or four miles in a high, narrow, regular ridge of above two thousand feet, called Queen's Mountain.

From this massive portion of the range, especially from the western end of it, several spurs make off southward between the waters of First and Second Broad, the chief of which are the Bickerstaft and Lookadoo Mountains, which are, in several points, nearly as high as the main chain.

The other range, the Brushy, is an independent chain which divides, for the greater part of its course, the waters of the Catawba and Yadkin, from a point a few miles northeast of Lenoir, for more than fifty miles, in a direction a little north of east. This chain also preserves through the greater part of its length a remarkable uniformity, in direction and elevation, many of its peaks rising above 2,000 feet. The sharp and conspicuous cone of the Pilot, and the Sauratown Mountains, which rise to a greater height than any part of the Brushy Mountains proper, are in fact only a continuation of this chain 20 miles beyond the Yadkin, which breaks through it at this point.

Besides these two principal chains, the western side of the plateau is diversified by many spurs of the Blue Ridge of great elevation, being in many cases much higher than the Blue Ridge itself. Among these may be mentioned the Saluda Mountains on the southern border, which constitutes the State line for a distance of more than twenty-five miles; the Tryon and White Oak range in Polk County, a spur of the Saluda separated from it by the Pacolet river, and from the Blue Ridge, (as is also the Saluda for the most part), by the deep and narrow gorge of Green River; the Hungry Mountains, which may be regarded as a continuation of the Tryon range, from which it is divided by the easterly bend of Green River, while it is separated from the Blue Ridge by the deep valley of Hungry River; the huge pyramidal masses about Hickory Nut Gap, as Sugarloaf, Bear Wallow, Pisgah, and the Pinnacle; the high ranges on the north side of the upper Catawba, upon which are the conspicuous summits of Mackey's Mountain and Wood's Knob; and, most notably, the long, regular and massive southerly chains of Linville and Jonas' Ridge. The last are parallel and approximate, in direction due south and separated by the deep and narrow rift of a thousand feet, through which flows the torrent of Linville river; and the former of them is divided from the Blue Ridge by the deep, regular, steep-walled, north and south valley of the North Fork. This region presents some of the wildest and most picturesque scenery to be found east of Rocky Mountains; as the Falls of Linville, (which make a perpendicular plunge of more than 100 feet), and the whole course of that river for upwards of 10 miles, through the deep chasm whose precipitous and often vertical walls rise hundreds of feet and at some points more than 1,000 on either hand; and, along the summit of the eastern ledge of Jonas' Ridge, the jagged peaks of Hawksbill and The Chimneys, and between them, on an isolated knob, the remarkable quadrangular column of Table Rock, whose level top lies nearly 4000 feet above the sea; and some 15 miles away to the north at the head of these spurs, the lofty, ragged summit of the Grandfather, nearly 6,000 feet high. The belt of country east of this, between the Blue Ridge and the Yadkin, having a breadth of fifteen or twenty miles, is corrugated by numerous southerly ridges making out from the Blue Ridge between the tributaries of Catawba and Yadkin, many of them more than 2,000 feet high.

Along the southeastern border of this plateau is another succession of sharp knobs and ridges running in a N. N. E. direction, from the southern edge of the State near Broad River, including the prominent peaks of King's Mountain, Crowder's Mountain, Spencer's Mountain to Anderson's Mountain, in Catawba county.

THE WESTERN DIVISION, or mountain plateau, is bounded eastward by the Blue Ridge, and on the west by the Smoky Mountains, (named locally in the northern portion Iron Mountains, and in the southern Unaka.) The general direction of the axis of the plateau is about E. N. E., its entire length, reckoned from its southwestern termination, in Georgia, to its northern, which is prolonged into Virginia 50 miles, is 275 miles, two-thirds of it, about 5000 square miles, lying within the territory of North Carolina. The following admirable description of this region was published by Prof. Guyot, in the American Journal of Science, in 1861:

"Although the elevation of the Atlantic plain at the eastern base of the mountains is only 100 to 300 feet in Pennsylvania, and 500 in Virginia, near James river, it is 1200 feet in the region of the sources of the Catawba. In the interior of the mountain regions the deepest valleys retain an altitude of from 2000 to 2700 feet. From the dividing line in the neighborhood of Christiansburg and at the great bend of New River the orographic and hydrographic relations undergo a considerable modification. The direction of the principal parts of the system is also somewhat changed. The main chain which borders the great valley on the east, and which more to the north, under the name of the Blue Ridge, separates it from the Atlantic plain, gradually deviates towards the southwest. A new chain detached on the east, and curving a little more to the south, takes now the name of Blue Ridge. It is this lofty chain, the altitude of which, in its more elevated groups, attains gradually to 5000 and 5900 feet, which divides in its turn the waters running to the Atlantic from those of the Mississippi. The line of separation, of the eastern and western waters, which, to this point, follows either the central chain of the Alleghanies, or the table-land region, passes now suddenly to the eastern chain, upon the very border of the Atlantic plain. The reason is that the terrace which forms the base of the chains, and the slope of which usually determines the direction of the water-courses, attains here its greatest elevation, and descends gradually to the northwest. The base of the interior chain, which runs alongside the great valley, is thus depressed to a lower level, and though the chain itself has an absolute elevation greater than that of the Blue Ridge, the rivers which descend from the summit of this last, flow to the northwest towards the great central valley, which they only reach in southern Virginia and North Carolina, by first passing across the high chain of the Unaka and Smoky Mountains through gaps of 3000 to 4000 feet in depth.

The southern division thus presents from southeast to northwest three regions very distinct. The first is the high mountainous region comprised between the Blue Ridge and the great chain of the Iron, Smoky and Unaka mountains, which separates North Carolina from Tennessee. It commences at the bifurcation cf the two chains in Virginia, where it forms, at first, a valley of only ten to fifteen miles in breadth, in the southern part of which flows New river; it then enlarges and extends across North Carolina and into Georgia, in length more than 180 miles, varying in breadth from twenty to fifty miles. The eastern chain, or Blue Ridge, the principal water-shed, is composed of many fragments scarcely connected into a continuous and regular chain. Its direction frequently changes and forms many large curves. Its height is equally irregular. Some groups, elevated some 5000 feet and more, are separated by long intervals of depression, in which are found gaps, whose height is 2200 to 3700 feet, but little above the height of the interior valleys themselves, with which they are connected. The interior, or western chain, is much more coutinuous, more elevated, more regular in its direction and height, and increases very uniformly from 5000 to nearly 6700 feet.

The area comprised between these two main chains, from the sources of the New River and the Watauga, in the vicinity of the Grandfather Mountain, to the southern extremity of the system, is divided by transverse chains into many basins, at the bottom of each one of which runs one of those mountain tributaries of the Tennessee, which, by the abundance of their waters, merit the name of the true sources of that noble river. Between the basin of the Watauga and that of the Nolechucky, rises the lofty chain of the Roan and Big Yellow Mountains. The northwest branch of the Black Mountain and its continuation as far as the Bald Mountain, separate the basin of the Nolechucky from that of the French Broad river. Between the latter and the Big Pigeon river stretches the long chain of the Pisgah and the New Found Mountains. Further to the west the elevated chain of the Great Balsam Mountains separates the basins of the Big Pigeon and the Tuckasegee ; next comes the chain of the Cowee Mountains, between the latter river and the Little Tennessee. Finally the double chain of the Nantehaleh and Valley River Mountains separates the two great basins of the Little Tennessee and the Hiwassee. The bottom of these basins preserves in the middle an altitude of from 2000 to 2700 feet. The height of these transverse chains is greater than that of the Blue Ridge, for they are from 5000 to 6000 feet and upwards ; and the gaps that cross them are as high, and often higher, than those of the Blue Ridge. In these interior basins are also found groups, more or less isolated, like that of the Black Mountain, which, with the Smoky Mountains, presents the most elevated points of the system.

Here then, through an extent of more than one hundred and fifty miles, the mean height of the valley from which the mountains rise is more than 2000 feet ; the mountains which reach 6000 feet are counted by scores, and the loftiest peaks rise to 6700 feet, while at the north, in the group of the White Mountains, the base is scarcely 1000 feet, the gaps 2000 feet, and Mount Washington, the only one which rises above 6000 feet, is still 400 feet below the height of the Black Dome of the Black Mountains. Here then, in all respects, is the culminating region of the vast Appalachian system."

There are several striking features ot this interesting region, which it is worth while to emphasize still further.

1. The general form of the plateau, as to contour, is that of a long, narrow loop, or a much flattened and somewhat distorted ellipse, being widened in the middle by a southward bulge in the region of the French Broad river, and the southern half having twice the breadth of the northern; the average being about 30 miles, the maximum 50, and the minimum not more than 15.

2. The narrowest part of the plateau (about the Grandfather) is also the highest, having an altitude of about 3500 to 4000 feet, while the average for the whole does not exceed 2600.

3. About the rim of this highest and narrowest part of the plateau (the highest table land east of the Mississippi), rise the culminating points of the Appalachian system, the Roan, the Grandfather and the Black, representing the three sub-systems into which it divides itself in this region, viz: the Smoky Mountains, the Blue Ridge and the transverse ranges, the Black being the highest point of the whole Appalachian system, and the Grandfather the highest point of the whole range of the Blue Ridge; the Roan, although one of the highest and hugest masses of the Smoky Mountains, is exceeded in elevation a few hundred feet in a more southern part of that range.

4. From the borders of this portion of the plateau eight considerable rivers take their rise, radiating to all points of the compass, viz: North Toe, Elk, Watauga, New River, Yadkin, John's River, Linville and North Fork, being the head waters of the Tennessee, Ohio, Yadkin and Catawba.

5. In a general view, the two chains,—the Blue Ridge and the Smoky,—are to be regarded as one, constituting with their cross connections, an expanded, as well as much elevated continuation of the Blue Ridge proper, (the eastern range of the Appalacian system), which separates the great Appalachian valleys,—Valley of Virginia and Valley of East Tennessee,—from the Atlantic plain; standing to this mountain system and to the Atlantic ocean as the great plateau of the Rocky Mountains does to that system, and to the Pacific; the whole broad backed swell having been carved and grooved transversely and variously by atmospheric agencies, into an irregular and double connected chain, the real crest of it, the dominant ridge of the whole, (the proper Blue Ridge in this view), being thrown to the western margin, (the Smoky Mountains); the Blue Ridge being only the eastern depressed margin of the first and higher plateau, or upper bench of the Atlantic slope; a view which would be obvious enough, but for the singular and altogether exceptional fact that the drainage of this plateau is thrown to the west, the streams rising along

its eastern and *lower border*, and breaking by deep chasms, through the more elevated and massive western barrier.

6. The Blue Ridge, then, is not so much a regular and well defined mountain chain, as the straggling broken line along which the mountain table land breaks off and drops down (about 1,500 feet) to the level of the second slope, or submontane plateau, already described, presenting the appearance of a huge scarped terrace-like wall.

Along this terrace edge, or near it, generally rises a low ridge or succession of hills and knobs, separated by "gaps" which are sometimes lower even than much of the adjacent plateau. At several points, however, this ridge is removed several miles westward of the actual margin of the plateau, and the waters are thrown off to the east, in such cases, by falls and rapids. The valley of upper Linville is a conspicuous example of this exceptional structure, the real bounding ridge here being Jonas' Ridge and the north end of Linville Mountain, the river breaking through the gap between them at Linville Falls. And another instance, with conditions a little modified, is presented on the eastern border of Henderson county, where the Blue Ridge as seen from the west, almost disappears, as at Reedy Patch Gap and Butt Gap and the whole space between, of 10 or 12 miles. Here the bounding eastward ledge, consisting of the Tryon and Hungry ranges is cut off and broken in twain as in the former case, but the valleys between have been grooved down by the torrents of Green and Hungry rivers, until they are no longer considered, at least for the greater part of their course, as belonging to the higher plateau.

7. Such being the character of the Blue Ridge, naturally enough, its highest summits and most imposing masses are not found generally on the ledge itself, but thrown off to the east or west, on its spurs, and at various and sometimes considerable distances. The Black mountains are a notable example, and Tryon and Sugarloaf and Swannanoa and many others.

The general course of the Blue Ridge across the State from the southwestern corner of Henderson county, near Cæsar's Head, to Fisher's Peak in the northeastern corner of Alleghany county, where it crosses into Virginia, is N. E. a little E., but its path between these points is a very crooked, broken and recurved line. From the head waters of Green River, it makes a quadrant sweep around Henderson county by east to north, holding this latter course by Reedy Patch and Hickory Nut gaps, and for 25 miles to the High Pinnacle, where the spur of the Black meets it and takes up the line. From this point it pursues for 30 miles a nearly direct line about N. N. E. to the upper waters of Linville, where it bends gradually more to the east for ten miles and then makes a sharp curve by east to south, around the head springs of that river to the Grandfather, from which point it reaches the southwest corner of Alleghany county near the Peak mountain by a zigzag lines—east, north, east, and again north; after which its course is nearly east, until it touches the border of Surry county, when it takes a N. E. course, in which direction it leaves the State at Fisher's Peak.

The chain of the Smoky Mountains is broadly contrasted with the Blue Ridge in its greater regularity both in direction and elevation, its greater elevation, and especially in the excessive depth of its gaps, which, from the peculiar structure of the plateau already noticed, become enormous chasms or water gaps of 3000 and 4000 feet depth, through which the drainage of the plateau escapes. These gaps are more than a thousand feet lower than those of the corresponding parts of the Blue Ridge.

Balds.—These are natural meadows which are found on the rounded tops of many of the highest mountains. They are treeless, and are in fact, like the savannahs of the east, simply prairies. The mountains are usually covered with heavy forests, quite to their summits, but a number of the highest knobs, especially in the Smoky chain, and in Mitchell and Yancey counties, have their dome-like tops quite bare of trees. The elevations of these *balds* is generally near or above 6000 feet. Their baldness of course has a different cause from that of savannahs and prairies.

The heavy forest growth of the valleys and lower slopes and benches of the mountains is gradually dwarfed toward the bald summits, so that these are surrounded by a fringe of stunted shrubby oaks, beeches, &c. Doubtless, therefore, the rigor of the climate on these exposed heights has much to do with their botanical features, the vegetation having a very *high latitude* aspect, as the abundance of firs, hemlocks, &c., testify. But this alone will not account for them, since there are many much higher peaks and ranges both in the Smoky and Black which are clothed with dense forests of large trees.

The most extensive and best known of these balds is that of the Roan. There is, in fact, a succession of them, five or six miles. Dr. Mitchell thus describes the Roan with its bald top: "It is the most beautiful of all our high mountains. With the exception of a body of rocks, looking like the ruins of an old castle, near its southwestern extremity, the top of the Roan may be described as a vast meadow, without a tree to obstruct the prospect; where a person may gallop his horse for a mile or two, with Carolina at his feet on one side, and Tennessee on the other, and a green ocean of mountains raised in tremendous billows immediately around him."

The Big Bald, a mountain of 5550 feet elevation, in the northwest corner of Yancey county, gets the name from the character of its conspicuous, bare, dome-like summit, which is covered with natural meadows like the Roan.

Geological structure and origin of mountains.—The simplest and the general and popular conception of the structure and mode of formation of mountains is, that they are the result of a simple upward bending of the strata, which will therefore be found sloping upward on both sides towards the axis of elevation. This is in fact the structure observed in many instances, and no doubt most of the existing mountains are the result of various subsequent modifications of such an original structure; but in most cases it has been entirely obliterated by denudation, that is, by the action of the atmosphere and the frost in disintegrating and breaking down the rocks, and of water in removing the debris. So that all the existing forms of land surface, its topographical features, the mountains, hills and valleys, are the result of a long continued process of atmospheric sculpture. The simple anticlinal structure resulting from the folding and flexure of the strata is not often observed. A very common modification results from a fracture along the crest of such an anticlinal fold, through which the atmospheric forces attack the edges of the softer and more disintegrable strata and scoop out a valley along the ridge; and the process may go on, undermining and removing also the harder and more resisting materials until a wide valley is opened between two monoclinal ledges bounding it on either hand; or, one or both of these may be entirely removed, leaving no signs of the former elevation except the opposite dips of the strata, or only an occasional projecting ridge or knob of refractory rocks; or the deepening and grooving may be continued far below the original valleys, so that *these* become the hills and mountains, with, of course, a synclinal structure, the strata on either side inclining towards each other *downward.* The mountains of this State do not present a well defined example of either the anticlinal or the synclinal structure; they are all *monoclinal; i. e.*, the rocks composing them all have one dip, often very confused, and generally quite steep; they are simply projecting ledges of the hard and difficultly decomposable rocks, left by the erosion of the neighboring softer strata.

The topographical features of the mountain region of the State above briefly sketched, are not accidental. There can be no doubt that here was once a lofty plateau higher than the highest summit of the Black, and comparable in elevation to the present great table land on the western side of the continent, between the Rocky Mountains and the Sierra Nevada. The destructive action of atmospheric agents, chemical and mechanical,—water, frost, oxygen, carbonic acid,—have by their incessant play through the uncounted centuries which make the lifetime of a continent, disintegrated and worn away the vast mass, until it is but a skeleton of what it was, transporting the ruins successively to lower levels, and finally to the sea. Of course in this process the softer rocks, as the shales, limestones and certain micaceous slates, would suffer a greater amount of abrasion than the harder masses, such as the silicious and horn blendic slates, schists and gneisses. Hence the present mountain chains are composed of the latter, while the rivers have scooped out their valleys through the tracts occupied by the former.

There are abundant illustrations of these statements throughout this interesting region. It will be sufficient to cite the great valley of Cherokee, hewn out of the limestone, and following that formation closely, far down into Georgia; the valley of the French Broad through Transylvania and Henderson, which has been excavated in a similar and easily disintegrable rock; and the valleys of Yadkin and Catawba. The rivers east of the Blue Ridge usually take a course at right angles to the direction of that chain, for the obvious reason that that is the line of quickest descent. But these two last named rivers form an exception to the rule, striking off for fifty or sixty miles in a northeasterly course, nearly parallel with the Blue Ridge, taking the tract of the softer rocks and making a grand easterly sweep around the harder strata of the Brushy and South Mountains.

The great geological fact underlying and explaining much that is peculiar in the grand topographical outlines of the State as above sketched, is the existence of a transverse line of movement, or axis of uplift in this part of the Appalachian system. This is sufficiently evident from one observation,—that the dips of the later formations are *north* along the northern border of the State, and *southerly* along the south and southeasterly outcrops of the same beds. And the dips are by no means insignificant, ranging from 15 to 70 degrees. To explain these facts there is required quite as great an upheaval along an east and west axis as is sufficient to account both for the excessive elevation of the continental mountain system in this region and for the great eastward protrusion of the Atlantic coast line.

VALLEYS.—There are no great valleys in this State comparable to the Valley of Virginia, or the Valley of east Tennessee. But each of the numerous rivers has hewn out a narrow valley for itself, in the bottom of which lies its present channel. The most considerable and best defined of these are found in the mountain region just described. The most notable and the largest among them is the *Valley of the French Broad*, which is about 50 miles long and has a varying breadth of 10 to 25 miles, having in Transylvania county a great extent of level and very productive "bottom" land; but for the most part it is traversed by many spurs, ridges and secondary chains of mountains from whose intervening valleys and gorges come the numerous tributaries of the F. R. River.

The other mountain valleys are of the same description, but are generally narrower and basin or trough-like, and have been excavated in the same manner by the rivers which drain the successive areas between the transverse chains already described and are flanked by numerous projecting spurs and ridges of the surrounding mountains, between which a multitude of subordinate tributary valleys ramify. There are in the valleys on all these streams considerable level areas, or "bottoms" of great fertility; as in that on *Valley River* in Cherokee, which is next in extent to that of the French Broad; parts of the *Tennessee Valley* and of the *Tuckasege V.;* of the *Valley of the Pigeon* and of that of *New River* in Watauga and Ashe; and there are many others of less extent, but of exquisite beauty and fertility. Many of these are thickly settled and highly improved.

The Valley of Nantehaleh is a very narrow and deep gorge between two approximate and very high mountain chains; and that of the lower Tennessee is similar, but deeper and more rugged.

Eastward of the Blue Ridge, in the piedmont region, are the *Valleys of the Upper Catawba and Yadkin*, already referred to, which may, in a general way, be considered as consisting of the entire basins or troughs between the parallel chains which enclose them, and so are 15 to 20 miles wide, but the level land along these streams and interjected between the mountain spurs, often quite to the foot of the Blue Ridge, as the fine valley of the North Fork in McDowell, is seldom more than a mile wide and frequently becomes very narrow, or quite disappears. Some of these openings, as *Happy Valley* on the Yadkin, and *Pleasant Gardens* on the Catawba, are among the most picturesque regions to be found in any country.

Of the same general description are the valleys of all the rivers in in their courses through the piedmont and hill country of the State,—the *Broad* and its tributaries, *Green River*, &c.

The Valley of the Dan River, which lies along the northern border of the State, from Stokes county to Person, has a large drainage surface, with undulating and hilly slopes of 5 to 10 and 12 miles, lying partly in this State and partly in Virginia, and presenting a variable breadth of "bottoms," among which are some of the best farming lands in the State. The bed of the river is generally 200 to 300 and occasionally even 400 feet below the adjacent ridges or divides. When this river returns into the State, in Warren county, some 20 miles above Weldon, after a wide detour into Virginia, having changed its name to *Roanoke*, the valley preserves its character, as above described, until it widens out into the broader "bottoms" and cypress swamps of the eastern champaign; but still presenting occasional bluffs, especially on the south side, while its flood plain often spreads out to a breadth of several miles. *The Valleys of the lower Yadkin and Catawba*, with those of their tributaries, chiefly the *South Yadkin and South Fork of Catawba*, (the former of which, about 50 miles broad, resembles that of the Dan in extent as well as in depth of excavation, that of the Catawba being very narrow), traverse the middle region of the State in a direction nearly at right angles to that of the Dan. At some points of their course, as at Mountain Island of the Catawba and the narrows of the Yadkin and through a considerable part of Montgomery and Richmond counties, the hills close in upon the narrow channel of the streams quite obliterating the valley, or reducing it to the smallest dimensions. But at many points, also, they open out into wide and fertile reaches of bottom land, often projecting in broad sinuses between the neighboring hills and presenting areas of sufficient extent for a succession of fine plantations. Similar bottoms, often of considerable extent, are found in the narrow valleys of the *Deep and Haw*, and ot the *Neuse and the Tar rivers*, which also lie in a direction but little E. of south, in their course through the hill country, the two former uniting to form the *Cape Fear*, which pursues the same course to the sea, and the two latter turning more to the east as they reach the seaboard plain, through which these, as that of the Cape Fear, resemble very closely the Roanoke valley spreading out, especially in their lower reaches, in some instances to a breadth of several miles of fertile "bottoms."

It would be tedious to mention all the valleys, even those of considerable extent and importance, as there is no county or corner of the State in which they do not constitute a very important part, and always the best part of the cultivated lands; and their bottoms contribute a very considerable proportion of the annual aggregate of the crops of the State.

RIVERS.—The river system of the State is very unique, being determined by the peculiar topography already described. The rainfall being very copious, numerous and abounding streams, make North Carolina one of the best watered (*or rather, the best drained*) countries in the world.

And since the highest mountains and tablelands of the eastern half of the continent are found here, these rivers, in making the descent to the sea level, develop an immense amount of mechanical power.

It also follows from the same topographical fact of the occurrence here of the culminating masses and peaks of the Appalachian Mountains, that the rivers of the State flow off to all points of the compass. Thus the New River takes a N. E. course to the Ohio; the other rivers of the mountain plateau flow N. W. and W. to the Tennessee (and the Gulf); and the course of those rising in the south and east slopes of the Blue Ridge is south, southeast and east, reaching the Atlantic at numerous points from the coast of Georgia around nearly to Virginia.

The mountain plateau is drained by six large rivers, or rather systems of rivers, and three smaller ones. In the extreme western portion of the State is the

Hiwassee River, with its two large tributaries, *Notteley River* and *Valley River*, draining the two counties Cherokee and Clay,—an area of about 650 square miles. The general course of these waters is west, and the descent from the upper valleys at the foot of the mountains, (about Valleytown, for example), to the State line, is some 8 or 900 feet, and their aggregate length (within the State) some 75 miles. Coming eastward, the next in order is the

Tennessee River and its affiliated streams, *Cheowah*, *Nantehaleh*, *Tuckasege* and *Oconaluftee*. These are all large streams, and, united, form a river, which, by the abundance of its waters, constitutes one of the principal sources of that great continental stream which carries its name for a thousand miles to the Mississippi. Its drainage area is about 1500 miles, including the counties of Graham, Swain, Macon and Jackson. The united length of these rivers is not less than 200 miles. The fall of the Tennessee, from the town of Franklin to the State line, where it cuts through the Smoky Mountains in a stupendous chasm of 4000 feet depth, is over 900 feet. The fall of the Tuckasege, (which is equal in volume of water to the Tennessee itself), from the Forks to its confluence with the Tennessee, is about 1000 feet, and that of Nantehaleh and of Oconaluftee nearly as much.

The third drainage area, that of *Pigeon River*, is about 500 square miles, being limited to Haywood county; and this stream is smaller than the Tennessee in the same proportion as its surface of drainage is less. Its length is 50 to 60 miles, and the fall from the upper valley to the border of the State of Tennessee about 1000 feet.

The French Broad River with its numerous large creeks and four considerable tributary rivers, *Mills River*, *Swannanoa*, *Ivy* and *Laurel*, is nearly as large as the Tennessee, and drains nearly as great a territory, measuring some 1,400 square miles. The fall to the State line below Paint Rock, counting only from the mouth of Little river, is 824 feet, and the aggregate length above 150 miles.

The Nolechucky receives its waters from the high culminating plateau previously described, draining the slopes of the Black, the Roan and Grandfather. Its principal tributaries are *Caney River*, and *North Toe* and *South Toe.* The aggregate length is 100 miles, and the fall from the plateau of the Old Fields of Toe to the State line, more than 1,500 feet; drainage area 600 square miles.

Elk River rises in the neighborhood of the Grandfather, and has a course of only some 12 or 15 miles within the State, draining a single narrow basin of not more than 30 square miles between the Yellow and Beech Mountains, and is a tributary of the

Watauga River, which it enters beyond the boundaries of the State. This drains an area of 100 square miles, lying between the last named range, the Blue Ridge, and the heavy cross chain of the Rich mountains. Its fall from the mouth of Boone Fork, is some 500 feet, and its length inside of the State about 20 miles.

New River differs from all the other streams of the State in that *it flows northward, into the Ohio.* Its drainage surface is quite large, covering the three counties of Watauga, Ashe and Alleghany. Its waters are chiefly contributed by two nearly equal rivers, North Fork and South Fork, which unite near the Virginia line, in the northeastern corner of Ashe, taking thence an east course along the margin of the State, which it re-enters about midway of Alleghany county, where it impinges against the Peach Bottom mountains, the last of the cross chains, and is deflected into a course a little east of north, towards the Kanawha Valley in Virginia. Its aggregate length, within the State, is nearly 100 miles, and its fall 700 feet, at least. This is one of the larger mountain rivers,—of the same order of magnitude with the Hiwassee, French Broad, &c. Drainage surface (in N. C.) 700 square miles.

There is a common feature of these streams that is worthy of special remark, viz: that through a considerable part of their very tortuous course across the plateau from the Blue Ridge to the Smoky, the amount of their fall per mile is frequently quite small, not greater than that of the rivers east of the mountains, the greater part of their descent occurring within the gorges through which they force their way across the Smoky chain, so that many of them present navigable channels of considerable extent. The French Broad, for example, has a fall of less than 3 feet to the mile from Brevard to Asheville.

And again, the dominancy of the western chain of mountains frequently asserts itself in a very striking manner, notwithstanding it is obliged, sooner or later, to give passage to all the streams of the plateau. The French Broad is a striking illustration as well as North Toe and New

River, (South Fork); all these being thrown off by the steeper slopes and more rapid torrents from the western escarpments and hurled against the very crests of the Blue Ridge, along which they wander lingeringly in slow and tortuous course, as if anxiously seeking the shorter passage to the sea; but finally turn, as if in desperation, and plunge with roar and foam against the frowning ramparts which bar their way to the west.

In addition to these rivers which flow west and north, there are several others which take their rise along the eastern and southern margin of the tableland whose course is eastward and southward, as *Linville River* which drops from the high tableland at Linville Falls; and *Green River*, which has cut its way down through a gradually descending narrow valley, or trough, along the edge of the plateau, for 20 miles before it breaks through the eastern barrier of the Tryon range; having a fall to this point, (from the road crossing near Saluda Gap), of not less than 800 feet; and to these may be added *Toxaway River*, whose head streams drain the tableland of the southern end of Jackson and Transylvania counties; and the head streams of the Chatooga, out of Casher's Valley and Horse Cove. Eastward of the Blue Ridge the rivers may be grouped into *four systems*.

The first will comprise the waters which drain the southern slope of the piedmont plateau, and which make their exit in a general course a little east of south, by the channels of *Broad River and South Fork* of *Catawba;* the latter rising in the flanks and spurs of the South Mountains, and the former receiving its waters, in part, from that range, (by way of *Buffalo Creek* and *First Broad* and *Second Broad rivers*, but chiefly from the eastern slope of the Blue Ridge, *Green River* being its largest affluent.) Broad River has, with its tributary rivers, a total length of 110 miles, and drains an area of 1250 square miles, including Polk, Rutherford and Cleaveland counties; and the South Fork, a length of 75 miles, draining portions of Burke, Catawba, Lincoln and Gaston,—some 800 square milas,—its confluence with the Catawba having determined an important corner of the southern boundary of the State. The fall of these waters, from the foot of the mountains to the State line, may be stated generally at about 900 feet, crossing the border at elevations of 600 and 500 feet, by the channels of Green and Catawba rivers.

The second river system is that which drains the northern half of the piedmont, and is represented by the two large streams, *Catawba* and *Yadkin*, whose general course is a few degrees north of east to the point where they leave this plateau, emerging by a sharp curve, in a southerly course at right angles to the former. It is noticeable that both these rivers receive the more part of their waters and all their larger tributaries from the north; those of the Catawba, *North Fork*, *Linville*, *Upper*

Creek, *John's River*, *Lower Creek* and the three "*Little Rivers*"; those of the Yadkin, *Lewis's Fork*, *Reddie's River*, *Mulberry*, *Roaring Creek*, *Big Elkin*, *Mitchell's River*, *Fisher's River and Ararat*, besides a multitude of creeks, large and small, entering on both sides.

These rivers, upper Yadkin and Catawba, are of nearly equal size, and the fall is nearly the same, being, for the Catawba, a little over 500 feet, counting from Old Fort to the great bend, a distance of 75 miles; and for the Yadkin, from Richlands to the bend, 100 miles. Their combined drainage area is more than 2500 square miles.

After entering the midland region of the State, these rivers properly belong to the fourth system and pursue a parallel course, which is a little east of south, but show very marked differences in other respects; the Catawba having an additional length, to the State line, of some 70 miles, a fall of 300 feet, and draining a narrow valley of 10 to 15 miles breadth, —an area of not more than 700 square miles, and receiving no important tributaries from it, while the Yadkin has an additional length of 150 miles, a fall of more than 700 feet, and drains a wide valley of an average breadth of 50 miles and an area of more than 5000 square miles; receiving, besides a number of large creeks, five considerable rivers, two from the west, *South Yadkin* and *Rocky River*, and three from the east, *Little Yadkin*, *Uwharrie* and *Little River*, thus becoming the largest river in the State. The aggregate lengths of these twin streams and their confluents in this State are respectively some 325 and 550 miles.

Both these rivers are navigable for the most part of their course through and even beyond the midland region, except at a few shoals and rapids, most of them easily surmounted by canals, jetties, &c. Such improvements were undertaken about 50 years ago, but never completed There were no serious obstructions on the Catawba, and that river was navigated for some years by flat boats, and the Yadkin also furnished an outlet for the produce of several counties up to the foot of the Blue Ridge. The Narrows, however, constituted an obstruction of a sufficiently formidable character to defeat the enterprise undertaken by the State for the improvement of that river.

The third river system is that of the *Dan* and its tributaries, which, with the *Roanoke*, (its continuation), drains the counties along the northern border of the State from Surry county to Northampton,—almost from the Blue Ridge to the coast; although in the middle part of its course it makes a northern curve into Virginia. It is the *longest river in the State*, its distance, measured along its course from the northern border of Stokes to the mouth, being more than 300 miles. and it is further notable as the only one of all the rivers rising in the Blue Ridge which reaches the Atlantic *within the State.* Its drainage area (in North Carolina) is about 3000 square miles, and aggregate of river lengths, 325 miles; its principal tributaries being *Town Fork*, coming in from the west, in Stokes county; and *Mayo River* and *Smith's River*, which enter on the north side, in Rockingham, and *Hico*, in Person. Its fall from Danbury to the sea is 686 feet. It is navigable the whole distance from the eastern border of Stokes, except at a few shoals and rapids, and these are easily overcome by canals and other simple contrivances of the system of slack water navigation; and in fact, such improvements were once partially effected and the whole length of the river navigated; and steamboats now ascend to the lower falls at Weldon, and flat boats are used on the other navigable stretches to the borders of Stokes county. It discharges its waters by several mouths into Albemarle Sound.

The fourth River system includes the four streams which rise along the southern slope of the easterly ridge, or watershed whose northern declivity is drained by the Dan, viz: Tar River, Neuse River, Haw River, Deep River and Cape Fear, (and the lower portions of the Yadkin and Catawba, as above described).

Tar River rises along the west side of Granville county and among the mountainous swells on the eastern edge of Person, and flows first in a S. S. E. course, and then more easterly, receiving several large tributaries, and drains most of eight counties, an area of nearly 5,000 square miles. The fall, from the junction of North Fork, is more than 400 feet, the last considerable water power occurring near Rocky Mount, on the Wilmington and Weldon Railroad, the seat of Battle's cotton factory. It is navigable to Tarboro', 14 miles east of the Railroad. Its aggregate length is 175 miles.

Neuse River has its head waters among the same highlands, in the south of Person and Orange counties, and pursues the same course as the Tar, to Smithfield, the head of navigation, in Johnston county, and then making a similar easterly turn, reaches Pamplico Sound at Newbern, receiving at this point a large tributary on the south side, in the *Trent River.* Its breadth at Newbern is two miles, and it rapidly widens to five, and at length to seven and eight miles. Its fall from the northwest corner of Wake county, where it takes origin in the union of three streams at one point, (*Flat River, Little River and Eno*), to Newbern, is about 340 feet; aggregate length, (adding that of two other large affluents, *Contentnea* and (another) *Little River*, which enter from the north), about 325 miles, and drainage area very near 5000 square miles.

Haw River and Deep River, the components of the *Cape Fear*, rise in

Rockingham and Guilford counties, and flow S. S. E., the latter making an eastward sweep from the southeast corner of Randolph along the southern border of Chatham, till it meets the former in the southeast corner of the latter county, the united waters pursuing the same average course (in the Cape Fear) to its mouth in the southeast corner of the State, 30 miles below Wilmington. Haw River receives two large tributaries, *Alamance Creek* and *New Hope River.* Its fall from the Piedmont Railroad crossing, in the northest corner of Guilford county, to its confluence with Deep River is 470 feet, affording with its affluents, many excellent water powers, a number of which have been utilized in cotton factories, flouring mills, &c. Deep River, which rises in the western part of Guilford county, has a fall of some 600 feet from the crossing of the North Carolina Railroad, and drives a number of mills and factories, chiefly in Randolph county. Its largest tributary is *Rocky River* in Chatham. The Cape Fear is navigable to Fayetteville, more than 100 miles above Wilmington; and its upper portion was once improved by the State at a cost of nearly $1,000,000, and navigated its whole length, as well as some 30 miles of Deep River, through the coalfields and iron beds. The fall from the confluence at Haywood is 135 feet. The aggregate length of the Cape Fear and tributaries is not less than 500 miles, including *Upper Little River*, *Lower Little River* and *Rockfish Creek* on the west, and two large navigable rivers from the east, viz: *Black River*, entering 12 miles above Wilmington and draining Sampson and portions of Cumberland, Bladen and New Hanover counties, and *Nroth East River*, confluent at Wilmington. The drainage is not less than 8,000 square miles. *New River*, with its branches, is nearly confined to Onslow county, rising in the border of the great swamps of Jones. For 15 miles this is a tidal river, 2 to 3 miles wide.

In the southeastern angle of the State are two other water courses of considerable size: *Lumber River*, which rises in Montgomery county, but derives its waters chiefly from Richmond and Robeson, passing the State line in Columbus, with a fall to this point of some 200 feet, and a drainage of 1,800 miles; and *Waccamaw River*, which rises in the lake of the same name in Green Swamp, and after a southerly course within the State of some 30 miles, and a fall of about one foot to the mile, enters South Carolina, and flowing parallel to the coast for about 50 miles, enters the Atlantic, with the last named stream, by way of the Peedee, at Georgetown. Both these rivers are boatable for considerable distance within the State, the latter quite to the lake.

In the northeastern part of the State are several broad navigable rivers which drain this much watered angle of the State,—an area of some 2,500 square miles, in a southerly direction, into Albemarle Sound. Of these the *Chowan* is the largest,—with the *Meherrin*, about 100 miles long, and navigable beyond the State line; and having a fall from the point where the latter crosses the border of some 40 feet. The other of these rivers, *Perquimans, Little River, Pasquotank* and *North River*, rise in the great tracts of swamps near the State line, and have a scarcely perceptible fall of less than one foot to the mile, terminating in wide bay-like arms of the sound. And the other rivers which drain the alluvial and swampy regions near the sounds are of the same character,—broad and navigable, but withlittle fall, and therefore of no interest in a manufacturing point of view.

On the south side of the Albemarle enter two such streams from the great swamps of Hyde and Tyrrell counties, the *Alligator* and the *Scuppernong*.

Pungo River is a wide stream of like character, which flows from these last swamps southward into Pamplico Sound, entering at the same point with the Tar, (or Pamplico) River, and is not less than three miles wide at its mouth. Midway between Tar and Neuse, is *Bay River*, 1 to 3 miles wide. Between the Neuse and Cape Fear are several other very short and broad tidal streams, as, *White Oak River*, from the swamps of Jones county, and *Newport* and *North River* in Carteret county; and south of the Cape Fear, *Lockwood's Folly* and *Challotte.*

It will be found, by summing the aggregates of the river-lengths of all the river systems of the State, that the total aggregate is about 3300 miles, (just the length of the Missouri from its source to the Gulf), and their total fall about 33,000 feet, or an average of 10 feet to the mile.

If, then, we imagine a river of about the average size of those above described, say the Haw, or the Neuse, with a length and fall equal to the above aggregates, we shall reach a very simple conception of the matter. Or perhaps we may even more readily grasp the totality of these results by taking one of the above described river systems as furnishing, in its length, fall, and drainage area, units of which the grand aggregates for the whole are simple multiples. The Neuse for example, drains an area of 5000 square miles, has a total length (with its tributaries) of about 325 miles, and the aggregate of the falls of the main river *and its principal affluents* is nearly 1100 feet, so that this river system, if the fall were three times as great, would bear the simple ratio of one-tenth to all the total aggregates for the State; that is to say, ten river systems equal to that of the Neuse, but with three times its fall will represent the extent and dynamical effect of the whole river system of the State.

Water Power.—It will be apparent from the foregoing rapid sketch, that the water power of the State is enormous and distributed over its whole territory except the immediate seaboard.

And only the larger class of streams has been included in the foregoing calculation, while hundreds of creeks, many of them large enough to be classed as rivers in other countries,—larger than the Tiber or the Arno—and of sufficient power for an indefinite number of mills and factories, have not even been named. In the piedmont and mountain regions especially, exist a multitude of streams, affluents of the great rivers, which in their descent of hundreds of feet from the upper slopes and table lands develop an aggregate amount of force, probably not much less than that of the main streams.

But it is not impossible to reach some definite conception of the amount of this mechanical power. We may arrive at such a result in several ways. The data already obtained for the aggregates of the river lengths and falls will serve as the basis of a first approximation to an estimate, if we add another which can only be obtained by an actual measurement of the power developed by such an average river as the Haw or the Neuse in a given amount of fall. Such a measurement of Haw River lately made at its confluence with Deep River, gives a force which may be expressed simply as 200 horse powers per foot of fall, after deducting ten per cent. for a slight rise in the river. If the half of this be taken as the average for the whole length of the stream, the additional datum required is 100 horse powers per foot of fall, for a river 3300 miles long and falling 10 feet to the mile. This gives a total mechanical effect of 3,300,000 horse powers.

A second approximation may be reached by starting from an entirely different point of departure. Given the average annual rainfall for the State, the proportion of it which escapes by evaporation and the average elevation of the surface above sea level, the dynamical effect of the descent of the residuum through the known vertical height is readily calculable. The average annual rainfall, as stated elsewhere, is certainly not under 45 inches. If the loss by evaporation is assumed to be 70 per cent., which is rather over than under the fact, the residuum to be accounted for by drainage is 13½ inches.

The average elevation of the surface may be obtained approximately from the following data, viz:

Area	of the State,	50,700	square	miles.		
"	" sounds,	3,300	"	"		
"	" land surface,	47,400	"	"		
"	" coast region,	15,000	"	"	Elevation,	50 feet.

Area	"	subeast'n, reg'n	9,000	"	"	"	200	"
"	"	middle "	12,000	"	"	"	650	"
"	"	piedmont "	6,000	"	"	"	1,000	"
"	"	mountain "	5,400	"	"	"	2,600	"

A simple calculation gives the average elevation of the land surface at 640 feet. This is different from the result obtained by others, from I known not what data, or assumptions. But the result can not be far from the truth.

The amount of water carried off annually by drainage is then 46,000,-000 tons. This will develop, in a descent of 640 feet, a total force of 3,-370,000 horse power.

The capacity of all the steam engines, stationary and locomotive, in England, as given by the Prussian Bureau of Statistics, is 3,300,000 horse powers; that of the United States, 3,800,000.

The artificial production of such an amount of force requires the consumption of more than 4,000,000 tons of coal.

Some notion may be obtained of the relative cost of water and steam power from the fact, mentioned by the State engineer of Maine, W. Wells, that the expenditure for the former, at the water works of the city of Philadelphia is less than one fifteenth of the average cost for the latter, in four cities, in which coal is $5.50 per ton.

The actual instrumental measurement of even the principal rivers of North Carolina will be a work of time and labor; but a few such measurements were made during the past autumn, which are given merely as first approximations, being made, of necessity, very rapidly and with imperfect appliances. The figures given are therefore subject to future revision and correction for errors which, however, can hardly be serious.

The Roanoke, measured at Haskins' Ferry, more than 50 miles above Weldon, and more than one-third of the distance from the latter point to Danville, gives a discharge of 177,000 cubic feet per minute, or 335 horse powers for every foot of fall. The entire manufacturing value of this stream, so far as its course lies within this State, is about 70,000 horse powers.

The discharge per minute of the Yadkin, measured at Brown's Ferry, near the N. C. Railroad bridge, where the breadth is 650 feet, is 155,155 cubic feet, which gives 294 horse powers per foot. The river at this point is not more than half the size which it attains before leaving the State. If therefore 300 horse powers be taken as an average for the fall of 850 feet from Wilkesboro' to the State line, the aggregate of horse powers developed is 255,000. The practical effect of this force may be seen from a statement of the amount of work which it is capable of performing, as for example in driving cotton mill machinery, being sufficient to turn 10,-200,000 spindles, which is four times as many as are found in Massachusetts, and far more than in all the factories in the United States.

The Catawba was measured at Marshall's Ferry, near Hickory, and gives at that point a force represented by 245 horse powers per foot; which, taken as an average for the fall of 750 feet from Pleasant Gardens to the State line, gives a total of 184,000 horse powers, or a capacity of 7,360,000 spindles.

The force of Haw River, and of Deep River, at the confluence, is for the first 200, and for the second, 120 horse powers; and that of the Cape Fear, therefore, 320, or nearly as much as that of the Roanoke; the aggregates are, for the Cape Fear, to Fayetteville, 45,000; for the Haw, from the Piedmont Railroad bridge, with a fall of 470 feet, and an average force one half of that at Haywood, about 50,000; and for the Deep, with the like assumption, 35,000; and for the three, 130,000; or an aggregate force sufficient to turn 5,200,000 spindles.

An approximation may be made to the power of any of the rivers of the State heretofore described, by a simple calculation based upon the relative drainage area and the fall. Such calculation will give for the South Fork of the Catawba, for example, a probable mechanical effect per foot of about 50 horse power in its middle course, and an aggregate of 25 to 30,000.

The sum of the powers above computed is more than 600,000, or nearly one-fifth of the whole theoretical estimate for the State, already given. And this aggregate only includes the main rivers, and would be largely increased even by adding the amounts for the larger affluents. So that it will be apparent that the theoretical estimate is quite within the limits of probability.

But there are several remarkable water powers in the middle and eastern sections of the State, which are worthy of more particular notice. One of the most notable of these is at the lower falls of the Roanoke which terminate at Weldon. The whole force of this magnificent river, developed by a fall of 100 feet in about 10 miles, could easily be rendered available by means of the canal which has its outlet at Weldon. The power of the Merrimac at Lowell is not comparable to this, and it is in the midst of cotton fields, and yet has never turned a spindle. Another fine water power is found on the Catawba at Mountain Island, 12 miles west of Charlotte, the fall being at least 40 feet and having the advantage of a similar canal. It drives only one large cotton factory, while it is a sufficient for a whole city of them.

On the South Fork of the Catawba in Gaston county, is a third noted power at High Shoals. The fall is some 30 feet, and although it has been utilized to the extent of driving the machinery of extensive rolling mills and some half dozen forges and puddling furnaces, not a tithe of the force is turned to account.

And there are many other important powers on the same stream, which is a succession of rapids for many miles as it breaks through the ledge of Spencers's Mountain, of the King's Mountain range.

A fourth valuable water power, as yet only utilized to a very small extent, is that at Lockville, in Chatham county, on Deep River. The fall here is 36 feet. And along this river, and the Cape Fear, are nineteen dams built by the State for the improvement of the navigation; and most of these are still standing at least in part, and about half of them have been recently put in repair by private enterprise, in developing the iron and coal interests of the region. Here there is a force of over 50,000 horse powers, (or 2,000,000 spindles), already rendered available, and yet wholly unused, although it is within the cotton region. There are about a dozen factories on this entire system of rivers, some 10 or 12,000 spindles, requiring some 300 or 400 horse powers, that is, about a four hundredth part of the whole.

But the most remarkable water power in the State is yet to be mentioned, and is one which has never been turned to the smallest account,—that at the the Narrows of the Yadkin, in Montgomery county.

At this point the whole immense volume of the waters of this, the largest river in the State, is suddenly compressed into a narrow, rocky gorge of the Uwharrie Mountains, a broad, navigable expanse of more than half a mile contracted into a defile of about 30 feet breadth,—through which the torrent dashes with an impetuosity to which the "arrowy" sweep of the Rhine, in its most rapid mood, is but sluggishness itself. The total descent of the Narrows and the Rapids, in a distance of some two miles, is not less than 50 or 60 feet; at the termination of which, at the confluence of the Uwharrie, the river attains a width of more than one mile.

This locality is about 30 miles from the nearest railroad. Those previously named are either on, or very near to some line of rail, and all are within, or on the margin of the cotton-growing zone, and in a region of abundant and various agricultural products, and except the first mentioned, are among the hills of the middle section, which is noted for its salubrity of climate.

Elevations, Profiles, &c.—A large mass of materials has been collected with a view to the construction of an approximative topographical map of the State, but it is still insufficient for that purpose. As many of the data, however, have an interest by themselves, a portion of them are given here. They are derived from various sources, besides the observations made in connection with the Geological Survey. A large part of the mountain region of the State has been triangulated, (partly by Prof. Guyot, and partly by the Survey), in a sort of secondary system, so as to locate, at least approximately, the prominent points and features with respect to each other, but as observations of that sort will be cf little general interest, apart from their mapped results, that portion of the work is reserved for a future volume.

Elevations—The altitudes given below are derived in part from railroad levels, and in part from barometrical measurements, (both mercurial and aneroid), from railroad benches, and partly from the latter with the aid of the barometer and pocket level. These several sources will be indicated by the following abbreviations: Railroad levels, R. R.; barometrical measurements, B.; aneroid, A.; barometer and pocket level, P. L. A large number of the barometrical altitudes in the mountain region I owe to the courtesy of Prof. Guyot, of Princeton, who has kindly communicated to me many of his results in advance of their publication elsewhere, with the reservation that a few of them may possibly require correction, to the extent of a few feet, upon a revision of the computations. And many of the measurements of the Survey marked P. L. are very rough approximations.

It is not easy to classify these data. The grouping by orographic relations, adopted by Prof. Guyot, is perhaps the most simple and intelligible, and will therefore be followed as far as practicable.

ALTITUDES IN THE SMOKY MOUNTAINS.

1. *The part of the chain beyond the State line in Tennessee and Georgia, south of the Hiwassee River, called the Frog Mountains.*

B.	........Big Frog, (Ga.),	4,220	Guyot.
B.	........Cowpen, (Ga.),	4,146	
B.	........Flat Top, (Ga.),	3,735	
B.	........Flat Top, (Ga.), (east end,	3,576	
B.	........Polecat Knob, (Ga.),	3,537	
B.	........W. N. Goss' house, (Ga.),	1,987	
B.	........Little Frog Mountain, Tenn.,	3,349	
P. L.	........Panther Knob, Tenn.,	2,960	
B.	........Ducktown, Tenn.,	1,780	Guyot.

2. *Between Hiwassee and Tennessee Rivers.*

P. L.	........Long Ridge, north knob,	3,373	
P. L.	........Long Ridge, south knob,	3,273	

P. L.	Sassafras Knob,	3,737	
P. L.	Unakoi, southwest peak,	3,637	
P. L.	Big Sassafras,	4,000	
B.	Big Beaverdam,	4,266	Guyot.
B.	Little Beaverdan Bald,	4,005	
P. L.	Wolf Pen Peaks of B. Bald.	3,112	
B.	McDaniel Bald,	4,653	
B.	Peak one half mile w. of last,	4,632	
B.	Hooper's Meadow,	4.632	
B.	Gap N. of McD. Bald,	4,287	
B.	Middle Ridge	4,671	
P. L.	Rattlesnake Knob,	4,364	
B.	Laurel Top,	5,365	
B.	Knob S. of last,	4,931	
B.	Knob N. E. of last,	5,366	
P. L.	Rough Ridge,	4,522	
P. L.	Sharp Knob,	4,991	
B.	State Ridge, first peak,	5,236	
P. L.	Hooper's Cabin,	5,127	
B.	Haw Knob,	5,480	
B.	Race Track, E. end,	5,480	
B.	Race Track, middle,	5,481	
B.	Little Snowbird,	4,355	
P. L.	Rocky Knob,	4,178	
P. L.	Slide Off,	4,067	
B.	Hangover,	5,600	Guyot.
R. R.	Tennessee River, State line,	1,114	

3. *Between Tennessee River and Big Pigeon*

B.	Bald Spot,	4,622	Guyot.
B.	Great Bald's Central Peak,	4,922	"
B.	Great Bald's South Peak,	4,708	"
B.	North Bald,	4,711	"
B.	Opossum Gap,	3,840	"
B.	Turky Knob,	4,740	"
B.	Spence Cabin,	4,910	"
B.	Eagle Top,	5,433	"
B.	Thunderhead Mountain,	5,520	"
B.	Snaky Mountain,	5,196	"
B.	Forney Ridge Peak,	5,087	"
B.	Corner Knob,	5,246	"
B.	Big Cherry Gap,	4,838	"
B.	Big St ne Mountain,	5,614	"
B.	Chimzy Knob,	5,588	"
B.	Mt. Buckley,	6,599	"
B.	Clingman's Dome,	6,660	"
B.	Mt. Love,	6,443	"
B.	Collins' Gap,	5,720	"
B.	Mt. Collins,	6,188	"
B	Road Gap,	5,271	"

4. *Group of Bullhead, Tennessee.*

B.	Alum Cave,	4,971	Guyot.
B.	Tomahawk Gap,	5,450	"

B.	Master Knob,	6,013	"
B.	Neighbor,	5,771	"
B.	Cross Knob,	5,931	"
B.	North Peak, (Mt. Safford)	6,535	"
B.	West Peak, (Mt. Curtis,)	6,568	"
B.	Central Peak, (Mt. LeConte,)	6,612	"
B.	Mt. Mingus,	5,696	"
B.	Right Hand, or New Gap,	5,094	"
B.	Mt. Ocona,	6,135	"
B.	Peck's Peak,	6,232	"
B.	Indian Gap,	5,317	"
B.	Top of Richland Ridge,	5,492	"
B.	Rheinhardt Gap,	5,220	"
B.	Laurel Peak,	5,922	"
B.	Thunder Knob,	5,682	"
B.	Three Brothers, central Peak,	5,907	"
B.	Mt. Alexander,	6,447	"
B.	Mt. Alexander, south peak,	6,299	"
B.	Mt. Henry,	6,373	"
B.	Mt. Guyot,	6,636	"
B.	Tricorner Knob,	6,188	"
B.	Raven's Knob,	6,230	"
B.	Thermometer Knob,	6,157	"
B.	Luftee Knob,	6,238	"
B.	Big Creek Knob,	5,990	"
B.	Starling Mountain,	5,952	"
B.	Big Cataluche,	6,159	"
B.	Hannah Gap,	3,524	"
B.	Big Pigeon River, near mouth of Fines Creek,	2,241	"

5. *Between Pigeon River and French Broad.*

B.	Bear Wallow Mountain,	4,658	Guyot.
B.	Bear Wallow Mountain Gap,	4,116	"
B.	Heab's Mountain,	4,468	"
B.	Sandy Mush Bald,	5,164	"
B.	Crabtree Bald,	5,336	"
B.	Max Patch Mountain,	4,700	"
B.	Max Patch Gap,	4,392	"
B.	Walnut Mountain,	4,335	"
B.	High Bluff,	4,703	"
B.	Indian Grave Gap,	4,288	"
B.	French Broad, State Line,	1,264	"
R. R.	Warm Springs,	1,326	"

6. *Between French Broad and Nolechucky.*

B.	J. Chandlers', on Shelton Laurel River,	2,031	
B.	Little Bald, Madison county,	4,876	
P. L.	Sugar Loaf, High Peak,	4,522	
B.	Big Butt,	4,877	
B.	Rich Monntain,	3,691	
B.	Bald Mountain,	5,552	
P. L.	Little Bald, Yancey county,	5,176	
B.	Egypt Cove, Proffit's House,	3,320	Guyot.
B.	Haw Knob,	4,924	

P. L.	Sampson Mountain,	4,774	
B.	Sampson Gap,	4,130	Guyot.
P. L.	Fire Scald,	4,774	
B.	Wolf's Camp Gap,	4,359	Guyot.
P. L.	Flat Rock Mountain,	4,924	
P. L.	Elk Wallow,	4,824	
B.	Toe River ford, near mouth of Jack's Creek	2,131	Guyot.

7. *Between Nolechucky and Watauga River.*

B.	Bakersville, (about)	2,550	
B.	Roan, High Knob,	6,306	Guyot.
B.	Roan, High Bluff,	6,296	"
B.	Grassy Ridge Bald,	6,230	"
B.	Cold Spring,	6,132	"
P. L.	Little Yellow Mountain,	5,195	"
P. L.	Humpback, (of Yellow Mountain,)	5,541	
P. L.	Avery's Yellow Mountain,	5,440	
R. R.	Cranberry Creek, at Cranberry,	3,051	Gardner
P. L.	Ragged Knob of Yellow Mountain,	5,240	
R. R.	Gap of Iron Mountains, near Cranberry,	2,784	"
B.	Elk River, at Lewis Banner's,	3,696	
B.	Beech Mountain	5,541	
R. R.	Beech Mountain Creek, mouth,	2,448	
R. R.	Watauga River, State line,	2,131	

8. *Between Watauga River and Head Waters of New River.*

B.	Jehiel Smith's house, Cove Creek,	3,035	
B.	Rich Mountain Bald, Watauga county,	4,681	
P. L.	Grassy Knob, of Rich Mountain,	4,480	
P. L.	Salt Rock Ridge, Rich Mountain,	4,631	
B.	Big Bald, Rich Mountain,	4,359	
B.	State Gap, (between B. B. and Snake Mountain,)	4,409	
B.	Elk Knob,	5,574	
P. L.	Snake Mountain,	5,594	
B.	White Top, Virginia,	5,530	Guyot.
B.	Miller's house, head of Meat Camp Creek,	2,824	
B.	John Green's, Meat Camp Creek,	3,180	
B.	Howard Gap, Rich Mountain,	3,679	
R. R.	Hodge's Gap,	3,330	
B.	H. W. Hardin's, floor,	3,169	
P. L.	Sugarloaf,	4,606	
P. L.	Harmon's Knob,	4,881	
P. L.	Pine Orchard Mountain, near Elk Knob,	4,800	
P. L.	Riddle's Knob, near Elk Knob,	4,800	
B.	Mouth of Elk Creek, (New River,)	2,898	
B.	Jas. Dobbin's, on Elk Creek,	3,057	
B.	Black Mountain,	4,622	
B.	Gap at head of Three Top Creek,	3,444	
P. L.	Paddy's Mountain, Ashe county,	4,300	
P. L.	Phoenix Mountain,	4,673	
P. L.	The Bluff,	5,060	
P. L.	The Bluff, south end,	4,620	
P. L.	The Bluff, ridge east,	4,500	

P. L.	........Rocky Knob,..................................	4,400....................
B.	........Three Top Mountain, middle knob,............	4,910....................
P. L.	........Three Top, east knob,.........................	4,950....................
P. L.	........Big Knob,....................................	4,770....................
P. L.	........Old Field Bald,...............................	4,850....................
B.	........Elijah Grier's,...............................	3,185....................
B.	........Falls of Longhope Creek, foot,................	3,675....................
B.	........Falls of Longhope Creek, top,.................	3,901....................
P. L.	........The Peak,....................................	5,100....................
B.	........Mouth of Three Top Creek, Worth's,..........	3,965....................
P. L.	........Mulatto Mountain,............................	4,680....................
B.	........Negro Mountain,..............................	4,678....................
B.	........Jefferson, C. H.,............................	2,940....................
B.	........Mouth of Cranberry Creek, New River,........	2,547....................

ALTITUDES ALONG THE BLUE RIDGE.

In Surry and Alleghany Counties.

B.	........Fisher's Peak, State line,......................	3,570....................
B.	........Cedar Ridge,..................................	3,210....................
B.	........Buzzard Knob,................................	2,790....................
B.	........Jack Lowe's house,...........................	1,472....................
B.	........Mill Creek, 2 miles from mouth,..............	1,380....................
B.	........C. C. McMichels, ground,......................	1,212....................
B.	........Rocky Ford of Mitchell's River,...............	1,130....................
B.	........Gideon Bryants, (river,)......................	1,277....................
B.	........Thompson's Gap,.............................	2,881....................
B.	........Saddle Mountain,.............................	3,376....................
B.	........A. M. Bryant's,................................	2,823....................
B.	........Bull Head Mountain,..........................	3,787....................
B.	........Bull Head Mountain, south peak,.............	3,883....................
P. L.	........Little Mountain,..............................	3,050....................
B.	........Roaring Gap,.................................	2,914....................
B.	........Cheek's Knob, Peach Bottom Mountain,.......	3,930....................
B.	........Edward's Gap, Peach Bottom Mountain,.......	3,579....................
B.	........Ferney Knob, Peach Bottom Mountain,........	4,150....................
B.	........Little Grandfather, Blue Ridge,...............	3,783....................

In Ashe County.

B.	........Thompkin's Knob, near Deep Gap,............	4,055....................
B.	........Deep Gap,...................................	3,105....................

In Watauga County.

B.	........Flat Creek, crossing,..........................	2,967....................
B.	........Clear Branch Gap,............................	3,186....................
B.	........Lookout Gap,.......................	3,198....................
B.	........Bent Branch Gap,............................	3,137....................
R. R.	........Cook's Gap,..................................	3,307....................
B.	........Boone, C. H.,.................................	3,242....................
B.	........Three Forks, of New River,...................	3,125....................
P. L.	........Rock Mountain,..............................	3,961................
B.	........Josh. Winkler's house,........................	3,104....................

B.	Col. Wm. Horton's floor,	3,115	
P. L.	Big Ridge, (of Blue Ridge)	4,072	
P. L.	Thunder Hill,	3,940	
P. L.	Blowing Rock Mountain,	4,090	
R. R.	Blowing (or Watauga) Gap,	3,779	
B.	Flat Top,	4,537	
R. R.	Shull's Mill Pond, Watauga R.,	2,917	
B.	Henry Taylor's house,	2,726	
B.	Gap at head of Watauga and Linville River,	4,100	Guyot.
B.	Grandfather,	5,897	"
B.	McCanless Gap, between Linville and Elk R.,	4,195	
P. L.	Peak Mountain, (near Grandfather)	4,924	
B.	Hanging Rock,	5,224	
B.	Ragged Ridge, between last two,	5,222	
B.	Hanging Rock Gap,	4,485	

In Mitchell County.

B.	Sugar Mountain,	5,228	
B.	Beech Knob, (near last)	5,067	
B.	Flat Top, (near last), Bluff of,	5,026	
P. L.	High Ridge of Soggy,	4.,956	
R. R.	Miller's Gap, Blue Ridge,	3,733	Gardner
R. R.	Toe River, at Old Fields of Toe,	3,558	"
B.	Dellinger's Gap, Blue Ridge,	3,389	
B.	Soapstone Gap, Blue Ridge,	3,360	
B.	Pisgah Gap, head of Brushy Creek,	3,437	
B.	Gap at head of North Fork, of Catawba,	3,407	
B.	Rattle Snake Spring Gap, near Linville Falls,	3,310	
B.	Gap ¼ mile north of last,	3,293	
B.	Linville River at Piercy's,	3,607	Guyot.
B.	Linville River Ford, near Pisgah Gap,	3,297	"
R. R.	Linville River Ford, near Horshaw's,	3,485	Gardner
R. R.	Barrier's Gap, Jonas' Ridge,	3,737	"
R. R.	Gap at head of Wilson's Creek,	3,772	"
R. R.	Head of Upper Creek, Barrier's,	3,614	"
B.	Old School House at head of North Cove, William English's,	2,025	
B.	Humpback, The Bluff,	4,262	
B.	Humpback, The Narrows,	4,255	
B.	Humpback, Mount Washington,	4,288	
B.	Toe River, ford near Childsville,	2,652	Guyot.
B.	Gillespie Gap, Blue Ridge,	2,795	

In Yancey County.

P. L.	Three Knobs, middle knob,	3,970	
B.	The Narrows, head of Buck Creek,	3,952	
B.	Gap at head of Buck Creek,	3,387	
B.	High Pinnacle,	5,701	Guyot.
B.	Rocky Knobs, south Peak,	5,306	"
B.	Rocky Knobs, Big Spring,	5,080	"
B.	Gap between High Pinnacle and Potatoe Top,	5,188	"

In Buncombe County.

B.	Greybeard,	5,448	Guyot.
R. R.	Mouth of Flat Creek, (Swannanoa R.,)	2,250	
R. R.	Swannanoa Gap,	2,657	
B.	Lyttle's Peak,	4,359	
B.	High Top,	4,380	
B.	Black Knob,	4,249	
P. L.	Dill's Knob,	3,790	
B.	Cane Creek Gap, head of Crooked Creek,	2,934	
B.	Hickory Nut Gap,	2,884	
B.	Sherrill's Porch,	2,597	
B.	Little Pisgah, near Hickory Nut Gap,	4,417	
P. L.	Weed Patch Mountain,	3,939	

In Henderson County.

B.	Bear Wallow Mountain,	4,233	
B.	Bear Wallow Gap,	3,465	
B.	Clear Creek Gap,	2,770	
R. R.	Reedy Patch Gap,	2,242	
R. R.	Broad River, (mouth of Reedy Patch Creek,)	1,473	
B.	Blue Rock,	2,674	
B.	Bald Mountain, (or Pinnacle,)	3,834	
P. L.	Miller's Mountain,	3,889	
P. L.	High Top, spur of Bear Wallow,	3,482	
P. L.	Turkey Knob, spur of Bear Wallow,	3,572	
B.	Ball Top, spur of Bear Wallow,	3,562	
P. L.	Round Top,	2,674	
B.	Bank's Mountain, spur of Bear Wallow,	3,696	
B.	Sugarloaf,	3,973	
B.	Stone Mountain, (spur of Sugarloaf,)	3,397	
B.	Hungry Mountain,	3,006	
B.	Hungry River crossing,	2,302	
B.	Top of ridge between Hungry Rivers.,	2,822	
B.	Little Hungry River,	2,602	
B.	A. J. Edney's Porch,	1,592	
B.	Chimney Rock, (Harris',)	1,059	
B.	Green River Gap, (Howard Gap road,)	2,174	
B.	Green River crossing, (Howard Gap road,)	1,622	
R. R.	Butt Gap, (Blue Ridge),	2,169	
R. R.	Saluda Gap, (old),	2,340	
B.	Saluda Gap, (new),	2,300	
B.	Corbin Mountain, (Saluda Mts.),	2,978	
P. L.	Grassy Mountain, (Blue Ridge),	3,078	
P. L.	Snaggy Mountain,	3,128	
P. L.	Harts' Knob,	3,053	
P. L.	Hammond's Knob,	2,978	
B.	Hendersonville, Brittain's,	2,167	
P. L.	Stone Mountain,	3,632	
P. L.	Chestnut Ridge,	3,730	
B.	Coley Mountain,	3,755	
B.	Pinnacle Mountain,	3,672	
B.	Crab Creek Gap,	2,422	
B.	Gap at head of Green River,	2,726	
B.	Sharpee Mountain,	3,355	

In Transylvania County.

B.	Shuford's, Little River, ground,	2,162	
B.	Mouth of Little River,	2,088	
B.	Thomas', ground,	2,805	
B.	Chestnut Mountain,	3,327	
B.	Rich Mountain,	3,788	
B.	Little River crossing, Jones' Gap road,	2,679	
B.	Jones' Gap,	2,925	
B.	Caesar's Head, (S. C.)	3,223	
B.	Slicken Gap,	2,873	
B.	Cantwell's Mountain,	3,555	
B.	Grassy Folly Gap,	2,828	
B.	French Broad, opposite Brevard,	2,109	
B.	Jesse Owens,	3,168	Guyot.
B.	Panther Tail, head of French Broad,	4,516	"
B.	Headwaters of French Broad, Jno. Owens,	2,739	"
B.	Cold Mountains,	4,631	"
B.	Owens' Gap,	3,579	"
B.	Gap south of Cold Mountain,	4,129	"
B.	Tennessee Creek,	3,041	"
B.	Canada Creek,	3,250	"
B.	Head of Saul's Creek, Tennessee Ridge,	3,213	"

In Jackson County.

B.	Great Hogback,	4,792	"
B.	Little Hogback,	4,560	"
B.	Gap between last two,	4,308	"
B.	Gap at foot of Little Hogback,	4,038	"
B.	Georgetown Mines, (Creek),	3,172	"
B.	George Pruit's,	3,201	"
B.	Jonathan Zackary's,	3,168	"
B.	Summit of road between Chatooga R. and Toxa-way,	3,586	"
B.	Summit of road between Fairfield and Casher's Valley,	3,563	"
B.	W. F. Passmore's,	2,877	"
B.	G. Green's, foot of Whiteside Mountain,	2,719	"
B.	Whiteside Mountain,	4,907	"

In Macon County.

B.	Sassafras Mountain,	3,812	"
B.	Little Terrapin,	4,078	"
B.	Black Rock,	4,364	"
B.	Fodderstack,	4,607	"
B.	Big Terrapin,	4,500	"
B.	Cowee Ledge,	4,402	"
B.	Chimney Top,	4,563	"
B.	Shortoff,	5,039	"
B.	Knob before Shortoff,	4,636	"
B.	Stuly Mountain,	4,506	"
B.	Scaly Mountain, north end,	4,780	"
B.	Scaly Mountain, center,	4,835	"

B.	Flatwood Gap,	1,475	Guyot.
B.	Tessentee River, at R. Conley's,	2,240	"
B.	Smith Ridge,	2,193	"
B.	White Rock Mountain,	4,648	"
B.	Fishhawk Monntain,	4,749	"
B.	Gap at foot of Osage Mountain,	3,803	"
B.	Chinkapin Mountain,	4,184	"
B.	Mud Creek Bald,	4,709	"
B.	Plateau between Mud Creek B. and Osage,	3,588	"
B.	Rabun Gap,	2,168	"
B.	Clayton Gap,	1,955	"
B.	Nona Mountain,	5,042	"

In Clay County and south.

B.	Standing Indian,	5,528	"
B.	Chimzy Mountain,	4,975	"
B.	Enota, Ga.,	4,811	"
B.	Bald, Ga.,	4,479	"
B.	Dome, Ga.,	4,600	"
B.	Tray, Ga.,	4,426	"
B.	Twin Tray, Ga.,	4,180	"
B.	Wiley, Hiwassee R., upper forks, Ga.,	2,000	"
B.	Tessuntee, Ga.,	4,477	"

ALTITUDES ALONG THE CROSS CHAINS.

Stansbury Mountains on State line.

B.	Angelico Gap, turnpike,	2,044	
R. R.	State line, R. R. crossing,	1,804	
B.	Stansbury Mountains, highest point,	2,599	
R. R.	Stansbury Mountains, R. R. crossing,	1,900	
B.	Pack Mountain,	3,937	
B.	Rocky Face,	3,163	
R. R.	Persimmon Creek,	1,755	

On Valley River.

B.	Murphy, C. H.	1,614	"
R. R.	Notteley River, 7 miles above mouth,	1,564	
B.	Mouth of Valley R., (Hiwassee R.),	1,514	"
B.	Valleytown,	1,911	"

On Long Ridge.

B.	Tatham's Gap,	3,639	"
B.	Joanna Bald,	4,743	"
B.	Winding Stairs,	4,476	"
B.	Waldroop Knob,	4,283	"
B.	Boulder's Knob,	4,301	"

Cheowah Mountains.

B.	Sherrill's, Cheowah River,	2,072	"
B.	Cheowah Maximum,	4,996	"

Fire's Creek Mountains.

B.	........Cold Spring Knob,..............................	4,446....................	
B.	........White Oak Knob, near Valleytown,............	4,301....................	
B.	........Beal's Knob,......................................	4,516....................	
B.	........Weatherman's Bald,..............................	5,000....................	
B.	........Corner Knob, (of three counties,)..............	5,259....................	

Valley River Mountains.

B.	........Barnett Mountain,................................	5,028....................	Guyot.
B.	........Chunky Gal,..	4,986....................	"
B.	........Medlock Bald,.....................................	5,258....................	"
B.	........Compass Bald,....................................	3,296....................	"
B.	........Tusquittah Mountain,............................	5,314....................	"
B.	........Koneheta,...	4,493....................	"
B.	........Valley River Gap,.................................	3,564....................	"
B.	........Red Marble Gap,..................................	2,686....................	"

Nantehaleh Mountains.

B.	........Burningtown Bald,...............................	5,243....................	"
B.	........Burningtown Bald, north end,.................	5,103....................	"
B.	........Rocky Bald,..	5,323....................	"
B.	........Toketa,...	5,372....................	"
B.	........Wayah,...	5,494....................	"
B.	........Nantehaleh Gap,................................	4,158....................	"
B.	........Monday's, Nantehaleh River, ford,.............	2,931....................	"
R. R.	........Tennessee River, mouth of Alarka Creek,......	1,590....................	
B.	........Little Bald,...	5,240....................	"
B.	........Catoogajay Mountain,............................	5,064....................	"
B.	........Albert Mountain,.................................	5,254....................	"
B.	........Nolen Mountain,..................................	5,094....................	"
B.	........Picken's Nose,....................................	4,926....................	"

Cowee Mountains.

B.	........Franklin, (C. H.),................................	2,141....................	"
B.	........Tennesse River, near Franklin,..................	2,020....................	"
B.	........Yellow Mountain,.................................	5,133....................	"
B.	........Cowee Mountains, chain N. W. of last,.........	4,772....................	"
B.	........Henderson's, Pine Creek,.......................	3,579....................	"
B.	........H. Baumgartner's,...............................	2,300....................	"
B.	........Ashe's,..	2,375....................	"
B.	........Watauga Gap,....................................	3,280....................	"
B.	........John Howard's,...................................	2,186....................	"
B.	........Grebble Gap between Catawba Creek and Little Savannah Creek,............................	2,565....................	"
B.	........Jones', Savannah Creek,........................	2,453....................	"
B.	........Wilson's, Savannah Creek,......................	2,291....................	"
B.	........Wild Cat Knob,...................................	4,452....................	"
B.	........Cherry Tree Spring Knob,.......................	4,490....................	"
B.	........Brushy Fork Gap,................................	4,287....................	"
B.	........Cowee Old Bald,.................................	4,977....................	"
B.	........Wessah Knob,....................................	4,576....................	"

B.	Wessah Gap,	4,253	Guyot.
B.	Little Bell Knob,	4,545	"
B.	Uhnalah Knob,	4,489	"
B.	Lost Knob,	4,203	"
B.	Y Knob,	4,360	"
B.	Rattlesnake Den,	4,597	"
B.	Rich Monntai ,	4,691	"

In Tuckaseye Valley.

B.	Quallatown, main store,	1,979	"
B.	Soco River, ford,	1,990	"
B.	Mouth of Bradley's Fork,	2,203	"
B	Mouth of Cullowhee River, (Tuck. R.),	2,066	"
B.	Mouth of Scott's Creek, (Tuck. R.),	1,977	"
B.	Mouth of Savannah Creek,	2,001	"
B.	Webster, (C. H.),	2,203	"
B.	Mouth of Cullowhee Creek, (Tuck. R.),	2,411	"
B.	Mouth of Bunch's Creek, (Oconaluftee R.),	2,379	"
B.	Mouth of Bradley's Fork, (Oconalufte R.),	2,203	"
B.	Mouth of Raven's Fork, (Oconaluftee R.),	2 476	"
B.	Mouth of Straight Fork, (Oconaluftee R.),	2,476	"

Balsam Mountains.

B.	Soco Gap,	4,341	"
B.	Road Gap, head of Scott's Creek;	3,357	"
B.	Old Field Mountain,	5,100	"
B.	Huckleberry Knob,	5,484	"
B.	Enos Plott's Balsam,	6,097	"
B.	Enos Plott's farm, north foot of chain,	3,002	"
B.	Jones' Balsam, (Junaluska), north point,	6,223	"
B.	Jones' Balsam, (Junaluska), south point,	6,055	"
B.	Gap south of last,	3,357	"
B.	Rockstand Knob,	6,002	"
B.	Brother Plott,	6,246	"
B.	Amos Plott's Balsam,	6,278	"
B.	Rocky Face,	6,031	"
B.	White Rock R dge,	5,528	"
B.	Black Rock,	5,215	"
B.	Panther Knob,	5,359	"
B.	Perry Knob,	5,020	"
B.	Westener Bald, north peak,	5,414	"
B.	Westener Bald, Pinnacle,	5,692	"
B.	Love's saw mill, Richland Creek,	2,911	"
B.	McClure's farm, Richland Creek,	3,285	"
B.	Gap at head of Scott's Creek,	3,357	"
B.	Richland Creek at Medford's,	2,938	"
B.	Lickstone Mountain,	5,707	"
B.	Deep Pigeon Gap	4,907	"
B.	Cold Spring Mountain,	5,915	"
B.	Double Spring Mountain,	6,380	"
B.	Richland Balsam,	6,425	"
B.	Chimney Peak,	6,234	"
B.	Spruce Ridge Top,	6,076	"

B.	........Lone Balsam,	5,898	Guyot.
B.	.. ..Old Bald, head of Richland Creek,	5,786	"
B.	........Reinhardt Mountain,	6,106	"
B.	........Beech Gap,	5,440	"
B.	........Rich Mountain Bald,	5,964	"
B.	........Mt. Hardy,	6,133	"
B.	........Tennessee Bald,	4,600	"
B.	........Court House Mountain,	5,788	"
B.	........Devil's Court House,	6,049	"
B.	........Sam's Knob,	6,091	"
B.	........Shining Rock,	5,988	"
B.	........Cold Mountain,	6,063	"

In Pigeon River Valley.

B.	........Hill's farm, Crabtree Creek,	2,714	"
R. R.	........Gap at head of Richland Creek,	3,411	
B.	........East Fork of Pigeon, Th. Lenoir's,	2,855	"
B.	........Forks of Pigeon, Col. Cathey's,	2,701	"
B.	........Waynesvile, C. H.,	2,756	"
B.	........Great Pisgah,	5,757	"
B.	........Little Pisgah, west,	4,724	"

In Valley of French Broad.

B.	........Hominy Cove, S. Davis's,	2,542	"
B.	........Sulphur Springs,	2,092	"
B.	........Asheville, C. H.,	2,250	"
R. R.	........Marshall,	1,647	
B.	........Gudger's, below Marshall, French Broad,	1,583	
B.	........Gahagan's, Laurel River,	1,705	
B.	........Lick Log Peak, Walnut Mountains,	3,607	
B.	........Cracker Knob, north of road gap to Laurel,	3,501	
R. R.	........Mouth of Ivy River, (French Broad,)	1,684	
B.	........Three Fo ks of Big Ivy,	2,276	"
B.	........Squire Blackstocks, Stockville,	2,216	"
B.	........Dillingham's, below Yeates' Knob,	2,568	"
B.	........Wheeler's, opposite Big Ivy Gap,	2,942	"

In Caney River Valley.

B.	........Mouth of Cattail Fork, (of Caney River),	2,873	"
B.	........Sandofer Gap, summit of road,	3,176	"
B.	........Burnsville, C. H.,	2,840	"
B.	........Green Mountain,	4,340	"

Black Mountains, N. W. Chain.

B.	........Blackstock's Knob,	6,380	"
B.	........Yeates' Knob,	5,975	"
B.	........Cock's Comb,	5,426	"
B	........Potato Top	6,393	"

Black Mountains, Main Cnai

B.	........J. Stepps'	2,360	"
B.	........Mountain House,	5,245	"

B.	Mt. Mitchell,	6,582	Guyot.
B.	Mt. Gibbs,	6,591	"
B.	Stepps' Gap, cabin,	6,103	"
B.	Mt. Hallback, or Sugarloaf,	6,403	"
B.	Black Dome,	6,707	"
B.	Dome Gap,	6,352	"
B.	Balsam Cone,	6,671	"
B.	Hairy Bear,	6,610	"
B.	Bear Gap,	6,234	"
B.	Black B other, (Sandoz),	6,619	"
B.	Cattail Peak,	6,611	"
B.	Rocky Trail Gap,	6,380	"
B.	Rocky Trail Peak,	6,488	"
B.	Cattail Gap,	5,720	"
B.	Deer Mountain, north point,	6,233	"
B.	Long Ridge, south point,	6,208	"
B.	Long Ridge, middle point,	6,259	
B.	Long Ridge, north point,	6,248	"
B.	Bowlen's Pyramid,	6,348	"

Craggy Range.

B.	Big Craggy,	6,090	"
B.	Bull's Head,	5,935	"
B.	Craggy Pinnacle,	5,945	"
B.	Cedar Peak, Beetree Mountains,	2,690	

Swannanoa Mountains.

B.	Young's Knob,	4,387
B.	Flat Mountain,	4,378
B.	Pinnacle,	3,885
B.	Ballard's Gap,	3,261
B.	Chestnut Flat	3,964
B.	Cedar Cliff,	3,850
B.	Mine Hole Gap,	2,587
B.	Busbee Mountain,	3,509

Mountains about Forks of Toe River

B.	Peak Mountain,	3,935	
B.	Brush Creek Mountain,	4,035	
B.	Brush Creek Gap,	2,927	
B.	Grassy Ridge,	4,145	
B.	Flat Rock, R. N. Penland's,	2,755	
B.	Bob's Yellow Mountain,	4,989	
B.	Bright's Yellow,	5,303	
B.	Toe River, ford near Autrey's,	2,547	"
B.	South Toe River, ford, Burnsville road,	2,532	"

ALTITUDES IN SPURS EAST OF THE BLUE RIDGE.

Tryon Range, &c.

B.	Tryon Mountain,	3,237
B.	Howard Gap,	1,886

B.	Pacolet River, Howard Gap road,	950
B.	Columbus, C. H.,	1,145
B.	Corner Stone, marked " N. C. " and " S. C.,"	1,111
B.	Whiteside Ford, Green River,	800
B.	Summit of road, near Earle's Mt.,	1,197
B.	Bush Mt.,	1,071
B.	Sandy Plains,	1,029
P. L.	Hogback, (S. C.),	3,028
P. L.	Glassy Mt., (S. C.),	2,978

South Mountains.

B.	Hickory Nut Mt. on Crooked Creek,	3,306
B.	Cane Creek Gap, near Brindletown,	1,508
P. L.	Silver Creek Knob,	2,822
B.	Deal's Knob,	2,922
P. L.	Big Hickory,	3,032
B.	Ben's Knob, (about)	2,801
B.	Henry's Fork of Catawba, Warlick's,	919
B.	Propst's Knob,	3,022

Mountains on Head Waters of Buck Creek and Catawba River.

B.	Wood's Knob,	3,634
B.	Greenlee Point,	3,165
B.	Gunter's Peak	3,949
B. L.	Chestnut Woods,	3,640
B.	Machie's Spring Peak,	3,994
R. R.	Buck Creek, ford at Carson's,	1,254
B.	Spencer Elliott's, Buck Cr ek,	1,670
R. R.	Marion,	1,405
B.	Mrs. Erwin's, Pleasant Gardens,	1,255

Linville Mountains, &c.

B.	Barnet Moore's, Linville River,	1,184
B.	John Warlick's,	1,272
B.	Old School House, near Linville River,	1,194
B.	Pinnacle of Linville,	2,869
B.	Highest point of S. end of Linville, (S. W. point),	3,766
B.	Spring at head of Paddy's Creek,	2,488
B.	J. H. Greenlee's porch,	1,476
B.	North Fork River, crossing, Linville Mt. road,	1,612
B.	Linville Gap, head of Paddy's Creek,	2,632
B.	Short Off, north summit,	3,105
B.	Table Rock,	3,918
B.	Hawksbill,	4,090
B.	Gap between Hawksbill and Table Rock,	2,921

Brushy Mountains, &c.

B.	Hibriten,	2,242
R. R.	Lenoir,	1,185
R. R.	Patterson,	1,279
B.	Col. J. C. Harper's,	1,265
R. R.	Warrior Gap,	1,352

B. ....Yadkin River, mouth of Warrior Creek,........1,208..................
A. ....Poor's Knob, Wilkes county,..................2,665..................
A. ....Cool Gap,......................................1,855..................
A. ....Wilkesboro, C H.,.............................1,043..................
A. ....Yadkin River at Wilkesboro ford,...............938..................
A. ....Taylorsville, C. H.,..........................1,264..................
A. ....Moravian Creek, road, above Wilkesboro,........1,211..................
A. ....Reuben Haze's,.................................1,093..................
B. ....De Journette's Store, Surry county,............1,405..................
B. ....Elkin Factory, Surry county,....................919..................
R. R. ....Elkin Factory, Surry county,................915..................
B. ....Richmond Hill, Yadkin county,..................1,030..................
B. ....Yadkin River, ford below last,..................805..................
B. ....Judge Pearson's,................................966..................
B. ....East Bend,.....................................1,088..................
B. ....Glenn's Ferry,..................................770..................
B. ....Brookstown, Forsyth county,.....................936..................

Pilot Mountain and region.

B. ....Dalton's,..991..................
B. ....Little Yadkin, near Dalton's, Salem road,........840..................
B. ....Wolfe's, 3 miles from Pilot,.....................877..................
B. ....Pilot Mountain, summit,.........................2,435..................
B. ....Pilot Mountain, foot of cliff,..................2,250..................
B. ....Spring on Pilot Mountain, N. E. side,...........1,761..................
B. ....Hollow Road Gap, at foot of Gordon's Mt.,.......1,238..................
B. ....Louis Creek, Mt. Airy road,......................934..................
B. ....War Hill, J. Worth's,...........................1,159..................
A. ....Flat Shoals Creek, Mt. Airy road,................944..................
A. ....Top of ridge 6 miles east of Mt. Airy, ...1,119..................
B. ....Ararat River, near Mt. Airy,.....................988..................
B. ....Stewart's Creek, road, near Mt. Airy,...........1,055..................

Sauratown Mountain.

B. ....Quaker Gap,......................................1,321..................
B. ....Moore's Knob,...................................2,583..................
B. ....Danbury, C. H.,..................................836..................
B. ....Dan River, ford near Danbury,.....................686..................
B. ....Town Fork, ford near Germanton,...................658..................
B. ....Germanton, C. H.,.................................732..................
B. ....Germanton and Salem road, top of ridge,...........979..................
B. ....Germanton and Salem road, Muddy Creek,............868..................
B. ....Germanton and Salem road, 4½ miles from S....1,015..................

King's Mountain and region.

P. L. ....King's Mountain,..............................1,650..................
B. ....Crowder's Mountain,.............................1,597..................
B. ....Ridge south of last,............................1,037..................
B. ....Grier Love's porch,...............................814..................
B. ....Dallas, C. H.,....................................834..................
B. ....Hoyle's Ferry,.....................................631..................
B. ....Spencer's Mountain,.............................1,271..................
B. ....Confluence of South Fork of Catawba,..............500..................

RAILROAD PROFILES.

Atlantic and North Carolina Railroad.

Carolina City, 10 feet.
Newbern depot, 12 "
Dover Swamp, 66 "
Kinston, 45 "
Summit, 135 "

North Carolina Railroad.

Goldsboro, 102 "
Little River, 86 "
Boon Hill, 160 "
Neuse River, 112 "
Clayton, 347 "
Walnut Creek, 219 "
Raleigh, depot 317 "
Snmmit, 503 "
Morrisville, 308 "
Cedar Fork Church, 418 "
Durham, 400 "
Summit, 515 "
Stone's Creek, 453 "
Summit, 630 "
Hillsboro', 539 "
Eno, second crossing, 524 "
Summit, 735 "
Mebanceseille, 687 "
Back Creek, 504 "
Haw River, 523 "
Graham, 677 "
Summit, 759 "
Rock Creek, 665 "
Summit, 778 "
Buffalo Creek, 686 "
Greensboro', depot, 843 "
Buffalo, second crossing, 796 "
Summit, 897 "
Bull Run, 731 "
Jamestown, 821 "
High Point, 943 "
Rich Fork, 649 "
Lexington, 776 "
Swearing Creek, 658 "
Summit, 682 "
Yadkin River, 616 "
Salisbury, 760 "
Charlotte, depot, 725 "

Carolina Central Railroad.

Wilmington, depot, 10 "
Northwest station, 50 "
Marlville, 65 "

Rosindale,	127	Feet.
Brown Marsh Swamp,	65	"
Brown Marsh Depot,	100	"
Balden Depot,	105	"
Bladenboro',	110	"
Big Swamp,	90	"
Lumberton, C. H.,	135	"
Lumber River, first crossing,	105	"
Lumber River, third crossing,	163	"
Moss Neck Station,	159	"
Red Banks,	176	"
Argyle,	175	"
Shoe Heel,	194	"
Laurinburg,	230	"
McLaurin's,	238	"
Gum Swamp,	184	"
Laurel Ridge,	245	"
Ridge near Old Hundred,	337	"
Joe's Creek,	249	"
Horse Pen Branch,	270	"
Ridge near Sand Hill Station,	412	"
Mark's Creek,	260	"
Beaverdam Branch,	224	"
Falling Creek, near Rockingham,	191	"
Rockingham, depot,	210	"
Rockingham, C. H.,	274	"
Hitchcock's Creek,	114	"
Peedee Rive-, (Yadkin),	105	"
Carr's Mount, near Wadesboro',	445	"
Big Brown Creek,	228	"
Lane's Creek,	335	"
Anson and Union line,	456	"
Summit, 22 miles from Wadesboro,',	593	"
Richardson's Creek,	455	"
Monroe,	586	"
Charlotte,	725	"
Sugar Creek,	650	"
Summit,	754	"
McCree's Creek,	663	"
Summit,	820	"
Long Creek,	597	"
Catawba River,	570	"
Rozell's Ferry road crossing,	893	"
Hoyle's Creek,	992	"
High Shoals Station,	1,001	"
Lincolnton,	866	"
South Fork,	649	"
Summit,	885	"
Indian Creek,	766	"
Muddy Fork,	820	"
Buffaloe Creek,	752	"
Summit,	958	"
Shelby, C. H.,	875	"
First Broad River,	689	"
Brushy Creek,	726	"

Summit,	943	feet.
Sandy Run,	773	"
Puzzle Creek,	840	"
Summit,	974	"
Second Broad River,	820	"
Summit, (G. Eaves'),	1,117	"
8.2 miles east of Reedy Patch Gap,	1,398	"
6.3 miles east of Reedy Patch Gap,	1,578	"
Reedy Patch Gap,	2,242	"

Raleigh & Gaston Railroad.

Weldon, depot,	72	"
Weldon, Roanoke,	30	"
Summit,	210	"
Gaston,	152	"
Summit,	307	"
Littleton,	380	"
Macon,	376	"
Warrenton Station,	451	"
Ridgeway,	415	"
Henderson,	505	"
Kittrell's,	417	"
Tar River,	296	"
Franklinton,	417	"
Cedar Creek,	370	"
Pacific Station,	449	"
Summit,	460	"
Wake county line,	384	"
Neuse River,	228	"
Summit,	335	"
Crabtree Creek,	228	"
Raleigh, depot,	303	"

Raleigh & Augusta Air-Line Railroad.

Cary,	495	"
Apex,	502	"
Lashley's,	334	"
Merry Oaks,	245	"
Haw River,	175	"
Deep River,	175	"
Sanford,	353	"
Summit,	427	"
Upper Little River,	360	"
Summit,	420	"
Crane's Creek,	260	"
Summit,	345	"
Lower Little River,	251	"
Sharon's Ridge,	508	"
Drowning Creek,	274	"
Summit,	450	"
Crossing of C. C. R. R., 5 miles east of Rockingham,	362	"

Western Railroad.

Sanford,	353	feet.
Egypt, depot,	262	"
Bottom of Coal Shaft, (below sea level,	198	"
Gulf,	279	"
Ore Hill, at furnace,	496	"

Piedmont Railroad.

Greensboro', Davies street,	829	"
Big Buffalo Creek,	738	"
Little Buffalo Creek,	741	"
Sugar Creek,	7[illegible]2	"
Morehead Station,	815	"
Reedy Fork Creek,	694	"
Brown's Summit,	800	"
Benaja Creek, first crossing,	695	"
Benaja Station,	678	"
Haw River,	655	"
Big Troublesome Creek	670	"
Little Troublesome Creek,	694	"
Reidsville,	828	"
Ruffin Station,	707	"
Pelham Station,	739	"
State line,	653	"
Dan River, (water),	385	"

North Western North Carolina Railroad

Greensboro, N. C. R. R. depot,	843	"
South Buffalo Creek,	859	"
Knight's,	942	"
Friendship,	892	"
North Fork of Deep River,	871	"
Whiteheart's,	976	"
County line,	974	"
Kernersville,	1,016	"
South Fork of Muddy Creek,	943	"
Hollow Road crossing,	959	"
Walker's Creek,	778	"
Middle Fork of Muddy Creek,	763	"
Summit,	940	"
Bushy Fork,	757	"
Ridge,	878	"
Bath Branch,	905	"
Salem, depot,	884	"

Railroad Survey from Greensboro to Cheraw.

Greensboro depot,	843	"
Silver Run,	779	"
Buffalo Creek,	738	"
Jamestown road,	850	"
Ballentine's Store,	843	"
Deep River,	625	"

Hinshaw's Ridge,	793	Feet.
Old Ashboro road,	701	"
Plank Road, opposite Ashboro,	855	"
Summit between Deep River and Pedee,	750	"
Henderson's Store,	661	"
Garborough's Store,	763	"
County line of Montgomery and Richmond,	628	"
Fayetteville Plank Road,	545	"
Old Scotch Fair Grounds,	560	"
Little Creek,	263	"
Catlege's Creek	158	"
Pedee (low water),	147	"
Carolina Central Railroad,	133	"
Hitchcock's Creek,	131	"
Solomon's Creek,	123	"
Mark's Creek,	100	"

Railroad Survey from Wadesboro' to Asheboro'.

Point opposite Wadesboro',	400	"
Peedee River	207	"
Mt. Gilead,	445	"
Summit,	750	"
Rocky Creek,	636	"
S. Zack's,	833	"
West prong of Little River,	698	"
Summit,	853	"
Little River,	713	"
Point opposite Ashboro',	846	"

Western North Carolina Railroad.

Salisbury,	760	"
First Creek,	665	"
Summit,	856	"
Walnut Branch,	690	"
Summit,	759	"
Second Creek,	665	"
Summit,	827	"
Third Creek,	710	"
Rowan and Iredell county line,	856	"
Statesville,	940	"
Third Creek, second crossing,	810	"
Summit,	930	"
Back Creek,	845	"
Summit,	958	"
Catawba River, (water),	762	"
Summit,	878	"
Mackline Creek,	778	"
Summit,	1,036	"
Hall's Store,	1,154	"
Drowning Creek, East Fork,	1,054	"
Drowning Creek, Middle and West Fork,	1,040	"
Drowning Creek,	1,070	"
Summit,	1,270	"

Bridge Creek,	1,145	Feet.
Summit,	1,273	"
Double Branch,	1,093	"
Conelly's Gap,	1,269	"
Ward's Branch,	1,195	"
Hunting Creek,	1,030	"
Morganton,	1,140	"
Silver Creek,	1,022	"
Muddy Creek,	1,090	"
Still House Gap,	1,355	"
Marion,	1,425	"
Opposite Carson's,	1,284	"
Catawba, opposite Mrs. Greenlee's,	1,294	"
Point Tunnel,	1,622	"
Mill Creek, fourth crossing,	1,510	"
Falls of Catawba,	1,941	"
Ridge between Mill Creek and Catawba,	2,269	"
Swannanoa Gap,	2,657	"
Swannanoa Tunnel,	2,510	"
Mouth of Flat Creek,	2,250	"
Summit,	2,304	"
Mouth of Swannanoa, French Broad,	1,977	"
Crossing of French Broad,	1,964	"
Alexander's Bridge,	1,796	"
Mouth of Ivy,	1,684	"
Marshall,	1,647	"
Rocky Bend,	1,446	"
Mountain Island,	1,364	"
Warm Springs,	1,325	"
State line,	1,264	"

Railroad Survey from Morganton to Cranberry.

Morganton, Main Street,	1,184	"
Catawba River, Fleming's ford,	1 019	"
Upper Creek, at D. Forney's,	1,011	"
Head of Steele's Creek, road crossing,	2 829	"
Head of Upper Creek, Old Mr. Barrier's,	3 614	"
Gap of Jonas' Ridge, B. Barrier's,	3,757	"
Gap between head of Wilson's Cr., and Linville R.,	3,772	"
Linville River, ford near Horshaw's,	3,486	"
Miller's Gap, (Blue Ridge),	3,733	"
Toe River, Old Fields of Toe,	3,558	"
Gap of Smoky (Iron) Mt. road,	3,784	"
Cranberry Cr., at Cranberry,	3,051	"
State line,	3,082	"

Railroad Survey from Asheville to Saluda Gap.

Asheville,	2,250	"
Swannanoa,	1,991	"
Stevens', 5 miles,	2,299	"
Branch, 6 miles,	2,262	"
Ridge, 8 miles,	2,466	"
Branch, 11 miles,	2,175	"

Ridge, 12 miles,	2,279	Feet.
Cane Creek, 14 miles, bank	2,124	"
Ridge, 15 miles,	2,269	"
Mud Creek, 17 miles,	2,118	"
Ridge 19 miles,	2,395	"
Crabtree Creek, 19 1-4 miles,	2,203	"
Ridge, 20 miles	2,311	"
Little Mud Creek, 24 miles,	2,138	"
Ridge, 29½ miles,	2,472	"
Green River, 32 miles,	2,057	"
Saluda Gap, 34 miles,	2,393	"

There is a large amount of material bearing on the topography of the State still in hand, which is not ready for publication, and there are also a great many surveys, of railroads and canals, and plank roads of which copies have not yet been obtained.

But any one who will take the trouble to study the above data with the State map in hand will be able to realize for himself the prominent and peculiar features of the topography of the State, and no one who does so can fail to see the important bearing which the subject has on the system of internal improvements, or to see the defects of our present system, if such it can be called; defects, the most glaring of which are due to a want of the necessary topographical knowledge on the part of the public, and of those who organized some of the dominant and most expensive parts of the scheme. A topographical map, though only approxmate, and even rude, will be of inestimable value in preventing the like expensive mistakes in the future. And this is especially true of the more interior or western extensions of our public works; the influence of the topography of this section ought to be controlling. It is proposed, as soon as all the existing sources of materials for the purpose are exhausted, and a few important connecting lines of barometrical levels can be run, to construct a relief map of the State, beside the geological map, on the walls of the Museum.

Latitudes and Longitudes.—Inasmuch as no astronomical observations had ever been made, (so far as appears from any record, with one exception, to be mentioned presently), to determine the geographical position of even the most important points in the middle and western sections of the State, it seemed desirable to ascertain at least approximately the errors of the positions commonly assigned to some of these points, For this purpose a good marine sextant and pocket chronometer were carried from Raleigh, as a base, (whose position has been accurately determined by the Coast Survey), and a series of double altitude observations of the sun were taken at a number of selected stations, from Charlotte and the neighborhood, to the western limit of the State. It will be seen that some of these determinations are quite different from the values of the co-ordinates usually assigned to these in our State maps. It is noticeable especially that all positions west of the Blue Ridge are placed *too far west* on the common maps, even those which are adopted and republished for their own use by the Departments of the General Government. Thus, for example, Asheville is too far west by about four miles, Waynesville by more than 2, Webster by more than 8, and Ducktown, (some 3 miles beyond the line), by 15 or 16. The last named is the most important. Observations were twice attempted at the State line, but the weather proving unfavorable, both attempts were failures. But a good series was obtained at Ducktown, and the result may be received as a pretty good approximation to the truth. And if so, the length of the State must be reduced from the common estimate by 15 miles or more; that is, this dimension will shrink to 470 miles. This result is confirmed by the fact that the longitude of Bristol, Tennessee, which lies northeast of this region, is misplaced on the same maps by more than 10 miles, as ascertained by the Coast Survey observations at that point, on the occasion already alluded to. This reduction will bring our western boundary (by a *second contraction*, but much more legitimate than the former), very nearly to the longitude of Cumberland Gap, beyond which the existing maps give it a wide projection. A consequence of this shrinkage will be a considerable loss of territory also, probably sufficient to reduce the total to a round 50,000 square miles; if the calculation be correct in other respects; which is improbable, however, since it was no doubt made without reference to the obscure and uncertain history and actual position of our boundary lines.

The determinations are the following, viz:

	Latitude.	Longitude.
Charlotte,	35° 15′ 49″	80° 49′.5
Corner stone of State line, about 30 miles south of Charlotte,	34° 50′ 20″	80° 47′.1
Lincolnton,	35° 32′ 21″	81° 17′.8
Corner stone in Polk county,	35° 14′ 9″	82° 10′.7
Corner stone in Polk county, as determined by Dr. Caldwell,	35° 15′ 11″	
Corner stone at confluence of South Fork of Catawba, (Dr. C.),	35° 9′ 23″	
Asheville,	35° 35′ 55″	82° 28′.5
Waynesville,	35° 29′ 18″	82° 56′.0
Webster,	35° 21′ 43″	83° 4′.1
Ducktown,	35° 2′ 50″	84° 6′.0

Observations were made or attempted at a number of other points, but without success, as the weather was unfavorable. An imperfect series of observations was gotten, for example, at Murphy, and at the confluence of the South Fork of the Catawba, two of the most important of the points selected, but they are too defective to give results worthy of confidence.

It is evidently a matter of some consequence that the State of North Carolina should know more of her whereabouts on the planet, and how much there is of her ; and it is proposed to extend the series of determinations, as it shall be convenient, so as to fix at least the boundaries and some of the more prominent physiographical features, and thus bring the State map into something like reasonable correspondence with facts. As it is, not only the boundaries, as was seen, are much misplaced, but our geographers, who plainly would not "respect even the Equator," if we had one among us, have mislocated the Blue Ridge, in some cases even many miles. So that it is impossible without confusion and serious error, to use the existing maps as the basis of a geological map of any detail.

CLIMATICAL.

The climate of North Carolina has a range corresponding to the variety of its topographical features, upon which, to an important extent, its various special or regional climates are dependent. The average climate of the whole State, of which that of the middle division is a fair representative, places it in the *warm temperate zone*, or on the southern margin of the temperate zone, the limits of that zone being taken at the isothermals of 40° and 60°. But on account of the peculiar geographical and topographical relations, its eastern margin being thrust outward a hundred miles beyond the position which the normal trend of the coast would give it, and almost into the edge of the great gulf stream, and its western end not only extending inland nearly five hundred miles, but being lifted into high table lands and lofty ridges and peaks, many of them more than a mile and a quarter in vertical height, the isotherms instead of keeping the parallels of latitude, are turned southward with a rapid curvature as they approach the western section, until at length they cross them almost at right angles.

So that while the mean temperature of one extremity is both elevated and regulated, (or approximated to an insular character in its distribution), that of the other is correspondingly depressed and carried up even to the colder half of the temperate zone, giving us the climate of the Gulf States (Alabama and Texas), on the one hand, and of New England on the other a truly continental range, within the narrow limits of one State. Indeed, if the length of the State were *north and south*, instead of east and west, stretching from South Corolina to New York, the variety of its climates would not be greater.

The influence of climate on human comfort, industries, progress, civilization is all-pervading and despotic. The climate of North Carolina is one of the most important factors of her present and prospective condition and history. It is therefore worthy of careful inve-tigation and discussion in any attempt to study or to set forth the resources, advantages and capabilities of the State. And hence a system of meteorological observations was organized in 1871, with a view to the elimination of the climatic peculiarties of all the different sections. Thirty stations were selected so as to cover the entire territory, and to give at least one observatory to every geographical, or topographical subdivision, and instruments and blanks were furnished and instructions given, (partly through the aid of the Smithsonian Institution in the first instance). This scheme contemplated only observations of the *temperature*, *rainfall*, *clouds and winds*, and omitted altogether two of the most important climatarchic elements, moisture and barometic pressure, mainly for want of means to furnish the necessary instruments, but partly also for want of observers of sufficient leisure, or skill, or interest. For appeal was necessarily made to the public spirit of individual observers, there being no remuneration offered.

Of some thirty stations, reports for one year and upwards have been received from 24, the average number reporting at one time being 12 to 15. It will be observed that several considerable tracts of the State are unrepresented, as for instance the region between Wilmington and Charlotte and Greensboro', and that north of Greensboro' and Statesville and west of Oxford, and especially the large and well marked climatographic subdivision between the Catawba River, the Blue Ridge and the southern border. The plateau of the upper French Broad, (Henderson and Translvania counties), is also well worthy of special observations, as well as that of Haywood county, and of Yancey ; and again in the extreme east, the whole peninsula between the two great sounds is one of the most peculiar tracts of country to be found in a dozen states, and peculiar too in many of those points especially connected with and determinative of one or more of the elements of climate ; yet in these different sections it has not been practicable to find observers, although they have been sought very diligently and instruments, &c. sent to parties supposed to be sufficiently interested and self-denying ;—and in a few cases reports have been received for one or several months. It is earnestly hoped that a better appreciation of the value of such observations to the whole State as well as to the particular section immediately concerned, not to mention the wider and higher interests of meteorological science, will lead to the early filling of these wide gaps and to the resumption of observations at other points where they have been intermitted for several years; for, as is sufficiently evident on the slightest consideration, or from an inspection of the tabulated results of the observations hitherto made, the value of these series is proportioned to the number of years which they represent.

It is due to the Smithsonian Institution, which has done so much for the climatology of the whole continent and for science of meteorology, to say that the Survey has, in several instances, availed itself of its observers, already secured and instructed and furnished. And after the making out of the table of temperatures, here given, for all the stations where observations are made for the Survey, or for which they were procurable from other sources, a number of others have been added from the proof sheet of a similar table, kindly furnished by Prof. Henry.

The stations thus added to the list are Gaston, Murfreesborough and Lake Scuppernong. The data for several other stations were obtained from the Agricultural Department reports, and from Blodget and from private records,—all derived however, I believe, from the records of observations procured by the Smithsonian Institution; and the results of the computations of these have been in several cases, (Warrenton and Kenansville, for example), averaged with those of the Smithsonian proof sheet.

The average for the different sections are the simple means of the averages for all the stations within their respective limits; that for the State is obtained from the sectional averages by giving to them a weight proportioned to their geographical extent; that is, to eastern, middle and western, a relative value of 5, 4 and 1, respectively.

Mean Temperatures.—The table given below, contains the results of the computation and discussion of all the accessible data; and it will be seen that they present many features of singular interest, notwithstanding the brief term of the observations at a number of the stations.

A full discussion of these results is reserved for a future occasion and a more complete and ample collection of materials; but there are some salient points which will not be affected by any amplification of observations, that are worthy of note.

By comparing the averages for the State with the corresponding figures for the different regions, it appears that the column for the middle section is almost identical with that for the entire State. These general averages are also repeated with notable exactness in the stational columns for Oxford, Chapel Hill and Albemarle, and the Charlotte column is but little variant. If a line be drawn through the three first named points, it will be very nearly direct, and will very well represent the isotherm of 59°. It is noticeably parallel to the Smoky Mountains and the coast, and is midway between them. And thus a system of lines connecting the different points of equal mean annual temperature would represent graphically one of the chief characteristics of the climate and show its intimate dependence upon topographical conditions. And similar charts for the seasonal and monthly means would bring to light many unsuspected peculiarities of the different regions and would develop most important bearings upon their special agricultural adaptations.

The representative stations, whose columns of averages are closely correspondent with those of the different divisions, are Poplar Branch for the eastern, Oxford for the middle and Asheville for the western. Such stations are of course the most important, and are indicated by these results as the proper points for permanent and completely furnished meteorological observatories.

It may be noted further that the columns for the spring and autumn means are, at almost all the stations, very nearly the same as the annual, and the average of the two is still nearer to it.

The influence of the Atlantic on the climate of the coast stations is observable chiefly in diminishing the difference between the temperature of summer and winter, and this is effected by an elevation of the latter; but this is only seen in the stations south of Hatteras. The difference in the January and July means for this part of the coast is about 33°, while the corresponding figures for the middle region is about 40°. The effect of the mountains upon the difference of the summer and winter means is similar, but less, the amount being about 35°; it is produced, however, chiefly by depressing that of the summer.

And it may be here observed that the difference in the general features of the coast region north of Hatteras, (the Sound region), and the lower coast is so marked as to justify the separation of these tracts into two climatic sub-divisions.

It is also worthy of note that the *hottest* month is *July*, and the *coldest*, *December*. In the northern portions of the continent January is the coldest month.

The average July temperature for the whole Northern Hemisphere is 71°; and that for January, 49°; the former figure represents the corresponding fact for the western division of North Carolina, and the latter for the southern coast.

MONTHLY, SEASONAL, AND ANNUAL MEAN TEMPERA-
THEIR AVERAGES FOR THE DIFFERENT

Name of Station.	January.	February.	March.	April.	May.	June.	July.	August.	September.	October.	November.	December.	
	°	°	°	°	°	°	°	°	°	°	°	°	
Asheville,	37	39	45	52	63	69	74	71	66	53	43	37	1
Albemarle,*	39	42	47	58	64	75	79	77	70	57	46	39	2
Bakersville,	34	37	38	54	61	66	72	74	65	50	43	36	3
Boone,†	33	34	36	49	57	65	69	70	62	47	34	30	4
Beaufort,	45	44	49	60	69	77	80	79	75	64	56	48	5
Charlotte,	38	43	49	60	69	77	79	76	73	57	46	40	6
Chapel Hill,	42	44	51	59	67	75	78	76	71	60	50	43	7
Davidson College,	42	41	50	58	66	74	76	80	64	57	45	43	8
Edenton,	41	44	45	60	66	76	79	80	73	59	47	37	9
Fayetteville,	39	42	45	62	71	77	81	79	71	60	49	40	10
Forest Hill,‡	40	40	40	59	64	68	71	71	63	53	41	41	11
Franklin,	38	42	45	54	63	70	70	70	65	52	42	41	12
Goldsboro',	43	48	51	61	69	78	82	79	74	62	51	44	13
Gaston,	37	42	38	54	66	74	78	76	68	58	47	40	14
Greensboro',	40	43	49	60	71	79	79	77	73	63	49	40	15
Kenansville,	49	45	50	58	68	76	80	81	71	59	48	44	16
Lake Scuppernong,	41	45	51	55	68	73	78	74	69	61	51	46	17
Lenoir,	36	40	45	56	66	73	76	73	67	55	43	37	18
Murfreesboro',	41	45	49	57	66	76	77	76	69	58	49	43	19
Murphy,	38	42	45	56	65	71	74	72	66	53	41	38	20
Newbern,	47	46	49	60	69	76	80	79	77	60	52	46	21
Oxford,	39	42	47	57	67	75	81	77	70	57	47	38	22
Poplar Branch,‖	43	44	45	57	68	75	81	80	75	60	49	43	23
Raleigh,	38	43	48	59	66	76	80	77	73	58	49	39	24
Statesville,*	35	39	44	54	62	72	76	74	65	54	43	35	25
Scotland Neck,§	41	43	48	54	65	75	76	74	70	56	45	38	26
Stagg's Creek,**	35	36	42	49	61	71	72	67	63	47	41	36	27
Smithville,	49	50	56	64	73	79	81	80	76	67	59	52	28
Tarboro',	39	42	42	58	68	73	80	77	72	59	46	37	29
Weldon,	42	41	45	57	69	76	81	77	69	56	43	37	30
Wilmington,	49	48	52	63	71	78	81	79	75	62	52	46	31
Warrenton,	42	40	43	55	65	75	80	78	68	61	49	39	32
Eastern Division,	44	45	48	60	69	76	80	79	73	61	49	43	33
Middle Division,	40	42	48	58	66	75	79	76	70	58	47	40	34
Western Division,	36	39	41	53	62	69	71	71	64	51	41	36	35
State,	41	43	47	58	67	75	79	77	71	59	47	40	36

*Station a few miles from town.
†December has observations for only one year.
‡Observations for several months incomplete.

TURES FOR A PERIOD OF YEARS, AT 32 STATIONS, AND REGIONS, AND FOR THE STATE.

	Spring.	Summer.	Autumn.	Winter.	Year.	Latitude.	Longitude.	Altitude in Feet.	No. Years Obs'rvat'n	Observers and Authorities.
	°	°	°	°	°	°	°			
1	53	72	54	38	54.3	35 36′	82 28′	2250	6½	Aston & Hardy.
2	56	77	57	40	57.8	35 18	80 11	650	4	Ag. Dep'tment.
3	51	71	52	36	52 5	36 3	82 6	2550	1	J. H. Greene.
4	47	68	48	32	48.7	36 14	81 39	3250	2	W. B. Councill.
5	59	78	65	45	62.0	34 42	76 40	12	6	J. Rumley.
6	59	77	58	40	58.8	35 16	80 50	725	3	G. B. Hanna.
7	59	76	61	42	59.5	35 54	79 17	570	17½	Mrs. C. P. Spencer.
8	58	76	55	43	58.0	35 32	80 51	850	2	W. C. Kerr.
9	57	78	60	40	58.8	36 4	76 41	30	2	Mrs. M. A. Hines.
10	59	79	60	40	59.7	35 5	78 53	75	1	J. M. Sherwood.
11	54	70	52	40	54.3	35 16	83 4	2500	1	Mrs. D. D. Davies.
12	54	70	53	40	54.4	35 13	83 15	2141	2	Mrs. A. Siler.
13	61	80	62	45	61.7	35 21	78 2	102	4	Ag. Dep'tment.
14	56	76	58	40	57.4	36 28	77 38	152	4½	S. I.
15	60	78	62	41	60.3	36 5	79 50	843	3	S. A. Howard.
16	60	79	59	46	61.3	34 58	77 58	60	2	S. I.
17	58	75	60	44	59.4	35 50	76 18	25	3	S. I.
18	55	74	55	38	55.5	35 57	81 34	1185	3	Dr. R. L. Beall.
19	58	76	59	43	58.8	36 26	77 1	75	4	S. I.
20	56	72	53	39	55.2	35 6	83 29	1614	2½	Wm. Beal.
21	59	78	63	46	61.8	35 6	77 2	12	2½	R. Berry.
22	57	78	58	40	58.2	36 19	78 41	475	7	Dr. W. R. Hicks.
23	57	79	62	43	60.1	36 14	76 00	10	2	J. M. Woodhouse.
24	58	78	60	40	59.1	35 47	78 41	350	4	P. A. Wiley.
25	53	74	54	36	54.5	35 47	80 53	940	7	Dr. J. A. Allison.
26	56	75	57	41	57.2	36 7	77 32	50	2	J. M. Smith.
27	51	70	50	36	51.8	36 26	81 33	3000	11½	J. O. Wilcox
28	64	80	**67**	50	65.7	34 00	78 5	20	8	Mil. Post.
29	56	77	59	39	57.8	35 52	77 40	50	1	R. H. Austin.
30	57	78	56	40	57.8	36 23	77 45	72	3	T. A. Clark.
31	62	79	63	48	63.0	34 17	77 58	50	3	Rev. D. Morrelle.
32	54	77	59	40	57.7	36 24	78 16	400	1	S. I.
33	59	79	60	46	60.3					
34	57	77	59	44	58.2					
35	52	70	52	37	53.1					
36	57	77	59	41	58.7					

‖Currituck county. S. I. Smithsonian Institution.
§Halifax county.
**Ashe county, near Jefferson.

The coldest station is Boone, (which is also the highest); and the warmest is Smithville. It would be a matter of much interest to have a record of observations for the plateau of upper Linville, at the foot of the Grandfather, nearly 1,000 feet higher than Boone. We should then have both extremes. The annual mean temperature for the western division is 53°.1. If we take only the three highest stations, (those nearest to this plateau), the average is 51°; the two highest give 50°.2; the single highest, 48°.7. The difference of the isotherms for Asheville and Boone is 5°.6, for a difference of 1,000 feet in elevation; and a difference of 300 feet between Asheville and Bakersville gives 1°.8, or 6° per 1,000 feet: so that it is quite within limits to place the isotherms for the Linville plateau at 45°. Taking that for Boone as representing the lower extreme, the isothermal range within the State is 17°: if the conjectural number for the Linville section be substituted, it is above 20°.

And there are many other regional and local climatic peculiarities which are well worthy of study, as for example, the very low range of the thermal means at the Statesville station, which is in fact climatically allied to the western instead of the middle section; and, by contrast, the higher range of the Lenoir station, which is more elevated and much nearer the Blue Ridge; and yet other phenomena not shown in the tabular abstracts, as the singular manner in which areas of sudden winter cold, approaching from higher latitudes protrude long and narrow sinuses across the State, leaving parallel tracts, east and west, little or not at all affected; and again the sudden reduction of the temperature over a limited tract, unconnected with any other area from which it could have been propagated, as if a tract of the upper strata of cold air had dropped from the clouds. These and a multitude of interesting meteorological phenomena must wait until another volume, for discussion, and even for adequate statement.

Such are some of the more notable points which are obvious from a simple inspection of the table and a comparison of its different parts among themselves.

If a wider comparison be instituted between these columns and similar abstracts of temperature observations for other states and countries, yet more important features emerge.

To begin with one of the last points mentioned,—the isothermal range,—while it is not less than 20° in North Carolina, it is 8° in New York, and 6° in Massachusetts. And any one who will take the trouble to trace the isotherm of 66° and 45° across the continent, as in Blodget's charts, for example, will be able to realize the marvellous extent of the climatic range which the territory of one State presents. The former, starting from the southeast corner of this State sweeps down through the southern half of Georgia and Alabama, many miles below Montgomery, and in fact touches Mobile Bay (isotherm 65°.8), and crossing the Mississippi a little above Natchez, makes a southward bend by Austin, Texas, and after a slight upward curve reaches the eastern escarpment of the great western plateau, and then "runs down the longitude" into Mexico, making its final appearance in southern California on the Pacific coast. The other line, of 45°, starting on the coast at Portland, Maine, and bending gently southward until it touches the northern edge of western Masschusetts, makes a sudden sweep to the north through Lake Champlain into the valley of the St. Lawrence, and then trends west a little south along the northern coast of Ontario, by Toronto, across the middle of Lake Michigan, and again with a northwest sweep through St. Paul, rises quite into the British Dominion in the valley of the Sascatchewan, beyond the parallel of 50°; and only after reaching the flanks of the Rocky Mountains does it touch, by a sudden southward plunge, the latitude of the Grandfather Mountain. So that these two lines enclose almost the whole United States and a portion of British America and Mexico.

The mean for the State, which is nearly 59°, if mapped, would enter its territory from Virginia, in Granville county, and leave it in Mecklenburg, and after making a wide curve into South Carolina and Georgia, around the southwestern end of the Appalachians, return to the parallel of 36½° about midway of the State of Tennessee.

If the geography of this line be traced through Europe and Asia, it will give a clue to still wider climatic relationships. It touches the European coast a little north of Lisbon, and passing through Madrid, hugs the upper coast of the Mediterranean round by Genoa, and bearing down through middle Italy by Florence, turns again east by Constantinople, Trebizond, and on through the heart of China, passing near Shanghai, reaches the Pacific in the latitude of southern Japan. And if the two extreme isotherms of the State, say only 48° and 66°, be followed around the globe, they will be found to enclose a zone within which lie nearly all the great centres of the population and power and civilization of the human race, both ancient and modern, in the old world and the new. But climate, even so far as dependent on temperature, is not wholly expressed by the annual isotherms. On the contrary, as long since pointed out by Humboldt, a most "important influence is exercised on vegetation and agriculture, on the cultivation of fruit, and on the comfort of mankind, by differences in the distribution of the same mean temperature through the different seasons of the year." "If in a thermic scale of different kinds of cultivation, we begin with those plants which require the hottest climate, as the vanilla, the cocoa, banana, and cocoa-nut, and proceed to pine apples, the sugar cane, coffee, fruit-bearing date-trees, the cotton-tree, citron, olives, edible chestnuts, and vines producing potable wine, an exact geographical consideration of the limits of cultivation will teach us that other climatic relations besides those of mean annual temperature are involved in these phenomena. Taking an example, for instance, from the cultivation of the vine, we find that in order to procure potable wine, it is requisite that the mean annual heat should exceed 49°, that the winter temperature should be upward of 33°, and the mean summer temperature upward of 64°. At Bordeaux, the mean annual, winter, summer, and autumn temperature are respectively 57°, 43°, 71°, and 58°. In the plains near the Baltic, where a wine is produced that can scarcely be considered potable, these numbers are as follows: 47°.5, 31°, 63°.7, and 47°.5." It will be observed that the corresponding numbers for the coldest station in North Carolina are all in excess of these last, viz: 48°.7, 32°, 68° and 48°; and also that those for the middle division of the State, (and the averages for the whole), differ but little from the typical series of Bordeaux, viz: 58°.2, 40°, 77°, 59°. And when it is further considered that the same determinant series, for the western section of the State, lies about midway between those of Bordeaux and the Baltic, viz: 53°, 37°, 70° and 52°; and that those for the eastern division exceed the Bordeaux series but little, being respectively 60°, 44°, 79°, 61°; it is apparent that, so far as the cultivation of the vine is concerned, the whole State lies within the favored tract. Middle and eastern North Carolina correspond to middle and southern France, and western North Carolina to northern France and Belgium. And all the climates of Italy, from Palermo to Milan and Venice, are represented. These points will be best understood, in the absence of illustrative charts, by a few comparative columns of figures, for a few representative localities, as follows:

Comparative Table of Mean Temperatures.

	Year.	Spring.	Summer.	Autumn.	Winter.
	°	°	°	°	°
State,	59	57	77	59	41
Middle Division,	58	57	77	59	40
Raleigh,	59	58	78	60	40
Oxford,	58	57	78	58	40
Marseilles, France,	58	56	73	59	45
Madrid, Spain,	58	56	74	57	44
Florence, Italy,	59	58	75	60	44
Eastern Division,	60	59	79	61	44
Poplar Branch,	60	57	79	62	43
Naples, Italy,	60	58	74	61	48
Western Division,	53	52	70	52	37
Ashevile,	54	53	72	54	38
Bakersville,	52	51	71	52	36
Paris, France,	51	51	65	52	38
Dijon, France,	53	53	70	53	35
Venice, Italy,	55	55	73	56	38
Smithville,	66	64	80	67	50
Mobile, Ala.,	66	67	79	66	52
Natchez, Miss.,	66	67	80	67	51
Austin, Texas,	67	68	81	68	49
Nicolosi, Sicily,	64	62	79	66	51
Alexandria, Eg'pt,	67	66	78	74	58
Jerusalem, Syria,	63	60	74	66	50
Nagasaki, Japan,	63	60	80	66	45
Boone,	49	47	68	48	32
Cambridge, Mass.,	50	48	70	52	31
West Point, N. Y.,	51	49	71	53	30
Chicago, Illinois,	47	45	67	49	26
Dubuque, Iowa,	49	50	72	52	22
Berlin, Prussia,	48	47	65	49	31
Munich, Germany,	48	48	64	49	32
Vienna, Austria,	51	52	69	51	32

AVERAGE MONTHLY, SEASONAL AND ANNUAL MAXIMA, MINIMA AND RANGE OF TEMPERATURE, FOR A PERIOD OF YEARS, AT 12 STATIONS, AND FOR THE DIFFERENT REGIONS, AND THE STATE.

NAME OF STATION.		JANUARY.	FEBRUARY.	MARCH.	APRIL.	MAY.	JUNE.	JULY.	AUGUST.	SEPTEMBER.	OCTOBER.	NOVEMBER.	DECEMBER.	SPRING.	SUMMER.	AUTUMN.	WINTER.	YEAR.	NO. OF YE'RS OF OBSERVATION.
Asheville,	Maxima,	63	65	71	80	82	83	86	85	81	75	68	63	82	86	81	65	86	6½
	Minima,	10	10	12	30	42	49	61	57	45	29	17	7	12	49	17	7	7	
	Range,	53	55	59	50	40	34	25	28	36	46	51	56	70	37	64	58	79	
Beaufort,	Maxima,		64	62	70	78	83	88	89	85	80	69	60	78	89	85	64?	89?	1
	Minima,		23	30	40	58	64	78	66	60	44	21	19	30	64	21	19?	19?	
	Range,		41	32	30	20	19	10	23	25	36	48	41	48	25	64	45?	70?	
Boone,	Maxima,	57	58	64	73	75	81	84	82	79	74	55	51	75	82	79	58	82	2
	Minima,	4	6	11	26	38	50	57	53	40	32	30	22	11	50	30	4	4	
	Range,	53	52	53	47	37	31	27	29	39	42	25	29	64	32	49	54	78	
Charlotte,	Maxima,	67	68	73	83	87	90	92	90	88	77	70	64	87	92	88	68	92	3
	Minima,	16	21	27	41	36	67	67	62	58	35	24	13	27	62	24	13	13	
	Range,	51	47	46	42	51	23	25	28	30	42	46	51	60	30	64	55	79	
Chapel Hill,	Maxima,	69	70	72	80	90	92	97	94	90	82	70	66	90	97	90	70	97	3
	Minima,	19	19	22	36	47	60	68	63	54	38	26	20	22	60	26	19	19	
	Range,	50	51	50	44	43	32	29	31	36	44	44	46	68	37	64	51	75	
Goldsboro',	Maxima,	71	75	81	89	94	98	102	97	94	87	78	70	94	102	94	75	102	4
	Minima,	21	20	25	38	50	59	69	64	73	37	28	17	25	59	28	17	17	
	Range,	50	55	56	51	44	39	33	33	21	50	50	53	69	43	66	58	85	
Lenoir,	Maxima,	62	66	71	82	85	88	91	87	85	82	67	63	85	91	85	66	91	3
	Minima,	14	15	14	36	47	58	66	52	50	29	18	9	36	50	18	9	9	
	Range,	48	51	57	46	38	30	25	35	35	53	49	54	49	41	67	57	82	

Murphy,	Maxima,	64	67	73	81	88	88	89	89	86	78	65	74	88	89	86	74	89	3
	Minima,	9	14	15	35	47	59	64	57	44	24	11	6	15	57	11	6	6	
	Range,	55	53	58	46	50	29	25	32	42	54	54	68	73	32	75	68	83	
Oxford,	Maxima,	63	66	73	85	88	93	96	93	88	78	68	63	88	96	88	66	96	7
	Minima,	17	17	20	35	46	58	67	59	52	35	26	12	20	58	26	12	12	
	Range,	46	49	53	50	42	35	29	34	36	43	42	51	68	38	62	54	84	
Poplar Branch,	Maxima,	74	73	72	80	87	92	95	92	93	82	72	68	87	95	93	74	95	2
	Minima,	23	22	21	35	45	58	69	65	40	28	21	19	21	58	21	19	19	
	Range,	51	51	51	45	42	34	26	27	53	54	51	49	66	37	72	55	77	
Weldon,	Maxima,	72	70	73	87	92	47	99	96	95	81	69	66	92	99	95	72	99	3
	Minima,	17	16	19	36	50	57	66	60	50	32	18	8	19	57	18	8	8	
	Range,	55	54	54	51	42	40	33	36	45	49	51	58	73	42	77	64	91	
Wilmington,	Maxima,	72	72	77	87	90	93	93	91	89	80	73	71	90	93	89	72	93	3
	Minima,	23	26	26	41	53	62	71	65	59	39	25	20	26	62	25	20	20	
	Range,	49	46	51	46	37	31	22	26	30	41	48	51	64	31	64	52	73	
Eastern Division,	Maxima,	72	71	73	83	88	93	93	93	91	82	72	67	88	93	91	72	93	
	Minima,	21	21	24	38	51	60	72	64	56	36	23	17	24	60	23	17	17	
	Range,	51	50	49	45	37	33	21	29	35	46	49	50	64	33	68	55	76	
Middle Division,	Maxima,	65	67	72	82	87	91	94	91	88	80	69	64	87	94	88	67	94	
	Minima,	16	18	22	37	44	62	67	59	54	34	23	13	22	59	23	13	13	
	Range,	49	49	50	45	43	29	27	32	34	46	46	51	65	35	65	54	81	
Western Division,	Maxima,	61	63	69	78	82	84	86	87	82	76	63	63	82	87	82	63	87	
	Minima,	8	10	13	30	42	53	61	56	43	28	19	12	13	53	19	8	8	
	Range,	53	53	56	48	43	31	25	31	39	48	44	51	69	34	63	55	79	
State,	Maxima,	68	69	72	82	87	91	93	92	89	81	70	65	87	93	89	69	93	
	Minima,	18	19	22	37	47	60	69	61	54	34	19	15	22	59	23	15	15	
	Range,	50	50	50	45	40	31	24	31	35	47	51	50	65	34	66	54	78	

Maxima, Minima and Range of Temperature.—The table pp. 76, 77, gives the average minimum temperature and the average maximum at a dozen stations where observations have been taken for the longest periods and are most complete, or where the point of observation is of high representative value; and also the means of the maxima and minima of the stations in each division of the State and the means for the whole State. Thus the lowest reading of the thermometer to be expected at Asheville in January is 10° and the lowest for the year 7° (in December); the highest for January or December 63°; the highest for the year, 86° (in July).

The lowest reading of all the stations is 4°, at Boone, (in Jan.), the highest 102°, in July, at Goldsboro. The lowest range of the thermometer for the eastern division of the State is seen to be 17°, and may be expected to be reached in Dec., for the middle 13°, and for the western 8°.

The greatest monthly thermal range is found in the winter months, and the least in July, (the latter being about half as much as the former); the greatest seasonal range is in spring and autumn, and the least in summer. The average of the yearly thermometric range for the whole State is 78°; the greatest yearly range is found at Weldon, 91°, and the least at Beaufort, 70°; no doubt Smithville gives still less.

The extreme limits touched by the thermometer are often very different in regions of the same, annual temperature. The most marked characteristic of littoral and insular climates is exhibited in the diminution of the thermal range,—the approximation of the maxima and minima, of the January and July temperatures, the elimination of wide, as well as of sudden fluctuations of the thermometer, which are so characteristic of interior and rigorous climates. It will have been observed, in the above comparative table of temperatures, that the points of nearly the same yearly means in the northern part of the continent are characterized by a wider thermal range than the corresponding points in North Carolina. The difference of the January and July temperatures for Cambridge, for instance, is 44°, while that for Boone is 36° (39° for Dec.), and as we recede from the coast, the difference becomes more marked, being 44½° at West Point, above 47° at Chicago, and 55½° at Dubuque. We have seen that the greatest difference in this State is that for the middle section, viz: 40°, while that for the coast is 33°, and for the mountains 35°.

But if instead of the differences of the monthly *means*, we compare the differences of the maxima and minima, the contrast will be still more striking. At Dubuque, the only point for which the necessary data are at hand, the range for January is above 59°, (from + 46° to —13½°), that for

July is 36°, (from 58° to 94°), and for the year 112°, (from — 18° to + 94°). The contrast which these figures present to the corresponding data, (53°, 27° and 80°), for the only point of observation in North Carolina which receives the same annual amount of heat, is very great. And if the absolute maxima and minima were compared, the result would be still more striking. Taking the highest and lowest accessible records for Dubuque in ten years, 99° and — 29°, (last winter it went to — 35°), the absolute range rises to 130°; while in Boone there is no record below 3° and none above 90°, so that the greatest absolute range is under 90°. And it is not greater for any part of the State. And those who have noticed the current weather reports of the last few years can hardly have failed to notice that during the prevalence of the most fearful cold for several days over the whole northern tier of States, 30°, 35° and 40° below zero, from Boston through New York to Iowa, the thermometer here in middle North Carolina scarcely reached the freezing point. And even during this present January, 1875, while the telegraph reports 20° to 25° *below zero* in various places north, the lowest record here in Raleigh during the same week is 27° *above zero.*

And so in midsummer, while the daily telegraphic reports from the north show 98° and 100°, the thermometer ranges here from 90° to 93°, rarely reaching 95°.

The importance of such climatic data to a proper understanding and estimation of the adaptation of a country or region to human industries and comfort and longevity, is only beginning to be appreciated. These are in fact the most important characteristics of climates, both as concerns vegetable and animal life, and it has come to be recognized as a sanitary fact of great importance that there is a most intimate relation between the death-rate in the human family and the range of the thermometer. "The severity of the strain of extreme climates on the human system is shown in a striking manner in the rapidly increasing death-rate according as the difference between the July and January temperatures is increased. Thus the mortality is 8 per cent. greater in England than in Scotland, the climate of the latter country being more equable or insular in its character; and it is found on advancing into the Continent of Europe, that the more extreme the climate becomes, so much the more is the death-rate increased." (Buchan). The same thing will no doubt be found in passing from the more littoral and equable climates of the American shores into the rigorous conditions which prevail in the interior. Blodget says, in a very full discussion of the relations of disease to climate, "All forms of disease of the respiratory organs *increase as the temperature decreases* with like conditions of humidity; and increases still more directly with the greater variableness of the climate."

Indeed, so close is the relation between climate and the physical well being of man, that certain classes of diseases are distinctly climatographical affections, and are eliminated by proper climatic conditions. So well recognized is this fact that one of the most interesting and elaborate of the reports of the last census of the United States contains disease charts,—maps of the geographical range of certain causes of human mortality.

And it is worthy of note, that one of the two tracts in the whole territory of the United States, which is absolutely or almost free from that scourge of rigorous and extreme climates, pulmonary consumption, is located by these census maps along the plateau east of the Blue Ridge in North Carolina, to which the nearest meteorological station is that of Lenoir, which has been pointed out above as contrasted in the equability of its temperature with stations more than 100 miles east, and of less elevation. One of the causes, (which, however, cannot now be discussed), is doubtless the fact that this region is sheltered on two sides by the proximity of the Blue Ridge, which here reaches its extreme altitude, and stands as a protecting wall against the two prevalent and weather-controlling winds from the interior, those from the southwest and northwest, (and indeed from the north as well).

Springs.—The list of springs given below is added here on account of the well known relation between the temperature of such sources (and that of wells, when they come from a depth of forty feet and upwards,) and the mean annual temperature, the former being a very fair expression of the latter. It will be seen that the observations with instruments receive a singularly strong confirmation from this source, as far as the evidence goes. The altitude is given, at least approximately, so that the effect of elevation may be eliminated, by allowing 3° for every 1,000 feet.

LOCALITY.	ELEVATION.	TEMP.
Cherokee, McDaniel Bald,	4,300 feet,	48°
Madison, Big Butt,	4,500 "	49
" Big Bald,	5,350 "	45
Yancey, Proffitt's,	3,300 "	49
" Black Mountain, about	6,500 "	40
" Burnsville, well,	2,800 "	52.6
" D. G. Ray's, near Burnsville,	2,900 "	52.5
Mitchell, Roan, about	5,000 "	49.3
" " Cold Spring,	6,100 "	45.1
" Flat Rock, Penland's,	2,800 "	51

LOCALITY.	ELEVATION.		TEMP.
Mitchell, Hump Back, Blue Ridge,	4,300	"	49.2
Watauga, Morris', " "	3,500	"	52.5
Alleghany, foot of Bullhead Mountain,	3,300	"	54.5
Transylvania, Little River, near Thomas',	2,800	"	54.2
Henderson, Bear Wallow Mountain,	2,800	"	52
Buncombe, Laurel Spring, Pinnacle,	2,700	"	52
" Hickory Nut Gap, Sherrill's,	2,700	"	54
" Mine Hole Gap,	2,600	"	54.5
McDowell, Hawksbill, about	3,500	"	51.8
" Shortoff,	2,800	"	55.4
" Paddy's Spring, Lin. Mountain,	2,200	"	54.8
" J. H. Greenlee's well,	1,400	"	56
Surry, Pilot Mountain,	1,760	"	54
Yadkin, Judge Pearson's,	950	"	57
" J. R. Dodges',	900	"	57.2
Alexander, Taylorsville, well,	1,260	"	57.1
Cleveland, Patterson spring, about	900	"	58
Moore, Carthage, 3 wells, about	450	"	60.3
Franklin, Dodd's Spring, (Emmons), about	300	"	60

If the reduction be made of all the above springs which are found in the mountain section to the average level of 2,600 feet, the average of all these temperatures so corrected will give 54° for the mean annual temperature of the region, which is very near that of the table. A similar reduction for all the springs of the piedmont section gives 57°, a result nearly coincident with that from direct observation.

Rainfall.—This important element of the climates of North Carolina is developed by the accompanying table, page 83. The variation in amount, in the different sections, is considerable, but the whole State belongs to the region of North America which is characterized by the largest precipitation, this region having its centre a little southwest of us, in Alabama, and extending to the Gulf coast and beyond the Mississippi and northward to the Ohio. Within this region the average annual precipitation is about 50 inches, the maximum rising above 60 in the centre, and the amount diminishing northward and westward, to about 40 in the north and northeastern States, 30 along the lakes and on the upper Mississippi; beyond which it falls to 15 and even 10 in some parts of the Great Plains, and reaching the minimum of 5 inches in a small tract of southern California. Over a limited belt of the Oregon coast it rises again to 50 and upwards. The average for the States along the Mississippi and eastward is probably a little above 45, and for the western half of the United States it is about 20, so that for the whole it is a little more than 30 inches. In the construction of the table for North Carolina, the stations are omitted for which the observations do not cover 2 years.

This table shows a very great variation in the amount of annual precipitation from station to station; and at some of them the amount is extraordinary,—far beyond the average even for this very term of years, 1871 to 1874; but the average for the whole State and for every region is notably high; although for a few stations, as Greensboro', it is abnormally low. In Blodget's rain chart there is only a small section in tht southeast corner of the State which is credited with so large an amonne as 48 inches, while a strip along the Blue Ridge is set down at 36 inches; and the average for the State has been commonly given as about 45 inches. But for the past few years the average is greater than this for the middle region and still larger for the two other divisions: so that the average for the whole rises above 53 inches. It is necessary that observations be continued through a long series of years, in order to eliminate the effect of irregularities and (perhaps) periodic variations in the amount of annual precipitation. But the present results seem to justify the conclusion that the average for the State has been heretofore placed at too low a figure, the deduction having been made from insufficient data, the stations being far too few and distant, and too partial in their distribution.

The quantity of rainfall is hardly more important than its distribution through the season of the year. Some portions of the earth which have an abundance of precipitation are almost uninhabitable on account of its unequal distribution; being overwhelmed by floods at one season and parched by drought at another. In this State, as may be seen from the table, the variation from month to month, and from season to season is very slight. On the whole, more rain falls in summer than in any other season, and the amount for winter stands next in order of magnitude. The most rainy month is July, and the next in order is February; but there is properly speaking no *dry* season or *wet* season, in any part of North Carolina.

The amount of precipitation in Europe, although very different from country to country, diminishing in general, with the distance from sea coasts and high mountains, is usually less than in this country. A few examples of notable localities in the old world are given by way of comparison, viz: London 21, Liverpool 34, Glasgow 21, Paris 23, Dijon 31, Marseilles 20, Bordeaux 34, Madrid 10, Berlin 24, Copenhagen 18, Milan 38, Rome 31, Naples 30, St. Petersburg 18, Pekin 27, Canton 69.

Average Monthly, Seasonal and Annual Rain Fall in Inches, for a Period of Years, at 18 Stations, and for the Different Regions, and the State.

Station.	January.	February.	March.	April.	May.	June.	July.	August.	September.	October.	November.	December.	Spring.	Summer.	Autumn.	Winter.	Year.	No. of Y'rs of Observation.
Asheville,	1.5	4.1	3.8	3.7	4.1	3.3	4.8	3.6	2.2	1.9	2.6	3.8	11.6	11.7	6.7	9.4	39.4	4½
Albemarle,	4.9	3.7	6.4	4.6	4.6	4.8	3.8	5.8	3.9	4.9	2.9	4.9	15.6	14.4	11.0	13.5	54.5	4
Chapel Hill,																	45.2	6
Charlotte,	3.7	7.5	3.7	4.0	3.7	3.9	3.6	6.3	3.3	1.9	3.8	2.8	11.4	13.8	9.0	14.0	48.2	2
Davidson Col.,	4.9	3.9	4.8	3.8	3.3	3.6	3.1	3.4	1.2	4.1	4.6	3.4	11.9	10.1	9.8	12.1	43.9	2
Franklin,	8.1	9.8	5.9	4.7	3.9	6.4	5.4	7.5	2.6	1.8	2.9	3.3	14.5	19.3	7.3	21.2	62.3	2
Goldsboro,	3.9	2.7	4.5	3.8	5.0	8.4	7.5	5.5	4.4	4.2	2.2	3.1	13.3	21.4	10.8	9.7	55.2	4
Greensboro',	0.9	1.5	1.6	1.4	3.5	1.6	1.4	2.6	1.7	0.7	0.9	2.1	6.5	5.6	3.3	4.5	19.9	3
Lenoir,	4.2	6.4	3.1	4.3	3.1	3.3	5.2	6.0	4.8	1.6	3.8	2.7	10.5	14.5	10.2	13.3	48.5	3
Murphy,	6.5	10.9	6.9	7.5	3.0	6.1	6.3	8.1	3.6	1.5	3.8	8.6	17.4	20.5	8.9	26.0	72.8	3
Newbern,	7.8	6.7	4.3	6.0	7.1	6.0	6.7	10.5	6.4	5.6	3.8	5.6	17.4	23.2	15.8	20.1	76.5	2
Oxford,	3.4	5.2	3.1	3.4	5.8	3.4	4.4	4.6	4.3	3.0	3.0	2.6	12.3	12.4	10.3	11.2	46.2	7
Poplar Branch,	3.9	5.3	3.7	5.9	5.1	3.8	4.0	5.3	3.2	4.5	2.8	2.3	14.7	13.1	10.5	11.5	49.8	2
Raleigh,	3.8	5.1	4.4	2.9	4.6	5.6	3.4	5.2	3.3	4.4	2.3	3.2	11.9	14.2	10.0	12.1	48.2	4
Statesville,	4.0	5.5	5.2	4.3	4.4	5.2	3.7	5.0	4.5	3.6	5.8	3.8	13.9	13.9	13.9	13.3	55.0	6
Scotland Neck,	3.5	5.7	3.3	4.3	6.1	2.3	4.6	7.5	5.0	2.2	4.2	4.4	13.7	14.4	11.4	13.6	53.1	2
Weldon,	4.0	5.3	3.1	1.6	5.4	2.8	5.2	6.6	4.2	4.2	3.4	3.1	10.1	14.6	11.8	12.4	48.9	3
Wilmington,	4.5	5.0	3.8	1.7	6.4	3.5	7.7	7.2	11.8	2.6	3.1	5.1	11.9	18.4	17.5	14.6	62.4	3
Eastern Divis'n,	4.9	5.1	3.8	3.9	5.8	4.5	5.9	7.1	5.8	3.9	3.5	3.9	13.5	17.5	13.2	13.9	58.1	
Middle Divis'n,	3.7	4.8	4.0	3.6	4.1	3.9	3.6	4.9	3.4	3.0	3.4	3.2	11.7	12.4	9.8	11.7	45.6	
West'n Divis'n,	5.4	8.3	5.5	5.3	3.7	5.3	5.5	6.4	2.8	1.7	3.1	5.2	14.5	17.2	7.6	18.9	58.2	
State,	4.5	5.3	4.0	3.9	4.9	4.3	4.9	6.1	4.5	3.3	3.4	3.7	12.9	15.4	11.9	13.5	53.1	

Snow.—The records of the stations are not full enough nor of sufficiently long continuance to give entirely satisfactory results, in regard to the amount and distribution of snow, but the observations of 17 stations in 1872, show that the total fall of snow for that year averaged 6 inches for the whole State, 4 inches in the mountains, and 6½ in the middle and eastern divisions; and the average for three years, (including 1872), for the State, deduced from observations at 5 stations, is also 6 inches, the largest average for a single station, 11½ inches, occurring at Boone. It is proper to state that the average for a larger number of years will probably be somewhat above the amount given by these last three, as this feature of the winters in this latitude is very variable, in some winters a fall of 4 or 6 inches occurring at one time, and at long intervals even 10 and 12 inches, as in 1857.

It is observable that the yearly amount of snow-fall is not greater in the mountains than in the cismontane regions. This result traverses the common impression; but there is a strong confirmation of it in the well known fact, attested by the most intelligent observers, that the wild mountain pastures do not become inaccessible to cattle grazing, by reason of the obstruction of snow, oftener than about once in seven years.

Frosts.—The first frosts of autumn may be expected about October 13; occurring once in the last three years on the 2nd., at three of the western stations, and as late as November 4, at one point of the eastern division; and the date of the last frost of spring is about April 21; occasionally falling however, as early as the 13th, and once in the three years, at some of the mountain stations, quite abnormally, as late as May 20.

There are portions of territory in the western region, that are exempt from frosts altogether. These are found in narrow zones along the flanks of various mountain ranges, and are known as "frostless belts." They are from a few rods wide to several hundred yards, and their boundaries are said to be very narrowly defined and to remain quite permanently fixed. Mr. Silas McDowell, a very intelligent observer in Macon county, seems to have been the first to call attention to this fact; and he has traced the limits of some of these tracts, and finds the lines so sharply drawn, that one half of a shrub will be frost-killed, and the other unaffected. It would occupy too much space to discuss here the causes of this phenomenon; suffice it to say, that it is due to the nocturnal sratification of the atmosphere of these mountain-enclosed basins, the different horizontal belts, having different degrees of humidity, whereby the surface radiation is controlled.

The point of practical interest is, that within these favored limits, fruits never fail. One of the most noted of these tracts is found along the eastward escarpment of the Tryon range, in Polk county, at an elevation of about 1500 feet. It is distinguishable at a distance of many miles by the numerous peach orchards which are spread along the face of the mountain in a narrow regular zone.

But similar areas are found in all parts of the mountain and piedmont regions, and are distinguishable, in the natural state, by the abundance of wild grapes. Such localities, not only beyond the Blue Ridge, but in the South Mountains and their spurs for example, and in the Brushy Mountains, are the most notable seats for orchards and vineyards, and are widely known for the abundance, and excellence and unfailing certainty of their crops.

Humidity.—The Survey has been able to procure hygrometric observations at only two points, and for a little more than one year. These two points are Wilmington and Charlotte. A special effort was made to have such observations at one station in the mountain region, but without success. This is regretted, as it is a matter of much importance, both in a sanitary point of view and in relation to agriculture, especially the cultivation of fruits. For at points "with thermal relations very similar, the results are nevertheless very different as regards the ripeness or unripeness of the fruit of the vine," for instance. In England, although the mean amount of annual heat is equal to that of many portions of North Carolina, such is the humidity of the atmosphere and so great the prevalence of clouds and fogs that vineyards are almost unknown, the strawberry is ripened artificially, and good peaches, apples, &c., are known only as importations. And yet there is no part of this State where the grape does not readily come to perfection, and where all the fruits suitable to the temperate zone, do not flourish. The observations at the two points named, for the eastern and middle divisions of the State, give the explanation, in the great dryness of the atmosphere, notwithstanding the large amount of rainfall,—so much in excess of that of England. The table below is intended only to exhibit this characteristic of the climate of the State, by giving the relative humidity for the three most important months in this respect, as representing the entire season of the ripening of grains and fruits; and the noon observation is deemed sufficient for the purpose.

RELATIVE HUMIDITY OF THE ATMOSPHERE, AT TWO STATIONS, FOR THREE MONTHS OF THE YEAR, 1873.

Time of Observation, 2 *P. M.*

	WILMINGTON.						CHARLOTTE.					
	JUNE.		AUGUST.		OCTOBER.		JUNE.		AUGUST.		OCTOBER.	
Day of Month.	Temp. of Air.	Humid-ity.	Temp. of Air.	Humid-ity.	Temp. of Air.	Humid-ity.	Temp. of Air.	Humid-ity.	Temp. of Air.	Humid-ity.	Temp. of Air.	Humid-ity.
1	70	70	85	74	69	57	72	54	89	54		
2	77	68	86	72	75	66	79	63	90	50		
3	83	66	87	58	72	58	84	53	90	52		
4	84	64	86	79	76	74	82	63	79	76		
5	89	51	79	84	78	70	81	80	77	61		
6	84	74	79	56	79	69	77	84	80	46	57	97
7	89	40	79	48	51	58			80	69	60	41
8	79	51	82	90	71	24	80	51	84	62	73	48
9	77	41	85	64	74	36	76	49	87	55	72	47
10	81	41	84	71	71	37	79	48	86	65	72	56
11	83	52	85	78	74		79	67	81	78	75	21
12	75	85	83	74	74		69	87	83	71	69	47
13	72	80	85	71	67	56	77	52	77	82	63	50
14	78	59	79	68	72	46	67	83	78	65	70	50
14	85	54	83	73	73	42	79	65	80	60	74	41
16	85	64	78	82	76	53	84	58	84	53	72	56
17	81	77	85	75	78	57	87	55	81	76	73	54
18	91	44	85		78	57	86	62	83	71	73	57
19	92	45	84	64	72	95	88	54	79	76	66	86
20	91	44	82	75	51	75	84	62	81	66	48	70
21	87	41	85	71	61	34	85	44	83	71	54	49
22	87	29	86	63	66	31	87	55	81	69	61	44
23	87	51	79	82	68	57	86	63	85	61	65	84
24	88	43	86	61	72	69	87	60	86	56	71	59
25	80	66	85	69	70	68	86	61	87	62	64	73
26	82	55	90	46	70	65	72	78			61	91
27	84	49	88	64	73	71	84	47			71	75
28	85	46	83	83	66	36	84	49			60	39
29	82	74	78	83	52	35	84	53			51	40
30	83	71	81	74	61	49	81	57			51	37
31			84	72	67	50					58	39

The table exhibits the great variability of the relative amount of moisture in the air during the period represented, the humidity being greatest in August, decidedly so at Wilmington; and the low degree of saturation during the hottest days is notable; as the temperature of the air rises towards 90°, the percentage of saturation commonly sinks to 50° and lower. These columns reveal the important fact that the excessive humidity of the atmosphere over the Gulf States and the lower and middle Mississippi valley is by no means able to follow the course of the southwest winds across the Appalachians. The importance of this fact in a climatological sense, and agriculturally, and especially in a sanitary point of view, is worthy of much emphasis.

The following comparative table of humidities shows the relative hygrometric condition of the atmosphere at several typical localities, and sets the fact of the relative dryness of the air in this State in a strong light.

The data, other than those for this State, are given by Blodget in his valuable work on American Climatology. This writer emphasizes the fact that the climate of the Gulf States and the Mississippi valley is very humid, and calls attention to the undoubted relation between the high percentage of moisture during the hot months and the excessive insalubrity of the whole region during the same season:

COMPARATIVE HUMIDITIES.

	Wilmington.	Charlotte.	New Orleans.	St. Louis.	London.
Jan'y,	57	78	85	68	85
Feb'y,	51	75	84	87	85
Mar.,	36	66	83	61	80
Apr.,	42	53	83	46	80
May,	61	65	84	66	75
June,	56	60	81	69	73
July,	61		82	70	77
Aug.,	71	64	87	78	77
Sept.,	73	65	85	80	74
Oct.,	55	56	80	63	83
Nov.,	53	57	84	71	86
Dec.,	60	73	82	68	84
	—	—	—	—	—
Year,	57	65	86	67	80

Atmospheric Pressure.—Barometric observations are in hand for only three stations, the two last named and Asheville; but there is not a complete series through an entire year for any of these points, and they have not been reduced or prepared for publication or discussion ; so that this department of the climatology is reserved for a later volume and a larger accumulation of data.

Clouds, &c.—Neither a copious annual precipitation, nor abundant humidity necessarily implies a prevalence of clouds and fogs. These elements of climate require to be ascertained independently. Excessive cloudiness, not less than excessive moisture, is unfavorable to many of the highest and most profitable forms of agriculture, to viticulture, for example, and to the ripening of fruits, and it also affects very directly the prevalence of certain forms of disease ; and it is a subject worthy of much fuller treatment in a general discussion of the climatology of the State, than can now be attempted, and indeed than the present data would justify. The table of relative cloudiness which follows, although not as full as is desirable, will serve to convey a reasonably just impression of the general character of this feature of the climate of the State, and of its particular sections. The term *fair* describes the days for which the average of the three observations of the clouds, morning, noon and night, is *less than one-third ; cloudy*, those for which this average is *above two-thirds ; and rainy*, the days on which rain fell, no matter how little or for how short time. So that it very often happens that the *rainy* days belong to the class of *fair* days. It will be observed that more than one-third, (about three-eighths) of the year is set down as fair ; about one-third, as cloudy ; leaving nearly a third, (from 100 to 112 days) unclassed ; being those which are partly cloudy, and partly fair, the cloudiness lying between one-third and two-thirds.

The greatest number of fair days is found in the eastern division, and the smallest number of cloudy and rainy ; and the middle region is credited with the largest amount of cloudiness.

Of the stations, Beaufort records the greatest number of fair days, and Oxford and Charlotte (along the mean isothermal), the greatest number of cloudy, and Charlotte and Newbern (and Wilmington) the most frequent rains, the number for these points being very much above the average for the State.

It is worthy of note that the number of rainy days, contrary to the common notion, is less in the western section than in the State at large, and less than in the other divisions except the eastern, with which it agrees in this particular ; and further, that there is greater cloudiness and more frequent rains along the immediate coast than in the eastern half of the State, or in the mountains, or in the State at large.

The fairest month, throughout the State, is October, and the greatest cloudiness is found in February; both these features being quite marked. And of the seasons, in all the divisions, autumn shows most fair weather, and winter the greatest prevalence of clouds; although rains are a little more frequent in summer, and as much so in spring. So that these two characters, cloudiness and raininess, are not necessarily proportional to each other.

The humidity of the atmosphere in this State does not often become palpable in the form of *fog*. An entire day of fog is of rare occurrence in any part of North Carolina. Quite a number of the stations record no fogs at all, or only for a fraction of one day in three years. Along the larger water courses, especially in the deep mountain valleys, morning fogs are quite frequent in the latter part of summer, and during the autumn months; in some sections, as at Franklin, Murphy, &c., half the mornings for a month in some years may rise foggy, but the mists lift before 10 o'clock. In the cismontane sections fogs occur about as frequently in winter as in autumn, but the total fogginess, averaged for the region, amounts to only about two days in the year.

Clouds; Aspect of the Sky; Average Number of Fair, Cloudy and Rainy Days, for a Period of Years, at Eighteen Stations, &c.

Name of Station.		January.	February.	March.	April.	May.	June.	July.	August.	September.	October.	November.	December.	Spring.	Summer.	Autumn.	Winter.	Year.	No. of Y'rs Observation
Boone,	Fair,	7	6	9	12	9	9	13	16	10	22	5	9	30	38	37	22	127	2
	Cloudy,	17	12	10	13	6	7	9	5	7	7	13	22	29	21	27	51	128	
	Rainy,	13	7	10	11	9	9	5	8	3				30	22	3	20	75	
Beaufort,	Fair,		10	19	19	23	24	30	18	19	19	23	17	61	72	61	27	221	1
	Cloudy,		13	3	0	0	0	0	0	0	0	1	10	3	0	1	23	27	
	Rainy,		5	10	8	6	9	5	7	8	5	7	10	24	21	20	15	80	
Charlotte,	Fair,	5	4	8	9	9	4	4	4	11	14	6	4	26	12	31	15	84	3
	Cloudy.	12	18	14	13	14	13	16	16	12	7	13	13	41	45	32	43	161	
	Rainy,	12	14	13	11	12	12	12	24	10	5	9	10	36	48	24	36	144	
Edenton,	Fair,	10	9	14	11	6	8	6	10	10	13	10	10	31	24	33	29	117	1
	Cloudy,	10	14	11	8	12	6	12	8	6	9	6	19	31	26	21	43	121	
	Rainy,	8	10	9	4	13	6	9	8	6	4	5	12	26	23	15	30	94	
Fayetteville,	Fair,	10	7	8	12	8	7	5	7	9	22	9	11	28	19	40	28	115	1½
	Cloudy,	13	15	9	10	11	5	9	6	9	6	12	13	30	20	27	41	118	
	Rainy,	4	10	9	7	12	9	13	14	6	4	7	11	28	36	17	25	106	
Franklin,	Fair,	8	7	11	11	16	9	9	16	21	10	13	8	38	34	44	23	139	2
	Cloudy,	13	15	13	10	10	10	9	6	7	4	6	17	33	25	17	45	120	
	Rainy,	9	9	12	10	5	9	8	10	4	3	9	8	27	27	16	26	96	
Greensboro',	Fair,	12	8	13	12	12	14	5	13	14	20	13	12	37	32	44	32	145	3
	Cloudy,	14	15	10	10	10	8	7	8	7	6	11	14	30	23	24	43	120	
	Rainy,	8	9	7	10	9	7	7	10	7	4	6	7	26	24	17	24	91	
Lenoir,	Fair,	12	7	13	10	13	11	12	11	14	20	11	11	36	34	45	30	145	3
	Cloudy,	13	15	9	9	11	10	9	10	8	7	12	13	29	29	27	41	126	
	Rainy,	8	10	8	11	9	11	9	0	6	4	8	7	28	30	18	25	101	

Murphy,	Fair,	5	4	10	9	13	8	9	9	14	20	10	4	30	26	44	13	13	3
	Cloudy,	17	14	14	14	10	11	10	6	8	5	11	19	38	27	24	50	139	
	Rainy,	14	12	13	12	7	9	10	8	6	3	9	12	32	27	18	38	115	
Newbern,	Fair,	11	5	11	10	12	6	6	4	6	14	7	9	33	16	27	25	101	2½
	Cloudy,	14	15	9	14	9	12	11	15	11	7	10	16	32	3[illegible]	28	45	143	
	Rainy,	12	6	11	11	12	9	13	17	11	6	12	13	34	39	29	41	43	
Oxford,	Fair,	9	6	11	8	9	8	7	6	11	13	8	9	28	21	32	24	105	3
	Cloudy,	14	17	12	14	13	12	13	13	13	8	14	18	39	38	35	49	161	
	Rainy,	9	11	8	3	7	7	8	8	6	4	6	8	23	23	16	28	90	
Poplar Branch,	Fair,	14	7	15	12	12	11	11	11	13	18	14	12	39	33	45	33	150	2
	Cloudy,	11	17	11	10	8	4	7	9	9	8	7	15	29	20	24	43	1[illegible]6	
	Rainy,	4	5	5	5	5	6	4	6	4	4	5	4	15	16	13	13	57	
Statesville,	Fair,	14	9	16	16	12	14	10	9	15	21	13	14	44	33	4	37	162	2
	Cloudy,	11	13	9	9	5	8	7	11	8	4	8	11	23	26	20	35	194	
	Rainy,	8	10	9	8	7	8	8	10	5	3	6	7	24	26	14	25	89	
Scotland Neck,	Fair,	13	6	15	12	15	19	14	16	17	23	15	11	42	49	55	30	176	2
	Cloudy,	8	14	8	10	12	6	6	8	7	4	11	12	30	20	22	34	106	
	Rainy,	8	9	8	9	10	8	9	11	8	3	7	10	27	28	18	27	100	
Stagg's Creek,	Fair,	9	9	14	11	14	14	10	15	16	21	16	16	39	39	53	34	165	2
	Cloudy,	17	12	12	11	6	4	7	7	6	2	6	10	29	18	14	39	100	
	Rainy,	12	11	10	12	10	8	5	6	4	3	9	5	32	19	16	28	95	
Tarboro',	Fair,	12	7	8	11	11	8	5	11	14	15	16	9	30	24	45	28	127	1
	Cloudy,	13	15	11	7	5	3	2	2	4	7	8	13	23	7	19	41	90	
	Rainy,	7	10	8	5	9	9	8	8	9	4	8	10	22	25	21	27	95	
Weldon,	Fair,	11	9	14	13	12	12	9	12	10	19	13	10	39	33	42	30	144	3
	Cloudy,	13	14	10	10	9	7	8	10	8	6	9	13	29	25	23	40	117	
	Rainy,	9	12	9	11	12	10	8	12	9	6	9	10	32	30	24	31	117	
Wilmington,	Fair,	13	6	10	12	13	10	7	9	8	14	13	10	35	26	35	29	125	3
	Cloudy,	11	14	11	11	9	9	8	11	12	6	10	13	31	28	28	38	125	
	Rainy,	9	12	10	6	13	16	14	14	11	4	7	14	29	44	22	35	130	

CLOUDS; ASPECT OF THE SKY; AVERAGE NUMBER OF FAIR, CLOUDY AND RAINY DAYS, &c.– (*Continued*).

		January.	February.	March.	April.	May.	June.	July.	August.	September.	October.	November.	December.	Spring.	Summer.	Autumn.	Winter.	Year.
Coast Region,	Fair,	13	6	12	11	12	9	8	8	9	15	11	10	35	25	35	29	124
	Cloudy,	12	15	10	12	9	8	9	12	11	7	9	15	31	29	27	42	129
	Rainy,	8	8	9	7	10	10	10	9	9	5	8	10	26	29	22	26	103
Eastern Division,	Fair,	11	8	13	13	12	13	11	12	13	18	14	11	38	36	45	30	149
	Cloudy,	11	14	9	7	8	4	6	6	6	5	8	13	24	16	19	38	97
	Rainy,	7	9	9	7	10	8	9	10	7	4	7	10	26	27	18	26	97
Middle Division,	Fair,	10	7	12	11	11	10	8	9	13	18	10	10	34	27	41	27	129
	Cloudy,	13	16	11	11	11	10	10	12	10	6	12	14	33	32	28	43	136
	Rainy,	9	11	9	10	9	9	9	12	7	4	7	8	28	30	15	28	104
Western Division,	Fair,	7	6	11	11	13	10	10	14	15	18	11	9	35	34	44	22	135
	Cloudy,	16	13	12	12	8	8	9	6	7	4	9	17	32	22	20	46	120
	Rainy,	12	10	11	9	8	9	7	8	4	3	9	8	28	24	16	30	98
State,	Fair,	11	7	12	11	12	10	9	10	12	17	11	10	35	29	40	28	132
	Cloudy,	12	15	10	10	9	8	8	10	9	6	10	14	30	26	25	43	124
	Rainy,	8	9	9	8	9	9	9	10	7	4	7	9	27	28	19	27	101

Winds.—The remaining table, of the winds, includes only those stations for which observations are complete for at least two years. There are others which it was desirable to add on account of their representative character, had their series of observations on this point been sufficiently complete and extensive; but enough are given to bring out the chief peculiarities of at least each of the principal subdivisions of the State, so far as this can be attempted in a partial and preliminary discussion. The direction only is given, and not the force, as the former is the more important characteristic in a region where violent and destructive winds are so entirely unknown, the average force, even in the most elevated and exposed parts, as at Boone, for example, being less than 1.8 for January, and not more than 2 (of the Smithsonian scale, that is "a gentle breeze") for any month of the twelve, and the greatest force recorded at this point (in two years) having never passed 5 (or "a high wind"). Indeed, the chief difficulty in obtaining complete records on this point arises from the fact that most observers fill a large part of the blanks with the entry *zero*, the breeze being a large part of the time insensible, except to close and patient observation. The figures in the table, opposite each of the letters indicating the points of the compass denote the number of days of the month (or season) at the top of the column during which the wind blows from that direction. These numbers were obtained by adding all the observations for the month, of each direction of the eight points of the compass, and dividing the result by three. The broken column of alternate figures and blanks, to the right of the columns for the seasons and year, are obtained, as will be obvious on inspection, by adding to the numbers, opposite which they stand, (in those columns), the numbers next above and below, as explained by the last column of the table, in the words *northerly*, *easterly*, &c.

WINDS: AVERAGE NUMBER OF DAYS OF THE MONTH, SEASON AND YEAR DURING WHICH THE WIND BLOWS FROM EIGHT POINTS OF THE COMPASS.

		JANUARY.	FEBRUARY.	MARCH.	APRIL.	MAY.	JUNE.	JULY.	AUGUST.	SEPTEMBER.	OCTOBER.	NOVEMBER.	DECEMBER.	SPRING.		SUMMER.		AUTUMN.		WINTER.		YEAR.			YEARS OF OBS'VATIN.
Boone.	N.	0	0	0	0	0	0	0	0	0	0	0	0	0	1	0	3	0	5	0	1	0	10	North'rly,	2
	N. E.	0	0	0	0	0	0	0	0	0	0	0	0	0		0		0		0		0			
	E.	0	3	1	1	0	0	0	0	0	0	0	0	2	14	0	2	0	15	3	6	5	37	Easterly,	
	S. E.	1	2	3	3	6	1	1	0	2	5	8	0	12		2		15		3		32			
	S.	2	1	0	1	0	0	1	0	0	0	0	0	1	14	1	7	0	15	0	3	2	39	South'rly,	
	S. W.	0	0	0	1	0	1	2	1	0	0	0	0	1		4		0		0		5			
	W.	22	23	21	24	16	14	13	13	28	23	19	28	61	63	40	47	70	75	73	74	244	259	Westerly,	
	N. W.	0	0	1	0	0	1	1	1	0	3	2	1	1		3		5		1		10			
Charlotte.	N.	3	6	4	4	1	2	2	5	6	5	4	6	9	32	9	31	15	34	15	33	43	130	North'rly,	3
	N. E.	1	4	3	2	5	4	4	6	5	3	3	1	10		14		11		6		41			
	E.	0	0	0	3	1	2	2	2	3	1	0	1	4	18	6	28	4	18	1	9	15	73	Easterly,	
	S. E.	1	1	1	2	1	4	2	2	2	1	0	0	4		8		3		2		17			
	S.	6	4	6	9	6	6	8	2	1	3	2	4	21	40	16	40	6	17	14	33	57	130	South'rly,	
	S. W.	7	5	6	4	5	5	7	4	2	2	4	5	15		16		8		17		56			
	W.	3	2	5	3	2	2	2	4	3	6	5	3	10	38	8	32	14	30	8	37	40	137	Westerly,	
	N. W.	3	3	5	3	5	1	3	4	2	3	3	6	13		8		8		12		41			
Franklin.	N.	2	1	3	1	1	1	1	1	0	3	1	0	5	14	3	11	4	12	8	24	20	61	North'rly,	3
	N. E.	2	1	1	1	2	2	2	1	1	2	1	5	4		5		4		8		21			
	E.	4	5	3	5	7	6	5	3	4	4	6	5	15	22	14	24	14	22	14	26	57	94	Easterly,	
	S. E.	0	2	0	1	2	3	2	0	0	1	3	2	3		5		4		4		16			
	S.	1	0	2	3	3	3	2	1	0	1	1	1	8	18	6	15	2	11	2	11	18	55	South'rly,	
	S. W.	2	1	2	2	3	3	1	0	2	1	2	2	7		4		5		5		21			
	W.	1	9	8	8	6	4	5	2	4	2	5	10	22	34	11	18	11	20	20	33	64	105	Westerly,	
	N. W.	6	2	2	2	1	1	1	1	0	2	2	0	5		3		4		8		20			

Greensboro'.	N.	2	2	1	2	1	1	1	2	2	2	2	2	4	36	4	25	6	40	6	47	20	148	North'rly,	
	N. E.	4	7	3	4	3	1	1	7	2	4	6	7	10		9		12		18		49			
	E.	1	1	2	1	3	1	1	0	1	0	0	0	6	18	2	14	1	17	2	21	11	70	Easterly,	
	S. E.	1	0	0	1	1	1	1	1	3	1	0	0	2		3		4		1		10			3
	S.	1	1	0	1	1	2	1	0	1	0	0	0	2	18	3	26	1	15	2	18	8	78	South'rly,	
	S. W.	5	5	4	5	5	7	6	7	4	4	2	6	14		20		10		16		60			
	W.	9	4	9	9	11	9	12	8	7	11	8	6	29	65	29	61	26	58	19	58	103	242	Westerly,	
	N. W.	8	6	10	7	5	4	4	4	6	6	10	9	22		12		22		23		79			
Lenoir.	N.	1	1	2	0	1	1	1	1	1	1	2	2	3	47	3	47	4	52	4	63	14	139	North'rly,	
	N. E.	7	9	5	6	7	3	5	8	8	6	6	6	18		19		20		22		79			
	E.	1	2	2	1	2	2	1	2	1	2	2	2	5	32	5	39	5	39	5	34	20	144	Easterly,	
	S. E.	2	3	2	3	4	4	5	6	5	6	3	2	9		15		14		7		45			3
	S.	1	1	0	0	1	0	0	1	0	1	0	1	1	21	1	24	1	22	3	18	6	85	South'rly,	
	S. W.	2	3	4	5	2	2	3	3	2	2	3	3	11		8		7		8		34			
	W.	2	1	2	4	10	7	5	3	1	2	2	3	16	53	15	48	5	40	6	51	42	192	Westerly,	
	N. W.	15	10	12	9	6	3	10	7	6	11	11	12	26		25		28		37		116			
Murphy.	N.	4	4	3	2	4	4	6	7	6	7	6	5	9	29	17	29	19	36	13	31	58	125	North'rly,	
	N. E.	1	1	1	1	1	1	1	1	2	2	2	1	3		3		6		3		15			
	E.	0	0	1	1	1	0	1	1	1	1	1	1	3	13	2	12	3	16	1	12	9	53	Easterly,	
	S. E.	3	3	2	3	2	4	1	2	3	2	2	2	7		7		7		8		29			3
	S.	2	3	3	3	4	5	5	4	4	2	2	2	10	29	15	29	8	22	7	23	40	103	South'rly,	
	S. W.	3	2	3	5	4	3	2	2	2	2	3	3	12		7		7		8		34			
	W.	3	5	8	5	6	4	5	3	4	4	4	5	19	48	12	23	12	30	13	36	56	142	Wester'y,	
	N. W.	6	4	7	6	4	4	2	3	3	4	4	5	17		9		11		15		52			
Newbern.	N.	0	1	1	1	0	[illegible]	1	1	1	3	0	0	2	22	2	19	4	34	1	36	9	121	North'rly,	
	N. E.	3	6	3	4	2	[illegible]	2	6	7	5	2	6	9		11		14		15		49			
	E.	0	1	1	0	0	[illegible]	1	1	1	0	2	1	1	28	4	32	3	29	2	27	10	116	Easterly,	
	S. E.	6	1	3	5	10	[illegible]	8	6	6	4	2	3	18		17		12		10		57			3
	S.	1	0	2	2	1	[illegible]	2	2	1	3	0	0	5	52	6	53	4	33	1	38	16	176	South'rly,	
	S. W.	10	8	6	13	10	15	9	6	4	4	9	9	29		30		17		27		103			
	W.	0	1	3	1	2	[illegible]	1	0	0	1	2	0	6	46	1	37	3	36	1	48	11	167	Westerly,	
	N. W.	6	6	5	3	3	[illegible]	2	3	2	7	7	8	11		6		16		20		53			
Oxford.	N.	2	3	2	2	4	[illegible]	1	2	3	4	4	3	8	47	4	32	11	49	8	54	31	182	North'rly,	
	N. E.	7	10	7	5	5	[illegible]	4	7	8	6	5	7	17		16		19		24		76			
	E.	0	0	0	0	0	[illegible]	0	0	0	0	0	0	0	23	0	23	0	23	0	25	0	94	Easterly,	
	S. E.	1	0	1	2	3	[illegible]	2	2	3	1	0	0	6		7		4		1		18			3
	S.	2	2	0	2	3	[illegible]	4	3	2	2	0	5	5	27	12	41	4	26	9	22	30	116	South'rly,	
	S. W.	4	3	6	6	4	[illegible]	9	6	4	4	10	5	16		22		18		12		68			
	W.	2	2	2	2	2	[illegible]	1	1	0	1	1	0	6	44	3	37	2	39	4	38	15	158	Westerly,	
	N. W.	11	5	9	6	7	6	3	3	4	6	9	6	22		12		19		22		75			

WINDS: AVERAGE NUMBER OF DAYS OF THE MONTH, SEASON AND YEAR DURING WHICH THE WIND BLOWS FROM EIGHT POINTS OF THE COMPASS.

STATION.		JANUARY.	FEBRUARY.	MARCH.	APRIL.	MAY.	JUNE.	JULY.	AUGUST.	SEPTEMBER.	OCTOBER.	NOVEMBER.	DECEMBER.	SPRING.		SUMMER.		AUTUMN.		WINTER.		YEAR.			YEARS OF OBS'VAT'N.
Poplar Branch.	N.	2	4	3	2	3	4	4	3	3	5	4	4	8	35	11	22	12	36	10	43	41	136	North'rly,	2
	N. E.	7	7	6	9	5	5	2	3	7	2	3	7	20		10		12		21		63			
	E.	0	2	1	1	3	1	1	2	2	0	0	0	5	35	4	23	2	25	2	28	13	111	Easterly,	
	S. E.	3	1	2	3	5	2	3	4	3	5	3	1	10		9		11		5		35			
	S.	6	2	1	2	2	3	9	5	4	1	4	6	5	38	17	50	9	32	14	29	45	149	South'rly,	
	S. W.	5	3	12	6	5	9	7	8	6	4	2	2	23		24		12		10		69			
	W.	2	2	5	4	3	2	1	8	2	3	4	5	12	42	11	36	9	33	9	31	41	142	Westerly,	
	N. W.	4	4	4	3	0	1	0	0	1	4	7	4	7		1		12		12		32			
Weldon.	N.	2	6	2	3	2	3	2	5	5	5	2	4	7	23	10	24	12	30	12	28	41	105	North'rly,	3
	N. E.	1	3	2	3	3	3	1	3	3	2	2	3	8		7		7		7		29			
	E.	1	1	3	1	2	1	1	2	1	1	1	0	6	23	4	17	3	15	2	13	15	68	Easterly,	
	S. E.	2	1	2	3	4	2	1	3	2	2	1	1	9		6		5		4		24			
	S.	6	3	4	4	3	8	11	6	4	5	2	4	11	27	25	42	11	25	13	26	60	99	South'rly,	
	S. W.	3	2	2	2	3	4	4	3	1	3	5	4	7		11		9		9		36			
	W.	7	4	8	7	3	2	3	1	1	2	5	5	8	23	6	24	8	28	16	34	38	109	Westerly,	
	N. W.	2	3	3	2	3	2	2	3	2	4	5	4	8		7		11		9		35			
Wilmington.	N.	2	3	3	1	1	0	2	2	3	5	2	2	5	27	4	21	10	40	7	44	26	132	North'rly,	3
	N. E.	3	6	3	3	4	4	1	4	5	5	7	6	10		9		17		15		51			
	E.	3	2	1	2	3	3	3	2	4	1	2	2	6	25	8	28	7	34	7	29	28	116	Easterly,	
	S. E.	5	1	2	1	6	3	4	4	5	3	2	1	9		11		10		7		37			
	S.	1	2	1	3	1	1	3	5	3	1	0	1	5	39	9	46	4	25	4	29	22	139	South'rly,	
	S. W.	6	6	8	12	5	12	10	4	3	4	4	6	25		26		11		18		80			
	W.	1	2	3	2	1	2	2	3	3	1	3	1	6	43	7	41	7	31	4	44	24	159	Westerly,	
	N. W.	7	7	6	4	2	3	2	3	2	5	6	8	12		8		13		22		55			

Coast Region.	N.	1	3	2	1	1	1	2	2	2	4	2	2	4	22	5	16	8	29	6	29	23	96	North'rly,
	N. E.	4	5	4	5	4	4	2	4	6	4	4	6	13		10		14		16		53		
	E.	1	2	1	1	2	2	2	2	2	0	1	1	4	29	6	29	3	28	4	28	17	114	Easterly,
	S. E.	5	1	2	3	7	3	5	5	5	4	2	2	12		13		11		8		44		
	S.	3	1	1	2	1	2	5	4	3	2	1	2	4	42	11	51	6	30	6	33	27	156	South'rly,
	S. W.	7	6	9	10	7	12	9	6	4	4	5	6	26		27		13		19		85		
	W.	1	2	4	2	2	1	1	4	2	2	3	2	8	44	6	38	7	34	5	42	26	158	Westerly,
	N. W.	5	6	5	3	2	2	1	2	2	5	7	7	10		5		14		18		47		
Eastern Divis'n.	N.	1	3	2	2	1	2	2	3	3	4	2	2	5	25	7	21	9	33	6	36	27	115	North'rly,
	N. E.	3	6	3	5	3	4	1	4	5	3	3	5	11		9		11		14		45		
	E.	1	1	1	1	2	2	1	2	2	0	1	1	4	26	5	24	3	23	3	23	15	96	Easterly,
	S. E.	4	1	2	3	6	2	4	4	4	3	2	1	11		10		9		6		36		
	S.	3	2	2	3	2	3	6	4	3	2	1	3	7	39	13	43	6	27	8	30	34	139	South'rly,
	S. W.	6	5	7	8	6	8	7	5	3	4	5	5	21		20		12		16		69		
	W.	2	2	5	3	2	1	2	3	1	2	3	3	10	40	6	31	6	31	7	29	29	141	Westerly,
	N. W.	5	5	4	3	2	2	1	2	2	5	6	6	9		5		13		16		43		
Middle Divisi'n.	N.	2	3	2	2	2	1	1	2	3	3	3	3	6	39	4	32	9	43	8	48	27	162	North'rly
	N. E.	5	7	4	4	5	4	3	7	6	5	5	5	13		14		16		17		60		
	E.	0	1	1	1	1	1	1	1	1	1	0	1	3	21	3	25	2	24	2	21	10	91	Easterly,
	S. E.	1	1	1	2	2	3	2	3	3	2	1	0	5		8		6		2		21		
	S.	2	2	1	3	3	3	3	1	1	1	0	0	7	26	7	31	2	19	4	19	20	95	South'rly,
	S. W.	4	4	5	5	4	5	6	5	3	3	5	5	14		16		11		13		54		
	W.	4	2	4	4	6	5	5	4	3	5	4	3	14	48	14	44	12	41	9	45	49	178	Westerly,
	N. W.	9	6	9	6	5	5	5	4	4	6	8	8	20		14		18		23		75		
Western Divis'n.	N.	2	2	2	1	2	2	2	3	2	3	2	2	5	16	7	15	7	17	6	18	25	66	North'rly,
	N. E.	1	1	1	1	1	1	1	1	1	1	1	2	3		3		3		4		13		
	E.	1	3	2	2	3	2	2	2	2	2	2	2	7	17	6	14	6	18	6	14	25	63	Easterly,
	S. E.	1	2	2	2	3	3	1	1	2	3	4	1	7		5		9		4		25		
	S.	2	1	2	2	2	3	3	2	1	1	1	1	6	20	8	18	3	16	4	13	21	67	South'rly,
	S. W.	2	1	2	3	2	2	2	1	1	1	2	2	7		5		4		5		21		
	W.	9	12	12	12	9	7	8	6	12	10	9	14	33	48	21	31	31	42	35	48	120	169	Westerly,
	N. W.	4	2	3	3	2	2	1	2	1	3	3	2	8		5		7		8		25		
State.	N.	1	3	2	2	1	2	2	3	3	3	2	2	5	29	7	27	8	35	6	38	26	129	North'rly,
	N. E.	4	6	3	4	4	4	2	5	5	4	4	5	11		11		13		15		50		
	E.	1	1	1	1	2	2	1	2	2	1	1	1	4	23	5	24	4	25	3	22	16	64	Easterly,
	S. E.	2	1	2	2	4	2	3	3	3	3	2	1	8		8		8		4		28		
	S.	2	2	2	3	2	3	4	3	2	1	1	2	7	32	10	35	4	23	6	24	27	114	South'rly,
	S. W.	5	4	6	6	5	6	6	5	3	3	5	5	17		17		11		14		59		
	W.	3	3	5	4	4	3	4	4	3	4	4	4	13	43	11	37	11	36	10	41	45	157	Westerly,
	N. W.	6	5	6	4	3	3	3	3	3	5	6	6	13		9		14		17		53		

The most striking general feature of the table is the *predominance of westerly winds* in all the divisions, and at nearly all the stations. A little closer inspection discovers that this predominance is most decided in the western region, and very slight in the eastern. It is worthy of note further, that while the winds which make up this result, in the average for the state, are nearly equally distributed to the three octants, S. W., W., and N. W., with a slight plurality of days to the first, in each of the different sub-divisions, it is due to the preponderance of a different octant, viz: of the S. W., in the eastern; N. W., in the middle; and W., in the western section; this preponderance being very marked in the last case. After the westerly winds, it will be observed that the next class in order of frequency is the northerly, except on the immediate sea-coast, where the preponderance passes to the southerly, from the great frequency of the winds from the S. W.; and the most infrequent in all sections and at nearly all the stations, are the easterly winds. And if only the E. octant is considered, it will be seen that in the general average for the State, the prevalence of this wind is limited to about two weeks; and if two stations be omitted, the average would fall to 11 days in the year for all the others. But at Franklin this octant is credited with a number of days only second to that of the W.; and at Wilmington it reaches nearly a month.

If the distribution of the winds be examined in reference to the seasons, it appears that in the State as a whole, the S. W. wind is preponderant in the spring and summer, and in the autumn and winter the N. W. and N. E. octants divide the sway with it almost equally; and the same statement holds for the eastern section with a more decided emphasis on the first of it, while in the middle region the prevalent winds are those from the three westerly octants with the northeastern, the N. W. having the advantage in spring, autumn and winter, the S. W. (slightly) in summer, the N. E. direction being more common in autumn and winter than the S. W., and of almost as frequent occurrence in spring and summer. In the western division the most common wind in all seasons is that from the W., its preponderance being most decided however, in winter and spring.

If the stations be considered individually, the most remarkable local peculiarities are, the prevalence at Boone of winds from the W. fully two-thirds of the year, at Lenoir the predominance of the N. W., at Greensboro of the W., and at Newbern of the S. W. octant; and the occurrence of E. winds for nearly two months at Franklin, while at Oxford this octant is wanting altogether.

These are some of the salient points, obvious on a cursory inspection of the table. A full discussion of this interesting and important branch of the climatology of the State will only be practicable when much ampler material shall have been collected. But enough is here given to exhibit the general features of the anemology of the State, and, it is hoped, to induce a wider interest in the subject, and fuller records. We do not in this latitude sufficiently appreciate the importance of the prevalent movements of the atmospheric currents in determining climates. The reason is our entire exemption from those deleterious and destructive winds which afflict so many of the fairest portions of the earth, as the hot and poisonous Simoom of Egypt and the neighboring countries; the burning Sirocco of Sicily and South Italy, and the frigid and tempestuous Bora from the Alps that ravages its northern coasts, the fierce Euroclydon; the stormy Levanter of the eastern Mediterranean shores; the hot and dust-laden Solano of Spain; the furious Pampero of the South American plains, or the biting and arid Puna of Peru; or even the unwholesome and disagreeable East Winds of Great Britain; or the Northeasters of the North Atlantic States; or the violent and freezing Northers of Texas and the great Plains; or the terrible Arctic gales that sweep the great prairie states of the Northwest. In this favored territory of North Carolina there is no distinct periodicity to the system of winds; the currents of the atmosphere are continually "boxing the compass," at least through the southern and western octants, hardly ever retaining one direction more than a few days together; the prevalent sweep of the great westerly continental current preventing the access of the damp and chill sea air, from the E. and N. E.; the cold N. W. winds being arrested and broken up in their passage across the numerous ridges of the Appalachians, among which also they are tempered by mingling with the warm southwest currents that roll up the intervening valleys; and the humid S. W. wind, (pluvius Auster) being drained of its excess of moisture and tropical heat in the ascent of the long southwest, Gulf-ward slopes, and later, the high table lands and lofty chains of the same mountain system, on the northwest border; so that none of the great continental currents, from the N. E., the N. W., or the S. W., reach this region, until they are quite bereft of their original and disagreeable characteristics. But as already intimated, it is not intended to attempt at present any thing like a general or exhaustive treatment of this department of our climatology.

Summary.—It may be fairly claimed upon the above exhibit, preliminary, brief and inadequate as it necessarily is, that there are few regions of the habitable globe where all the elements of climate are more admirably blended and attempered, both to human comfort and physical well being, and to that variety and productiveness of industries which is most conducive to the collective prosperity of a people.

Sanitary.—And as to salubrity, it must be evident to any one who has considered the topographical features of the State as hereinbefore described, and the prevalent climatic conditions, as developed in the present chapter, that the conditions of insalubrity cannot exist otherwise than locally and exceptionally. And the case becomes still stronger when the underlying geological structure is taken into account, which is almost every where favorable to ready and complete drainage, so that the waters of the most copious rains disappear from the surface in a few hours at most. And the sanitary statistics of the United States census reports show that the death rate for this State for 1870, for example, is much less than the average for the United States,—less than one per cent. against an average of more than one and a quarter, and if the comparison be carried back to include the reports for 1860 and 1850, the rates are still in nearly the same ratio, viz: 1.14 to 1.31; and as has been stated already in another connection, so far as concerns one of the most prevalent and fatal affections, consumption, one of the two small areas of total exemption in the whole United States is found in North Carolina; and if the figures which express the ratio of deaths from this cause to total mortality, for the entire State, be compared with the average for all the states, the contrast will be found not less striking than that of the general averages above given.

BOTANICAL.

It has long been known to botanists that the territory of North Carolina presents one of the finest fields in the United States for collection, on account of the great variety and interest of its vegetable productions. Many plants of northern habit, such as are common in the White Mountains, for example, and along the northern lakes, find their southern geographical limit in the mountains of this State; and quite a number of others spread from the Gulf and the Mississippi Valley to the Cape Fear and even to Pamplico Sound. So that the flora of this State is continental in character and range, combining the botanical features of both extremes as well as of the intermediate regions.

The results of the preceding discussion of the climatology of the State furnish ample explanation of the fact. The close connection between climate and organic life, and the decisive control which meteorological conditions exert over the whole character and range and form of its development render it practicable to infer the latter from the former, at least as to general outlines.

But it happens that the botany of North Carolina has received much earlier attention and a far greater amount of study, and has been much more fully worked out than its climatology, so that the inferential process has needed to be reversed, and the range and character of the climate to be deduced from botanical data. This is due in large part to the attractive nature of the field to the botanical explorer, which has engaged the interest and study of some of the most famous botanists of both Europe and America, from the time of Bartram's tour, in 1776, and of the elder Michaux, 1787, and of the younger, an equally distinguished botanist, in 1802, to the later explorations of Nuttall, and of Dr. Gray and Mr. Carey, who traversed the higher ranges of our mountains in 1841, and especially of the Rev. Dr. Curtis, to whom the State owes a debt, in this regard, which she does not yet fully appreciate. It is due to him more than to any one else,—to his skill and zeal in his favorite science, that North Carolina stands among the foremost of the states in respect to the completeness as well as the scientific accuracy of the knowledge which the world possesses of her singular botanical wealth.

In witness of the remarkably wide range of vegetable forms, corresponding to the variety of climatic conditions, may be cited the fact of the occurrence within the limits of the State on the one hand, of the white pine, (pinus strobus), and the black spruce, (abies nigra), which are found along the Appalachians from North Carolina to the White Mountains and Canada, and of the hemlock spruce, (abies canadensis), whose range reaches from our mountains to Hudson's Bay ; and on the other, of several species of magnolia and the palmetto, which have their northern limit in the southeast part of the State and spread thence to the Gulf. And the same point might be illustrated even more strongly to the botanist, by the mention of other but inconspicuous species, among the lower orders of plants, as the mosses, lichens, &c.

And as concerns the variety of plants which characterizes the flora of the State, it is sufficient to mention the fact that Dr. Curtis' Catalogue contains nearly 2,500 species, leaving out the mushrooms (fungi), of which there is about an equal number, or almost 5,000 in all.

Dr. Cooper in his general description of the "Forests and Trees of North America" in the Smithsonian Report for 1858, says: "Coming next," (from the Canadian), "to the Appalachian province, we find a vast increase in the variety of our forest trees. In fact, looking at its natural products collectively, one of the most striking, as compared to the rest of the world between the 30th and 45th degrees o north latitude, is its richness in trees, which will compare favorably with almost any part of the tropics. It contains more than 20 species which have no representatives in the temperate climates of the old world, and a far greater number of species of the forms found there." Some of our most valuable timber trees are wholly wanting, as the hickory. And while there are not 50 indigenous species of trees in Europe which attain a height of 50 feet, there are above 140 in the United States, and more than 20 of these exceed 100 feet. Says Dr. Curtis, "In all the elements which render forest scenery attractive, no portion of the United States presents them in happier combination, in greater perfection, or in larger extent than the mountains of North Carolina."

And in order to realize the extent to which this richness of forest development is concentrated within the area of this State, it is only necessary to call attention to the distribution of a few kinds which are dominant and characteristic. Of species found in the United States (east of the Rocky Mountains), there are

Oaks,	22,	and	19	in	North	Carolina.
Pines, (trees),	8,	"	8	"	"	"
Spruces,	5,	"	4	"	"	"
Elms,	5,	"	3	"	"	"
Walnuts,	2,	"	2	"	"	"
Birchs,	5,	"	3	"	"	"
Maples,	5,	"	5	"	"	"
Hickories,	8,	"	6	"	"	"
Magnolias,	7,	"	7	"	"	"

And as to the first and most important group of the list, Dr. Curtis has called attention to the very striking fact that there are more species of oaks in this State "than in all of the States north of us, and only one less than in all the Southern States, east of the Mississippi."

It will be observed that the kinds of trees which characterize this flora include chiefly such as are most valuable in the arts. The long-leaf pine alone is the basis of industries whose annual products in this State are not less than $3,000,000. The juniper and cypress have long been a source of large revenues to the whole eastern region. And it is worthy of mention in this connection, that besides the present crop of trees, there are, over large areas of the swamp lands, several successive generations of buried forests, whose timber is in good preservation, ready to be exhumed when the present growth shall have been exhausted.

The most characteristic and prevalent species of the middle region are the oaks. Several kinds of white oak, so much in demand, and so highly prized in ship-building and numerous domestic arts, are abundant in all parts of this division and especially in the mountains. There are also large tracts of white pine on both sides of the Blue Ridge. The hickories are found everywhere, and the black walnut is plentiful in the river bottoms and on the fertile slopes of the mountains, so common as to be used for fencing; and the wild cherry, mahogany (black birch), and several species of maple furnish abundant cabinet materials; and to these should be added the extensive forests of holly in the eastern region.

Nearly every one of the 20 kinds of timber admitted to the New York shipyards as suitable for building vessels is found in this State in abundance; and since the forests of the North Atlantic States are very nearly exhausted, and timber for ship building is brought to the coast from the upper Mississippi, and even foreign governments are exporting large supplies for their navy yards from the interior of the continent, it is evident that our forests have a value and are entitled to a consideration which they have never received among us. We have still some 40,000 square miles of forests of which the larger part is as yet unviolated by the woodman's axe. And I think it safe to say that the intrinsic value of this heritage alone is such, that within ten years it will be seen, that it exceeds the present total valuation of the entire property of the State. And it is time for the people of the State and its legislators especially, to begin to realize and take account of the fact, that here is one of the most valuable, as it is also one of the most undeveloped and little considered of her natural resources. And its value is appreciating more rapidly than that of any other kind of property in the State; and this from two causes, the operation of which is incessant and rapid, and the results inevitable and soon to become actual, viz: the rapid exhaustion of the more accessible forests of the continent and the constantly accelerating consumption of their products, and the increase and cheapening of the means of transportation to those parts of the world where the demand is greatest.

The people of this latitude for several generations have been accustomed to regard and to treat the forests as a natural enemy, to be extirpated, like their aboriginal denizens, human and feral, by all means and at any cost, and "a man was famous according as he had lifted up axes upon the thick trees." Too many of our people have yet to learn that "all that has been changed," and the time has come not only to cease from the wanton and thoughtless, but even from the ordinarily legitimate distruction of forests, in the way of "clearing new grounds," &c., and even to begin the work of undoing,—of repairing the mischief and waste of our predecessors and our own, by planting our old fields with the seeds of future forests and fortunes.

In most of the countries of Europe forestry comes in for a very large share of attention of both citizen and government. The conservation, propagation and improvement of forests, constitute an important department of public administration, as they are reckoned an indispensable element of national wealth; and the schools and colleges and officers which abound everywhere in this interest, are a sufficient evidence of the important place which the subject occupies in public and private economies.

We shall doubtless come to that some day; and at our present rate of progress, very soon, as to a large part of the State. In some portions of it already there is not timber enough to repair tho annual decay of the fences; and yet the old habit continues of abandoning half worn fields to sedge and sassafras, and pines and briars and gullies, and of clearing "new grounds," at a greater expense than would be necessary to restore the old, taking no account of the value of the forests destroyed in the process, which is almost always greater than that of the land after it is cleared; and this, while there is at least three times as much land cleared as can be properly tilled by the present agricultural force of the State. And the plan of fencing adopted when the whole country was forest-covered, and as one means of disposing of a considerable part of it, is still continued long after not only this state of things has ceased to exist, but also the main purpose of fencing at all, which was to render available for cattle grazing the rich natural pasturage which abounded in the "forests primeval," but have been long since extirpated, except in the higher and almost unpeopled regions of the mountains.

And as the pasture plants of our original forests have disappeared almost entirely from our flora, and as under a similar reckless system of forest destruction to our own, the forests of the old world have been impoverished and reduced to mere shreds and shadows of their probable original variety and extent, so will the most characteristic and valuable elements of our unequalled forests disappear, one by one. How this can come to pass is already but too evident to any one who has observed the woful destruction within a single generation of the long-leaf pine, for example, the most valuable forest tree of them all, or of the juniper, or the palmetto, both on our own coasts, and especially of South Carolina; or of the white pine of the northeastern and lake states and of Upper Canada.

Agricultural.—First, *as to the variety and kinds of agricultural products*, it is obvious that they will be proportioned to, as they are dependent on, the same climatic conditions as the indigenous vegetation. And when it is considered that, as shown in another connection, every agricultural product found in the census tables of the United States, except perhaps the sweet orange, is grown in this State, from cotton, tobacco, jute, figs, sugar-cane, and the like, to rye, buckwheat, maple sugar, &c., and that, in short, everything which can be produced in the temperate zone is producible here, it is seen that there is yet another and a strongly confirmatory expression of the wonderful combination and adjustment of climatal elements above disclosed by direct observation.

And second, *as to soils*, the peculiar geological structure of the State, to be discussed in a future chapter, furnishes the material for every possible variety and commixture; and in fact there is no description or combination unrepresented, from the black and deep peaty soils of Hyde and the great swamp tracts of the seaboard, and the alluvious, marls, and light, sandy and porous Quaternary accumulations of the eastern champaign to the clayey, sandy and gravelly soils of the hill country and of the mountains, the result of the decomposition in situ of every variety of rock,—granite, gneiss, schists, slates, sandstones, &c.

And there is one notable feature of these soils which is worthy of a passing remark. It has often attracted the interested attention of geologists from more northern regions, that the soils of this latitude are far deeper, that the decomposition of the geological formations has penetrated much further than in high latitudes. While in New England, for example, the solid rock is generally found within a few feet of the surface, here it requires a penetration of 30, 50 or even 100 feet to pass through the overlying debris of disintegrated strata, as seen every where in railroad cuts, wells &c. This is doubtless due, in large part, so far as it is not explained by the foliation and tilted position of the rocks, to climatic influences. The easily permeable strata are subjected throughout the year to the chemical action arising from a large and continuous percolation of comparatively warm aërated waters; while in higher latitudes, not only are the quantity of water and the temperature and the chemical activity reduced, but for one half the year, the soil is locked up by frost from all access of decomposing agencies.

So that not only are the products of the soil profoundly influenced by climatic agencies, but even the depth and composition of the soil itself are greatly modified by them.

Zoological.—Not only the vegetable but the animal kingdom is dependent, and is equally dependent on climatic influences; and is in fact, both directly and indirectly by reason of its intimate correlations to and dependence on the former, but another and equally exact exponent of underlying causal conditions and relations of climate, as well as of the outgrowing vegetable adjustments. What the original fauna of North Carolina may have been, how rich and various and abundant, before the balance of nature was disturbed by the civilizing and exterminating hand of man, will never be fully known. But it is well enough ascertained that many of the larger animals which are now found only on the other side of the Mississippi, or in the Rocky Mountains, as the elk and the buffalo, once pastured in the open woods and the rich mountain meadows of the State; and the traditions of the last of their retreating columns still linger among the older inhabitants of the mountain region. These may serve as an illustration of changes wide and great which have affected the whole animal kingdom, and make it, as we now see it, something vastly different from what the first European settlers found.

But there is left enough to record in a very impressive manner the bearing of the peculiar climatography of the State. When Agassiz undertook the study of the animal life of this continent, he had no sooner begun his collections from the Middle and Southern Atlantic States than the transitional character of the North Carolina fauna attracted his attention; and he found, as the botanists had done earlier, that the limits of northern and southern species meet and overlap along this median area. And more singular still, on account of the peculiar conformation of the coast line and its relations to the great oceanic currents, already adverted to, the limitations of the range of the animal population of the sea are even more sharply defined by the far-projecting Cape of Hatteras than is either flora or fauna of the land. This will be apparent on opening any work on marine conchology, for example, in which the range of species is defined; the most common, the continually recurring definitions are, *Massachusetts to North Carolina, Cape Cod to Cape Hatteras, North Carolina to West Indies, Florida to North Carolina.*

These points are noticed, not merely as a matter of curious interest, but because they have a profound significance when considered in their proper connection.

CHAPTER III.

GENERAL PRINCIPLES.

In order to a proper comprehension of the relations of the North Carolina geology, by such as are not familiar with geological literature and nomenclature, it is needful to sketch, at least briefly, the outlines of the general system of geology which has resulted from the study of the rocks in various parts of the earth.

The first and broadest distinction among the rocks, founded on their most obvious features of structure, give rise to the division of them into two great classes; one, including those rock masses, in which there are divisional planes, more or less nearly parallel, which separate them into layers, or strata, the so-called *Stratified Rocks*, as sandstone, clay, slate, &c.; the other, such as are without any such arrangement, or structural sub-divisions,—the *Unstratified Rocks*, as granite, trap, porphyry, &c. Since granite of several varieties is the prevalent, or characteristic form this class, they are also designated as the *Granitic Rocks;* and as a minute and extensive study of them discloses the fact that they are crystalline, and owe this constitution to the fact of their having been at one time in a state of fusion from heat, they are also called *Igneous Rocks.* And so the stratified rocks, being studied as to their origin, and found to be universally formed by the accumulation of sediments, of sand, mud, &c., formed by the action of moving waters, as in rivers, lakes, seas, &c., are denominated *Sedimentary Rocks.*

But many of these are also found to be much altered since their formation, both as to position,—being often inclined to the horizon at high angles and variously crumpled and distorted, and as to constitution, being no longer simply consolidated deposits of sand, gravel, clay, &c., but more or less changed by chemical action, aided by heat, moisture and pressure, into a crystalline form scarcely distinguishable, in some cases, from the igneous rocks themselves, except by their bedding; and even this is not infrequently obscured, or almost obliterated; so that they form a transitional term between the sedimentary and igneous rocks and are called, from their altered condition, *Metamorphic,* and also from their disturbed and irregular bedding *Fohiated Rocks.*

Most of the rocks of North Carolina belong to this sub-division,—the granites, gneisses, &c., as do those of most of the mountain chains of the continent, having been thus modified by the very circumstances of disturbance and contortion to which they were subjected in the process of upheaval.

The mode of formation of the different kinds of stratified rocks can only be understood by observing the different conditions which now determine the deposition of one or another of these kinds of materials in moving water.

Thus it is seen that the materials brought down by rivers and floods from land surfaces, or abraded from sea shores by the action of waves, are deposited in a certain order of arrangement; the coarser gravels and sand drop at the first slackening of the current, as the waters debouch into the bays, estuaries, &c., and along the shores, and the finer materials are carried further out and into deeper water; and it is found that at depths greater than a few hundred feet, and in all open seas, but little less else is deposited besides calcareous sediments, consisting of the hard parts of minute organisms which inhabit the still depths and secrete their solid particles from the carbonate of lime held in solution by the sea water and continually supplied by the rivers,—accumulations which are afterwards changed into chalk, limestone, marble, &c.

By widely extended and long continued observations in many parts of the world, it is ascertained that the sea level is everywhere and continually changing with respect to its shores, now advancing, now receding, and that these oscillations are due to the alternate rising and sinking of the land masses. And as the sea encroaches upon the land, the coarser sediments that were dropped along the shores, are gradually carried back into deeper water and overlaid by finer and finer materials, first sand, then clay, and at length, by the still finer calcareous mud. And hence the usual order of arrangement among stratified rocks; first the coarser conglomerates and sandstones, followed by clay slates and shales, and finally by limestones. Hence also the former deposits contain, for the most part only the remains of land plants and animals, often beds of driftwood, while the fossils found in the shales and limestones are entirely of marine origin, the remains of shell fish, corals, fishes, &c.

It is obvious that in the progress of the changes above considered, as the sea advances upon the land, its successive deposits will be laid down over all the irregularities, the excavated river channels, the upturned and broken rocks and the hills and valleys of the land surface; and so, when in the reverse process, the ocean bed gradually rises to the air and becomes dry land again, it will be re-peopled by animals and plants, and channelled anew by rivers, and its surface eroded by rains and frosts into hills and valleys as before, to be again invaded by the sea and buried under additional accumulations of sediments.

But these animals and plants will not be the same as those which occupied the same space formerly and have left their fossil remains imbedded in the previous deposits, laid down ages before; neither will the marine forms which the next encroachment of sea brings, be a repetition of the species whose remains were deposited in its former advance. Everything will show the marks of change. Old forms of life will have passed away and new ones occupied their places. And these different accumulations will be distinguishable, one from another, both by the breaks of continuity which separate them, being in geological language, *unconformable*, and also by their different fossil contents; being thus grouped into *formations* and *systems*.

And furthermore, an extensive comparison of observations made in all quarters of the globe has shown that the life forms, whose successive developments have left their impress upon the rocks, have not only undergone great changes from age to age, from formation to formation, but that these changes have been in certain determinate directions,—involve more than mere change, and indicate also progress; and the steps of this progress every where follow the same order, so that, the order of succession of different formations having been made out, in one part of the world, the same order is found to hold in every other part.

It is not meant that the entire series is completely represented every where; which indeed could not happen, inasmuch as sediments are deposited only over those portions of the earth which are submerged, and not on the land surface existing at the same time; on the contrary, some of its terms are generally wanting, and any number of them may be; but those terms which exist, preserve every where the same relation to each other of upper and lower, newer and older, and observe the same order of progression of living forms, the study of whose relations and successions in their ancient types, in the lower formations, is styled *Palæontology*.

The *geological chart* which follows, will illustrate to the eye, in one view, these several points. It represents graphically the relations of superposition, succession, relative age, and shows the sub-divisions and the relations of the different series in different regions, to one another and to the complete, typical series.

GEOLOGICAL

TIME.	AGE.	SYSTEMS.	SUB-DIVISIONS.
CÆNOZOIC.	Mammalian.	QUATERNARY.	TERRACE. CHAMPLAIN. GLACIAL.
		TERTIARY.	PLIOCENE. MIOCENE. EOCENE.
MESOZOIC.	Reptilian.	CRETACEOUS.	UPPER. MIDDLE. LOWER.
		JURASSIC.	OOLITIC. LIAS.
		TRIASSIC.	KEUPER. MUSCHELKALK. BUNTER-SANDSTEIN.
PALEOZOIC.	Amphibian.	PERMIAN.	PERMIAN.
		CARBONIFEROUS.	UPPER. LOWER. SUB-CARB.
	Ichthyan.	DEVONIAN.	CATSKILL. CHEMUNG. HAMILTON. CORNIFEROUS. ORISKANY.
	Molluscan.	SILURIAN.	UPPER. LOWER. PRIMORDIAL.
AZOIC. Eozoic.	Archæan.	HURONIAN.	HURONIAN.
		LAURENTIAN.	LAURENTIAN.
		IGNEOUS.	IGNEOUS.

CHART.

NORTH AMERICAN REPRESENTATIVES.	NORTH CAROLINA REPRESENTATIVES.	OHIO REPRESENTATIVES.
Terrace. Loess. Champlain Clays. Drift.	Gravel, Sand and Clay Beds of Eastern Counties.	Terraces, Drift, Erie Clay, &c.
Sumpter Clays. Yorktown Marls. Claiborne Beds.	(Wanting.) Shell Beds, Marls. Limestones. Clays.	Wanting.
Sandstones. Rotten Lime stones. Marls. Lignites. (Wanting.)	Greensand. Shell Marls.	Wanting.
Arenaceous Limestones. Sandstones, (Rocky Mountains.)	Wanting.	Wanting.
Red Sandstones. Shales. Conglomerates. Marls. Coal Beds.	Red Sandstones. Coal Measures. Conglomerates, Shales.	Wanting.
Dolomites, &c. (Missouri, Nebraska.)	Wanting.	Wanting.
Upper Coal Measures. Lower Coal Measures. Conglomerates. Limestones.	Wanting.	Coal Measures. Conglomerates. Limestones.
Catskill Group. Chemung Group. Hamilton Shales, &c. Corniferous Limestones. Oriskany Sandstones.	Wanting.	Erie Shales. Limestones. Sandstones.
Helderberg Limestones, &c. Saliferous Group. Niagara and Clinton Limestones. Hudson River Shales. Trenton Limestones. Potsdam Sandstone.	Wanting?	Limestones. Shales. Conglomerates, &c.
Huronian.	Silicious, Chloritic, Clay and Conglomerate Slates.	No outcrop.
Laurentian.	Gneiss, Granite, Hornblende Slates, &c.	No outcrop.
Igneous.	Granite, Syenyte, Porphyry, &c.	No outcrop.

The chart presents an example of the absence of certain formations and systems and sub-divisions. In the North Carolina series, there is a wide gap from the Huronian, one of the earliest formations, to the Triassic, all the intermediate systems, which make up so large a part of the geology of the rest of the continent and of the world, being unrepresented;—the Silurian, so grandly developed over the state of New York and the northwest, and the great Carboniferous, the most important of the whole, on account of its immense stores of mineral fuel. The meaning of this is obviously, that during the long period occupied in the deposition of these immense systems, in many parts of the world several miles thick, the surface of North Carolina was dry land. The Ohio series represents still other points; formations present here are wanting there. And again, as seen in the lower part of the chart, systems may exist in localities where they do not come to the surface,—outcrop, being overlaid by later formations.

Nor is it necessary to assert that there is absolute synchronism between the formations in distant parts of the globe which show the same, or corresponding organic forms; but only that these different groups of animals and plants, the fauna and flora, follow each other in the same order; although in fact it is probable that in most cases the corresponding groups are at least approximately synchronous.

From this will be apparent the origin and meaning of the terms *age*, *epoch*, *horizon*, in geology.

It is evident that only in the sedimentary rocks will fossil remains be found. But it is worth while to state that their occurrence is comparatively rare even in these, where they have been subjected to those great mechanical convulsions and chemiccal transformations described by the term metamorphism, that is, in the older and altered sedimentary rocks. It may be for this reason that no fossils have as yet been found in the rocks which occupy most of the surface of North Carolina, and are found only in the sandstones and shales of our coal formations and the marls and other recent deposits near the coast.

Formations, which are synchronous, *i. e.* were deposited at the same time in different parts of the world, are described as *equivalent*, or as belonging to the same horizon; and this equivalency is made out mainly from the identity, or correspondence of the fossils which they contain; but also partly from stratigraphical considerations of order of succession, conformability, &c.

From a comparison of the series of sedimentary rocks in many parts of the world, geologists have reached by gradual approximation a complete series, which is supposed to represent the successive stages in the progress of the life and of the physical conditions and changes determining the life of the globe.

Thus the formations are all grouped into a definite number of *systems*, corresponding to different *ages*.

The annexed chart shows the relative position and age of the different systems, and their general characterization according to the predominance of different organic forms.

IGNEOUS ROCKS.

The *Igneous* or granitic rocks of course occupy the lowest position in the chart, being the oldest, and therefore underlying all the other younger and derivative formations.

This series of rocks nowhere occupies very extensive areas of the earth's surface. The prevalent species are granite, syenyte, porphyry, &c.

LAURENTIAN SYSTEM.

The lowest group of stratified or foliated rocks is called *Laurentian*, after the Canadian Survey, in which is described an enormous development of them along the St. Lawrence, reaching a thickness estimated at more than 45,000 feet.

These rocks are found throughout the length of the Appalachians, in the Ozarks, and quite widely in the Rocky Mountains, and also in other parts of the world. This is not only the oldest of the series of stratified rocks, but is also one of the most extensive, both in vertical thickness and in horizontal area. Most of the metamorphic rocks of North Carolina probably belong to this horizon. The prevalent species are granite, gneiss, syenite and other hornblendic rocks, dioryte and crystalline limestone; and these contain much magnetic and specular iron ore, frequently in very large beds; and beds of graphite are also common.

HURONIAN SYSTEM.

The second system in the series is called *Huronian*, from an extensive area of these rocks on the north shore of Lake Huron. They also occur in Northern Michigan; and a narrow belt along the entire Appalachian range is supposed to belong to this system.

The most abundant and characteristic species are silicious and argillaceous slates and conglomerates, micaceous and hornblendic schists and slates, chlorites, quartzytes and diorytes ; with cherty, jaspery and epidotic beds, and much specular iron ore.

Like the preceding, this formation is destitute of fossils, and so its horizon cannot be determined with the same degree of certainty as those of later periods. And hence these two series, with the first, are grouped into one age, under the name *Azoic*, which means *without life*, or simply (Dr. Dana) *Archæan*, (*ancient*). The term *Azoic* is open to the objection that these rocks are not now, as formerly, supposed to have been deposited before the introduction of organic life ; the beds of graphite and graphitic gneisses and slates are commonly referred to a vegetable origin ; and the limestones and iron ores are supposed to have been accumulated through organic agency, as now. But all traces of their origin have been obliterated.

Within a few years this term has given place to *Eozoic*, (*life-dawn*), from the discovery of a supposed organism of low order, but its organic character is still in doubt.

These rocks occupy a considerable extent of surface in this State.

SILURIAN SYSTEM.

The azoic (or archaean) rocks are succeeded by those of the *Silurian* system. It includes stratified rocks of every description, sandstones, clay-slates, shales, conglomerates, limestones ; and abounds in marine fossils ; among which, the various kinds of shell fish (mollusca) predominate and hence the period is characterized as the *Molluscan Age*.

The organic forms of this age are all of a low order, and only in the upper terms of the series have remains of land plants or vertebrate animals been found.

The rocks of this series have a very wide distribution. They occupy the larger part of the surface of the State of New York, where they were first and most minutely studied in this country, and from which most of the sub-divisions were established and named, and their characteristic fossils ascertained. It is found in some of its sub-divisions, throughout the northwestern states, and in the Alleghanies of Pennsylvania and Virginia, in Kentucky, Tennessee, Alabama, Texas and Missouri, and in the Rocky Mountains ; and it is also largely developed in the old world.

In some localities, and especially in its lower formations, the rocks have been changed into crystalline schists, gneisses and even granites, and their fossils obliterated. The best examples of this metamorphism are found in New England.

This formation, so far as known is not represented in this State, except in its lowest term, the primordial, which crosses the northwest border from Tennessee, in a few points along the Smoky Mountains.

DEVONIAN SYSTEM.

In the *Devonian* system, (so called from Devonshire, Eng.), the fossils belong largely to higher types; land plant and *fishes* being abundant and the latter the predominant type of organic life, so that it is known as the *Ichthyan* or *Fish Age*. Rocks of this series are found in many parts of Canada, of New England, New York and Pennsylvania, West Virginia, and in various parts of the Mississippi Valley, and west as far as Utah The series occupies also an important place in the geology of other continents. The sandstones of this horizon are the chief source of petroleum. The former name of the group is "Old Red Sandstone."

CARBONIFEROUS SYSTEM.

The distinctive feature of this system is the enormous development of its fossil vegetation preserved in the form of coal. The most valuable beds of this mineral in Europe and America occur in the formations of this age; in Asia and the western side of North America, however, the coal beds are generally of a later date. Limestones abound in these formations, and the lower terms are largely made up of conglomerates, grits and coarse sandstones. The coal measures, which are found mostly in the Carboniferous proper, are underlaid very generally by extensive beds of these latter rocks.

The seams of coal, which are sometimes very numerous and of various thicknesss, from that of paper to 40 feet and more, are commonly interstratified with shales, slates and sandstones.

The coal is simply the result of a chemical transformation of vegetable matter, accumulated very much as beds of peat are now seen to form in various parts of the world. The extent of these beds, which are frequently called *basins*, from the basin or trough-like form into which they have been thrown by the folding or bending up of the strata, is often very great. The largest in the world is the Alleghany Coal Field, which extends from the southern edge of New York, nearly 700 miles, to the middle of Alabama, and is estimated to contain an area of more than 60,000 square miles. The great coal basin of Illinois and Indiana is nearly as large, and there are many others of great extent in different parts of the continent, amounting in all to about 200,000 square miles, while the whole of Europe hardly contains one-tenth of that amount.

The most abundant plants in the coal are ferns: but trees also abound of very peculiar forms, related to some of the more insignificant tribes of the present day, such as the club-mosses, rushes and the like. The highest class of plants of the coal age is a species of tree related to the pines. Animals also of a higher organization than any found in the preceding formations, make their appearance, such as frogs, salamanders and other amphibious creatures and reptiles; hence the designation *Amphibian Age.*

The English and many of the continental coal beds also belong to this horizon. They are of great extent in the British Islands, occupying an area of some 12,000 square miles, and in some localities, of a thickness of many thousand feet.

PERMIAN SYSTEM.

The next group in order, the *Permian*, is scarcely known in this country, only a few of its characteristic fossils having been discovered in one or two states west of the Mississippi; where, however, the strata containing them are regarded as more properly a continuation of the carboniferous, to which they are conformable.

The preceding systems are grouped together under the general designation *paleozoic*, (*ancient life*); on account of the transition to higher forms, which is observed in passing to the next series of systems, the *Mesozoic*, (*middle life*), which consist of the Triassic, Jurassic and Cretaceous, and are characterized collectively as the *Reptilian Age*, from the predominant type of its animal life.

TRIASSIC SYSTEM.

The lowest of these, the *Triassic*, is represented very scantily on the Atlantic slope, being limited to the narrow tracts of sandstones, with shales and conglomerates, so well known in the Connecticut Valley; which extends also, with few interruptions, from the Hudson River in southeastern New York to the upper border of South Carolina. These rocks are, however, developed on a great scale in the states west of the Mississippi, from Nebraska to Texas and New Mexico, as well as in California and the adjoining states; and it is of common occurrence also in Europe. The famous *brown sandstone*, so much used in building in New York and elsewhere, is obtained from this formation, mostly in the Connecticut Valley; and the same rock is characteristic of it in North Carolina. But the important feature of it here and in Virginia, is the occurrence of extensive and valuable seams of coal; and while the strata of this series are generally poor in fossils elsewhere in the Atlantic slope, there have been found in this latitude many new and interesting organic forms, both vegetable and animal.

JURASSIC SYSTEM.

The rocks of this system, named from their extensive occurrence in the Jura Mountains of Switzerland, are not known in this country except on the Pacific Slope, in California and northward, and in some of the spurs of the Rocky Mountains. They are abundant in England and on the continent, and are notable on account of their remarkable fossils, the bones and teeth of enormous, walking, swimming and flying reptiles.

CRETACEOUS SYSTEM.

The name Cretaceous is due to the occurrence of the chalk beds of England in this period. These beds are a soft friable limestone, composed almost entirely of the shells of minute marine animals, and are formed, as the recent soundings and dredgings in the Atlantic and other seas have shown, only in very deep waters. Chalk is scarcely found in this series in North America. The Greensand of New Jersey represents the system, in part, on the Atlantic slope, and it is found also in a narrow zone, at a short distance from the coast, and at very moderate elevations above sea level, in the South Atlantic and Gulf States, from the Neuse River, round to the Mississippi; but in a large part of this area it comes to the surface only in very limited tracts, being generally overlaid by newer formations. There is a vastly larger area on the western side of the continent which is occupied by rocks of this series, which there consists of sandstones, limestones, shales, &c., to the depth of several thousand feet, and contains extensive beds of coal. These rocks are also remarkable for the presence in them of the bones and teeth of enormous and uncouth reptiles corresponding in size to those of the preceding (Jurassic) period in Europe. Many of the genera of living plants also occur first as fossils in the Cretaceous beds of the West.

TERTIARY SYSTEM.

This system, like the former, is represented by a narrow zone of beds of no great thickness near the Atlantic coast, and spread out over a large territory in the Gulf States, in the Rocky Mountain region and in California.

To this group are referred all the formations which contain, in a fossil form, any of the plants or animals now living. Its accumulations of more or less indurated sand and clay, marls, shell beds and lignites reach, in some places, a thickness of six or eight thousand feet. Coal of an inferior quality called lignite, or fossil wood, is found in these formations in the Rocky Mountain region. The system is subdivided into three subordinate groups called Eocene, Miocene and Pliocene. It is found, in some of its divisions, in British America as far north as the Arctic sea, and also in Greenland, carrying in both, an abundance of fossil plants, similar to many which are now living in North Carolina and southward.

Tertiary rocks abound in other parts of the world, in southern England, in France, (as the famous Paris Basin), and in central and southern Europe, in the Pyrenees and some of the higher Alps. They cover also extensive tracts in Asia, India, China and Japan, and in Egypt. The period during which these formations were deposited is called the *Age of Mammals*, on account of the great abundance of fossils and bones of many species of this class of animals, as the camel, horse, rhinoceros, elephant, mastodon and many other strange forms having but little resemblance to any living species.

It is evident that the topography of the continent has undergone vast changes, especially since the Cretaceous age, during which deep sea sediments were accumulated several thousand feet thick over a large part of the area now lifted into the great ranges and table lands of the Rocky Mountains. The character of the Tertiary sediments shows that these mountains and plateaus were elevated in part during their deposition, a large proportion of them being of fresh water origin, and the great coal beds having been deposited in wide marshes and lagoons.

The major part of the eastern side of the continent was dry land during the deposition of the Tertiary, which appears therefore only as a fringe on its eastern and southern borders, and occurs on and very near the surface in its two lower members, over considerable part of the eastern division of North Carolina, furnishing nearly all the calcareous marls of this region.

QUATERNARY SYSTEM.

At the close of the Tertiary period, the physical condition of the earth seems to have undergone a great revolution, so that the sub-tropical climate and products which extended over the northern portions of the continent, and even to Greenland, were presently replaced by the artic rigor of the Greenland of to-day, the vast ice sheet which caps the polar regions having pushed its margin down to the latitude of southern Pennsylvania and Ohio, and along the higher Appalachian valleys to the very borders of the Southern States. This change was accompanied, and no doubt largely, if not mainly produced by great changes in the topography of the continent, the chief of which was doubtless an elevation of the sub-polar regions and a great increase of frozen land surface. One consequence of these vast changes was the extinction of nearly all the pre-existing races of plants and animals. The formations accumulated during this period, known as the Glacial or Ice Period, are frequently called *Post-pliocene* and *Post Tertiary*, but more commonly *Quaternary*; and since it has been ascertained that they were formed mainly by the action of ice, they are called *Drift* or *Glacial Drift.* They consist of beds of pebbles, gravel and sand, and of clay mingled with stones, called bowlder clay, and scatted rock masses, more or less rounded, called bowlders, often of great size. These materials were abraded by the great ice masses in their southward movement, from the underlying rocks, and were either left in confused heaps, when the ice melted, or have been partially arranged in more or less nearly horizontal beds,—stratified by the subsequent action of water. These accumulations of course contain no marine fossils, and the remains of land animals and even plants are seldom abundant. The stratified drift is found especially in terraces or benches flanking the large streams or in areas which were occupied by lakes or broad estuaries.

From the above account of the origin of these formations, it is evident that they will be found mostly in high latitudes, (or in elevated and mountainous regions further south); but in the Middle and even Southern States are found Quarternary beds of pebbles, gravel, sand and clay, large tracts of these regions having been submerged during at least a part of the glacial period and covered with the material swept down from adjacent highlands and from the more northern zone by the great floods to which the melting ice gave rise.

Beds of drift abound in the New England and northern states; and in the Mississippi valley quite to the Gulf, are found great areas of stratified Quaternary sands, clays, &c., derived from more northern sources. On the Atlantic slope also, in Virginia and North Carolina, beds of a similar character and age extend inland more than 100 miles from the coast. Quaternary beds are very abundant in England and among the Alps, as well as elsewhere on the continent, and in all high latitudes of both hemispheres.

These accumulations are every where the superficial deposits, with the unimportant and occasional exception of some recent alluvions, so that they terminate the geological series in the ascending order, and close the record of the earth's changes, to the Human or present Era.

CHAPTER IV.

OUTLINES OF THE GEOLOGY

OF NORTH CAROLINA.

It is proposed in this chapter to give only a brief summary of the general geology of the State; presenting only the principal and broadest results of the work hitherto done in the investigation of its general relations, as to the age, structure, stratigraphy, lithology, mineralogy and geopraphical extent of its formations; and omitting all details, for which reference is made, first to the volumes of the Survey already published, by those who have investigated the several departments; especially to the reports of Dr. Emmons for 1856 and 1858, and to the Annual Reports of the Survey for 1867 and 1869, and to the several papers in the Appendix to this volume; and second, to the next volume of the report, to follow this in about a year, in which it is hoped to add something on the mineralogy, topography and stratigraphy, but especially to investigate the *lithology* of the North Carolina rocks, which subject has never received the attention which its importance and significance merit.

By reference to the Chart given above, and the map at the end of the volume, it will be seen that the surface of this State is pretty equally divided between the lowest, or oldest, and the upper, or newest systems, the larger part of the series having no representatives; the eastern half being occupied by the later formations, and the western by the earlier; and that the only one of the intermediate groups which appears, covers but an insignifiicant area in the middle region. The complete series for the State is as follows: Quaternary, Tertiary, Cretaceous, Triassic, Huronian, Laurentian and Igneous. These groups will be considered in order, beginning with the lowest.

LAURENTIAN.

This system is represented on a very large scale in North Carolina. It occupies a belt about 20 to 25 miles wide and of a nearly north and south direction, across the northern part of the sub-eastern section, the capital being located upon it. It extends northward to the Virginia line, the southern part of it towards the Cape Fear and beyond, and its entire eastern margin, being covered up by Quaternary sands and gravels. This belt consists of light colored and grey gneisses, which occasionally pass into granite, but more frequently into felspathic, quartzose (and rarely hornblendic) schists. In some localities the mica is entirely wanting and then the rock is either a dull-reddish, brownish, or whitish massive felspathic rock, trachyte, euryte, felspar porphyry, &c.

The rocks of this belt are usually quite fine grained. The predominant element in their composition is felspar, although quartz is abundant; the proportion of mica, which is usually biotite, is very small. The strike of the strata is generally between 20° and 30° east of north, and the dip east, usually at a high angle, from 65° to 80°, and down to 40° and 45°. The rocks are much disturbed and very irregular in position.

The following analysis will serve to give a general ieda of the character and chemical composition of the rocks of this belt, the sample being selected from the Raleigh quarries and as nearly a typical specimen as possible.

Silica,	69.28
Alumina,	17.44
Sesquioxide of iron,	1.08
Protoxide of iron,	1.22
Lime,	2.20
Magnesia,	0.27
Potassa,	2.76
Soda,	3.64
Manganese oxide,	.16

At one point on the Cape Fear, the felspar of the gneiss is partly replaced by calc spar.

There are a few points some distance to the eastward of the general boundary of this belt, where there are local and limited outcrops of gneiss and granite, appearing through the general covering of sand, most of which are indicated on the map, as at Weldon, Rocky Mount and two other points in Edgecombe, and one in Wilson. The granite for the United States post-office, in Raleigh, is obtained from Edgecombe. It is of light grey color, and shows no gneissic or foliated structure, being undistinguishable from true granite. The rock at two other of these localities is of the same general description, but much coarser grained, and is likewise used for building purposes. Ledges of coarse syenite and diorite dikes occur occasionally in this tract, and with the former grains and sometimes considerable masses of magnetic and titanic iron. There is also one occurrence of serpentine in the upper part of Wake county.

Besides the minerals just mentioned, iron pyrites, copper pyrites and specular iron are found occasionally, mostly in quartz veins, but also in the gneiss rock itself In one locality on the Cape Fear River, near the mouth of Buckhorn creek, there is a bed of red hematite nearly 40 feet thick, together with a slaty manganese garnet, interstratified with the gneiss, and the two minerals are combined in some parts of the bed into a mineral which differs little from knebelite.

The second area of rocks which I have referred to the Laurentian, and the lower division of it, extends from the southern border of the State, where that is crossed by the Catawba river, in a northeast direction almost to the Virginia line at a point near the town of Roxboro, in Person county, and re-appearing in a triangular tract 8 or 10 miles to the eastward, crosses the northern border about midway of Granville county. There is also another small area in the southern part of Orange including the University, which probably belongs here, although it is not represented on the map. It will also be seen that there are several other small patches of the same color in different parts of the map, indicating other scattered outcrops of allied rocks. The main body is from 10 to thirty miles wide and has an area of about 3,000 square miles.

The characteristic and prevalent rocks are syenyte, doleryte, greenstone, amphibolyte, granite, porphyry and trachyte. Dr. Mitchell says of these rocks: "There is no well defined gneiss, mica slate, serpentine or limestone," among them. "Mica is rare, and in its stead there is chlorite, or hornblende, but even these are not in general well characterized;" and Dr. Emmons, "Trap-dykes are numerous at most places where the rock is exposed. At certain points they are so numerous that the rock is obscured. The dykes are not composed of one material, but consist of the common amphibolic trap, quartz, felspar and thin seams of epidote; forming together a network of eruptive rocks. When they decompose, the hornblende trap appears in dark green stripes, and many have assumed the structure of a laminated rock." Mica is in fact rare throughout the series except at a few points where the rocks are granitic, and even in them the proportion of it is very small. The most common rock is of a hornblendic character; and traps, trachytes, granulytes and porphyries are confusedly and angularly wedged in among each other, with frequent veins of epidote crossing the felspathic species in every direction.

The following analysis, by Dr. Genth, of one of these typical trachyte porphyries, the leopardite of Mecklenburg and other localities will show the general character of a considerable proportion of the rocks of this series.

Silica,	75.92
Alumina,	14.47
Sesquioxide of iron,	0.88
Magnesia,	0.09
Lime,	0.02
Soda,	4.98
Potassa,	4.01
Loss by heating,	0.64
	100.01

This analysis is taken from the American Journal of Science and Arts for March, 1862.

The absence of anything like stratification or foliation is conspicuous throughout the region. In the northern part of the outcrop in Granville county, and in the southern, near the Catawba River, the doleryte dikes are of so coarse a texture as to present striated faces of labradorite crystals ½ and ¾ of an inch broad.

One of the largest terranes or outcrops of a single kind of rock is the syenytic ledge which crosses the southeastern side of Mecklenburg, and occupies a breadth of several miles along the west side of Cabarrus, being traceable for many miles by the huge dark bowlder-like masses which stand thick through the forests and fields, many of them 10 to 15 and 20 feet in diameter. Another quite extensive outcrop is that of a very coarse light-colored, easily decomposed felspathic granite, which crosses the railroad a few miles west of Salisbury, in Rowan county, and extends southwest many miles into the southern end of Iredell. The crystals of felspar which weather out of the rock in great quantities, are often two to three inches in length, and frequently twinned. A similar ledge is seen also on Long Creek, in Gaston county. Ledges of very coarse pyroxenyte and hornblendyte are common, and one of these in the west side of of Guilford county seems to pass into Lherzolyte. And in the tract beyond the Blue Ridge, in Mitchell county, on the Nolechucky River, occurs an enormous ledge of doleryte, extending several miles along the river, much of it very coarsely porphyritic, and on the west side of the river is a heavy outcrop of coarsely crystalline hornblendic rocks, among which is a dark gray mass which seems to be hypersthenyte, and within a few miles in three different directions are three chrysolyte hills.

The area of rocks of this series near the southern border of the State, on the lower Yadkin (Peedee) is a very coarse grained porphyritic granite, (in a portion of which, at least, the felspar is triclinic), intersected by a succession of heavy dolerytic dikes.

In the traps and occasionally the granites of this series, iron pyrites is disseminated in small grains and thin films, and in some of the syenytes magnetite is a common constituent, and it is also found occasionally in veins of several feet thickness, as in the great ledge above mentioned, in which these veins are common, both in Cabarrus and Mecklenburg.

Besides these and epidote, the most common mineral, specular iron occurs in at least one locality in considerable quantity, in a quartzytic rock in the upper part of Mecklenburg. Agate and rutile are found in Mecklenburg, and agate and opal in Cabarrus. Along the southern edge of the belt are many productive veins of pyrites carrying copper and gold, in Alamance, Guilford, Cabarrus, Rowan and Mecklenburg.

If there be any significance in structure or in lithological characters, this singular body of rocks seems entitled to be placed at the very base of the Archæan age, certainly at the bottom of the Laurentian; and even below these, if there be any older rocks exposed anywhere,—the true Azoic or Igneous. In the direction of this notion certainly point the absence of stratification, the non-occurrence of limestone, and the great predominance of syenytes (mostly hyposyenyte), and other iron-bearing and basic rocks. I have only placed them as the lower Laurentian, however, since there seems to be a general disinclination to suppose that the primal igneous core anywhere shows itself to human inspection. This belt may well be characterized as the geological axis of the State.

The group of rocks just described is bounded on the northwest by a series of gneisses and feldspathic and occasionally hornblendic slates, which extend westward with little interruption to the Blue Ridge, and, except a narrow zone of a few miles breadth along the course of that chain, includes the whole mountain region to the flanks of the Smoky Mountains, through the greater part of its length. These are considered to belong to the Laurentian proper.

The portion of this series which lies east of the Blue Ridge is the largest connected area of Laurentian in the State, and covers not less than 16,000 square miles. Its resemblance to the Raleigh belt is very marked, especially in the southeastern part, which consists of a succession of schists and gneisses and slates, for the most part thin bedded, and only occasionally showing granite-like masses and syenytes, which, however, are generally in the form of dikes. There is a narrow tract of coarse granite, described by Dr. Emmons as a series of veins, along the southeast margin of the zone, across Gaston and Lincoln counties. A few miles west of this is a narrow terrane of syenytes and other hornblendic rocks and granites, which extend northward across Lincoln and Catawba counties, reaching the Catawba river at the great bend. It is seen about 4 miles west of Lincolnton, at Newton, and in the railroad cuts near Catawba Station, and beyond. The predominance of hornblendic rocks, the absence of mica, and the general absence of stratification have seemed to justify the reference of this belt to the lower part of the series, along with the preceding central zone.

Proceding westward we find the rocks occasionally more micaceous, mica slates and slaty gneisses becoming in some localities quite common; and there comes in along the centre and southern portions of the tract a series of mica schists and slates, some of which seem to be more or less talcose, and very felspatthic, which weather into a spongy, purplish-brown, soft rock, easily cut with the axe, which is much used for chimneys, and as a substitute for soapstone. In places these slates are hard and abound in imperfect crystals of garnet, and occasionally of staurolite and cyanite. These rocks may be seen in the railroad cuts and hills about Hickory, and in the eastern ridges of the South Mountains, and in the middle and southern parts of Polk county. It is noticeable that these schists and slates every where occupy the ridges and higher swells and do not reach the level of the river channels, so that they overlie the gneisses, and are to be referred to an upper division of this formation, or more probably to the next system, the Huronian. These rocks extend across the Catawba into Caldwell and Alexander counties and are seen in the southward spurs of the Brushy Mountains, from Gunpowder Creek to Middle Little River. The rocks of this tract are generally fine grained but toward the western side of it there is a body of coarse porphyritic grey gneiss, sometimes so rough and nodular as to appear like a conglomerate, the nodules being lenticular and rounded masses of cleaveable felspar and quartz of various sizes, up to an inch and more in length, the dark gray argillaceous mica-schist matrix lapping around and enclosing them and filling up accurately the interstices,—a true augen-gneiss. This rock is seen conspicuously in the vertical and overhanging cliffs on the turnpike just below Blowing Rock in Caldwell, in the steep mural ledge of Hickory Nut Mountain on Crooked Creek in McDowell, in the large masses of porphyroidal gneiss near Hickory Nut Gap, in the naked ledges about Flat Rock and the quarries near Hendersonville, and again on Little River near Jones' Gap. And there is a wide belt of light colored fine-grained, very felspathic, easily decomposable gneiss, in McDowell county, very conspicuous in the railroad cuts about Marion, and for eight or ten miles eastward. It is in places much seamed and jointed by numerous divisional planes, and often has little or no signs of bedding. On the other hand the gneisses of Cleveland and Rutherford are very slaty, frequently passing into mica slate; and they are notable as being abundantly impregnated with minute crystals of iron pyrites, so that copperas has been made from them on a large scale.

Hornblende slates are not of very frequent occurrence, but there is a very persistent ledge along the Blue Ridge, across the southern and eastern sides of Henderson county, and also in the Saluda and Tryon ranges and a few miles east and south of Hickory Nut Gap. And a number of small local outcrops of hornblende rocks, slates, and (occasionally) syenytes, are found here and there throughout the region, but constituting a very insignificant proportion of the whole. Chorite slates occur in a few localities, as on Lower Creek, in Caldwell county, and a granular talco-chloritic rock of a grey to olive color, impregnated with titanic iron is found in the northern part of the same county. In this county also are several dikes of serpentine, one quite dark and compact, and filled with minute reticulations of chysotile veins; the others of a grey color and granular texture, one containing asbestos, chysotile and baltimorite, and walling a gold vein. A few other similar dikes are found in other sections of this belt.

The limestones of Forsyth, Yadkin and Stokes, probably belong to this series, being interstratified with its normal gneissic rocks. They are coarsely crystalline for the most part, and schistose, in places abounding in crystals of a brown mica, (phlogopite). These limestones are slightly magnesian and therein agree with those of the typical Laurentian of Canada. The following analysis made by Dr. Genth for the Survey, will show the composition of this rock at one of the best known localities, Bolejack's quarry, near Germanton:

Quartz and Silicates,	15.42
Carbonate of Lime,	74.53
Carbonate of Magnesia	8.22
Carbonate of Manganese,	0.34
Carbonate of Iron,	1.49

At some of the outcrops, which are generally limited to two or three rods in thickness, and a few hundred yards in length, the limestone seems to graduate into neighboring gneisses. It is only in this northeastern part of the area that limestone occurs.

The rocks of this belt are very much disturbed and irregular in their position, but the strike is very uniformly northeasterly, between 50° and

65° E. of N., and the dip is quite prevalently east, the average lying between 30° and 50°. Large veins of manganese garnet are of frequent occurrence.

Besides the minerals already mentioned incidentally, gold is found both in the superficial gravel and in veins in many parts of the region, but especially in Caldwell, Burke, McDowell, Cleaveland and Polk counties. The largest gold field, and one of the most noted in the Atlantic States, is that of the South Mountains in the centre of the territory indicated. With the gold are associated a number of interesting mineral species, as zincon, monazite, &c., of which mention will be found in Dr. Genth's paper in the Appendix. The well-known zincon locality of Henderson county belongs here. Magnetic, specular and titanic iron are found in several parts of the region, the magnetic and titanic being most abundant in the extensive beds which cross the northwest side of Guilford county, extending into Davidson on the south, and Rockingham on the north. But both of the two first named species often occur in veins and also in a granular form, impregnating the gneisses and schists. Brown hematite beds are common in the talcose mica schists. Corundum was found by Dr. Genth in the iron ores above mentioned from Guilford, to gether with chromite. And I have since found it in crystals in Forsyth, and also the mineral rensselaerite. Graphite occasionally replaces mica in the mica slates and gneisses.

Another considereble area of Laurentian rocks is found beyond the Blue Ridge, occupying most of the mountain plateau between that and the Smoky Mountains, and in places constituting the materials of these chains. As stated before, this area may very properly be considered as only a continuation of the preceding, from which it is divided by a very narrow and interrupted belt of Huronian slates, which also divide it transversely in the region of the Yellow Mountains, into a southern and northern tract. The rocks of both of these, like those of the preceding area, are foliated for the most part, and consist of indefinite alternations of the same kinds of metamorphic strata,—gneiss, hornblendic, feldspathic and micaceous schists, and occasionally chloritic and talcose slates. Mica schists are less common than in the more eastern belt, while the hornblendic are much more common. The former are very generally garnetiferous, and occasionally cyanitiferous; and they are found mostly in the northeastern portion of the southern tract. The hornblendic slates and syenytes, (the latter of which occur not infrequeutly), are also often highly garnetiferous. These rocks are more abundant in the middle portions of the tracts, although not confined to these. The most extensive hornblendic terrane of the region and of the State, is found in the angle between the forks of New River, in Ashe and Watauga counties, in the Rich Mountains, Elk Knob, &c., to Negro Mountain, near Jefferson.

Very large veins of a very coarse granite abound along the median parts of the tract, especially in Mitchell and Yancey. The quartz, mica and feldspar are found in huge masses instead of small crystals. These veins are extensively wrought for mica, which is obtained in large plates, 10 to 20 and even 30 inches in diameter. Some single veins have yielded hundreds of tons within the last 3 or 4 years. And these mines are not now opened for the first time. On the contrary, they were wrought on a much larger scale by the Mound-Builders ages ago; and most of these veins are honey-combed with ancient tunnels and shafts, which were located and excavated with more skill and success than the modern workers have yet attained. Their market was evidently the populous regions north of the Ohio, whose numerous mounds contain, in their multitudes of ornaments and utensils of this mineral, the evidence of the extent of this curious ancient commerce.

One of the most remarkable and interesting features of the geology of this belt is the line of *chrysolyte* ledges, (*dunyte*), which occur along the median zone of it, outcropping in massive dikes, which form rough, jagged hills at intervals of half a score of miles, more or less, from the Rich Mountains of Watauga through Mitchell, and the intervening counties to Clay. Some of these ledges are nearly a mile long and several hundred yards wide. They are not in line with one another, but are scattered over a zone 10 to 20 miles in breadth. It is worthy to be noted that they occur in the middle zone, where the rocks are most disturbed and irregular in position; that they are associated with the most massive outcrops of hornblendic rocks,—syenytes, schists and actinolyte rocks, and with heavy veins of coarse porphyroidal granite, and that they thus claim a very low horizon.

The masses of chrysolyte are more or less distinctly granular, and are in fact, a chrysolytic sandstone, of a yellowish to dull, or dark olive-green color. The composition of this rock Dr. Genth finds to be as follows:

Silica,	41.89
Protoxide of iron,	7.39
Nickel oxide,	0.35
Magnesia,	49.13
Lime,	0.06
Loss by heat,	0.82
Chromic iron,	0.58
	100.22

It weathers into rough, jagged, honey-combed, and laminated or slaty-looking ridges, and decomposes into a dark, gravelly, barren soil, of the following composition; (sample from Hampton's, in Yancey county):

Silica, (8.08 sol.)	63.15
Oxide of iron,	8.53
Alumina,	3.41
Lime,	0.22
Magnesia,	2.38
Sulphuric acid,	0.10
Chlorine,	0.02
Phosphoric acid,	0.18
Organic matter,	17.00
Water,	4.50
	99.49

n which the absence of potassa and soda is notable, and the abundance of iron, and of organic matter especially, the latter no doubt exceptional and accidental. The most common and characteristic minerals of the North Carolina dunyte are chlorite, talc, asbestos, chalcedony and chromite, the last in scattered grains and in coarsely granular irregular veins, or pockets. In many places several other species are quite common, for example, bronzite, nodular masses of enstatite, a bright, green, granular, hornblendic mineral, which Genth makes kokscharoffite, serpentine, and a curious cup-foliated variety of talc, &c. One of the most interesting and valuable minerals, and one which is also of common occurrence, is corundum, which occurs in tabular, cleaveable masses and in crystals. For a particular account of this and the other associated minerals, the reader is referred to Dr. Genth's and Mr. Smith's papers in the Appendix, and to Dr. G.'s special paper on corundum, constituting No. 1 of "Contributions from the Laboratory of the University of Pennsylvania," and to Prof. Shephard, in the American Journal of Science, August, 1872.

Crystalline limestone occurs in three or four small ledges (beds), of a foot or two in width to a rod or more, in one small tract on the French Broad, in and a few miles below Marshall, in Madison county. It is associated, at one of these outcrops, with a greenish hornblendic rock, and is filled with minute, rounded grains of green coccolite. There are also occasional dikes of serpentine and of pyroxenyte; one of each may be seen along the Swannanoa road in Buncombe. And the hornblende slates are sometimes epidotic, as in Mitchell near Flat Rock. The rocks of this belt are very much disturbed,—broken, crumpled and folded, especially along the middle of the tract; but the general strike is about N. 50° E., and the prevalent dip is S. E., at every possible angle, but generally between 40° and 60°. Along the median zone, however, for several miles, the prevalent dip is N. W.

Besides the minerals already mentioned incidentally, magnetic iron is of frequent occurrence, and may be set down as a characteristic mineral of the series; one of the largest iron beds in North America is found among the hornblende slates and syenytes of the Iron (Smoky) Mountains in Mitchell; and specular iron is also found occasionally. Copper pyrites exists in large bedded veins among the syenytes and hornblende slates of Jackson, Macon, Haywood, Watauga and Ashe, and also sometimes in the grey gneisses and mica schists, as at Ore Knob and Peach Bottom, in Ashe and Alleghany.

This mountain tract of Laurentian rocks contains between 3 and 4,000 square miles of surface; which, added to the areas of the previous tracts, gives an aggregate of more than 20,000 square miles occupied by this formation, or nearly one-half the territory of the State.

HURONIAN.

The next system in order of superposition follows in the true order of time, without break of geological continuity. By reference to the map at the end of the volume, it will be seen that the Huronian system, represented by the apple-green color, occupies several disconnected areas, separated by intervening tracts of the older and underlying formation. There are in fact 5 principal outcrops, with two or three subordinate ones, which may very properly be referred to one or another of the former as detached fragments of them. The most easterly of them lies against the first or Raleigh belt of Laurentian on the east, with an easterly dip; and is mostly covered by the sands and gravels of the Quarternary. The outcrops may be seen however along the bluffs of the streams and occasionally in jutting ledges on the swells between, from the Roanoke near Gaston to the Neuse about Smithfield and the mouth of Falling Creek, in Duplin. The rocks are quartzyte and clay slates, grey, light-colored and drab and greenish. At some points the quartzytes are argillaceous, and at others as a few miles west of Smithfield it approaches a fine conglomerate. The clay slates are occasionally slightly hydro-micaceous.

This series reappears on the west side of the Raleigh granite with an opposite or westward dip, quite steep at first at about three miles from the city, but gradually becoming less. The bottom beds are argillaceous and talcoid, and at two lines of outcrops less than a mile apart, and three to four miles from Raleigh, these slates become highly pumbaginous, the main seam of 12 to 20 inches in former case, and three feet in the other, containing 50 per cent. and upwards of graphite. The more eastern of these beds is nearly vertical to 75° N. W., and the other 40° to 60°, probably forming an anticlinal, and a heavy body of micaceous white slaty quartzytes follows closely along the west side of the graphite. Alter-rations of argillaceous, talcoid and quartzytic beds continue for five and or six miles, when they disappear beneath a narrow trough of Triassic sandstones; beyond which they emerge along an irregular, but approximately N. E. and S. W. line, in the great central mineral-bearing slate belt, so widely familiar to miners and geologists. This tract extends quite across the State in a breadth of 20 to 40 miles, and is composed of silicious slates and clay slates chiefly; the former being often brecciated and conglomerate, the pebbles sometimes a foot and upwards in diameter, frequently chloritic, and often passing into hornstone and chert and occasionally into quartzyte. The clay slates are generally thin bedded, often shaly, grey, drab, banded, blue and frequently greenish, from an admixture of chlorite, sometimes talcoid or hydro-micaceous; and very often they may be better described as conglomerate slates, being composed of flattened and differently colored soft slaty fragments of all sizes, from minute particles to an inch and more in diameter. Near the middle of the breadth of this body of slates in Montgomery county, in a very heavy ledge of silicious slates, occurs a silicious conglomerate which is filled for hundreds of feet with very singular silicious concretions, some of which Dr. Emmons has described under the name Palæotrochis; but the rock for several miles, as well as at this particular locality, contains a multitude of rounded and ovoid masses from the smallest size to that of a hen's egg; showing the wide prevalence of conditions favorable to the operation of concretionary forces.

Quite characteristic also of this belt is the occurrence of extensive beds of pyrophyllyte slate, white and greenish, in places with disseminated crystals of chloritoid. Pyrophyllyte also occurs at several places in stellate-fibrous aggregations and also foliated like talc.

The talcose, silicious and chlorotic slates are more abundant towards the base of the series, the east side, and the clay slates predominate on the west.

A notable characteristic of this belt of rocks is the abundance of quartz veins, the fragments often covering and whitening the knolls and the roads for rods together, so that one can ascertain with considerable accuracy when the boundary of these rocks has been passed by the sudden and marked change in this respect. These rocks have been so fully described by Dr. Emmons, that there is no need to particularize further.

The strike is conformable to the general trend of the mountains and coast, and of the preceding formation, and the dip is prevalently *west* at high angles, but towards the western side of the tract, and conspicuously in widest part of it there is a breadth of several miles of easterly dips.

Besides the minerals already named, one of the most characteristic and abundant is specular iron, micaceous, granular and massive, which occurs in large veins and bedded masses, sometimes associated with slaty and jointed quartzytes, and silicious slates, and again with white, red and dark banded and jaspery slates. Magnetic iron is also not uncommon, and in a few localities there are large veins of brown hematite. Several of the most noted copper mines in the State occur in this formation, and it abounds in gold mines, both vein and gravel. Several silver and lead mines have also been wrought along its western border. The list of its minerals however, will be found in Dr. Genth's paper in the appendix.

The belt is bounded on both sides by the Laurentian, already described, on which it lies unconformably, and from which its materials were derived. The stratigraphy therefore indicates the horizon of these rocks to be the Huronian, and the lithology agrees well with that determination; and the reasonable course therefore seems to be, to place them as Huronian, until some evidence shall be found of an organic character, to lift them to a higher geological plane. The absence, or at least the non-discovery of fossils hitherto, in an extensive body of slates like those of the middle and west portions of this tract, so little altered and so well adapted to the preservation of even the most delicate organisms, and in a region so much studied, and on account of numerous mines, offering so good opportunities for the discovery of fossils if any existed, is certainly so far confirmatory of the sub-Silurian theory of these deposits. This is the principal area of Emmons' Taconic in this State.

The third belt, broken and interrupted, and of small extent, may be identified as the King's Mountain belt. Its greatest breadth is only five or six miles; its direction is marked by the high ledges of quartzyte slates which constitute King's Mountain, Crowder's Mountain, Spencer's Mountain and Anderson's Mountain, disappearing towards the great bend of the Catawba River. The rocks are quartzytes and clay slates; the former, sometimes cyanitic, often micaceous and slaty, and passing into mica schists occasionally; and the latter often talcose, or hydro-micaceous. Limited lenticular beds of crystalline limestone occur at intervals all along the outcrop. The strike of the rocks coincides with the general direction of the belt, which is 10°—20° north of east, and the dip W., at high angles, generally 45° to 80°. The clay slates are plumbaginous along the western side of the outcrop, and to the northward of Mt. Anderson is a bed of impure graphite, in places two and three feet thick. The limestone is grey, bluish and light colored to white, and fine to coarse granular, schistose in structure, with tremolite, and disseminated crystals of iron pyrites. Some of these beds are dolomytic, as shown by the following analysis by Dr. Genth, of a sample from a quarry near Lincolnton :

Quartz and Silicates,..............................	13.62
Carbonate of Lime,..............................	46.57
Carbonate of Magnesia,..............................	37.63
Carbonate of Manganese,..........................	0.21
Carbonate of Iron,...	1.97

The most valuable and characteristic mineral of the belt is magnetic iron, which is found throughout the length of it, cropping out at intervals of a few miles in large bedded veins, sometimes over 20 feet thick. The ore is usually granular and slaty, talcose or chloritic, and frequently more or less specular. At one of the largest veins it is highly epidotic. There are also frequent veins of limonite.

In the direction of the continuation of the line of this belt, near the northern border of the State, in Surry and Stokes counties, is another body of quartzytes and mica slates, with occasional argillaceous and hydro-mica slates, constituting the range of the Pilot and Sauratown Mountains. Some of these quartzytes are flexible—itacolumite, and there is a bed of conglomerate near the base of the series. The dip in the western part of the range of the Pilot is N. W. about 20°, and in the eastern about the same amount, in the opposite direction ; and the easterly dip also holds for the Sauratown range ; while in the gap between, there is much less regularity, and the prevalent dip seems to be N. W., and at angles varying between 30°an 60d°.

The fourth belt of Huronian rocks is coincident in general direction, and partly in position, with the Blue Ridge. Towards the S. W. it crosses that chain and occupies a belt of two or three miles across the plateau of the upper French Broad; the rocks here being gray and bluish clay slates and hydro-mica slates, with very limited and occasional outcrops of quartzyte and of a light colored to gray and bluish schistose, compact to slightly granular limestone. With these are associated occasional beds of limonite. The rocks of this belt may be seen in Swannanoa Gap, in a large body of quartzo-argillaceous and quartzitic slates, and of mica slates and drab, bluish and greenish clay slates, all dipping south eastward at an angle of 30° to 60°. About the foot of the mountain the quartzytes become gneissoid, and in places occur coarse grits, and beds of chloritic and calcareous slates. The breadth of these rock at this point is 6 to 7 or 8 miles; but the greatest development of this series of rocks is seen a little further northeast, in the Linville Mountains, which are composed almost wholly of sandstones and quartzites of various degrees of metamorphism, in some places almost or quite vitrified, and so jointed that the bedding is entirely obliterated. These quartzytes are sometimes slightly micaceous or chloritic, and sometimes flexible,—itacolumitic.

The dip is very irregular and confused, but seems to be predominantly westward. Several beds of compact, light-colored and grey limestone crops out along the western base of the mountain in the valley of North Fork, and almost to the head of it, the upper beds being on the west side of the valley.

Linville River seems to occupy a rift in these slates, which is more than 1,000 feet deep, with precipitous, and in places, vertical walls on either hand. The mural mass of Table Rock, the jagged peaks of the Chimneys, &c., and the sharp top of Hawksbill, are all recurrences of the Linville quartzytes, with characters unchanged.

Following northeastward along the line of these rocks, we find them recurring in the form of quartzytes, itacolumites, clay, micaceous, chloritic and talcoid slates in the various spurs of the Blue Ridge, and occasionally constituting the eastern escarpment of that chain in its southward bends, to Surry county, where these rocks cross into Virginia. At this point, in Fisher's peak and the knobs of the Blue Ridge south of it, are ledges of hard and gnarled grey and glistening argillaceous and quartzo-argillaceous and gneissoid slates, which are often specked with magnetite and martite crytals; and in Watauga and Caldwell these become martite schists, and again micaceous specular schists, which are rich ores of iron.

But the most remarkable part of this belt, both for breadth and peculiar lithology, is found in the region of the Grandfather and Yellow Mounsins, about the head waters of Toe River, Linville, Elk and Watauga. On upper Linville, and towards the base of the Grandfather and the head waters of Watauga, there are limited beds of argillaceous and hydra-mica slates and shales; but the prevalent rocks are feldspathic and quartzose slates and grits, sometimes gneiss-like, and chloritic and epidotic schists, with epidosites, the latter sometimes enclosing bright red rounded grains of jasper. Along the high spurs of the Grandfather, to the northwest,—the Yellow Mountains, are large bodies of greenish epidotic sandstone, feldspathic and quartzose; and along the northward spur of Hanging Rock, hard and gnarled dark grey quartzo-argillaceous slates prevail; but these are also much veined with irregular masses and reticulations of epidote. Passing eastward to the Watauga, from Valley Crucis up the river, the prevalence of epidotic and chloritic, massive or obscurely bedded rocks, is most striking. Some of the masses are much veined with fine seams of white quartz, while others are amygdaloidal, sprinkled with grains of gypsum and quartz and epidote; while still further east, across the Rich Mountains, occur chloritic amygdaloids in which the grains are feldspar, which are much weathered so as to leave the surface of the rock deeply honey-combed. Alternating with these conspicuous and dominant masses along the river, are the slate and gneiss-like grits of Linville, and occasionlly silvery, grey, greenish and spotted argillaceous and felspathic slates and shales.

On Elk River occurs a greenish quartzo-felspathic, thick bedded, compact to friable slate and grit, which gradually passes into a nacreous light-colored, coarse slate-conglomerate,—a fine grained argillaceous quartzyte, filled with rounded and flattened pebbles of white and reddish quartz and of hard quartzo-argillaceous slates.

This conglomerate outcrop has a breadth of several hundred yards on Elk, and extends nearly east and west several miles into the mountain slopes on either hand.

The rocks of this rugged region are much disturbed, but the prevalent dip is eastwardly, and the strike a little east of north.

There remains one other Huronian tract, whose formations compose the most westerly rocky zone of the State, including the mass of the Smoky Mountains and its eastern escarpment for the more part of its course, from the head waters of Laurel River in Madison county, near the Big Bald, to Cherokee; widening southward, until it includes almost the whole length of the latter county, in the transverse section of its strata. This belt I have elsewhere provisionally named the "Cherokee Slates."

Two sections of these rocks are given on the map, as they occur on the French Broad, and along the Hiwassee, through Cherokee.

Beginning at the State line in the latter county we encounter, for several miles, a succession of conglomerates and clay slates, drab, blue and green, with presently gneiss-like slates and grits and quartzo-felspathic rocks, and occasional beds of staurolitic and garnetiferous hydro-mica slates. These slates with their characteristic crystals are very persistent, being seen conspicuously in Georgia, on the Morganton road; and also northeastwards 4 or 5 miles in the spurs of the Smoky. Near Murphy the grey gneiss-like slates are thickly sprinkled with transverse crystals of mica; and this remains a prominent feature of these slates on Valley River, 12 or 15 miles above Murphy, and on the Tennessee near the mouth of Tuckasege, and on Hiwassee 8 or 10 miles above Murphy. The dip of the rocks, which is generally steep, 40° to 60, and 80° and 90° S. E. for several miles from the state line, until Long Ridge is passed, after which it turns to the N. W., to within 3 or 4 miles of Murphy, where the easterly dip is recovered. About Murphy the crystalline dolomitic limestone is encountered, with accompanying beds of shining clay slates and shales and a thin bed of quartzytes, which lie along the valley of Valley River, to its head; being accompanied throughout by frequent outcrops of limonite. This limestone and its accompanying iron ore and clay slates is repeated on Peachtree Creek, 4 or 5 miles east of Murphy, and this reduplication seems to follow up the east side of the wide valley of Valley River, parallel with the former, which keeps to the northwest side, at the distance of 2 to 3 miles, and less, towards the head of the valley. To the southeast of this valley, in the Koneteh Mountains, and across the upper Hiwassee into Clay, is a succession of clay slates, with gneiss-like gray slates, as described above, and staurolitic mica slates. A little above Valleytown a small body of quartzytes is passed and then a heavy bed of shining dark clay slates, which run nearly north from this point through the Valley River Mountains and into the Nantehaleh Mountains to the east of Nantehaleh River towards the mouth of that stream. These slates are much disturbed, broken and crumpled. Beyond these are light colored and grey argillaceous, and occasionally micaceous slates and shales, with alternations of gneissoid slates for two or three miles, after which, on Nantahaleh, come in, with a change of the dip to the west, the gneisses and hornblende slates of the Laurentian.

The reversals of the dip in the section below Murphy are easily traceable across the valley of the Cheowah and the Tennessee, on the latter, a little below the mouth of Tuckasege. The Tennessee river section shows much fewer and smaller beds of conglomerates than the Hiwassee, and also less of clay slates and mica slates, but a greatly exaggerated development of the quartzose slates, gneisses and grits.

The limestones of Valley River follow the valley of Notteley river southwestward into Georgia, crossing the Toccoa (Hemptown creek tributary) 12 miles S. E. of Ducktown. To the northestward they pass through Red Marble Gap of the Valley River Mountains, and outcrop along Red Marble Creek, and several miles below its mouth, are last seen at Blowing Cave. These limestones are generally white, but are often found of various colors,—pink, grey, black, mottled and banded. They are accompanied by large beds of white, compact to granular steatyte, which is massive to more or less schistose in structure. Tremolite is of frequent occurrence in the limestones, which, as already intimated, are dolomytes at least in part, as shown by the following analyses of Dr. Genth:

	I	II	III
Quartz and Silicates,	0.44	2.56	0.32
Carbonate of Lime,	97.86	94.51	54.10
Carbonate of Magnesia,	1.29	2.12	44.44
Carbonate of Manganese,	0.18	0.21	0.52
Carbonate of Iron,	0.23	0.60	0.62

I and III are white and fine grained, from Valley River, the former near Taylors; II is the red or pink marble from Blowing Cave, on Nantehaleh river.

The section on French Broad begins at the State line near Paint Rock in Madison county. The vertical cliffs along the river gorge at this point are gray and light colored quartzose sandstones and quartzytes with occasional thin beds of dark gray clay slate. Passing up the river, we find these quartzytes interbedded with and finally replaced by shales, and then by thick bedded grits and conglomerates, or breccias. These are succeeded by heavy beds of argillaceous slates and shales, brown and gray, and at Warm Springs, about 6 miles, by compact blue and gray limestones and a calcareous gray sandstone, and half a mile above, by vertical cliffs of much jointed quartzytes, which continue for nearly two miles with little interruption, and give place, just below the mouth of Laurel river, to blue and gray clay slates and coarse comglomerates, which outcrop again 5 or 6 miles southwest on Shut-In-Creek. Above Laurel river come in heavy beds of greenish and reddish felspathic quartzytes and gneissoid rocks for more than a mile, and then gray, dark blue, and spotted argillaceous slates, after which the gneisses and hornblende slates and crystalline limestones of the Laurentian succeed. This cross section would make nearly ten miles in a direct line. The disturbance, the folding and crushing of these strata has left them in such disorder that it is difficult to make out their position with any satisfaction, but after leaving the almost horizontal strata of the cliffs at Paint Rock, the dip, which is generally between 40° and 70°, is predominantly easterly, but with many exceptions, until the Warm Springs belt is passed, after which the dip is reversed, for the most part, through a section of several miles about Laurel River. The limestones of the Warm Springs section pass westward into Tennessee, and northeastward up the valley of Laurel River and through the Smoky range, making their final disappearance into Tennessee; the Smoky Mountains beyond this point being composed of older formations.

This series of rocks pass southwestward across Shut-In Creek and up Warm Springs Creek and Meadow Fork, through the New Found Mountains, across Pigeon River, and over to the head waters of Oconaluftee River, widening out so as to take in almost the whole course of that stream to the Tuckasege. But the limestones which pass out on the Pigeon Valley from Warm Springs do not again cut into the Smoky, which is composed, for this interval, from Pigeon to the Tennessee, of clay slates, blue and grey, micaceous and talcose, and of quartzose slates and gneiss-like beds, schists and quartzytes.

This belt of rocks is colored on the map throughout like the other Huronian belts, and for the same reasons, viz: that they succeed the Laurentian, and differ from them strongly in degree of metamorphism and general lithological character, so that the transition from one to the other is obvious along the whole extended line of contact, and that they have yielded no fossils, which alone could authorize their reference to a later age. And although the fact of unconformability can not be asserted for any one of the sections, this may arise from the circumstance that the disturbance and dislocation of the strata along this line are extreme, and that no detailed or minute examination has ever been attempted, and of course nothing short of such examination would suffice in such a region. And another circumstance of weight is the immense body of these rocks, which must be allowed, on the French Broad for example, after every reasonable reduction for folding, a thickness of several miles. Add these to the primordial or the lowest members of the Lower Silurian and they receive a most incredible development downwards, since the rocks along the Tennessee border referred to this horizon have already a very great thickness.

However, as stated above, these rocks have only been located *provisionally*. And it is right to say further that the only examination I have made of this western Smoky belt, was a mere reconnoisance, mostly on horseback, made in a few weeks of the autumn of 1866. The only hopeful way of attacking the complicated problem of their age is to trace their connection with the

SILURIAN,

As this formation is developed in Tennessee, where they have been so thoroughly studied by Prof. Safford. And I am glad to acknowledge the service which he has rendered towards the solution of the problem by running his French Broad section across the State line to Warm Springs and a little beyond. In this section he makes the Paint Rock sandstones to be Chilhowie, or Potsdam, and the grits and conglomerates below and above Warm Springs to be Ocoee, or sub-Potsdam, and the limestone he refers to the Knox Dolomite, which is above the Potsdam.

And Prof. Bradley of Knoxville University, has kindly furnished me within a few days, a manuscript copy of a paper which he proposes to publish soon, giving some conclusions from a recent study of the rocks of Cherokee and of the lower Tennessee and Nantehaleh sections of them. Extensively familiar already with the Primordial formations in other parts of the continent, and living in the midst of a region of Lower Silurian formations, which have been so well described and mapped by Safford, and with whose characteristics he is familiar from his own explorations, Prof. B. is well qualified to attack this knotty problem from the only direction which offers any prospect of its solution. He refers the conglomerates, sandstones and quartzytes and their associated slates, to the Primordial, (Ocoee and Chilhowie of Safford), and the limestones of Valley River to the Knox formation, regarding these beds as continuations, or folds of the same rocks in Tennessee and Georgia, basing his conclusions on stratigraphical and lithological considerations, having found no fossils. If Prof. B. is able to continue his investigations among these confused and complicated geological obscurities and to unravel the tangled skein of their history, he will doubtless render an eminent service to science as well as make an important contribution to the geology of North Carolina.

If these identifications shall prove to be valid, they will carry not only this belt but the preceding, which lies along the line of the Blue Ridge; since this belt connects itself directly with the slates and conglomerates of Tennessee through the large and peculiar body of epidotic and chloritic sandstones and the slates and conglomerates of the Yellow Mountains and along Elk River. And the King's Mountain belt will probably follow, as this is almost certainly geologically indentical with the Sauratown and Pilot Mountain section, and the latter are almost continuous with the eastern fragments of the Blue Ridge belt in Surry county. But this conclusion will not involve the great middle and eastern belts which must still remain Huronian, until determined independently to belong to a later series; both because they are widely separated from the others, and because they have lithological and stratigraphical characters of their own, which would prevent their following any determinations of horizon for the others, which should be based on these considerations alone.

If the rocks of the Smoky or Cherokee belt are not Silurian, the formation is wanting in North Carolina.

TRIASSIC.

There are in this State two narrow fringes of an eroded and obliterated anticlinal, which belong to this system; the smaller, or Dan River belt, from 2 to 4 miles wide, following the trough-like valley of that stream, (about N. 65° E.), for more than 30 miles, to the Virginia line; the other, the Deep River belt, extending, in a similar trough, 5 to 15 miles wide, (and depressed 100 to 200 feet below the general level of the country), from the southern boundary of the State, in Anson county, in a N. E. direction, to the middle of Granville county, within 15 miles of the Virginia line. They are separated, therefore, by a swell of country 100 to 75 miles wide, which rises along its topographical axis to 8 or 900 feet above the sea, the troughs themselves having respectively an elevation of 5 to 600 feet and 2 to 300 feet. The belts are convergent in the direction of the Triassic beds of Virginia, with which they were doubtless once connected, (as well as with some small intervening outliers) in one continuous formation.

The dip of the Dan River beds is about 35° N. W., (20° to 70°) and of those of Deep River 20° S. E., (10° to 35°). The rocks are sandstones, clay slates, shales and conglomerates, generally ferruginous and brick-red, but often gray and drab. The shales are occasionally marly, and these and the sandstones are sometimes saliferous. Many of the beds consist of loose and uncompacted materials, and are therefore easily abraded.

The most important and conspicuous member of the series, is a large body of black shales, which encloses seams of bituminous coal, 2 to 6 feet. This coal lies near the base of the system in both belts, and is underlaid on Dan River by shales, and on Deep River by sandstones and conglomerates; the latter constituting the lowest member of the series, and being in places very coarse. And near the eastern margin in Wake county, where the belt reaches its greatest breadth, (some 15 miles,) the conglomerates are of great thickness and very coarse, uncompacted and rudely stratified, resembling somewhat the half-stratified drift of the mountain slopes, the fragments often little worn and sometimes 10 and 12 inches in diameter, and evidently derived from the Huronian rocks of the hills to the eastward. The conglomerates of the Dan River belt are among the upper members of the series, and are mostly fine and graduation to grits and sandstones.

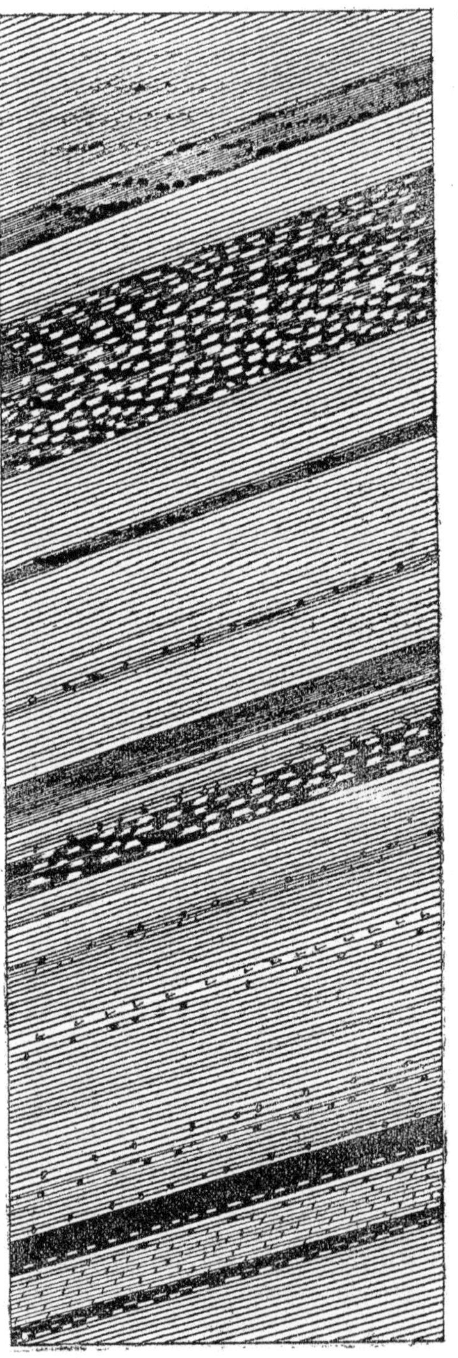

SECTION OF EGYPT COAL SHAFT, CHATHAM COUNTY; 460 FEET DEEP.

The black shales near the base of the system contain beds of fire clay and black band iron ore, interstratified with the coal. They are also highly fossiliferous, especially on Deep River. Silicified trunks of trees are very abundant in the lower sandstones, as may be seen conspicuously near Germanton, in Stokes county, the public road being in a measure obstructed by the multitude of fragments and entire trunks and projecting stumps of a petrified Triassic forest; and similar petrifiactions are abundant in the Deep River belt, occurring in this, as in the other, among the sandstones near the horizon of the coal.

The accompanying section shows the rocks of the Deep River region, down to the coal. The section is that of the shaft of the Egypt mine, which was opened some 20 years ago and wrought quite extensively, both before and during the war. It is in the main, a copy of that given by Admiral Wilkes, in his report to the General Government in 1858, on the Deep River coal region. The prevalence of shales and slates is notable, as well as the very small proportion of sandstones; in both respects, the section is exceptional. Below the slate at the end of the shaft, come in the bottom sandstones and conglomerates. The shaft is located 500 yards south of the outcrop.

Emmons reports 5 seams of coal, separated by black slates, shales, black band iron ore and fire clay; and in general, he finds a remarkable similarity to the coal deposits of the Carboniferous formation.

The coal with its shales outcrops along the northern margin of the belt at various points, for more than 15 miles; and many shafts having been sunk to, and through the main seam, which is the upper one, it is ascertained to be very persistent in all its characteristics and associated beds.

The outcrops may be traced almost continuously to the gulf, 3 miles west of Egypt. The annexed map of the outcrop at this point is copied from a local survey made in connection with some mining operations carried on here during the war. And the section (on the line A—B) is added from a shaft recently sunk to a depth of 20 feet through the two upper seams of coal and the intervening stratum of black band. The dip is 32° south. The section is as follows:

Black slates and shales,	8 feet, (from the surface).
Fire clay and ball ore,	4 "
Coal,	4 "
Black band, nearly	2 "
Coal,	1½ "
Black slates,	——, at bottom.

Outcrop and Section of Coal at the Gulf, Chatham County.

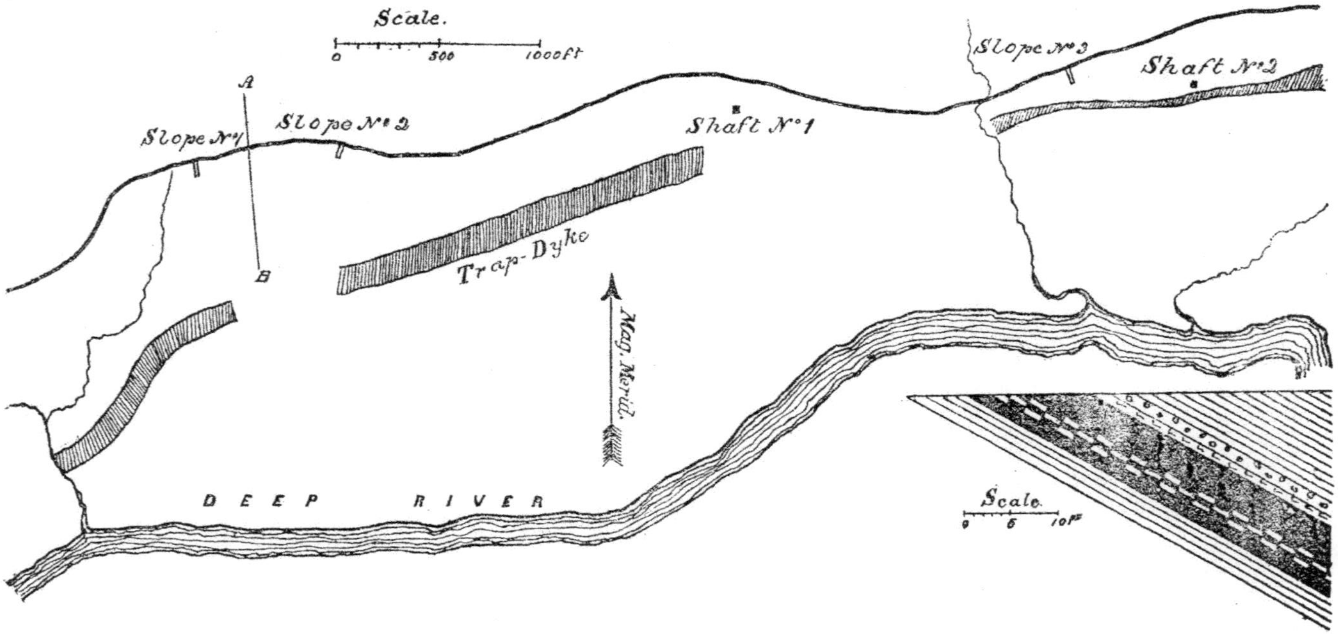

Scale.
0 500 1000 ft
Slope No. 1
A
B
Slope No. 2
Trap-Dyke
Shaft No. 1
Mag. Merid.
Slope No. 3
Shaft No. 2
DEEP RIVER
Scale
0 5 10 ft

On Dan River the coal first shows itself on the surface about 3 miles east of Germanton, being imperfectly exposed in a ravine. The coal is about 3 feet thick. Some 6 or 7 miles further east, at Stokesburg, there are outcrops of three seams in succession, the upper about 3 feet thick, with a heavy body of bituminous shales ; the other two were not well enough exposed for measurement, but they were explored by a very intelligent gentleman who reports one of them as much thicker than the top seam. The black shales and slates crop out at various points about the town of Madison ; and near Leaksville a slope was driven some 60 feet on the coal seam which is here 3 feet thick, and with a dip of 34° and considerable quantities were mined during the war. It is classed as a semi-bituminous or dry coal. The outcrops show that the coal is continuous through the whole length of the belt in this State, which is above 30 miles.

The thickness of the Triassic series Dr. Emmons estimates at about 3,000 feet on Deep River; but owing to the steeper dips of the Dan River beds, the thickness of all the strata represented there would be about 10,000 feet. But their actual vertical depth to the underlying Archæan rocks, is probably less than a thousand feet, in either case. What was the original thickness of the formation when first elevated, and before the wasting by denudation began, can only be remotely conjectured; but it must have been very great, as will appear from the following considerations: 1. The beds on Dan River, measured at right angles to the dip, gives a minimum thickness for that side of the formation of near 10,000 feet: 2. In the section of the Deep River belt, which is exposed in the valley of the Yadkin, not only is there a width of 6 miles with the usual dip of 20°, but there is an additional outcrop more than a mile in breadth, *ten miles south* of the principal belt, which preserves the southeasterly dip of nearly 20°, and hence the calculation for a minimum thickness at this margin must be based on a breadth of 16 miles, which gives a thickness of more than 25,000 feet: 3. There is no way of accounting for the present position of these beds with their opposite and considerable dips, but by supposing an uplift of the intervening tract, such and so great, that if the movement were now reversed, it would carry this swell of nearly 100 miles breadth into a depresssion much below the present level of the troughs in which these remnant fringes lie, so that there has been an erosion not only of 10 to 20,000 feet of the broken arch of Triassic beds over this area, but also of a considerable thickness of the underlying rocks on which they had been deposited: 4. While this erosion of the central parts was going forward, the margins must have suffered a very great amount of waste, so that the beds which remain, are probably but a small part of the original series. It is probable that these beds at one time covered the larger part of the middle section of the State, almost to the flanks of the Blue Ridge.

The present area of Triassic in the State is about 1,000 square miles, about one-third of it estimated to be underlaid with coal; but since there are outcrops of black shales and of lignites in other parts of the Deep River belt at great distances from the area commonly set down as coal-bearing, there is a strong probability that coal will be found over a much larger territory.

Another point worthy of note has been mentioned incidentally, viz: that the materials of the coarse conglomerates which characterize the the eastern belt (and its eastern margin), as compared with the western, were evidently derived from the Archæan rocks *to the eastward;* the the large pebbles and bowlders (sometimes 10 to 15 inches thick), may often be traced to the very ledges a few miles east, from which they were torn. And the rudely stratified condition of these beds, and the coarseness and miscellaneous character of their materials, being made up of slightly worn fragments of rocks of various degrees of hardness, indicate a derivation from neighboring and steep highland or mountain slopes; and indeed they are of such likeness to some Quaternary, semi-stratified accumulations, as even to strongly suggest a sub-Triassic glaciation. If it be true that the materials of this formation came, even in large part, from the east, and it seems impossible to resist the conclusion, and if their extent, horizontal and vertical, was at all such as has been shown to be probable, it follows that there existed in Triassic times a large coastward tract of elevated and probably mountainous territory. The changes, therefore, in the topography of this portion of the continent, in comparatively late geological ages, have been much greater than is generally supposed, involving such a depression of this Atlantic tract, that the whole of it was swept over and planed down still further by the great gravel floods of Glacial times; and a tranverse upthrust of more than a thousand feet, along a nearly east and west axis, sufficient to throw off the margins into high opposite dips across a anticlinal bulge of nearly 100 miles breadth.

A very marked peculiarity of the Triossic formation in this State, in all its outcrops is the frequency of dolerytic dikes. These beds are every where intersected, in various directions, by these ledges of dark grey, generally fine grained traps; the thickness being usually not more than a few yards to 2 or 3 rods, and the length not generally exceeding a few hundred yards, but occasionally extending to several miles. These traps are sometimes brecciated, and occasionally contain serpentine and chlorite; and magnetite and pyrite in disseminated grains are quite common. The sandstones and shales are usually blackened on either side of these trap dikes to a distance of several feet or yards, proportioned to the size of the dike, and not unfrequently they have undergone complete metamorphism.

It is due to Prof. Dana that we are able to describe these dikes as *dolerytic* instead of *diorytic*, his investigations among the traps of the Connecticut valley having determined this point for them, and the examination of a typical specimen of the North Carolina traps, sent for comparison at his request from the very full collection in the Museum, having extended the conclusion to those of this State also. Of valuable minerals, besides the coal, iron ores are the chief, there being several beds of limonite, (frequently in the form of a coarse gravel), which are persistent for many miles and of 1 to 3 feet thickness.

Fossils.—In addition to the vertebrate remains of the North Carolina Triassic, of which a complete list is found in the Appendix by Prof. Cope, the following species of other orders are given by Dr. Emmons:

MOLLUSCA.

Posidonia ovalis.
" Multicostata.

CRUSTACEA.

Cypris ——.

PLANTS.

Chondrites interruptus,
" gracilis.
" ramosus.
Gymnocaulus alternatus.
Equisetum columnaroides.
Calamites disjunctus.
" arenaceus.
Strangerites oblongus.
Pecopteris falcatus.
" carolinensis.
Cyclopteris ——.
Acrostichites oblongus.
Sphenoglossum quadrifolium.
Cheilanthites ——.
Dyctuocaulus striatus.
Cycadites acutus.
" longifolius.
Zamites graminoides.
" obtusifolius.
Podozamites lanceolotus.
" longifolius.
Pterozamites decussatus.
Walchia diffusus.
" longifolius.
Lepacyclotes circularis.
" ellipticus.

The coal mines are not wrought, and have not been re-opened, except for a few months, since the resumption of the Survey, so that there has been little opportunity to add any thing to the pre-existing knowledge of our Triassic palæontology.

CRETACEOUS.

This formation is visible in North Carolina only in the river bluffs of the southeastern portion of the State, from the Neuse, (and its tributary, Contentnea), southward. Dr. Emmons also speaks of it as occuring on

Tar River. It is best exposed in the bluffs along the Cape Fear between Fayetteville and Wilmington. The rocks of this system (every where very slightly compacted) are, for 50 to 60 miles below Fayetteville, sandstones, clay slates and shales, 30 to 40 feet thick, in many places dark to black and very lignitic, with projecting trunks and limbs of trees, and at a few points, full of marine shells. These beds Dr. Emmons regards as probably eocene. For 40 to 50 miles above Wilmington, and in all the other river sections, the rock is a uniform dark, greenish gray, slightly argillaceous sandstone, massive, and showing scarcely any marks of bedding. This sandstone every where contains a small percentage of glauconite, and is in fact the representative of the true Greensand.

The following analysis of a specimen from a representative outcrop at Blackrock bluff, 20 miles above Wilmington, on the Cape Fear, is from Emmons:

Silica,	93.43
Oxide of Alumina and Iron,	9.00
Carbonate of Lime,	11.40
Magnesia,	0.20
Potassa,	0.38
Soda,	0.42
Organic Matter,	4.80
Water,	3.80
	100.43

The above is a fair sample of this formation in all its northern and eastern outcrops, as it appears on Tar River, about Kinston, in Lenoir county, as well as on South River and Black River, in the southwestern corner of Sampson county; but westward, higher up the Cape Fear, the beds lose entirely their glauconitic and calcareous character, and become more clayey and frequently black-lignitic, with embedded trunks, limbs and leaves of trees; and not unfrequently it is composed of sandy accumulations exhibiting much false bedding. These beds extend a hundred miles up the Cape Fear from Wilmington. It is probably the same lignitic member of this series, which appears at low water in the Neuse, at the railroad bridge near Goldsboro. The Cretaceous beds of North Carolina are not usually very rich in fossils, the greensand containing generally scattered specimens of belenmites, ostræa larva, exogyra costata and an occasional anomia; but at several points on the Cape Fear the exogyras are very numerous, and at Kelley's Cove, about 40 miles from

Wilmington, there is a stratum of 2 to 4 feet which is filled with marine shells. And at Snow Hill, in Lenoir county, on Contentnea Creek, is a line of bluffs on the south side of the stream, several hundred yards in length, and 20 to 40 feet high, the lower portion of which, to the height of 10 or 12 feet is a cretaceous sandy marlyte, filled with shells, many of them of new species and representing several new genera, but containing known species enough to enable Prof. Conrad, to whom by good fortune the unique collection in the museum from this locality was submitted, to determine the horizon as that of the Ripley group. For a description of these Snow Hill species and a synopsis of the Cretaceous shells of the State, the reader is referred to Prof. Conrad's paper in the Appendix. It is probable therefore that all the cretaceous beds of North Carolina, so far as visible, should be referred to the upper cretaceous. These beds occupy everywhere the lowest position, and nowhere expose a thickness above 50 or 60 feet, so that there is nothing on which to ground even a conjecture of their vertical extent.

Very few species of the higher orders of animals have been found in these beds. In addition to the list of Prof. Conrad, Dr. Emmons gives Belemintella americana, B. Compressa, and one or two large Saurians; and there is a large femur of a chelonian in the State collection.

TERTIARY.

The two lower subdivisions of this formation, Eocene and Miocene, are extensively exposed, chiefly along the watercourses and in the ravines and bluffs, and in the wells and plantation ditches of the eastern counties.

Eocene.—The distribution of the rocks of this subdivision is more limited than that of the Cretaceous and much more so than that of the Miocene, which overlies it. The boundaries of it, north and south, are the Neuse and the Cape Fear; and it is found on the Neuse to within 2 or 3 miles of the railroad crossing, near Goldsboro', and at one point, in an isolated outcrop on the river bluff 7 or 8 miles further west; and it occurs in limited outcrops throughout the triangular region between Newbern and Goldsboro' and Wilmington. It consists of a light-colored and yellowish consolidated marlyte, as in the steep bluffs on the Neuse 10 miles below Goldsboro, and again, 15 to 20 feet thick, 10 miles above Newbern, and in the Natural Wells near Magnolia, containing, in this form, 40 to 80 per cent. of carbonate of lime; or of a shell conglomerate as seen about Newbern, and 8 or 10 miles up the Trent river,—a rock much used for building in Newbern, and burned for lime, while in some limited localities it is made up of silicious casts of shells from which all the carbonate of lime has been dissolved, constituting a true buhrstone; or of a white calcareous sandstone, more or less compacted, as on the Neuse near Goldsboro, and near the railroad through Duplin and Sampson counties, and in Onslow and in Jones on the Trent, and along the North East River for the most part of its course to within a mile of Wilmington; or of a gray and hard limestone, as about Richlands, in Onslow, at Rocky Point, 20 miles north of Wilmington, and 7 miles north on the North East River; or of a coarse conglomerate of worn shells, sharks' teeth and fragments of bones and stony pebbles, as in the upper part of Wilmington and at Rocky Point; or of a fine shaly infusorial clay, light gray to ash colored, as in Sampson county near Faison's depot. Outside of this region, there are two or three small patches of Eocene; one capping a hill 350 feet above the sea, on the railroad 7 miles east of Raleigh, a silicious shell conglomerate of 2 or 3 acres in extent and 6 to 10 inches thick; the second a ferruginous, and calcareous sandstone of 4 or 5 feet thickness, on the top of a hill in the southeastern corner of Moore; this last containing some shells and many echinoderms. These fragments, or outliers show that this formation, limited as it was in thickness, had a vastly greater horizontal extent than would have been suspected, and they carry the shores of the Eocene seas quite into the hill country of the State and nearly 150 miles from the present coast line, and to an elevation of nearly 400 feet.

Some of the clay and sand beds on the upper Cape Fear may belong to the Eocene as Dr. Emmons conjectured; but as they do not contain fossils, only a minute study of the stratigraphy can decide.

Fossils—In addition to the organic remains described in the papers of Cope and Conrad in the Appendix, the following are given by Dr. Emmons.

Cidaris Mitchellii,
Cidaris Carolinensis,
Pecten membranaeea.
Scutella ———,
Microcrinus conoides,
Echinocyamus parvus.
Scutella Lyellii.
Gonioclypeus subangulatus.
Lunulites contigua.

There is a small collection of Eocene fossils in the Museum, which have not yet been studied, that will doubtless add something to the list of species already recorded.

Miocene.—This sub-division of the Tertiary extends over nearly the whole seaboard region, from the sea shore and the western margins of the Sounds, 50 to 75 miles inland. It has a much greater horizontal extent than the preceding, and a greater thickness, but is less continuous, being found in disconnected patches often of quite limited area, and exposed, like the preceding, only in river bluffs, ravines, ditches, wells, &c. It consists of beds of clay, sand and marl which are locally filled with shells (more or less decayed), to a thickness of 2 or 3, to 6 or 8 feet, and occasionally 10 or 20. The distribution of these shell beds, as far as known, will be best ascertained by a reference to the maps. These beds of blue marl as they are called, are found for the most part in the right banks of the large rivers and on the north slopes of the divides or swells of land between the rivers, the probable explanation of which has been given in the chapter on topography. And the formation thickens,—deepens, towards the northern border of the State, the beds being much thicker on the Tar and Roanoke than on the rivers south of them, and in fact being of such thickness here as to conceal both the Eocene, if it exists, and the Cretaceous, with a few quite local exceptions.

These shell beds are very rich in fossils, which are often in perfect preservation. The vertebrates will be found in Cope's Appendix. The new species of shells which have been discovered in the course of the present Survey, are described in Conrad's Appendix. The following list contains the species given by Emmons, a few of the names being changed to agree with Conrad.

Echinus Ruffinii,
Lunulites denticulata,
" oblonga,
Murex umbrifer,
" globosa,
" sexcostata,
Ecphora quadricostata,
Pyrula spirata,
" reticulata,
Fasciolaria distans,
" elegans,
" Sparrowi,
" alternata,
" nodulosa,
" acuta,
Galeodia Hodgii,
Terebra dislocata,
" unilineata,
" neglecta,
Dolium octocostatum,
Dactylus carolinensis,
Oliva ancillariæformis,
" canaliculata,
" ———,
Erato lævis,
Voluta mutabilis,
" obtusa,
Amphidetus Virginanus,
Astræa bella,
" ———,
Busycon carica,
" contrarium,
" canaliculatum,
" rugosum,
Fusus equalis,
" exilis,
" lamellosus,
" moniliformis,
Cancellaria carolinensis,
" reticulata,
Eupleura caudata,
Ptycosalpinx multirugatum,
" porcinum,
Buccinum multilineatum,
" moniliforme,
" bidentatum,
" obsoletum,
Cypræa carolinensis,
" pedicula,
Mitra carolinensis,
Marginella olivæformis,
" limatula,
" constricta,
" ovata,

Conus adversarius,
" diluvianus,
Pleurotoma lunata,
" flexnosa,
" limatula,
" commnnis,
" elegans,
" tuberculata,
Pyramidella reticulata,
Eulima lævigata,
" subulata,
Terebellum etiwanense,
" constrictum,
" Burdenii,
Turritella constricta,
Petaloconchus sculpturatus,
Litorina lineata,
Trochus philanthropus,
" ———,
Orbicula lugubris,
Cæcum annulatum,
Crucibulum costatum,
" ramosum
" multilineatum,
" dumosum,
Fissurella redimicula,
Pecten comparilis,
" eboreus,
" clintonius,
" peedeensis,
" Mortoni,
" Jeffersonius,
" Madisonius,
Verticordia ———,
Axinæa subovata,
" lentiformis,
" arata,
Chama corticosa,
" congregata,
" striata,
Arcinella spinosa,
Corbicula densata,
" cuneata,
Lucina Pennsylvanica,
" contracta,
" crenulata,
Caryatis sayana,
Callista reposta,
Dosinia transversa,
Artemis concentrica,
Metis biplicata,
Tellina alternata,
" polita,
" flexuosa,
Macoma lusoria,
" inflexa,
" elevata,
Lunatia catenoides,
Neverita percallosa,
" Emmonsii,
Natica canrena,
" fragilis,
Pyramidella arenosa,
Chemnitzia reticulata,
Cerithium moniliferum,
" ———,
" annulatum,
" bicostatum,
Scalaria multistriata,
Astarte undulata,
" curta,
" clathra,
Delphinula quadricostata,
Tornatina cylindrica,
Dentalium attenuatum,
" thallus,
Trochita centralis,
Crepidula fornicata,
" spinosa,
" plana,
Ostræa Virginiana,
" Carolinensis,
Plicatula marginata,
Mytilus incrassatus,
Arca lienosa,
" scalaris,
" incilis,
" centenaria,
" idonea,
" transversa,
Nuculana acuta,
Nucula proxima,
Astarte concentrica,
Crassatella undulata,
" Gibbesii,
" melina,
" alta,
" Marylandica,
" protexta,
Pholas costata,
" oblongata,
Mercenaria Rileyi,
Venus tridacnoides,
" cribraria,
" athleta,
Circe multistriata,
Mulinia variabilis,
Donax lateralis,
Mactra congesta,
Pteromeris perplana,

Rangia clathrodonta,	Mactra similis,
Solen·ensis,	Siliquaria equalis,
Glycimeris reflexa,	" Carolinensis,
Pholadomya abrupta,	Pholas Memmingeri,
Carditamera arata,	Cardium magnum,
Pleuromeris decemcostata,	" sublineatum,
Glycocardia granula,	Cardita carinata.

QUATERNARY.

The *Quaternary*, or *Postpliocene*, the final term of the geological column, occupies a larger area of the surface of the State than any of the preceding, as will be seen from the map. The whole eastern part of the State, a tract extending more than 100 miles from the coast, and rising to an elevation of 4 to 500 feet along its western margin, is covered for the most part with a superficial deposit of shingle, gravel, sand and clay, the coarser material predominating westward and becoming successively finer towards the coast. Almost the whole of the Tertiary and Cretaceous, and a considerable part of the Triassic, as well as a broad belt of the Archæan rocks, are concealed by a thin covering of this formation. It terminates inland along a very sinuous line, which curves sharply to the west along all the divides between the great river channels, having been swept away by denudation from their slopes as well as their valleys proper, throughout the more elevated parts of the formation, while further east, at lower levels, the present river channels themselves have been excavated through these deposits. Along railroad cuts, in gullies and washes on road sides, and wherever a section of these superficial deposits is exposed, they are found to be very irregularly bedded, showing beach structure and every kind and degree of false bedding, fine and course materials, gravel and earths being generally commingled. Towards the west, the lower parts of the earthy beds are filled for several feet with quartz pebbles of various sizes to several pounds weight. The elevation of the more western of these beds, on the top of some of the higher hills, is 4 to 500 feet, in Harnett, Moore, Richmond and Anson, conspicuously about Carthage, Rockingham and Wadesboro'. Their thickness does not often exceed 20 or 30 feet, and is generally not more than 10 or 15. Some of the best exposures of them are found at the entrance of the hill country above Fayetteville and along the Carolina Central Railroad, through Robeson, Richmond and Anson counties. They consist here of gray and purplish-white clay, sometimes quite pure, serving for brick or potter's clay, and again very sandy. These gradually become more sandy and gravelly, and at last coarse pebbly, with the rise of the surface towards the west.

Three periods are distinguishable in this formation in North Carolina, the Glacial, Champlain and Terrace; the first two quite readily.

Glacial.—Over the more eastern parts of the formation, where the elevation above tide does not exceed about 100 feet, there lies upon eroded surface of the underlying Eocene, Miocene or Cretaceous, a thin stratum of a few inches to a foot, (rarely more), of tolerably coarse pebbles, often with shark's teeth, coprolites and rolled fragments of bones, washed from the older rocks; and along the river bluffs, notably of the Cape Fear, this stratum, which lies frequently in a level line for hundreds of feet just above the water's edge, consists of a single layer of scattered pebbles and bowlders, often a foot and more in diameter, on a smooth floor of Cretaceous, for example. The underlying rock was evidently planed down by the currents and drifting ice which carried these bowlders from the Archæan hills of Chatham, to which they are readily traceable. And this erosion of the surface and scooping out of the broad river valley no doubt took place during the *Glacial period*, or the earlier part of the Quarternary age, which was *a period of elevation* in this part of the Atlantic slope, in common with the more northern portions of the continent, as is evident from the fact that the bed of the Cape Fear at Wilmington, for example, was grooved down to a depth of about 100 feet below the present sea level. This has been shown both by excavations and pile driving; the latter being carried down to the depth mentioned, through the peaty alluvion which has filled up the old bay-like 2 miles breadth of the river at this point, and reduced it to about 100 yards, and the excavations having brought up, from a depth of 70 feet, huge trunks of cypress trees, together with just such bowlders of Chatham rocks as those along the higher reaches of the river, as above described, some of these stones being more than a foot through. This stratum of pebbles between the older formation and the Quarternary often contains fossils, as previously stated, in the form of teeth, bones, coprolites, &c., but rounded and worn, evidently derived from the denuded underlying formation, Tertiary or Cretaceous.

Here, however, have been found the best preserved and entirely unworn specimens of Mastodon teeth and bones, *possibly* derived from the preceding formation, but from their mechanical condition, almost certainly belonging to the beginning of the Quarternary age or the Glacial Period.

Further evidences of a Glacial period in this latitude will be presented further on, in the Quarternary of the piedmont and mountain regions.

Champlain.—Along the bluffs of the Cape Fear below Fayetteville, one of the most persistent and regular beds is the sand and gravel deposit of 10 to 20 feet, with its torrential stratification, flow and plunge structure, and every evidence of violent movement of the transporting currents, which, in the later or Champlain period of the great ice age, filled up and obliterated the river channel and valley even, in large part: the comparatively insignficant water-way of the present river having been reëxcavated in later times through this deposit, which is doubtless the Orange Sand of Hilgard, so conspicuous on the Mississippi.

Towards the coast, and at levels but little above tide, there are regular stratified and nearly horizontal beds of ash colored clays, frequently more or less sandy. An example may be seen on the lower Neuse, along both shores of its broad bay-like mouth, 5 to 15 miles below Newbern. These beds are 5 to 10 and 15 feet thick, extending but a few feet above tide, and abound in littoral and estuary shells, undistinguishable specifically from those now living alongshore, some 30 or 40 miles east. And similar beds exist on the sound near Beaufort. It is probably that a large part of the gray and ash-colored clays near the coasts of the sounds, east of Pungo and Chowan rivers, also belong to this period, as they seem to overlie the miocene marls,—and they may be considered the continuations and representatives of the fossiliferous clays of the Neuse, just described. But a closer study of the stratigraphy than has yet been made, or the discovery of fossils will be necessary to settle the question of their age.

Above these gravels and clays there is a thin stratum (1 or 2 to 4 or 5 feet) of marine sand, and in some places of drift sand, which is spread over the surface of wide tracts, from the immediate coast at some points, quite to the western limits of the formation, and is found at all elevations. It is this stratum which gives rise to the name of "sand hills."

The Champlain period was evidently one of depression, as indicated by the marine shell beds of the Neuse for instance. But the marine sands, as well as the stratified beds on the hills towards the western margin of the formation, show a depression of more than 400 feet, and at some points of 500; but it is worthy of note that the depression along the northern border of the State was only about half as great as towards the south.

This completes the description in brief of the great Quartenary area of the State. But isolated patches of shingle and pebble and rudely statified gravel beds are found capping the hills and benches that flank the great river valleys of the State, at various elevations above present water level, 50 to 150 and 200 feet, and even more, and at all distances, up to 2 or 3 miles occasionally. These beds extend quite to the foot of the mountains, even to an elevation of 1,200 and 1,500 feet above the sea. The beds are generally not more than 3 or 4 to 6 or 8 feet thick, increasing towards the mountains to 10 and 20 occasionally. The coarser pebbles are generally collected in a stratum at the bottom of the bed and immediately upon the irregularly eroded surface formed by the upturned edges of the Archæan rocks, which preserve perfectly their form and bedding in the quartz and mica seams, and in the differently colored earths into which they have passed by weathering, showing that denudation had overtaken the forces of disintegration, and that the whole region was planed down to the living rock, and all soils and earths swept away.

The gold gravels are no doubt to be referred to this period. The most notable and extensive of these are found on the flanks of the spurs and low ridges of the Uwharrie Mountains in Montgomery county and along the foot hills and inclined upper valleys and benches of the South Mountains. Some of these beds on the head waters of Silver Creek and Muddy Creek, and First Broad and Second Broad Rivers,—Brindletown, Brackettown, &c., are 20 and sometimes even 30 feet thick. They consist in their upper portions where they lie against the steeper slopes of the mountains, of masses of ferruginous earth or soil, showing slight evidence of incipient stratification, the lower part of the mass for 1 or 2 to 4 or 5 feet being filled with angular and slightly worn fragments of hard rocks, mostly quartz. At a few points where these accumulations have descended upon a slight depression or ancient ravine, the old dark soil remains beneath, with its roots and stumps and trunks and leaves of trees, grass and fruits, &c., and not unfrequently the lower 3 to 6 feet is bleached to a light colored earth, by the chemical action of the organic matter; while the upper part of the bed is brick-red.

Such are some of the richest gold gravels of the State, on Silver Creek, for example, in Burke county, which have often yielded ten dollars a day to the hand. No better example of these pnenomena can be found than on the flanks and around the base of the Pilot Mountain, in the mines of Col. J. C. Mills. The gold-bearing gravel beds of Montgomery are of the same description, the famous Christian Mine among others.

Evidently these materials have descended the slopes of the mountains and ridges, at whose bases, or on whose lower and gentle inclines they are found. By what force? Certainly not of water. Neither are they *moraines*—accumulations at the foot of descending ice masses. They are simply beds of *till*, which have crept down the declivities of the hills and mountains, exactly as a glacier descends an Alpine valley, by successive freezing and thawing of the whole water-saturated mass, both the expansion of freezing and gravitation contributing to the downward movement; and with each thawing and advance, the embedded stones and gold particles dropping a little nearer the bottom. If these till beds are followed down the slopes into the valleys and bottoms of the streams to the flood-plain, they will be found to have changed character with every rod of advance, all the gold having been dropped either on or near the foot of the slopes, the pebbles being more exclusively quartz, and more and more rounded, and accumulated in a stratum at the bottom of the bed, or constituting the whole of it.

Accumulations of the character above described as till, or *initial drift*, may be seen everywhere on the hills and slopes of the piedmont region, and, less conspicuously, even into the eastern territory, of the Quaternary proper. Any where on the hills or declivities about Raleigh for example, notably in the railroad cuts, may be seen masses of earth 4 or 8 feet thick along the lower portion of which the angular quartz fragments have begun to accumulate; frequently the vein is visible beneath from which the fragments have been moved but a few feet or inches down the slope. Of course no movement can take place at such a depth now; that must have ceased with the arctic cold which could freeze the soil to such depths.

The railroad cuts through the piedmont region, especially from Morganton to the foot of the Blue Ridge furnish many admirable sections of hill side drift. The most interesting is 9 miles beyond Morganton, known as Leonard's cut. On the upper slope of a high hill a cut of 80 feet exposes a bed of peat and drift wood 15 feet thick with the underlying soil filled with stumps and roots. Above the peat is a bed of rudely statified gravel and sand, 10 to 15 feet deep, on which grows the present forest. In the peat are numerous shining wing-covers of beetles and seeds of many species of plants, cones of several kinds of pine, and of hemlock, squirrel-gnawed hickory nuts, seed pods of kalmia, &c. No species have been observed which are not found at present living in the region, although the hemlock and white pine are not found nearer than the Blue Ridge, some 30 or 40 miles away. The bottom of this cut is 100 feet above the surface of the Catawba River, 1 mile distant. Nearly all the hills of this region are shown by these railroad sections to owe their present form and pressure mainly to the drift beds which fill up and round out their flanks, to a thickness of 1 or 2 to 15 or 20 feet, and occasionally much more, and frequently crown their summits, or even make up their whole mass, the present ravines being excavated along, or across the crests of the old buried hills and rocky ledges. In several of these railroad sections there are plainly distinguishable two periods of drift, the lower, of different materials, frequently indurated, generally by an iron cement, and its surface eroded and covered with a second pebble and gravel bed. And in some of them again, for example that of Hemphill cut near Old Fort, is a bed of gray indurated and in places sandy clay, in which are embedded not only a stratum of earth and pebbles small and large, but in one part of it many huge rounded and polished, yellowish quartz bowlders, some of them weighing 2 and 3 towns, a true *bowlder clay*.

On the table land beyond the Blue Ridge these drift beds are quite as abundant and well characterized. The cut at Swannanoa gap is a good example. This drift bed begins almost at the summit, within one or two hundred yards, and there are frequent additional examples on the road to Asheville, where such an accumulation may be fonnd on the summit of the highest knob overlooking the town and not less than 300 feet above the French Broad, a mile distant. This bed has long furnished cobblestones for the pavements of the town. Some of these stones are peculiar, as the heavy black compact tourmaline pebbles, and these have been traced to their source in a vein on a foothill of the mountains 6 miles above, towards the Blue Ridge. Similar accumulations are found along the valley of the French Broad to Tennessee, on the slopes and benches of the mountains on either hand, sometimes to a height of one or two hundred feet, generally in the form of terraces. But along the slopes and benches among the mountain ranges are frequent accumulations of earth and slightly worn fragments of quartz and other hard rocks, which it is difficult to account for except on the supposition of an intensity of cold and an accumulation of ice and an exaggeration of the amount of rainfall which are not easy to conceive.

It is not possible to give a just impression of many of the phenomena above described without the help of illustrative diagrams, and it is proposed to give in the next volume some of the numerous sections which have been taken of these Quaternary strata in all parts of the State.

Glaciers.—There is no evidence of the former existence of glaciers in this State, unless of the most local and limited character; but there is strong evidence of their non-existence over nearly the whole area of the State, conspicuously in the piedmont and mountain regions, in the mode of occurrence of the till and pebble beds already described. These beds adjust themselves accurately to all the inequalities of surfaces, which are composed of the irregularly eroded edges of foliated, or bedded rocks, of variable disintegrability; whereas the whole surface would have been evenly planed, or smoothed and rounded, (if not polished and grooved and striated), as in Glacial latitudes; and the total absence of this latter sort of evidence may be at least taken as confirmation of the conclusion reached on other grounds.

But the conclusion seems to be inevitable that, in the modified sense, which is obvious from the preceding descriptions, the whole middle and western sections of the State have been extensively and profoundly glaciated,—by the action of frost and flood, so that the prëexisting soils and earths and the more disintegrable rocks were removed and rapidly accumulated in the ravines and valleys, which were often in part, or entirely obliterated by the floods of sand and gravel constantly thrown into them from the steeper slopes, more rapidly than they could be removed by the same volume of water with its diminished velocity, after reaching the gentler inclinations of the ordinary flood-plains of the rivers; so that for the most part, their channels have, in the course of post-glacial ages, been re-excavated by the slow erosion and transport of these vast accumulations of debris, to successively lower levels and to the sea, leaving only occasional and accidental patches and benches at different elevations, to bear witness of so great changes.

Recent.—This brings us to the subject of *terraces*, which represent the latest period of the Quaternary. These are nearly level-topped accumulations of drift, such as have been described, along the sides of the river valleys, against the shoulders of the enclosing hills, or the foothills of the mountains. Two or three such terraces, besides the flood-plain, are frequently found, one above another, the highest sometimes more than 100 feet above the river. Examples of these are to be seen on all the large rivers of the State, but more conspicuously in the mountain and piedmont regions, as on thë Yadkin, below Patterson, and on the French Broad, below Warm Springs.

These terraces or benches are the remnant patches of former flood-plains, as the torrents of the closing glacial epoch subsided and shrunk gradually towards their present dimensions, cutting for themselves successively deeper channels through the loose drift which had filled up the old valleys, and thus lowering their flood-plains bench by bench. The gradual elevation of the land also, which, as has been seen, was depressed several hundred feet, no doubt aided in the formation of these terraces, by successive accelerations of the currents.

Sand dunes, or wind-drifis of sand, as incidentally intimated above, overlie the drift in places towards the coast. Instances may be seen on the hills about Wilmington, and very conspicuously in the peninsula between the Neuse and Pamlico rivers, which is traversed from river to river in a north-west and south-west direction by a line of sand hills sometimes fifty and sixty feet high, marking an ancient dune, and a stage also in the retreat of the shore in later Glacial times.

Modern.—The sand dunes of the present coast line, in constant formation and movement and transformation, have already been described; as have also the marshes which are formed by the silting up of the narrow fringe of sounds that line the whole coast, as well as the extensive peat beds that make up a large part of the so-called swamp lands.

In addition to these may be mentioned again the alluvions, especially those along the lower reaches of the great rivers, in their course through the great eastern plain to the sea. The flood-plains of some of these rivers are several miles wide for considerable stretches, as of the Roanoke in Bertie and Washington counties, and of the lower Cape Fear and Tar. Over these river flats, of course, alluvial deposits are still accumulating. Islands are also forming near the mouths of some of the rivers, and off-shore accumulations are making along the margins of the sounds, and wide flats and shoals which gradually become marshes. Tens of thousands of acres have in this way been added to the land surface from the sounds and bays within a generation or two, and the great sounds themselves are visibly shallowing and narrowing, and will finally, and in no very long period of time, become mere continuations of the channels of the rivers which empty into them.

Human.—Some evidences of the presence of prehistorical races of men in this State have been given incidentally in another connection. The Mound Builders seem to have carried on extensive mining operations for plate mica in the mountain region. From the great extent and number of their works, open cuts and tunnels, they must have occupied the country for ages. There are enormous heaps of excavated earth which, as well as the excavations, are covered with the largest forest trees two or three hundred years old, and with the decayed trunks of a former generation.

There are also a few mounds in the river valleys further west, one in Macon county of a circular form, 25 feet in height, with a level top about 50 feet in diameter.

There are many beds of kitchen middens also along the shores of the bays and sounds, composed chiefly of oyster shells with fragments of bones and of pottery: some of them 3 to 5 feet thick and covering an acre or more. These however, were no doubt made by the Indians. And there are throughout the State relics of these tribes, arrowheads, stone hatchets, soapstone vessels, and a few implements of copper and of iron have been discovered. These relics are generally found buried in the river bottoms, where they were either interred with the bones of their owners, or, perhaps quite as often, silted up by river floods, just as they were left in their settlements and camps, which were generally in such situations. An extensive camp or village of this sort was brought to light a few years ago in the valley of Dan River, on the plantations of Judge Settle and Gov. Reid. An unusual freshest cut extensive channels through the sediments of the river bottoms, which are here half a mile wide and some two miles long, exposing two tiers of Indian relics, one consisting of hearths of broken stones, about 20 inches wide and 5 to 6 feet apart, scattered up and down the river flat for more than a mile. On and about these hearths were numerous fragments of bones of wild animals, often partly charred, and a great accumulation of river shells, and of stone implements and of ornaments. This stratum was on a level 3 to 6 feet below the original forest-covered surface of the river flat. Above this, 1, 2 and 3 feet are numerous skeletons, orderly disposed and with personal ornaments attached.

Similar exposures of Indian graves and of buried relics of camps or settlements are frequently made of late years; as on the upper Yadkin and the Catawba for example a few years ago, and on the Roanoke, a mile below Weldon, in a recent railroad excavation.

Such is a very brief sketch of the geological history of North Carolina. It would have been more full if the means had been furnished for such plates and illustrations as are absolutely essential to a proper presentation of the matter. However, as to the Triassic and later formations, found only in the eastern parts of the State, Dr. Emmons has given a pretty full account of them in the volumes for 1856 and 1858.

In addition to the geological chart in the previous chapter, the following diagram, after Lyell, gives a very good idea not only of the general order and position of the different systems, but of the order and position of the different formations found in this State.

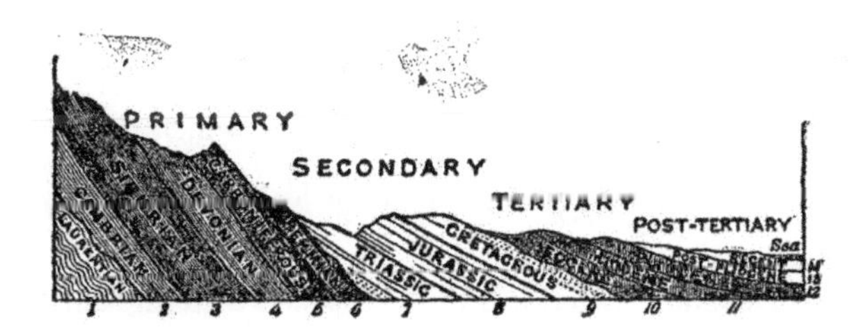

It will be seen that the Primary or Archæan rocks, at the left hand end of the figure are very highly inclined, as in this State, (Cambrian for Huronian); that the Triassic is moderately inclined as here; the lower Tertiary very little; while the Post-Tertiary, or Quaternary is almost horizontal. Out of the 14 formations, the series in North Carolina includes 8, viz: 1, 2, 7, 9, 10, 11, 13, 14.

CHAPTER V.

ECONOMICAL GEOLOGY.

Under this head will be treated such of the mineral substances in the State as have a practical or money value in arts and business. These will be best considered in several sections: 1, Soils; 2, Fertilizers; 3, Metalliferous Ores; 4, Minerals useful or marketable in the natural state; 5, Mineral Waters.

SECTION I. SOILS.

The soils of North Carolina divide themselves, on a mere inspection of the map, into three classes, Clayey, Sandy and Peaty, according to the predominance of one or another of three characterizing elements; and these answer, at the same time, to geographical divisions; the first class being prevalent in the middle and western sections; the second, in the champaign or eastern; and the third being characteristic of the swamp soils near the coast. Of course such a classification is very rude, and subject to much modification and qualification. In fact all these classes are found together in each section of the State; and indefinite gradations between them.

Probably a majority of the soils of the middle and western regions would come under the common designation of *loam*, which is about half clay and half sand (or gravel); while a larger part of the eastern soils would be classed as *sandy loam*, of which about two-thirds are sand. There are, however, in the eastern as well as the western counties, of alluvial, clayey loams, (about two-thirds clay), especially in the wide river bottoms, and around the margins of the great swamps,—the white oak and beech flats.

The soils of the "sand hills" of the eastern counties, already referred to as covered with marine and drift sands, are to be classed as *sand*, i. e., as consisting of above 90 per cent. of sand.

It is hardly necessary to state that all soils are derived from the decomposition of rocks. Considered as to origin, soils may be classed as *sedentary* and *transported*, (after Prof. Johnson); i. e., as derived by decomposition in situ, from the rocks on which they lie, or as composed of these materials removed and deposited in new situations, by the agency of water or ice, and so, as consisting of *drift* or *alluvium* or *colluvium*; the first being a collection of the unsorted and confusedly commingled debris of disintegrated rocks; the second, of the finer materials, sorted and more or less arranged,—stratified, in quiet or gently moving currents; and the last a mixture of these fine sediments with more or less coarse gravel and fragments of rock. From what has been previously said, it is evident that these *transported* soils correspond geologically to the Quaternary rocks and are found almost exclusively in the east, while the sedentary are exclusively middle and western, and consist of decomposed granites, gneisses, schists, slates, &c.

Of course the soils will vary in chemical composition, and in fertility according to the character of the rock from which they were derived; so that a geological map would furnish the basis of a soil map.

The principal mineral components of soil in general, are *Silica*, *Alumina*, *Potassa*, *Soda*, *Lime*, *Magnesia*, *Iron*; but besides these, there must be present, to make a productive soil, a small per centage of compounds containing several other elements, phosphorus, sulphur, chlorine, nitrogen and carbon. And these components, except the last two, can only be derived from the rocks. And since all rocks are derived from granites originally, the granites must contain whatever is found in any soil. The chief elements of the granites are *quartz*, *felspar*, *mica*, *hornblende*. These minerals vary much in composition; thus there are several species of felspar, which is essentially a silicate of Alumina and an alkali, this alkali being potash or soda, or both in different proportions, and lime being present in some of them. And while mica is normally a silicate of alumina with potash and magnesia, some species also contain soda and iron. And so there is a great variety of hornblendes, which are mainly silicates of magnesia and lime, with generally alumina and iron, and in some species also soda or potash, or both.

Quartz or silica is the predominant element in granites and most other rocks, and also of soils. Alumina, the base of clay, is the next in order of abundance in rocks, and also in soils; this is derived chiefly from the decomposition of felspar and mica. Potash and soda are also derived chiefly from the felspars, but in part also from mica, and to a small extent, from hornblende. The lime comes mainly from hornblende, but a little is contributed by some kinds of felspar. The hornblendes and some of the micas furnish magnesia. And hornblende is also the chief source of the iron of soils, but some of the micas furnish it also. There are also many other minerals, some of them even occurring as rock masses, which sometimes furnish these different soil elements in abundance. Thus lime is furnished by limestone, magnesia by dolomite and by talc, serpentine, &c.

The other elements of mineral origin, phosphorus, sulphur and chlorine, are derived from other mineral species which are universally diffused, though in very small quantities, as phosphorus from apatite, sulphur from pyrite and from gypsum, chlorine from common salt and from apatite, &c. Thus it is evident that soils will vary indefinitely in composition and fertility according to their source in the mineral kingdom. And thus also the bearing of geology upon agriculture becomes obvious.

From the previous general description, and from the preceding account of the geology of the State, it is apparent that the range of its soils is such as to include almost every variety and grade.

The plan of the Survey includes as complete an investigation of these soils as is practicable. It is proposed to analyze the soils in connection with the underlying rocks, and to classify and map them. Meanwhile the soils have been graded in a preliminary way, over a large part of the State, the estimation being based upon natural growth, physical characters and actual yield. As soon as practicable a map of these observations will be published. Some progress has also been made in the work of systematic analysis, according to the general plan. Nothing like a complete discussion of these analyses, or a general classification of the soils of the State upon the basis of their results, can be attempted at this stage of the work. But for the benefit of those who are not familiar with the subject of soil analysis, and the relations of chemical composition to fertility, and the most common and obvious causes of infertility, and the methods of removing it, so far as indicable by chemistry, and in a word, the function and value and limits of analysis in practical agriculture, the following table is given as furnishing standards of comparison.

	FERTILE SOILS.				BARREN SOILS.			IMPROVABLE SOILS.		
	I.	II.	III.	IV.	V.	VI.	VII.	VIII.	IX.	X.
Silica, Insol.	51.71	87.16	71.55	43.00	95.86	70.50	94.80	77.85	90.22	82.30
Silica, Soluble.	2.50	...	...	0.03	0.02	...	...	0.10	...	0.10
Alumina.....	2.90	5.67	6.93	6.40	1.64	0.76	0.65	10.11	2.11	8.70
Oxide of Iron.	10.87	2.22	5.17						3.95	
Oxide of Manganese	0.35	0.36	...	...	...	...	...	...	0.96	...
Lime.........	5.10	0.56	1.23	0.21	0.10	0.01	0.01	2.00	0.54	0.02
Magnesia	0.14	0.31	1.08	0.12	trace.	trace.	trace.	1.81	0.73	0.01
Potash	1.43	0.12	0.35	0.16	...	...	trace.	0.18	0.07	trace.
Soda.........	2.07	0.02	0.43	0.18	...	...	trace.	0.34	0.01	trace.
Phosphor. Acid	0.32	0.06	0.43	0.30	trace.	...	...	0.08	0.37	0.15
Sulphuric Acid	1.10	0.03	0.04	0.04	...	...	...	0.01	trace.	0.01
Carbonic Acid.	6.94	0.08	...	...	—	...	...	...	...	...
Chlorine.....	1.30	0.04	trace.	trace.	trace.	...	...	0.01	0.01	0.01
Organic Matter	12.58	3.39	10.20	48.10	1.85	25.20	1.50	3.95	1.04	3.35
Water	...	...	...	...	...	2.70	1.20	5.75	...	6.00

I, is a soil from near the famous Zuider Zee, Holland, and is an alluvium of the Rhine. After Prof. Johnson.

II, is from the banks of the Ohio; a fertile corn soil. J. F. W. Johnson.

III, a Scotch wheat soil, of great fertility. Prof. Johnson.

IV, a Hyde county corn soil, which produces 50 and 60 bushels to the acre. From Emmons.

V, called the most barren soil in Bavaria. Prof. Johnson.

VI, a gallberry soil, Dover Swamp, Craven county; rather coarse sand and vegetable matter; the rains wash the vegetable matter from the surface sand, leaving a black ground sprinkled with white grains; the sample is a "fair representative of a large part of Dover Swamp, and of a large area of flat low lands in the middle section of the eastern counties." Emmons.

VII, a sandy soil from Bladen county, near Elizabethtown, common in the region. Emmons.

VIII, a brown soil, tenacious when wet, common in the eastern counties; generally overlies the marl, miocene or eocene; specimen from plantation of Sam'l Biddle, Craven county, overlying eocene marl; found also near Elizabethtown on shell marl. Emmons.

IX, a German soil, from Brunswick. J. F. W. Johnson.

X, a light yellow gallberry soil, common in Onslow county. Emmons.

The difference between these three classes of soils is obvious from the above analyses at a glance. Those of the first section are seen to contain in large proportion all the mineral elements of plant food; while the second set are deficient in most of them; and in the third, the principal elements are present, but some are wanting, the analysis shows which in each case, and so indicates the character of the fertilizer to be employed in order to develop the fertility. If but one element be absent, which is required by a given crop, the soil is as unproductive as to that crop, as if all the elements were wanting, and the addition of the single missing substance will convert the barren into a fertile soil.

Thus in VIII and IX, there is a deficiency of sulphuric acid and of chlorine, which may be easily remedied by the addition of gypsum and common salt; and in X there is, besides, a deficiency of potash and soda, and the percentage of lime and magnesia is small, so that ashes would be required in this case, in addition.

It is to be kept in mind, however, that a soil may be unproductive as to one crop, while it is fruitful for another; which is owing to the simple fact that plants require very different proportions of the different mineral substances which enter into their composition. Hence one class of plants is denominated lime plants, another potash plants, &c., according to the predominant constituent of its ash.

QUANTITIES (POUNDS) OF THE PRINCIPAL MINERAL ELEMENTS ABSTRACTED FROM AN ACRE OF SOIL BY SOME OF THE COMMON CROPS.

MINERALS.	KIND OF CROP AND QUANTITY PER ACRE.								
	COTTON, 400 lbs.	TOBACCO, 1,260 lbs.	WHEAT, 18 bus.	CORN, 50 bus.	POTATO'S, 50 bus.	RYE, 33 bus.	OATS, 30 bus.	HAY, 2 tons.	CLOVER, 2 tons.
Phosphoric Acid...........	75 lbs.	22	17	50	46	20	7	16	22
Potash	120	118	18	78	161	20	18	68	78
Soda	7	15	6	30	32	6	4	19	4
Lime......................	150	88	16	25	9	8	18	31	77
Magnesia..................	30	19	13	18	9	6	17	13	28
Chlorine..................	3	21	1	29	7	3	5	21	8
Sulphuric Acid...........	7	17	2	34	15	4	3	14	7
	372	300	73	264	279	67	72	182	222

The above table will give an approximately correct view of the relative proportions of the different mineral elements removed from an acre of soil by some of the principal crops of the State:

Cotton—Four hundred pounds *lint*, with seeds, stalk, &c. *Tobacco*—Twelve hundred and sixty pounds *dry leaves*, with stalk, &c. *Wheat &c.,—entire plant.*

The larger part of this mineral matter is of course found in the stems thus, in the case of cotton, the 400 pounds of lint carry off but 7 pounds from the soil, the seed not quite 30, the stem having to account for nearly 300. Tobacco, however, removes two-thirds of the amount credited to it, in the leaves, one-third only going to the stem.

This will suffice to bring into a general view the relations of the ordinary crops to the composition of the soils on which they are grown, and it will serve also to show the relations of fertilizers to soil improvement and restoration.

The soils whose analyses are given below, may be graded, and their general character and value ascertained, at least approximately, by reference to the above tables; and the defects of such as are wanting in any essential elements, will also be apparent, so that the proper fertilizer will be indicated; and a reference to the following section will show whether such defiiciencies may be supplied by the marls, peats, or other domestic resources, or whether foreign fertilizers are needed.

Most of the soils heretofore analyzed, it will be seen, belong to the eastern region, a large proportion of them being from some sort of swamp; as this class of land is very extensive, and constitutes altogether the most valuable portion of that region.

SWAMP SOILS OF THE EASTERN COUNTIES.

Bay River Swamp, Craven County.

	1	2	3	4	5
Silica, Insoluble,........	69.28	62.64	75.05	71.24	71.30
Silica, Soluble,.........	12.05	3.86	6.75	9.95	5.90
Alumina,..............	4.90	9.65 (Alumina and Oxide of Iron)	2.94	7.58	1.23
Oxide of Iron,..........	1.46		0.52	1.36	1.39
Oxide of Manganese,....		0.64			
Lime,.................	0.29	0.68	0.15	0.11	0.12
Magnesia,..............	0.09	0.58	0.03	0.16	0.13
Potash,.....	0.24	0.90	0.13	0.08	0.08
Soda,..................		0.68	0.16	0.07	

Phosphoric Acid,.......	0.04	trace,	0.08	0.04	0.06
Sulphuric Acid,........	0.03	0.43			trace,
Chlorine,..............	0.03	trace,	0.06	0.06	0.02
Organic Matter,........	9.60	19.60	5.60	6.00	17.50
Water,................	2.10		9.00	3.00	2.30

1. The first of the above analyses is that of a class of land called *second swamp*. The sample was obtained within half a mile of the village of Jackson which is situated on the river. The soil is dark to gray in color, and somewhat gravelly. It is flat and lower than the more sandy margin of the river; the growth is beech, maple, tupelo, &c.

There is a large body of this second swamp land; several cotton farms have been opened in it since the war, and the ordinary yield, without manure, is a bale to the acre.

There is a large area also of open beech flats with much palmetto, 8 or 10 miles N. W., on South creek, of which the soil does not differ much in appearance, nor probably greatly in quality, from the above; it is more clayey.

Number 2 is a light to dark gray soil, from the outer rim of Bear Creek swamp, 6 or 7 miles below Jackson; ordinary swamp growth, tupelo, poplar, maple, ash, sweet gum and white bay. 3 is the subsoil of same at the depth of 2 feet, lighter colored and more sandy. 4 is still deeper, about 4 feet.

Number 5 is the swamp soil proper, higher in level than the last, towards the centre of the swamp; black, peaty, much fibre of wood half decayed; about 2 feet deep to fine white sand; covered with thick growth of short canes and shrubs, an occasional short leaf pine being the only tree. This represents a large body of the interior of this swamp; and the corresponding belt also of most of the great swamps of the region.

Blount's Creek Swamp, Beaufort County.

	6	7	A
Silica, Insoluble,.....	59.24	55.46	77.50
" Soluble,....................	1.86	1.26	
Alumina,........................	13.78	11.52	6.90
Oxide of Iron, ...			
Lime, ...	1.62	2.60	0.50
Magnesia,.......................	1.08	0.54	0.10
Potash,.........................	0.79	0.81	0.02
Soda, ...	0.69	0.52	0.03
Phosphoric Acid,................	trace	trace	0.40

Sulphuric Acid,..................	0.22	0.14	0.18
Chlorine, ...	0.06	trace	
Organic Matter,..................	20.80	27.40	15.40

Number 6 is from a cypress swamp on Major Blount's farm, very dark to black, with much half decayed vegetable matter, soil 3 to 4 feet deep, growth large cypress, poplar and tupelo: when fresh brings 50 bushels of corn to the acre, and is very durable. A is a similar soil from the same plantation analyzed by Dr. Emmons. 7 is from a field which had been reclaimed from a swampy condition and cultivated, chiefly in corn for many years; the sample was selected from a small spot of about a quarter of an acre in the middle of a field which had within a few years ceased to produce, the corn *frenching*, as it is called, after growing to the height of 6 or 12 inches. The analysis does not indicate the cause; if the iron had been separated from the alumina, perhaps the cause would have appeared in a deficiency of the former.

This Blount's Creek swamp is quite flat, and requires much ditching; it is also quite extensive, and includes several grades of swamp land, much of it more sandy, and more elevated and with much less vegatable matter, and no cypress.

Open Ground Prairie Swamp, Carteret County.

	8	9	B
Silica, Insoluble,................	80.84	1.52	32.50
" Soluble,....................	3.70	0.00	
Alumina,.........................	2.69	0.39	2.00
Oxide of Iron,....................	1.18	0.15	
Lime,............................	0.44	0.36	0.65
Magnesia,.........................	0.22	0.14	0.30
Potash,...........................	0.07	0.06	0.07
Soda,.............................	0.02	0.13	
Phosphoric Acid,.................	0.08	0.06	
Sulphuric Acid,..................	0.06	0.00	trace
Chlorine,.........................	trace	0.02	trace
Organic Matter,..................	7.70	87.25	52.70
Water,............................	2.50	9.60	11.20

Number 8 is from the margin,—the oak fringe of this great swamp, near North River, about 8 miles north of Beaufort; it is light gray to ash-colored, with a growth of white oak, gum, maple, pine and palmetto; the situation is low and flat. This marginal belt of semi-swamp is from a half mile and less in width to above a mile. The surface rises towards the interior and is covered by a soil, if it may be called such, represented by No. 9 which is 2 to 3 feet deep, and upwards (to 8 or 10, according to report), and lies on a bed of white sea-sand. It consists of a loose open mass of half decayed woody matter, of a brown color, and is in fact a superficial, uncompressed lignite; for it will be observed that the analysis includes nearly 10 per cent. of water, so that the dry substance would give but 3½ per cent. of inorganic matter, not more than would be accounted for by the ash of the woody matter. The growth is a dense thicket of spindling shrubs with small scattered maples and bays. Dr. Emmons reports as the result of an analysis by him, only 3 per cent. of organic matter. This is of course worthless as a soil, and unimprovable. B is a sample analyzed by Dr. Emmons from another portion of the swamp border, where the soil is 3 to 5 feet deep, black and peaty and covered with briars and bushes and brambles. This soil is reported to have given a remarkable yield of potatoes in an experiment made for the Literary Board.

White Oak Swamp, Jones County.

	10	C
Silica Insoluble,	64.74	60.00
" Soluble,	3.60	10
Alumina,	3.33	11.03
Oxide of Iron,	0.30	
Lime,	0.10	1.50
Magnesia,	0.29	0.30
Potash,	0.05	0.01
Soda,	0.02	0.02
Phosphoric Acid,	0.06	0.31
Sulphuric Acid,	0.21	
Chlorine,	trace	
Organic Matter,	22.80	25.00
Water,	4.20	2.71

Number 10 is a sample of soil from Mr. E. L. Franke's plantation on the southwest margin of the swamp. The growth is tupelo, poplar, ash, cypress, pine and bay. The soil is black, and 2 to 3 feet deep, increasing in depth inwards. This soil has proved very productive in corn, and the soils a little further out, on the very fringe of the swamp produce also fine cotton. C. is an anylysis by Dr. Emmons of a sample from the same plantation. Mr. F. informed me that the wooded and fertile belt of the swamp in this part of it, is between 1 and 2 miles wide, and is succeeded by half a mile of reeds, and towards the central part becomes higher, sandy, briary and poor.

Lousin Swamp, Lenoir County.

	11	12
Silica, Insoluble,.......	87.82	92.60
Silica, Soluble,........................	1.80	2.20
Alumina,..........................	1.07	1.56
Oxide of iron,........................	0.20	0.21
Lime,..........................	0.09	0.13
Magnesia,..........................	trace	0.13
Potash,..........................	0.05	0.08
Soda,..............................	0.00	0.00
Phosphoric acid,......	0.08	0.06
Sulphuric acid,....	trace	0.06
Chlorine,..........................	0.02	trace
Organic matter,......................	7.20	3.00
Water,..................	1.20	0.50

Number 11 is a sample of low flat land, a sort of second swamp, characterized by a growth of willow, oak, pine, black and sweet gum; it is light gray in color, and of a quite fine texture, so that it has the appearance of clay; and is of good quality. Number 12 is the subsoil, and as will be seen, supplies some substances which are deficient in the soil itself, and suggests deep plowing as a means of renovation. There is a large quantity of land throughout the eastern region, which answers to the above description. The sample was obtained from the woods on the plantation of L. A. Mewbern, 7 miles from Kinston.

Swamp near Morehead City, Carteret County.

	13
Silica, Insoluble,..............................	69.07
" Soluble,..........................	6.80
Alumina,..................................	4.25
Oxide of Iron,..............................	1.12
Lime,....................................	0.20
Magnesia,....................	0.07

Potash,......	0.07
Soda,......	0.00
Phosphoric Acid,......	0.13
Sulphuric Acid,......	0.08
Chlorine,......	trace
Organic Matter,......	13.00
Water,......	4.80

Number 13 is a sample from a newly cleared swamp on the lands of the Rev. Mr. Carrow. The soil is of a gray color, and lumpy; the growth, tupelo, ash, maple, poplar and bay; a good corn soil.

Big Swamp, Robeson County, and Eagles' Island, Brunswick County.

	14	15	16
Silica,......	52.20	32.36	62.22
Alumina and Oxide of Iron,...	6.09	4.92	20.35
Lime,......	1.16	0.56	1.54
Magnesia,......	0.55	trace	0.23
Potash,......	0.60	0.96	0.46
Soda,......		.26	0.00
Phosphoric Acid,......	0.34	0.45	trace
Sulphuric Acid,......	0.65	1.30	0.23
Organic Matter and Water,....	38.41	59.19	12.43

Number 14 is a sample of black, boggy, soft soil, 5 to 10 feet deep, from under the railroad bridge, Big Swamp. There is a scattered growth of tupelo and cypress, with a few small ash and maple trees between. It contains in abundance all the elements of the richest soil.

Number 15 is from Eagles' Island, opposite Wilmington; the growth, cypress, tupelo, &c., with abundance of canes. It is a famous rice soil,—such as, when cleared and ditched, was estimated at one hundred dollars per acre before the war.

No. 16 is a sample of the same soil from a field just below, of Mr. Northrop, which has been in cultivation for about one hundred years in rice. It is ash-colored and of close texture, and now produces well, grass, clover and garden vegetables, and is still a very strong soil, needing only phosphoric acid.

Dead Land, or Exhausted Swamp or Frenchy Soil; Wayne and New Hanover.

	17	18	19
Silica Insoluble,..........	65.97	47.27	59.02
" Soluble,............	4.63		0.11
Alumina and Oxide of Iron,	8.10	3.73	7.09
Oxide of Manganese,......	0.13		
Lime,.......	0.24	0.50	0.68
Magnesia,...............	0.22	0.44	0.42
Potash,......	0.40	0.42	0.36
Soda,...................	0.18	0.00	0.28
Phosphoric Acid,..........	0.07	0.12	0.04
Sulphuric Acid,...........	0.25	0.85	0.03
Chlorine,.....	trace		trace
Organic Matter,...........	18.12	46.50	26.55
Water,..................			5.60
Sulphide of Iron,..........	1.12		

Number 17 is from a plantation near Boon Hill, Wayne county, (Atkinson's.) The soil is black, produced well for several years, and then began to fail,—to *french* in patches, which gradually widened until they occupy a large part of a field, flat, low and swampy, and of the same general appearance and natural growth as number 18, which is from the plantation of Jas. Murphy, on Black River, New Hanover county. The latter sample was obtained from a barren patch of a few rods, in the middle of a large field, which had a number of such scattered over it. The field had all produced alike well for three years, and then began to fail in this way. The soil was dark brown to black, 3 to 5 feet deep; the original growth, poplar, tupelo, white and red bay, maple and a shrubby thicket. No. 19 is a similar grade of soil from the lands of J. Foy near Pollocksville, Jones county. This, as well the others, contains in good proportion most of the elements of fertility.

It will be seen that the analyses do not reveal the source of the difficulty, perhaps for the same reason suggested in regard to number 7.

This is a point deserving further investigation and more minute chemical analysis; especially since there is a considerable area of this description of land.

Marsh Soils—White Marsh, Columbus County, &c.

	20	21	22
Silica, Insoluble,	37.47 }	54.42	3.71
" Soluble,	9.95 }		0.40
Alumina,	3.43 }	16.45	2.52
Oxide of Iron,	0.55 }		
Oxide of Manganese,		0.54	
Lime,	0.45	1.18	3.08
Magnesia,	0.58	0.07	0.05
Potash,	0.09	1.18	0.49
Soda,		0.70	0.84
Phosphoric Acid,	0.22	0.25	0.05
Sulphuric Acid,	0.10	1.46	1.40
Chlorine,	0.03		0.00
Organic Matter,	41.90 }	20.92	87.80
Water,	5.30 }		
Sulphide of Iron,		1.09	
Chloride of Sodium,		1.63	

Number 20 is from White Marsh, a few miles southeast of Whiteville on the plantation of Col. V. V. Richardson. The marsh is treeless—a natural meadow, matted with coarse water grasses, weeds, and a few scattered button-bushes. It is overflowed a considerable part of the year. It is dark gray to black soil, three to four feet deep, and shakes under the tread; but is dry and solid enough for cattle-grazing in summer and autumn. The analysis shows a very rich soil, capable of indefinite production, if drained. There are some 2,000 acres of this open grassy marsh in view from one point.

Number 21 is from the wide marsh which borders Newport river at Dr. Arendell's place, 7 miles above Morehead City. This marsh is one to two miles wide, and has been formed within a generation, filling up the old wide channel of the river and reducing it to a narrow serpentine bayou of a rod or two in breadth. The soil is of a dark, bluish gray color, and full of decaying grass roots and stems, and five to ten feet deep. It is seen from the analysis to be not only a very rich and inexhaustible soil, but to be capable of serving as a fertilizer for the neighboring region.

Number 22 is from a marsh on Tar river, one mile above the town of Washington, on the plantation of Gen. Grimes. It extends a considerable distance along the river shore, and has a depth of soil of five to ten feet. The analysis indicates a valuable fertilizer, for which purpose it has been used to some extent. Indeed, all of these marsh sediments, of which there is a great and increasing area, scattered along all the lower reaches of these wide rivers, and on the shores of the sounds and bays, must one day become a most important source of manure to all the coast region, which is everywhere penetrated by bayous and other navigable water-ways, for their transportation and distribution.

Semi Swamps and Alluvions, in several Counties.

	23	24	25	26	27	28	29
Silica, Insoluble,...	85.15	94.05	75.95	81.70	87.79	81.25	90.13
" Soluble,.....	1.57			0.40	0.00	6.15	3.67
Alumina,........	5.02	1.15	5.15	5.85	6.58	3.44	1.48
Oxide of Iron,....		0.71	9.60	0.07		1.85	6.70
Lime,..........	1.67	0.26	0.59	1.96	0.73	0.17	0.45
Magnesia,........	0.38	0.09	0.29	0.62	0.43	0.25	0.05
Potash,..........	trace	0.16	0.08	0.72	0.41	0.11	0.13
Soda,............	.45			0.84	0.57		
Phosphoric Acid,..	0.02		trace	0.00	0.06	0.05	0.02
Sulphuric Acid,...	0.03	0.15	0.08	trace	trace	trace	trace
Chlorine,.........	.01				trace	trace	trace
Organic matter,...	4.41	3.25	8.40	7.40	1.44	5.50	2.34
Water,..........	1.32			1.45	0.55	1.40	0.50
Sulphide of Iron,..	0.24				1.08		

Number 23 is a sandy and somewhat gravelly loam of Columbus county, of a gray color, flat, heavily timbered; growth, willow oak, maple, ash, sweet and black gum and poplar. It is found near Whiteville, farm of V. V. Richardson, and represents a large area of land in the eastern counties, which can be identified by the above characters. It contains all the elements of a good soil, but potash in too small proportion. No. 24 is from the sloping margin of a white oak flat, one mile east of Rocky Point, in New Hanover; it is gravelly and sandy, and produces fair corn crops. 25 is from the flat itself just mentioned, of which the characteristic growth is white oak, but there are also black gum, hickory, horn-beam, ashe, buckeye, may apple. It is shown by the analysis to be a strong soil, with all the elements of fertility in abundance, except phorphoric acid. 26 is from a gray alluvial tract which stretches for a mile or two south of the Neuse, near Goldsboro, a sort of sandy second bottom; the growth is willow oak, sweet gum, maple, white bay, &c. The analysis shows a good soil except as to phosphoric and sulphuric acid. No. 27 is the sub-soil of the last, at the depth of 3 feet; and in it one of the defects of the soil proper is abundantly supplied. 28 is a sample of the flat, gray, alluvial wheat lands north of Albemarle sound, obtained 1 mile east of Woodville, Perquimans county. The analysis explains the fertility of these noted soils. 29 is from the "pine flats" of Johnston county; the sample is from Selma, and was obtained in the new grounds of Mr. Noble; it is of a light gray color, presenting the appearance of a clay, very lumpy, and disposed to adhere in angular masses, when plowed or spaded; the principal growth is long-leaf pine, with small oaks, gum and other semi-swamp vegetation. It is evidently a soil of good quality. Flats of this description are very extensive, in many eastern counties.

Gallberry Soils.

	30	D	E	F
Silica,	90.83	88.40	70.50	82.40
Alumina and Oxide of Iron,	1.24	2.92	0.76	8.70
Lime,	0.26	0.01	0.01	0.02
Magnesia,	0.08	0.01	trace	0.01
Potash,	1.46	trace		trace
Soda,	0.32	trace		trace
Phosphoric Acid,	0.09	0.00		0.15
Sulphuric Acid,	0.27			
Organic Matter,	5.45	4.20	25.20	3.35
Water,		3.09	2.70	6.00

Number 30 is from a gallberry flat of several miles extent in the upper part of New Hanover county, one mile north of Burgaw Savannah. It is covered with a various shrubby thicket, somewhat brambly, almost the only tree being a stunted short leaf pine, and the growth of this rather sparse. It will be observed that the analysis shows about 95 per cent. of sand, (leaving out the organic matter and water), and an insignificant amount of alumina and iron; the other ingredients being in fair proportion; it is a much better soil than that of most gallberry lands. The next analysis, D, is that of a sample from Sampson county, by Dr. Emmons, and shows a hopelessly poor soil. There is a considerable quantity of such land in this and in Duplin and Johnston counties. The color is brownish gray and drab. Similar to this and even more deficient, is the next soil, represented by analysis E. The specimen is from the great Dover Swamp, and according to Dr. Emmons, from whom the analysis is taken, represents a large proportion of it. F is given by Emmons as an example of the better kind of gallberry land, of considerable extent in Onslow. The color is described as "light yellow and texture fine." This soil has a fair proportion of alumina and iron, in which this class of land is usually deficient, and no excess of organic matter as is common. So that it differs much from a true gallberry soil, which consists essentially of a coarse white sea sand with organic matter and little else, and is represented by the analyses D and E. These gallberry tracts are generally flat and wet, and are characterized by a dwarfed vegetation as well as by the prevalence of the bush from which they are named.

Savannah Soils.

	31	32	33	34	G.
Silica, Insoluble,	87.80	92.66	86.89	79.86	80.59
Silica, Soluble,			4.05	8.80	0.10
Alumina,	6.91	1.31	2.77	3.99	7.00
Oxide of Iron,			1.16	1.85	3.40
Lime,	0.77	0.22	0.20	0.26	0.36
Magnesia,	0.41	0.40	0.11	0.11	0.18
Potash,	0.41	0.86	0.02	0.16	0.10
Soda,		0.34	0.17	0.14	
Phosphoric Acid,	0.19	0.12	0.11	0.06	?
Sulphuric Acid,	0.02	0.13			trace.
Chlorine,	trace		0.09	0.18	trace.
Organic Matter,	2.80	4.88	4.55	3.40	3.70
Water,			0.55	1.60	4.00

Number 31 represents the Burgaw Savannah in the northern part of New Hanover county, on both sides of the railroad, 25 miles above Wilmington. This sample was taken within half a mile of the upper or northern margin. The soil is dark gray to black colored to the depth of about a foot, and is composed of very fine sand with little clay, but is pasty when wet, with impalpable humus, which renders it as impervious to water as pipe clay. At the depth of two feet the color is light yellow, and at three feet the quantity of clay is considerably increased. 32 is another sample from the middle of the same savannah. It contains more sand and organic matter, and much less clay than the former. It is obvious from these analyses that this is a fair soil, and if drained, marled and aërated, it would no doubt produce well. The growth consists of a number of species of short grasses with sarracenias and other flowering plants in abundance, the savannah being merely a prairie. 33 is from the Big Savannah in Beaufort county, which has been described previously, and is the largest prairie in the State. It is of the same description as Burgaw as to growth, except that there are occasional small persimmon bushes scattered among the grass, but these do not seem to pass one or two years growth. The soil is of a gray to light yellowish color, and consists of very fine sand, much resembling clay in appearance. 34 is the subsoil of the same at the depth of 20 inches. This is seen from these analyses to be a fair soil, but not so well constituted as that of Burgaw. G is a savannah in Craven county on the Atlantic railroad; analysis from Emmons. These savannahs may be considered as capable soils if drained; and therein lies the difficulty, on account of their very close texture, which no doubt constitutes the controlling cause of their treeless condition.

Upland Sandy Soils of the East.

	35	36	37	38	39	40	41	42	43	44	45
Silica, Insoluble,	89.00	91.96	88.32	89.56	81.53	93.32	74.95	90.35	90.52	87.46	88.20
Silica, Soluble,	2.67	1.24	1.88		0.73	0.70	7.70	4.35	1.40	0.00	1.64
Alumina,	2.40	1.24	1.77	6.37	9,17	0.23	7.00	1.22	6.48	1.73	1.91
Oxide of Iron,	0.24	0.52	1.35			1.13	4.06	0.42		2.69	2.45
Lime,	0·23	0.08	0.20	0.82	0.78	0.03	0.08	0.20	0.53	0.79	1.68
Magnesia,	0.10	0.09	0.29	0.49	0.96	0.11	0.14	0,76	0.00	0.48	0.32
Potash,	0.04	0.08	0.19	0.17	0.39	0.10	0.07	0.06	0.96	0.22	0.25
Soda,				0.40	0.22	0.04	0.09		0.21		0.48
Phosphoric Acid,	0.04	0.04	0.15	0,02	0.08	0.03	0.01	trace,	0.04	0,12	0.09
Sulphuric Acid,	0.01	0.03	0.06	0.02	0.05	0.02	0.00	trace,	0.43		0.15
Chlorine,	0.02	0.01	0.05	trace,	trace,	trace,	0.02	0.02	0.00	0.30	trace.
Organic Matter,	4.90	4.15	5.80	1.30	4.80	2.15	5.10	2.50	1.00	3.75	2.70
Water,	0.40	0,80	0.80	0.95	1.15	1.50	1.50	0.30		2.95	0.65

Number 35 is a specimen of the level, upland, sandy soil, so common in the eastern section. The sample was taken at Faison's depot, in Duplin county, in the forest. This and number 45, obtained one mile north of Wilson, represent the most common type of cotton lands of the region, not only in these counties, but in Wayne, Pitt, Lenoir, Edgecombe, &c. The growth is an open woods, consisting of a mixture of long and short leaf pine, mostly the latter, with an undergrowth of rather small oaks of several species, (prevalently post oak and black oak), and a subordinate shrubby growth of dogwood, sourwood, blackjack, &c. The analysis shows it to be a very sandy loam with a sufficiency of organic matter, and all the essential mineral elements of plant food *in moderate quantities.* The sand is tolerable fine, but the texture is not close enough to retain moisture well, and its supply of organic matter is easily exhausted. It is plain that these soils under cultivation will require marl to keep up the supply of mineral elements and frequent green crops to restore the easily exhausted humus.

The subsoil is yellowish brown and a little more clayey, and so compact as to stand in vertical walls, in ditches and wells, almost as well as rock. 36 is a similar soil, a little more sandy, from Mr. Jas. Joyner's place at Marlboro in Pitt; 37 is from the same, and is a garden soil in which the cabbage is affected with the disease known as the *big root,* which is common in the region. The only suggestion contained in the analysis is connected with the deficiency of clay and the consequent want of coherence,—porosity of the soil, which probably permits, or in some way promotes parasitic, or fungoid growths upon the roots.

Number 38 is from the flattish slope of the ridge which forms the north shore of Waccamaw Lake, in Columbus county. The sample is from a point in the forest near the depot. It is, from the analysis, a soil of a better general constitution than the preceding. 39 is the subsoil of the above at a depth of two feet, and is much better than the soil, indicating the advantage of deep plowing in this case

Number 40 is a leaner and more sandy soil from the border of the great White Oak Swamp in Onslow. This is a slightly rolling upland, and the soil is of a yellowish brown color. There is a scattered growth of pines, long and short leaf, and an undergrowth of scrubby oaks. There is a large area of similar soil in the region. The subsoil, at the depth of 20 inches, (analysis 41,) is, like that at Waccamaw, much better than the soil, in most respects.

Number 42 is a sandy upland, of the same character as the preceding; the sample is from the slightly undulating border of Pine Log Swamp, two miles northwest of Whiteville, Columbus county. The growth is the same as in the last case, with the addition of dogwood and blackgum. 43 is from the vineyard of Col. D. M. Carter, one mile from Washington, Beaufort county. The tract had been long cultivated, but was at the time the sample was obtained, planted with scuppernong vines, of several years standing. 44 is from a piney, blackjack swell of land on the eastern edge of the village of Selma, Johnston county; and is representative of a common class of soils which will be recognized from the description. It is yellowish brown in color, and composed predominantly, of moderately fine sand.

The obvious defects of all these soils are due to the excess of sand and the consequent small proportion of clay, and in part also to the chemical state of many of the other elements which are present in fair proportion. It is largely a quartzose granitic sand of so permeable texture, that the mineral elements are carried off by solution almost as fast as formed from the gradually decomposed rocky constituents.

The advantages of the addition of humus, from any source, and of the calcareous marls, so abundant in the region, will be obvious when the analysis of some of these in the next section, are compared with those of the soils.

Sand Hill Soils.

<table>
<tr><th></th><th>46</th><th>H</th></tr>
<tr><td>Silica,</td><td>92.12</td><td>94.80</td></tr>
<tr><td>Alumina and Oxide of Iron,</td><td>5.29</td><td>0.65</td></tr>
<tr><td>Lime,</td><td>1.13</td><td>0.01</td></tr>
<tr><td>Magnesia,</td><td>0.03</td><td>trace</td></tr>
<tr><td>Potash,</td><td>0.64</td><td>trace</td></tr>
<tr><td>Soda,</td><td>0.35</td><td>trace</td></tr>
<tr><td>Phosphoric Acid,</td><td>0.00</td><td></td></tr>
<tr><td>Sulphuric Acid,</td><td>0.33</td><td></td></tr>
<tr><td>Chlorine,</td><td>trace</td><td></td></tr>
<tr><td>Organic Matter,</td><td rowspan="2">0.60</td><td>1.50</td></tr>
<tr><td>Water,</td><td>1.20</td></tr>
</table>

The first of the above analysis, No. 46, is that of a tolerably fine, nearly white sand, from the ridge of dune which crosses the peninsula of Pamplico, in a northwest direction, in Pamplico county; the sample was gotten not far from Grant's store, in the open "piney woods," or "pine barrens," characterized by a scattered growth of long-leaf pines and tussocks of wire grass, with patches of shining bare sand between. And yet the analysis does not look half so poor as the soil is in fact. It consists however of rounded and smooth grains of wind-drifted sand, mainly of white quartz, but partly also of particles of marine shells, and black iron sand. H is an analysis by Dr. Emmons from the sand hills of Bladen near Elizabethtown. This, it will be seen, is sterility itself. And yet even such lands, mainly through the force of their subsoil, often produce certain kinds of plants very well; for example, the scuppernong, the cassena, and the ground pea.

The preceding examp es are all of *transported* soils, belonging for the most part, to the drift, which consists of the debris of the older rocks, lying west and above. Those which follow are mostly *sedentary* and granitic.

SOILS OF THE MIDDLE REGION.

Tobacco and Wheat Soils of Granville, Orange, Person, Caswell.

	47.	48.	49.	50.	51.	52.
Silica, Insol.,....	94.10	58.56	85.70	79.83	71.60	81.35
" Soluble,..	1.10		6.95	3.77	3.90	0.49
Alumina, ...	0.71	30.18	1.90	5.30	5.89	5.94
Oxide of Iron,..	0.65		1.48	3.38	10.59	3.19
Lime,..........	0.13	3.03	0.16	0.07	0.22	0.91
Magnesia,......	0.14	1.42	0.24	0.16	0.25	0.51
Potash,........	0.07	0.19	0.12	0.10	0.02	0.43
Soda, ...		1.33				0.69
Phos. Acid,....	trace	trace	0.06	0.11	0.32	0.11
Sulph. Acid,...	trace	trace	trace	0.03	0.04	0.18
Chlorine,......	0.01	trace	0.02	0.02	trace	trace
Organic Matter,	2.40	4.55	3.05	6.25	5.40	3.90
Water,........	0.20	1.40	0.45	0.30	2.20	1.70

Number 47 is a light colored, sandy and gravelly soil, from Prospect Hill, Orange county, formed by the decomposition of a very quartzose felspatic granite. The growth includes several species of oak of moderate size, with a few small specimens of hickory, dogwood, sourwood and blackjack, and an occasional pine. The sample was taken from the farm of Mr. E. Birch, which produces tobacco of the finest quality, which is sometimes sold at two dollars a pound. It is evidently a lean soil, and the yield is small; though the texture of the leaf is superior. A dressing of gypsum and bone-dust would raise the quality of this soil very much as these would supply the only elements of fertility which are deficient. Number 48 is a soil of somewhat similar physical appearance and growth, but with a larger proportion of hickory and a heavier forest, found on the eastern slope of a high broad-backed ridge near Gillis' Copper Mine, on the Person and Granville line. The soil is derived from an epidotic feldspathic rock and hence has a large proportion of lime, magnesia, iron and alumina; but phosphoric acid is present in only very small quantities. Numbers 49 and 50 are specimens of the noted Hico tobacco lands in the northern part of Person. These soils are derived from feldspathic and hornblendic slates and gneisses, and are characterized by fine forests consisting of several species of oak, hickory, dogwood and occasional pines. These soils are a sandy and somewhat gravelly loam, of a light orchreous color. The former is from the farm of Mc. M. McGehee, and the latter from Mr. J. Pointer's. It will be observed that both these soils, and especially the former, have a good proportion of potash and lime, the most important elements of a tobacco soil; and the decomposing gravelly particles of rock restore the waste of cultivation to a considerable extent. But ashes and gypsum would add much to their fertility.

Number 51 is a fine wheat and corn soil from the plantation of Mr. J. Davis, on Spew Marrow Creek, in the northern part of Granville county. It is a dark gray to black, gravelly soil, with a thick growth of hickory oak and dogwood. The yield of this land per acre has sometimes been above 100 bushels of corn and 50 bushels of wheat, without manure There is a large level body of such land about Shiloh church. The fertility is due to the syenytic and dolerytic rocks from which the soil is derived.

Number 52 is another fine wheat soil from the banks of Neuse River in the southeast corner of Orange county, the noted Cameron plantation, which is a wide level alluvial tract of several thousand acres. The soil is a light ash-colored clay apparently; the analysis however shows it to be mostly sand; but the texture is very fine. The growth is white oak, willow oak, hickory, black and sweet gum and elm. The analysis shows a very rich and durable soil, with all the main elements of fertility in large percentage.

Blackjack Soils.

	53	54	55
Silica, Insoluble,..............	85.33	64.96	50.07
" Soluble,..............	2.50	0.00	12.20

Alumina, ...	2.51	12.75	8.48
Oxide of Iron, ...	4.99	8.87	17.49
Oxide of Manganese, ...			0.70
Lime, ...	0.04	4.37	0.08
Magnesia, ...	0.07	1.33	0.76
Potash, ...	0.07	0.72	0.10
Soda, ...		1.52	0.10
Phosphoric Acid, ...	0.09	0.15	trace.
Sulphuric Acid, ...	trace.	trace.	0.00
Chlorine, ...	trace.	trace.	0.22
Organic Matter, ...	3.10	3.95	8.00
Water, ...	0.90	2.00	2.40

The first of these specimens is from Leasburg, on the west border of Person county. It is an ash-colored, gravelly soil, overlying hornblendic and feldspathic rocks at the depth of a few feet. The growth is thickety, and composed of small blackjacks, post oaks and hickories. Plaster and salt would supply the most obvious defects, and doubtless much increase its productiveness, which is naturally low. Number 54 is from a gladey, blackjack flat, ten miles southeast of Charlotte, Mecklenburg county. The soil is a light gray, gravelly loam. The growth is almost exclusively blackjack, with an occasional post oak. The underlying rock of this region is syenyte and doleryte. It is evidently a very fine and durable soil, needing only thorough draining to develop its fertility.

There is a large area of land of similar quality and origin to these two samples, overlying the amphibolic and syenytic rocks of the Greensboro and Charlotte belt of granitic rocks. The surface is generally quite flat, or but slightly undulating. The color is generally light to slightly yellowish gray, and sometimes dark gray and greenish, and in composition, the soils are generally a very gravelly clay, pasty and boggy in wet weather.

Number 55 is from a flattish, gladey, blackjack woods, in the southern part of Granville county, three miles south of Taylor's Bridge. The soil is derived from a coarse, dark trap (doleryte) dyke of several hundred yards breadth. There are some oaks among the growth, of which blackjack is the most characteristic.

Soils of the Piedmont and Mountain Sections.

	56	57	58	59
Silica, Insoluble, ...	76.88	71.64	54.87	77.06
" Soluble, ...	0.67	0.00	0.78	3.84

Alumina,	12.46	11.47	14.61	6.97
Oxide of Iron,	3.57	4.27	13.74	4.07
Lime,	0.51	1.64	1.17	0.10
Magnesia,	0.33	0.14	1.69	0.29
Potash,	0.16	2.42	2.38	0.11
Soda,	0.45	1.09	0.70	
Phosphoric Acid,	0.09	0.08	0.15	0.05
Sulphuric Acid,	0.02	0.04	0.03	trace.
Chlorine,	trace.	trace.	trace.	0.06
Organic Matter,	4.60	5.49	7.25	6.65
Water,	1.07	1.30	2.05	1.10
Sulphide of Iron,	0.11	0.03	0.05	

Number 56 is from the forest in the suburbs of the town of Hickory, Catawba county, the growth being small to medium sized oaks, black-jack, dogwood, sourwood and pine. This locality is on the top of a broad flattish ridge, some 3 miles from the Catawba River and more than 300 feet above it. The soil is light colored and evidently sandy, a little ochreous with iron oxide. The analysis is of a fair soil, having all the substances required by the cultivated plants in pretty good proportions. No. 57, from the wood at the railroad bridge near Morganton, is plainly of a much better composition, having a very large per centage of lime and potash, and is well adapted to the production of tobacco. The growth is much more luxuriant than in the preceding case, consisting of oaks, hickory, dogwood and pine. This is also a light yellowish sandy loam. The last two are representative soils, standing as good averages for the respective regions for several miles around.

No. 58 is a representative of the best class of uplands in Caldwell county. The specimen was obtained from the high ridge 100 yards above the college in Lenoir, in a heavy oak grove. It is a red soil from the abundance of iron, and contains, like the specimen from Morganton, remarkable percentages of the alkalis and alkaline earths, and so is notably adapted to the production of tobacco, as well as grain crops.

Number 59 is a yellowish brown colored soil from a high chesnut ridge in Mitchell county, a terminal spur of the Little Yellow Mountains in the bend of the North Toe River, 3 or 4 miles south of Wiseman's at the Toe R. crossing. The growth is chesnut, spanish oak, chesnut oak, sourwood, ivy, (kalmia), and much wild indigo; a combination which is always indicative of infertility. The analysis shows low percentages of most of the valuable soil ingredients. The soil is gravelly, and the rock particles are not thoroughly decomposed; and the infertility arises as much from this circumstance, that is from the mechanical state ot the substances present, as from any deficiency of them; and this difficulty, as well as the other, in part, would be much alleviated by the use of quick-lime and ashes. There is a great deal of land of the above description among the foot hills and low spurs of the mountains: while the higher ranges have generally a productive soil and are covered with luxuriant forests; the former being composed of argillaceous and micaceous slates and schists, while the latter are more frequently made up of syenytes and hornblende gneisses and slates.

This completes the list of soils, as far as analyzed: but it is only a beginning of the work which ought to be accomplished in this direction, and which would be, if the survey were in a condition to employ a chemist constantly.

SECTION II. FERTILIZERS.

MARLS.

Marl is very abundant in North Carolina and very widely distributed, and of several kinds, the principal of which are four, viz: Green-sand, Eocene, Miocene and Triassic. The former has generally but a small percentage of carbonate of lime, 5 to 30; the second, usually 40 to 95; the third, 20 to 60; and the fourth, generally less than 50. The last is of little consequence as a fertilizer, because of the very limited extent of its outcrops, and it is scarcely used where abundant. It will be remembered as a frequently recurring term in the Egypt coal section, described in the previous chapter. These marls are more extensively exposed than elsewhere in the northwestern part of Wake county and in the edge of Orange, between Morrisville and Durham. There are frequent outcrops of a bed of marl and impure limestone, 2 to 4 feet thick, over a territory of 15 or 20 square miles, the nearly horizontal strata coming to the surface in ravines and gullies, and exposed in ditches, wells, &c. Near Brassfield turnout, on Mr. W. Rochell's place, is an exposure of nearly 4 feet of alternate thin beds of a compact, light gray and red arenaceous limestone, with strata of uncompacted brick red, marly clay between. This middle portion has the following composition:

Carbonate of Lime,	24.07
" " Magnesia,	7.52
Silica,	47.20
Alumina,	15.84
Oxide of Iron,	4.76

This would evidently prove a valuable addition to some of the lean soils of the region, which are deficient in alkaline matter. The upper indurated strata contain more than 90 per cent. of carbonate of lime, and the lower about 60 ; and both require to be burned before they are available for agricultural uses. Lime was made at this point during the war, and used for building purposes in Raleigh. And some 40 years ago, a few kilns were burned for the same purpose, at a point a few miles southeast-ward. There is an outcrop of a very similar character at Mr. H. Witherspoon's, 2 miles east of B.

Greensand Marl.—This is the great fertilizer of New Jersey, which has renewed the face of nearly the whole state agriculturally, within a generation, and mostly within a decade or two. The discovery of a marl bed in that region is justly regarded as an event of more importance than that of a gold or copper mine. One of the chief occupations cf the railroads in that state is the transportation of this natural manure from its depositories to the farms of almost every county. Prof. Cook, the State Geologist, mentions the fact that the amount transported in 1867, was about one million tons, and the quantity is constantly increasing, with the discovery of new deposits, and the construction of every additional mile of railway, so that the amount for 1869 was estimated at double the above. No one passing through the State in any direction can fail to notice the marl heaps that line the track at every turnout, and almost every farm in some sections.

As to the benefits which that state has derived from the use of this fertilizer, the following remarks of Prof. Cook are sufficient : " Thousands of acres of land which had been worn out and left in commons, are now, by the use of this fertilizer, yielding crops of the finest quality. What are supppsed to be pine barrens, by the use of marl are made into fruitful land. Bare sands, by the application of marl, are made to grow clover, and then crops of corn, potatoes and wheat."

The composition of this fertilizer will be understood from the following specimens of analysis from the " Geology of New Jersey, 1868."

	1.	2.	3.	4.	5.
Silica,.........................	51.16	73.10	49.40	36.03	38.70
Alumina,....................	6.10	12.60	8.90		30.67
Oxide of Iron,...........	17.68		18.66		
Lime,.......................	3.48	1.62	2.52	15.19	7.79
Magnesia,....................	2.04		3.25		1.21
Potash,....................	4.27		6.31		4.47
Phosphoric Acid,.........	4.54	1.20	2.69	1.23	1.41

Sulphuric Acid,..........	0-43	2.16	0.26		0.31
Water,.	9.13	8.26	7.55		11.22

The most valuable ingredients of these marls are potash and phosphoric acid. It was long supposed that their high fertilizing effect was due to the potash chiefly, but it has been ascertained that the phosphoric acid is the constituent which determines the agricultural value. Number 1 is one of the best varieties, containing unusually high percentages of both these important elements; although some pits are richer in one, or the other. Number 2 is one of the poorer sorts. These two samples represent the famous Squankum beds, some of which are wrought by companies on a large scale. Number 3 is from the pits of the West Jersey Marl Transportation Company, and contains a very high percentage of potash. Number 4 is pronounced "A marl of the first quality and a fair sample of those of the neighborhood." Number 5 "Is a good sample of the blue marl." And yet neither of them is rich in phosphoric acid or lime.

This greensand is widely distributed over the southeastern half of New Jersey. It occurs in horizontal beds of great thickness and various composition. The characteristic compound however is, of course, the *green sand*, which consists of minute rounded grains of a green colored mineral, soft enough to be crushed by the nail, and known in mineralogy as *glauconite*, a hydrated silicate of alumnina and iron, with potash and magnesia. The different strata contain different proportions of this mineral mixed with clay, quartz sand, and sometimes a considerable percentage of carbonate of lime. Some of the best layers of marl contain 90 per cent. and upward of the green sand. An average of some two dozen analyses given by Prof. Cook gives 75 per cent., the range being from about 30 to 90. In North Carolina the proportion of green sand is very small, not often passing from 5 to 10 cent., and only occasionally rising to 25 or 30.

By reference to the map and to the previous chapter, it will be seen that this marl occurs throughout the southeastern region of the State, between the Neuse River and the Cape Fear. The following analyses will furnish the means of comparing these marls with those of New Jersey, and also of estimating their agricultural value:

	A	B	C	D	E
Silica, Insol.,............	93.43	37.00	91.00	79.00	89.70
" Soluble,.........		1.46	0.20	0.60	
Oxide of Iron and Alum.	9.00	6·40	4.70	8.80	5.00

Phosphate of Iron,......		1.60			
Carb. of Lime,..........	11.40	33.40	1.00	2.75	1.50
Magnesia,...............	0.20	13.60	0.70	1.60	0.20
Potash,...............	0.38	1.43	0.23	1.75 }	0.25
Soda, ...	0.42	2.12	0.26	0.30 }	
Sulphuric Acid,........				0.20	
Organic Matter,.......	4.80	1.60		2.00	
Water,...............	3.80	1.80	1.50.	2.33	3.51

The above are from Emmons, reproduced because the report in which they occur is out of print and little accessible. The first two represent the upper and lower beds at Blackrock, on the Cape Fear. C is described as representing the greensand marl as it exists near Kinston and at Mr. D. Fowler's, in Bladen. D and E are from Tar River, near Tarboro', the former from Gov. Clark's plantation, and the latter from Col. Bridgers'. The analyses given below have been recently made:

	1	2	3	4	5	6	7	8
Silica, Insol.,..........	70.91	75.66	51.50	82.38	79.76	77.94	76.63	68.91
" Soluble,...........								
Alum. and Ox. of Iron,...	7.58	6.68	7.59	11.88	6.62	6.62	4.23	9.91
Lime,....................	9.22	8.15	20.21	2.86	0.60	6.58	9.19	8.89
Magnesia................	1.08	0.85		0.14	0.98	0.43	0.30	1.20
Potash,..................	0.68 }	0.54		0.67 }	1.00	0.88	0.51	0.62
Soda,....................	0.32 }			}		0.65	0.11	
Phosphoric Acid,.........	0.04		trace	0.14		0.12	0.73	0.24
Sulphuric Acid,..........	2.12	1.47		1.53	0.44	0.48	1.83	4.21
Carbonic Acid,............	7.23	6.53	15.87			5.27	6.00	5.76
Water and Org. Matter,...	0.82			4.45	5.75	1,93	0.46	0.26

Nos. 1 and 2 are from the bluff of Livingston's Creek in Brunswick county, at the railroad bridge, and present a fair average of the greensand marls of that creek. No. 3 is from the bank of the Cape Fear at Parsley's Mill, Wilmington. No. 4 is from Rockfish Creek at railroad crossing, on the upper border of New Hanover. No. 5 is from the mill on Southwest Creek, some 4 miles from Kinston. No. 6 is from the marl pits of Mr. W. Taylor, on Lousin swamp, 7 miles north of Kinston. No. 7 is from the bank of the creek at Suggs' Mill, Wheat Swamp, some 9 or 10 miles northwest of Kinston. No. 8 is from the cretaceous shell bluff in Snow Hill, Greene county.

It will be seen that the proportion of greensand and silica are very different in these specimens from those found in the New Jersey beds. There is, however, a good percentage of lime generally, and of potash and magnesia. And in fact these marls have been used with very great advantage in many places. Mr. Flowers, above mentioned, states that an application of five to seven hundred bushels to the acre has sometimes more than quadrupled the crop of corn, and Mr. J. F. Oliver, 3 miles further down, prefers the greensand to the more calcareous shell marls. And Dr. Emmons states that Gov. Clark had used the marl, marked "C" with good success for many years. Some of the analyses given above show a large percentage of sulphuric acid, (sulphate of iron), as Nos. 1, 4, 7. These must be used with some caution on account of their acid quality. They should be thrown out of the pits long before using and exposed to the leaching action of the rains; or better, treated with a small percentage of lime or of shell marl, which would not only correct the acidity, but increase the value by replacing the sulphuric acid with gypsum.

The quantity of marl which may be profitably used varies with its quality and the condition of the land. But these greensand marls may be applied in quantities of from 500 to 1000 bushels per acre. The richer marls of New Jersey are applied in quantities varying from 100 to 500 or even 600 bushels. But it happens in this state generally, that where this species of marl is found, the better qualities of shell marl are also accessible, and, requiring to be used in much smaller quantities, they are much cheaper. But where these cannot be had, the greensand marls are unquestionably well worthy of the attention of the farmer. Their distribution is easily seen by a glance at the map. They come to the surface, as stated, along the banks of the Cape Fear and Livingston's Creek, on Black River and South River, on the Neuse and its tributaries about and below Kinston, along the Contentnea and Moccasin, and at a few points even as far north as the Tar River.

Eocene Marl. The marls of the next formation, which are always found overlying the preceding, when the two occur together, are, as already described in another connection, either a calcareous sand, passing in places into a friable sandstone, coarse, or fine, or a fine calcareous clay, or a conglomerate shell limestone, more or less compact and occasionally semicrystalline. They are composed of comminuted shells, corals and other marine exuviæ. The extent, and many localities of outcrops of these marls, have been previously noted. The following analyses will show their chemical constitution and agricultural value:

	8	9	10	11	12	13
Silica, ...	3.54	4.95	1.22	7.27	20.39	40.11
Ox. of Iron and Alum.	0.97	2.30	1.30	1.63	3.83	5.23
Lime, ...	51.74	50.59	52.90	48.55	39.96	27.73

Magnesia,..........	0.50	0.58	1.07	1.39	1.42	trace
Potash,............	1.28	0.85	0.25	1.06	0.79	1.34
Soda, ...	0.36	0.00	0.05	0.00		0.46
Phosphoric Acid,....	0.35	trace	0.34	0.10	0.39	0.44
Sulphuric Acid,.....	0.49	0.18	0.08	0.20	0.24	0.75
Carbonic Acid,......	40.61	40.29	42.33	39.35	32.46	20.96
Water and Org. Mat.,	0.16	0.26	0.46	0.45	0.52	2.98

The first four specimens are from New Hanover county; number 8 from a point about a mile N. E. of Wilmington, the locality called Hard Scrabble; the others from Rocky Point and vicinity; 9 from D. T. Durham's place, one mile west of R. Pt., the marl lying so near the surface as to be exposed in the ditches and even the furroughs of the wide river flats, which extend from the North East River at Rocky Point for nearly a mile in this direction and several miles along the course of the river; No. 10 from a plantation known as Green Hill, some 2 miles above R. Point, in a situation quite similar to the last; Mosely Hall, the next plantation above, furnishing sample 11. These marls are all of the same description, viz, white, rather coarse, friable, shell and coral sandstone, easily removed with a pick, or even a hoe. The only point south of the Cape Fear where I have seen this formation is the bluff of Black Rock. Here it is quite similar to that just described, but it is only a few inches thick apparently, and lies in immediate contact with the greensand of that bluff. It is found however all along the course of North East River and the other streams north of Wilmington, and every where within a few feet of the surface. At the Davis place, 7 miles above the city on the N. E. River, as well as at Rocky Point, the formation occurs both in the form just described and as a compact limestone, which is valuable both for building purposes and as a source of lime, for which it was largely used during the war: it has also served as a flux for iron smelting.

It will be seen that these samples, which are representative for the region of the Cape Fear, have a chemical constitution not different from that of ordinary limestones, the percentage of carbonate of lime ranging from about 90 to 95. Of the same character are the outcrops along the North East River and its head waters through Duplin and (the eastern side of) Sampson counties, as for example, on Maxwell's Creek, near the bridge at Chinquepin, at Mr. Jcs. Shines, some 7 miles east of Mt. Olive Depot, and at Mr. Henry's in Young Swamp near Faison's Depot. The outcrop near Kenansville, at Rev. Mr. Stallings' differs from the preceding only in its somewhat lower percentage of carbonate of lime; it is represented by No. 12. No. 13 is from Dr. Roberts', near Mt. Olive, and is a good representative of the marl beds of the immediate neighborhood, at Jesse Flowers', Kornegay's, Benj. Carr's, &c. In this region the Eocene marl has been commingled with a considerable percentage of the underlying greensand, and contains numerous sharks' teeth, rounded fragments of bones and coprolites.

	14	15	16	17	18	19	20	(20)
Silica, Insoluble, ...	5.60	11.86	11.50	4.88	15.28	27.54	52.82	3.82
Silica, Soluble, ...					1.16	1.78	2.64	0.74
Ox. of Iron and Alum., ...	2.43	3.53	3.87	1.60	2.86	4 40	6.68	1.62
Lime, ...	46.88	44.55	42.85	50.80	41.70	28.98	20.94	50.04
Magnesia, ...	1.11	0.23	0.67	0.67	0.06	4.60	0.65	1.72
Potash, ...	0.52	0.96	0.60	0.37	0.34	0.51	0.55	trace
Soda, ...	0.20	0.36	0.28	0.42	0.20	0.00	0.03	0.14
Phosph. Acid, ...	0.47	0.06	0.43	0.45	0.24	0.43	0.27	0.34
Sulphu. Acid, ...	0.70	0.38	0.30	0.33	0.50	0.13	0.21	0.45
Carb. Acid, ...	37.03	34.98	33.83	40.60	32.33	27.20	15.90	40.55
Water and Org. Matter, ...	5.06	3.22	6.37	0.27	5.47	4.80	0.10	0.58

Nos. 14 and 15 are from Onslow county, which is for the most part underlaid with marl and limestone of this period. The first is from the pits of Dr. Duffy, near Richland, who makes much use of it, and with great benefit to his land. Dr. D. also uses the shell marl. No. 15 is from E. L. Frank's, Cohorn Creek, on the borders of White Oak Swamp. About Richland, on Chapel Run and other streams, are cliffs of limestone, as well as on some parts of Dr. Duffy's plantation. This marl extends southward towards Jackson, being in places compact, as about the Alum Spring and Crane Ponds, and again loose and uncompacted, and sometimes much mixed with the greensand, which seems to have been washed up by the waves and re-deposited with this formation, as about Mt. Olive. A specimen from E. F. Jamin's shows only 49.28 per cent. of carbonate of lime.

No. 16, (as well as 15), is a friable, rather fine-grained calcareous sandstone, of a grayish to yellowish white color, and is found on the banks of Trent River, some six miles above Trenton, in Jones county. No. 17 is from Mr. J. A. Heath's, 8 miles southeast of Kinston, Lenoir county. No. 18 is from Maj. Blount's place, some 7 or 8 miles above Kinston, on the Neuse. A very similar specimen is from Jno. E. Wooten's, about 5 miles Southeast of Kinston. This last has a slight sprinkling of the green grains from the lower formation. Dr. Emmons gives two analyses of Eocene marls from Jones county, which had been used as fertilizers, both from J. H. Haughton's place, the first showing 85.20 per cent. of carbonate of lime, the second 56.06; also another from W. Wadsworth's in Craven, which contains 71.22 per cent. Mr. W. used 75 to 100 bushels to the acre, and found that quantity as much as his poorer soils would take with advantage.

No. 19 is from Col. S. Biddle's on Neuse River, some 10 miles above Newbern. Emmons gives an analysis of a sample from the same point which shows 78.60 per cent. of lime carbonate. This marl is a very fine clay-like mass, of a light ash color. Col. B. "killed" a considerable field some 40 years ago by a dressing of 600 bushels, so that it has not fully recovered yet. With smaller quantities he obtained very profitable results. A specimen analyzed for Col. E. R. Stanly, (Newbern), gave 85.20 per cent. of carbonate of lime.

No. (20) is a marl sent by Mr. Geo. Allen (Newbern), and is still richer in lime, and contains a high percentage of magnesia in addition. No. 20 is from Cox's Ferry 10 miles above Goldsboro, where there is an outcrop of some two miles extent along the bluff on the south side of the river. The same marl is reported as occurring 5 miles still further west. The marl here is much mixed with gravel, having been evidently disturbed by currents since its first deposition.

The Eocene marl is found at a few points along the Contentnea in Greene county, but not in its original position or purity. On the contrary, one only finds patches of it mingled with green sand, abraded from the underlying formation. A sample from Hon. Jos. Dixon's, a fine grayish white sand, slightly coherent, gives 30.14 per cent. of lime carbonate, and is evidently a valuable marl.

It will be seen that these marls usually contain a very large percentage of lime and are therefore to be used with care, especially on thin soils. Fifty to seventy-five bushels to the acre is sufficient. The quantity may of course be increased with every addition of organic matter,—peat, muck, green crops. These marls never fail to improve the land and largely increase its yield, when judiciously applied. This would be so, if they contained only lime, but there are also valuable percentages of magnesia, potash and phosphoric and sulphuric acids.

Miocene Marls.—These are commonly known as *shell marls*, or *blue marls*. They are found in limited patches or "beds," and are scattered over a much wider territory than either of the preceding, and being nearer the surface, and so, more accessible, have been much more extensively used, and are consequently much better known. They are found throughout a large part of the eastern region, from South Carolina to Virginia; in fact, they occur in all the counties of eastern North Carolina, except those lying between, and north of the great sounds, and two or three small outcrops have been observed in Chowan, and in the northern part of Currituck. The western boundary of these beds, is very nearly represented by a line parallel to and 3 or 4 miles west of the Wilmington and Weldon Railroad, from Halifax to Goldsboro. Southward, the inland boundary is found to be generally but little west of a line connecting the latter point and Lumberton, that is, a line parallel to the coast and about 65 miles distant from it.

The area included within the above limits is about one-fourth of the state,—a much larger territory than the whole state of Massachusetts, or New Jersey.

These beds, even along the western boundary, are seldom found at an elevation exceeding 100 feet above the sea.

The analyses given below, of specimens gathered from the whole region, will give the means of judging of the value of these deposits, and of their importance to the agricultural development of a large section of the state.

Blue Marls South of the Cape Fear.

	21	22	23	24	25	26	27
Silica, ...	6.97	61.61	18.84	58.25	25.28	39.36.	5.65
Ox. of Iron and Alumina,	0.86	2.80	2.72	11.28	3.02	3.47	3.30
Lime, ...	47.62	19.60	41.48	13.49	37.52	28.96	48.51
Magnesia, ...	1.03				0.12	0.16	1.96
Potash, ...	0.37		0.56		0.22	0.75	0.23
Soda, ...	0·15		0.09		0.25	0.17	0.30
Phosphoric Acid, ...	0.19		0.18		0.40	0.11	trace.
Sulphuric Acid, ...	0.41	0.06	0.64		0.40	0.18	0.31
Carbonic Acid, ...	38.15	15.37	32.07	10.59	29.02	22.73	39.80
Org. Matter and Water,	4.25		3.42		2.98	4.11	0.60

No. 21 is from a point in Robeson county, 3 miles north of Lumberton,—farm of B. Godwin. It is a gray earthy mass, with many shells, in every stage of decay, most of them small. It is very rich in lime, and has several other valuable ingredients. The proportion of sand is unusually small. It has been used with excellent effect on the farm. The bed is within three feet of the surface. Similar beds are reported 3 miles northwest of this point, and on Lumber River 1 to 2 miles above and below Lumberton, and 10 miles south, on Hog Swamp. No. 22 is found near Whiteville, Columbus county, half a mile south, in the slight acclivity just across the swamp. It is composed largely of comminuted shells, and is brown in color. The materials have evidently been disturbed since their deposition, and the bed in consequence conforms nearly to the inclination of the ground. It is a marl of fair quality, but much less valuable than the preceding. No. 25 is from R. D. Sessions', 4 miles from Whiteville,—a solid shell-marl, of light color. Nos. 23 and 24 are from the north bluff of Waccamaw lake. The bed is within three feet of the surface. The upper portion of the bed represented by 23, is full of decomposed shells and is very rich in lime; the lower portion (24) is quite clayey in appearance, and in fact, contains many black, smooth phosphatic (probably coprolitic) nodules. Such nodules are of frequent occurrence in the marls of both this and the preceding age,—Miocene and Eocene; they are of no more value agriculturally, than so many flint pebbles, unless ground and treated with acid. Four miles below Wilmington, on the Cape Fear, at Col. McIlhenny's, there is a marl bed which is a light colored conglomerate of shells, small and large,—a sort of shell limestone,—containing 73.32 per cent. of carbonate of lime. It lies near tide level, and belongs evidently to the richer class of marls. No. 26 is from the bluff at the mouth of Livingston's creek, near the landing known as "The Barn," (a corruption of Le Bon Secours.) The bed lies at the top of the bluff 35 to 40 feet above the river. It is a mass of decomposing shells and a sandy earth. At some points the shells are mostly oysters, while at others, within a rod or two, scarcely an oyster shell is to be found; and arcinella spinosa abounds, and many other rare, and especially small species. The marl is above an average in quality, and has the advantage of unusual accessibility. No. 27 is a specimen of shell marl sent to the laboratory from the plantation of Mr. Canady, on Town Creek in Brunswick county. It is an uncommonly rich marl.

Besides the above samples, which have been analyzed, the Museum contains a number of others whose general character may be ascertained approximately by comparison with similar ones among these. For example, there is an outcrop of a "red marl" in the ravine nearly a mile northeast of Brinkley's Depot in Brunswick, which resembles that near Whiteville, but contains less sand and more lime. There is also a blue marl at Applewhite's, 4 or 5 miles south of Brinkley's Depot, which is of average quality. Three miles south of Brown Marsh Depot, across the marsh and near its eastern margin at W. Smith's, is a large bed of marl whose appearance is about the same as that of number 27. It has been well opened, but little used. At Jack Allen's, some 90 miles above Wilmington, near the top of a high bluff, about 100 yards from the right bank of the river and at an elevation of nearly 100 feet above it, is an extensive bed of "red marl" (brown), quite like that at the Barn, (No. 26). This marl has been extensively and profitably used. There is no marl higher up the river, that I could hear of. But below this point there are many occurrences of such beds, as at Owen's Hill,—mostly oyster shells ; about Elizabethtown, above and below, (a sample from Cromarty's gave Dr. Emmons 40 per cent. of carbonate of lime); at Brown's Creek, and again at Walker's Bluff, where the marl is nearly 20 feet thick, and about 50 feet above the river, and overhanging it. It abounds in shells, at one point exclusively oysters (O. mauricensis). Again the marl appears at Brown's Landing, and at D. F. Flower's, who has long used both this and the greensand marl very successfully. The miocene marl on his place is of a brown color, and full of shells. At a point near this, some 2 miles from the river, the shells are all oysters (O. mauricensis), and perfectly sound, as at Walker's Bluff. Shell marl is also abundant, and has been profitably used at D. A. Lamont's, a few miles below. In the southern part of Brunswick it is said to be abundant, both on the Waccamaw River and between that and the coast, eastward of the Green Swamp.

Blue Marls of New Hanover.

	28	29	30	31	32	33	34
Silica,	37.24	43.21	49.17	65.94	45.17	25.34	26.35
Ox. of Iron & Alumina,	2.09	4.57	2.98	4.72	4.12	1.61	5.47
Lime,	30.45	27.50	25.20	14.32	25.50	34.43	33.03
Magnesia,	1.88	0.41	0.52	0.54	0.57	0.59	0.59
Potash,	1.60	0.49	0.45	0.77	0.55	0.66	0.91
Soda,	0.34	0.00	0.03	0.46	0.10	0.00	0.02
Phosphoric Acid,	0.38	0.51	0.74	1.22	1.33	0.39	1.67
Sulphuric Acid,	1.10	0.49	0.32	2.25	trace	1 34	0.28
Carbonic Acid,	25.16	21.31	19.50	9.47	19.44	30.53	24.89
Org. Mat. and Water,		1.51	1.09	0.31	3.22	0.11	6.89

The larger part of New Hanover county contains blue marl, as well as deposits of the two preceding and underlying formations. The first of the above samples is from the left bank of the Cape Fear at Parsley's mill, about a mile above Wilmington. The bed lies immediately on the Greensand, 6 or 8 feet above water. The color is light gray, and shells are abundant, and generally small and much decayed. The analysis shows a marl of very good quality, with an unusually large percentage of potash and magnesia. This marl is very easy of access and probably abundant, and would be of great benefit to the sandy soils of the neighborhood. Near the Carolina Central depot is another outcrop of the bed, the upper part of which is a solidified conglomerate, the shell bed lying beneath and, for the most part, concealed. Near market street also in the middle of the city beds of shells crop out in the cellars. It is used to some extent as a dressing for the streets, and serves as a cement to give solidity to the mobile sea sand of which they are composed.

Nos. 29 and 30 are the upper and lower strata of an outcrop at Mr. Armstrong's, 4 miles north of Rocky Point. Nos. 31 and 32 are from Wm. Thompson's, a few miles west of Rocky Point,—upper and lower strata; 33 and 34 from J. McIntyre's, 6 miles west; the latter remarkable for its large proportion of phosphoric acid. Marls of similar quality are found still further west, on Moore's Creek, at Mrs. F. A. Colvin's and other places. They have been used to some extent in many portions of the upper end of the county, and always with decided advantage. The reason will be obvious on an inspection of the above analyses, all of which show, besides a large percentage of calcareous matter, notable quantities of potash, magnesia, phosphoric acid, and most of them, of sulphuric acid also.

Blue Marls of Sampson and Duplin.

	35	36	37	38
Silica,	33.64	38.23	29.38	55.99
Oxide of Iron and Alumina,	3.17	5.15	4.27	7.48
Lime,	33.58	29.19	33.35	16.46
Magnesia,	0.71	0.58	0.93	1.73
Potash,	0.31	0.75	0.52	0.91
Soda,	0.32	0.04	0.13	
Phosphoric Acid,	0.61	1.40	0.39	0.32
Sulphuric Acid,	0.79	1.57	0.89	1.56
Carbonic Acid,	26.16	21.41	26.37	13.67
Organic Matter and Water,	0.71	1.68	377	1.88

No. 35 is from the farm of J. C. Pass, a mile and a half west of Faison's Depot. This is a very good marl and abounds in shells. It is of an ash color and apparently exists in large quantity. Another well known outcrop in the same neighborhood is at Dr. Thompson's, whose crops are a sufficient evidence of its value. It is found again in the railroad cut near the depot, and a few miles south on the railroad; and at Giddensville, 5 or 6 miles northwest, the marl is within a few feet of the surface; a specimen from this point gave 49.80 per cent. of carbonate of lime.

No. 54 is from the farm of Jas. King, some 10 miles from the depot, southwest. Marl is found over the whole of his farm, even in the well at the depth of 10 feet. There is probably no better illustration of the value of this species of marl as a fertilizer, than this farm affords, having been brought by a liberal use of it, from the condition of one of the poorest farms in the region to that of the most productive. This locality is on the waters of Six Runs Creek, and marl seems to be abundant throughout the considerable section drained by this stream; although unfortunately it is used by very few, so little contagious is a good example. Marl is also abundant about Magnolia, as at the Natural Wells; at Strickland's; at Whitaker's, 3 miles east on Kenansville road, represented by No. 37; here quite light colored and shelly; and at A. H. Grady's, 5 miles northeast of Kenansville, represented by No. 38. This latter is a dark gray, compact marl, streaked and spotted with decayed shells. It lies within two or three feet of the surface and is of unknown thickness. Indeed this marl may be found in almost every neighborhood of these counties, but unfortunately its value is not generally appreciated and its use is very limited, although I have never found the farmer that has tried it and concluded that it did not pay.

Blue Marls of Lenoir, Onslow, Craven and Carteret.

	39	40	41	42	43	44
Silica, Insoluble,....	76.74	46.46	46.42	67.61	36.60	55.28
" Soluble,.......	0.64			0.36		
Ox. of Iron and Alum.	6.20	3.51	5.00	2.20	6.94	2.92
Lime,...........	5.45	21.79	25.21	16.28	27.20	21.04
Magnesia,...........	0.16	0.14	0.13	0.09	0.87	0.23
Potash,..........	1.04	0.73	0.31	0.26	0.55	0.51
Soda,..............	0.00	0.68	0.30	0.50	0.45	0.14
Phosphoric Acid,....	0.24	0.16	0.20	0.85	0.05	0.43
Sulphuric Acid,.. ...	0.29	0.70	1.05	0.32	0.50	1.96
Carb. Acid,........ ...	4.40	16.80	19.20	11.43	23.20	16.40
Org. Mat. and Water,.	4.80	9.03	3.20	0.97	4.00	1.60

On New River, Onslow county, shell marl is of common occurrence, immediately overlying the Eocene, which has been seen to be so nearly universally present in this region. On Dr. Duffy's place for example, there is a Miocene shell bank, of average quality, containing probably more than 50 per cent. of carbonate of lime. A few miles lower, at R. Barber's, is a bed which has been opened and used to some extent. This is represented by No. 39. It is very sandy, and of poor quality. Nos. 40 and 41 are from Mr. Rhodes' place, some 2 miles from New River; a gray marl, very shelly, of good quality; it has more than doubled the yield of the land to which it was applied. No. 42 is from Mr. T. J. Jamin's, lower down, and is of light color and without shells, probably Eocene. There is also a bed of fine gray shelly marl 5 miles north of Jackson, at Jonas Jones' place, which contains large clam shells in abundance. No. 43 is from Glenbernie, 3 miles above Newbern, on the Neuse. It is a brown marl, full of broken shells. The white (Eocene) marl also crops out extensively beneath it in the slope facing the river. Shell marl is found abundantly below Newbern, in both banks of the river for many miles. It is constantly eroded by the play of the tides, and the fossil shells and corals of both the Miocene beds and the overlying Postpliocene are strewn in great numbers along the beach with the remains of living species. In Carteret county, at Newport, marl is obtained in a ravine crossing the railroad. A specimen forwarded by Dr. Arendell, gave 30.55 per cent. of carbonate of lime. It is a sandy, ash-colored earth, full of small shells in good preservation. No. 44 is from Lenoir. The sample was obtained from the farm of J. L. Mewbern, 7 miles north of Kinston, in an extensive level tract known as Lousin Swamp. This bed is notable for the fine mastodon jaw, and other striking fossils whilch it has furnished. A similar body of marl is found between this point and Kinston, in Briar Swamp. But the Eocene and Cretaceous marls are more common in this county than the Miocene.

Blue Marls of Wayne, Wilson and Nash.

	45	46	47	48
Silica, Insoluble,................	75.66	73.44	24.70	35.73
Silica, Soluble,...................				1.21
Oxide of Iron and Alumina,......	6.24	5.25	6.01	7.95
Lime,..........................	8.17	8.50	34.97	25.01
Magnesia, ...	0.85	0 55	2.26	0.82
Potash,.........................	0.51		0.02	0.80
Soda, ...	0.02		0.24	0.48
Phosphoric Acid,................	0.32	large	0.32	0.07
Sulphuric Acid,.................	1.47	2.08	1.08	0.60
Carbonic Acid,..................	6 24	6.14	29.06	20.15
Organic Matter and Water,.......	0.52		0.44	7.18

Marl is abundant in the neighborhood of Goldsboro, and northward on the waters of Little River. In a field of Dr. Kirby, near the limits of the town, a bed has been opened, which is a gray sandy marl, with many shells and fragments of bones, and containing 13 per cent. of carbonate of lime. Two miles northeast of Goldsboro, at B. Whitfield's, a similar deposit has been opened, which evidently contains a larger proportion of fertilizing ingredients than the preceding. No. 45 is from the pits of J. A. Howell, 4 miles north of Goldsboro; and at 3 miles, John Robinson's, another bed of the same character has been opened. It will be observed that the marls of this region are very sandy, and are of course less valuable on that account, and yet they produce very marked results on the thin sandy soils of the section. A field in the immediate vicinity of the last mentioned deposits, which had been marled nearly 30 years ago, shows a two-fold increase of crop to the present day. On Nahunta creek, in the northern part of the county, marl is also found. A bed 1 mile east of Pikesville Depot, a deposit of considerable thickness was opened several years ago, which is composed of a very fine sandy mud, thickly sown with small shells (chiefly mulinia and arca), overlaid by about 10 feet of a stratified, sandy clay. The percentage of lime is not probably greater here than on Little River.

In Wilson county marl is abundant, in the middle and eastern parts, especially on Tossnot creek. The beds here are richer in lime than those of Wayne. They abound in small shells which are generally little decomposed. A deposit only half a mile north of the town of Wilson (at Farmer's) abounds in coral stems as well as shells. It is of average quality. No. 46 is from Hominy creek, 1½ miles from Wilson (at Barnes'). This is much like the bed on Nahunta. No. 47 is from Tossnot, some 6 miles east (Col. J. S. Woodard's). This bed is 15 feet thick, and lies within 5 feet of the surface. This marl has been used with very good effect both on corn and cotton land. The proportions of magnesia and potash are notably large. One mile distant, (at Wm. Woodard's), another bed has been opened, which however is more sandy than the last and less valuable. A third deposit in the same neighborhood, (4 miles from Wilson), at Mrs. Farmer's, resembles the preceding, but is white with the multitude of small shells. Marl occurs also in the southern part of the county on Moccasin creek, and beds of it have been opened on both sides of the railroad.

No. 48 is from Nash county, (Col. W. D. Harrison's), 3 miles west of Battlesboro, on Beech Run creek. The bed is reached at the depth of 7 feet, and is 20 feet thick. The general appearance of this marl is like that on Tossnot. The analysis is that of a good marl, above average quality. On the northern border of the county, on Fishing creek, is an extensive outcrop, extending a long the creek more than a mile (with interruptions). At the famous locality where the skeleton of a whale has long been known as lying quite across the bed of the stream, into Halifax, about two miles above the railroad crossing, on the farm of J. M. Mayo, the marl bed is at least 20 feet thick. The bones above referred to are embedded in it, at the bottom of the stream. Most of the skeleton has been carried off by curiosity hunters, and not more than 3 or 4 vertebræ are left. It belongs to the same genus as the Quanky specimen. The marl is of at least average quality.

Blue Marls of Halifax and Edgecombe.

	49	50	51
Silica,	63.47	42.75	44.57
Oxide of Iron and Alumina,	4.18	5.64	8.96
Lime,	12.99	27.03	19.27
Magnesia,	2.87	0.32	1.80
Potash,	0.48	0.75	1.00
Soda,	0.21		0.35
Phosphoric Acid,	0.38	0.29	0.09
Sulphuric Acid,	0.61	1.67	0.33
Carbonic Acid,	12.68	20.40	17.60
Organic Matter and Water,	2.13	1.15	6.40

Marl is found in abundance along the course of Quanky creek, and about Enfield. No. 49 is from the right bank of the creek above named, near the town of Halifax, on the farm of Maj. Fenner, who used it with advantage before the war. The bed lies deep, 25 to 40 feet below the surface, overlaid by gray and bluish stratified clays. At this point some very large bones were obtained, belonging to an unknown genus of whales, of which an entire upper and lower jaw and several large vertebræ are in the Museum. They are described by Prof. Cope in the Appendix. This marl is found along the banks of the creek two miles higher up, where also cetacean vertebræ are common.

No. 50 is from the border of Beach Swamp, 1 mile east of Enfield, at W. F. Parker's. The same marl is found at various points north and east of Enfield; at Dr. Whitaker's; W. Burnet's, 3 miles lower on the swamp; and 4 miles southeast, at J. W. Whitaker's, and at G. W. Phillips'. It is also found on Tar River about Rocky Mount. No. 51 represents a bed lying half a mile below Battle's Factory. It is also struck in digging wells in the neighborhood. Five miles lower, on the farm of Mr. T. Battle, is a very sandy marl with few shells, cropping out in the river bank, which gave only 3.41 per cent. of carbonate of lime on analysis

About Tarboro marl is of common occurrence. In a field of W. S. Battle, one mile north of the town, a bed of gray shelly marl is found within a few feet of the surface. The bed is 8 feet thick, with 4 feet of bluish, stratified clay overlying it. At the Panola farm, (in the upper part), a bed of red marl appears at the foot of a cliff overlooking the river. At Bell's Bridge on the river, and again at Dr. Baker's farm, 3½ and 4 miles north of Tarboro, a light gray sandy marl of fair quality appears. Southward also, it is equally abundant, as at Cromwell's, 3 miles from Tarboro, where it is very common in the farm ditches, and is full of shells. Much benefit has been derived from the use of marl in this county, which is the pioneer in this improvement. The large farmers about Tarboro commenced the use of it a generation ago, and their success led to its general use in the county and the neighboring counties. Pitt and Greene have fallen in with the practice more extensively than any other. Mr. Elias Carr, in the lower end of the county, has used marl for a long time and with most evident beneficial results, although the bed from which he generally procures his material contains, (according to an analysis of a sample I obtained from his heaps), but 5.57 per cent of lime. Another bed less used gave 10.37. But this last, if properly opened, would no doubt prove much richer than on the surface.

Blue Marls of Greene and Pitt.

	52	53	54
Silica, Insoluble,	49.66	44.14	38.86
" Soluble,			
Oxide of Iron and Alumina,	4.99	7.08	5.43
Lime,	20.25	20.28	27.32
Magnesia,	0.37	2.77	0.93
Potash,	0.37	0.60	0.43
Soda,	0.34	0.05	0.20
Phosphoric Acid,	3.75	2.02	1.72
Sulphuric Acid,	2.02	1.91	1.41
Carbonic Acid,	11.72	16.06	20.12
Organic Matter and Water,	6.48	5.09	3.58

Marl is abundant about Greenville, Pitt county. It appears in the river bluff at and below the bridge, and on Col. Yellowley's farm, one mile distant, a large amount has been used. A sample from this gentleman's pits gave the analysis No. 52. It is notable as containing an extraordinary percentage of phosphoric acid, and it is otherwise more than an average marl. No. 53 represents the marls on Little Contentnea and Sandy Run, on the borders of Pitt and Greene. The sample was obtained at the road crossing, 14 miles north of Snow Hill, where large quantities have been dug for many years. It is found all along these streams, and has been used on most of the farms near them for many years, notably at the Streeter place on a large scale. Elias Carr, lower down the Contentnea, also used large quantities and with very striking results. About Marlboro, above and below, marl is everywhere, and it is very generally and profitably used. At D. N. Joyner's one mile east, is a bed 10 feet thick, and again two miles east, at George Joyner's, is an extensive exposure. The bed at Marlboro on Middle Swamp is said to be 20 feet thick. It occurs again at Farmville, one mile north; and three miles northwest, at Capt. Barrett's, there is a bed 13 feet thick. Again at the old Bynum place, four miles from Marlboro, and at Wm. May's, five miles north on the Contentnea, are other outcrops. Following down the course of the Contentnea to its mouth, marl is found on almost every farm. No. 54 represents the marls south of Marlboro towards Snow Hill. The sample is from Mr. Grimsley's, three miles north of Snow Hill, whose bed is 10 to 12 feet thick, and filled with shells and abounds in fragments of whale vertebræ; and there are other outcrops between this point and Marlboro, as at Dale's, Edwards', &c. No part of the state is better supplied than this region.

Blue Marls of Beaufort and Pamplico

	55	56	57	58	59	60
Silica, Insoluble, ...	81.50	36.94	62.69	74.43	74.50	76.21
" Soluble, ...	1.88					
Oxide of Iron and Alumina,	4.85	6.77	7.95	3.49	9.28	4.00
Lime, ...	5.31	29.16	14.16	11.50	5.32	10.00
Magnesia, ...	0.20	0.32	0.68	0.19	0.29	0.21
Potash, ...	1·07	0.92	0.54	0.18	0.31	0.36
Soda, ...	0.44	0.04	0.13	0.27	0.15	0.50
Phosphoric Acid, ...	0.18	0.11	0.25	0.06	0.12	trace
Sulphuric Acid, ...	0.18	0.81	0.51	0.31	1.75	
Carbonic Acid, ...	4.12	22.72	10.90	9.02	9.30	8.00
Organic Matter and Water, .	0.68	2.08	2.18	1.23		

Shell marl is found in Beaufort county on both sides of the Pamplico River; on the north, from Washington to Pungo River. No. 55 is from the northern margin of the Big Savannah, near Pungo River. It lies at the depth of 5 feet beneath the soil; is ash-colored, fine-sandy, with small shells little decayed. The same description of marl is found on the north side of Jackson Swamp, (at H. F. Harris's,) just below Bath, but apparently more calcareous, and of better quality. On the shores of Pungo River, the banks of oyster shells, accumulated by the Indians, are used instead of marl. No. 56 is from M. J. Grist's, near Washington; it is exposed in the farm ditches. No. 57 is from Maj. Blount's farm on the south side of the river, on Chockowinity Creek. This is a red marl, composed almost entirely of decomposed oyster shells. It is very abundant and within a few feet of the surface. At Durham's Creek also marl occurs on Mr. C. Bonner's farm. It is represented by No. 60; is quite sandy, and the shells small and not much decayed. The same description of marl occurs on South Creek also, a few miles below Aurora, at Swindell's and Reeves,' represented by 59. In the Bay River region it is also abundant, occurring at and around Jackson in the wells and farm ditches; and also some 8 miles lower down on Bear Creek. The marls on both sides of Pamplico River are of the same appearance and character. They are mostly composed of small shells, and are quite sandy, having therefore a smaller proportion of lime than is common. They are represented by No. 58; the sample was obtained from a tract on Bear Creek, opened by Dr. Abbott and others. The same sort of deposits is found on Smith's Creek and Beard's Creek; so that the whole peninsula seems to be underlaid by it.

Blue Marls of Roanoke River.

It is reported that there is shell marl about Hill's Ferry and in various parts of Martin county and in Washington near Plymouth, but I have not seen samples from any of these localities.

Blue Marls of the Meherrin River.

	61	62	63	64	65	66
Silica, Insol..........	58.83	56.31	58.58	63.00	13.43	43.69
Silica, Soluble,........		1.26	1.68		1.08	0.69
Ox. of Iron and Alum.,	3.62	6.88	7.23	4.65	1.73	7 60
Lime,...............	14.60	17.51	15.63	15.96	43.04	24.04
Magnesia,...........	0.41	0 79	0.26	0.50	0.40	0.93
Potash,.............	0.93	0.73	0.47	0.25	0.86	0.85
Soda,...............	0.70	0.15	0.30		0.12	0.62
Phosphoric Acid,....	0.18	0.08	0.21	0.25	0.54	0.09

Sulphuric Acid,.. ...	2.82	0.48	0.12	trace	0.28	0.32
Carb. Acid,.........	10.23	14.00	11.20	12.20	33.61	16.90
Org. Mat. and Water,.	9.37	1.60	4.00	2.50	5.39	4.30

Along the northern border of the State, on the waters of the Meherrin, the occurrence of shell marl is very common, especially about Murfreesboro. It is found in the town in a ravine a few hundred yards south of the principal street, on the farm of Mr. Southall, 200 or 300 yards from the river. This marl is represented by No. 61. It very much resembles the beds of Halifax, on Quanky. It crops out in the river bank, at the landing near the town, extending 12 feet above water, and forms the bed of the river for several miles down, as at Beeman's Fishery. The similarity to the Quanky beds appears also in the abundance of whole vertebræ, which are said to be so numerous as to form a serious obstacle to the movements of the seine. On Kirby's Creek, 3 miles from Meherrin, at Watson's Mill, is a vertical cliff more than 30 feet high, the larger part of which is composed of marl. The following section will show the mode of occurrence of the e deposits in this section.

1. Brown earth,...	3 feet
2. Sandy stratified clay,..................................	3 "
3. " " " full of small shell prints,...........	5 "
4. Bluish marl with small shells,..........................	6 "
5. " sandy clay, with shell fragments,................	10 "
6. Blue marl with large shells,............................	7 "
7. Water level.	

The lower stratum is represented by No. 62. The same bed appears in the cliff overlooking the mill pond, and again under the dam below the mill, two miles lower down the creek, at the road crossing (Vaughan's Mill). Whale bones are also abundant here. No. 63 is from this point. It will be observed that the marls of this neighborhood are of a very uniform composition, and of middling quality. No. 64 is from the bank of the river at the Branch place on the state line, 2½ miles from the Branchville Depot. The appearance is the same as at Murfreesboro, and the extent of the outcrop, several miles up and down the river. No. 65 is from a mussel bed at Wm. Harrell's near Harrellsville, in the southern part of Hertford county. It is doubtless of Indian origin, and evidently an uncommonly good fertilizer. No. 66 was sent to the Museum by H. A. Gilliam, from the Chowan river above Edenton.

Three additional analyses are given below of samples from beyond the state line on the upper waters of the Chowan.

	67	68	69
Silica,	59.12	33.80	43.00
Oxide of Iron and Alumina,	5.00	0.92	3.88
Lime,	12.99	34.55	25.09
Magnesia,	4.75	0.29	2.52
Potash,	0.30	0.18	0.47
Soda,	0.15	0.25	trace
Phosphoric Acid,	trace	0.48	0.41
Sulphuric Acid,	0.00	0 00	0.00
Carbonic Acid,	13.90	26.70	22.20
Water and Organic Matter,	3.50	2.90	2.40

No. 67 is from Flat Swamp creek, a mile north of Branchville. It is the same marl in appearance and character as that on the Meherrin, and the bed is extensive. The same marl occurs on the Nottaway, half a mile below the railroad crossing, (No. 69). At Dr. Massenberg's, 2 miles north of the railroad between the Nottaway and Blackwater, a bed of marl, partly red and composed of comminuted shells,—a beach accumulation, and partly blue, like the last, crops out in the lower scarp of a hill about 30 feet in height. It is exposed to a depth of 8 to 10 feet. No. 68 is from this point. There is another appearance of this marl at Franklin on the Blackwater. These beds were explored and analyzed in the hope and with the prospect of inducing the Raleigh and Gaston Railroad to inaugurate the business of transporting marl on a large scale, for the supply of the region through which it passes.

Other analyses, complete, or partial, have been made from time to time with the purpose of encouraging and extending the use of this valuable, but insufficiently appreciated resource of our defective agriculture. There remain a few localities to be explored: but the above exhibit is sufficient to accomplish the purpose in view, viz: of showing the unlimited extent, the wide distribution and the inestimable value of these manurial resources. Some analyses of New Jersey marls were given in the beginning of this chapter, for the purpose of affording means of comparison to such as have not access to the New Jersey Reports. The specimens given were all of Greensand marls, to which class most of the beds used in that state belong. But in the limited tract of that state,—less than the extent of one of our smallest counties, in which shell marl like ours, is found, it is highly appreciated and extensively used, being transported many miles. The two analyses following, from the New Jersey Report for 1868, will show the comparative excellence of these marls and ours.

	1	2	3
Silica,	59.30	50.20	65.53
Oxide of Iron and Alumina,	5.91	5.33	11.67
Lime,	15.30	19.71	2.71
Magnesia,	0.69	0.50	2.65
Potash,	0.97		1.12
Soda,	0.58	0.63	
Phosphoric Acid,	0.45	0.70	2.00
Sulphuric Acid,	3.56	2.09	6.70
Carbonic Acid,	9.09	15.05	
Organic Matter,			2.12
Water,	2.80	6 15	5.17

Of the first two of these marls, Prof. Cook says, that the land in the neighborhood was exhausted, so that it was too poor for wheat, and some of it even for rye. "Forty years have elapsed, and competent authorities estimate that the land has increased in value tenfold. The whole country about this marl outcrop has become a wheat-growing region instead of raising poor crops of rye." Its "effects are said to be visible for 30 years." There is a large trade in these marls. "The general practice is for the seller to dig it out and sell it from the bank." "The average price per ton-load is about fifty cents, though at some pits it is a dollar a load. "The pits are generally kept free of water by pumping, which is done by water power or steam, or the water is syphoned off."

On comparing these analyses with those of the North Carolina blue marls above given, it is obvious that they are hardly up to the average and much inferior to a very large proportion of them. And yet the difference in the estimation is immense, and on the wrong side. The third of the above marls is so poor that it would hardly rank with the most inferior kinds here, that are thought to be scarcely worth handling.

But in order to furnish the means of forming a more definite and precise notion of the value of these deposits, absolutely and relatively, the following table is added. It is founded on the estimates which are arrived at in other parts of the world, the English tables being the basis. The values for phosphoric acid and potash are adopted from Prof. Cook's table, as they seem reasonable, and for the purpose of comparison ; the former no doubt existing as phosphate of lime and the latter as silicate of potash.

Phosphoric Acid,........................	9 cents	per		pound.
Potash, ...	2 "	"		"
Sulphuric Acid,........................	4 "	"	10	pounds.
Lime,.................................	2 "	"	12	"
Magnesia,.............................	2 "	"	10	"
Soda,.................................	2 "	"	5	"

The sulphuric acid exists as gypsum, (or is readily convertible into that form by the addition of lime.) With these data it is easy to arrive at an estimate of the value of a y marl whose analysis is known. And it will be found that the range of valuation per ton of the two latter classes of marls, Eocene and Miocene, is from 2 or 3, to 6 or 8 dollars. Thirty per cent. of lime,—a very common proportion,—gives a value at once of $1.00 per ton. And one per cent. of phosphoric acid gives $1.80: and some of the analyses show 2 and 3 and upwards, making, for this item alone, $3.60, $5.40 and more, per ton. According to the best information I can get, the marl does not cost generally more than 25 or 30 cents per ton for throwing out;—a common price is half a cent per bushel, which is but 10 cents per ton,—counting 20 bushels to the ton, as done in N. J. And it does not cost more generally to distribute it; put the cost at 50 cents per ton in the field. (The marl is supposed to be found on the farm). If the marl be worth but $2.50 per ton, the profit is 500 per cent. on the outlay. If the results reach the half of this, or one-tenth even, it may be asked, what other farming operation in the state can compare with it in profitableness? But one of the most important considerations in estimating the value of a fertilizer has not been reckoned at all in the above count, viz: durability. While the effect of the high-priced commercial manures disappears with the season, or at most in two or three crops, an application of marl is good for a lifetime. Such is the testimony of all who have made the experiment among us. And similar results are attested elsewhere. Prof. Cook, of New Jersey, says of the use of marls there, "It gives lasting fertility to the soil. While all other fertilizers are exhausted and the soils become poor, I have never seen a field which has once been well marled that is now poor."

And another point worthy of mention is, that there are several other ingredients in the above marls, besides those taken into the above estimates, that are often of great importance, as soluble silica, the oxides of iron and organic matter.

From what has been said it is evident that, in the case of a very large number of the marl beds of which analyses are given, there is a large margin for transportation; the margin being the value, as estimated by the above table, less the cost of throwing out; for it is worth that amount any where in the State; so that if the value of a given marl be $3.75 at the pits, it may be profitably transported 300 miles, at $1.25 per ton per hundred miles. Of the New Jersey marls Prof. Cook says, estimating the range of values at $3.50 to $8.50 a ton, "I believe, in comparison with the prices paid for concentrated manures, they are worth that price to the farmer. I am confirmed in my opinion of their value by the testimony of successful farmers who have used them 20 years or more, and who assure me they can better afford to incur an expense of $5 or $8 a ton, than to farm without them, or to use any other purchased fertilizers." Unfortunately there is no such confirmatory experience in this latitude, because, so far from incurring any such expense in transportation, there are few who have tried the experiment of hauling it even one or two miles, and its transportation by rail is unheard of. On the contrary it is not uncommon to find farmers in whose ditches and furroughs even, the marl obtrudes itself, paying $60 and $70 a ton for commercial manures, and leaving the marl untouched. But it is plain from the facts and figures above given, that while the marls are naturally distributed over one quarter of the territory of the State, they are profitably accessible to at least one half.

The question is often asked me whether there are any minerals in the eastern section of the State; the answer is, the mineral wealth of that section, *in the form of marl*, is worth ten-fold more than that of all the rest of the state beside, great and various as that is. If the money spent in gold-getting alone, which is not less than 12 or 15 millions since 1820, had been spent in marl-getting, the State would be worth more than double its present aggregate valuation. For at the rate already given, that sum would have marled 3 millions of acres,—more than the total surface now in cultivation; that is, it would have produced a result at least equal to to the adequate marling, (at the rate of 10 tons to the acre), of every acre now in cultivation, leaving out of the calculation the interest, that is, the results of the increased production during several decades of years. And I think the farmers of those neighborhoods where marl has been most persistently and judiciously used will testify that on an average, an acre, which has been properly marled, is worth three unmarled. Of course there are instances of the injurious, because injudicious use of marl, such as have been referred to in the account of some of the stronger sorts. But it is possible to use too much stable manure, or Peruvian Guano, or to eat too much wheaten bread, or Irish potatoes; and it would be just as wise to condemn altogether the use of these articles on that account, as to refuse or abandon the u.e of marl for such a reason; as some farmers and neighborhoods have allowed themselves to do. It has been stated that 50 to 75 bushels of Eocene, or white marl is sufficient for an acre. Of blue (or shell) marl an ordinary dressing is from 8 to 12 tons, (or 150 to 250 bushels), to the acre. And in each case it is better to apply it in two or three doses, in successive years. The quantity should vary with the proportion of lime, and the condition of the soil; the more lime, or the poorer the land, the less the dose. The effects of over marling may be corrected by deep plowing, and by the application of muck or peat, or by turning under green crops,—weeds, peas, &c.

Peat, Muck, &c.—The value of peat as a fertilizer is scarcely appreciated among us. Dana has called attention in the "Muck Manual," to its remarkable similarity to the dung of the cow; and Prof. Johnson shows that it is rendered equal to stable manure by the addition of one per cent. of commercial potash, (or 5 of ashes), and one per cent. of a super-phosphate. And he further states it is often equal in practical effect to stable manure, and in some cases even superior; and this is doubtless due, in part at least, to the fact that it contains on an average, (deduced by him from the analyses of 30 specimens), 1½ per cent. of nitrogen,—more than three times as much as stable manure,—and in some cases even gave 2½ per cent. and upwards. The term peat is not very precise, but is applied to "the substance which results from the decomposition of vegetable matter under or saturated with water, whatever its appearance or properties," such as is everywhere accumulated in bogs, swamps and marshes, and in high latitudes, is found in any situation where moisture is abundant. Its characteristic constituent is *humus*, or vegetable matter in a state of decay. But owing to the various circumstances under which the accumulation takes place, the proportion of this substance to the earthy or inorganic matter,—the *ash*, varies very widely. Of the 30 specimens examined by Prof. J., some contained but 2 per cent. of ash, and others 20, 30, and even 60. A pure peat he considers as containing about 5 per cent. The composition of this ash is important. The following is in round numbers the average given by the same high authority; potash and soda nearly 1 per cent. each; lime 24; magnesia 3; alumina 6; oxide of iron 19; sulphuric acid 7½; chlorine ½; phosphoric acid 2½; sand 25. Muck is used generally to designate smaller and more earthy and less decayed swampy deposits, an impure or *unripe peat;* but it is not possible to say where peat begins and muck ends; the general nature and uses and value agriculturally are the same, the latter being less valuable, in proportion as it contains less humus.

Peat and muck abound in the eastern portion of this State, and are so widely distributed, that a large proportion of the farms, and almost every neighborhood have their own local supply within easy reach. But the inexhaustible source of this material for the region, is the great swamps previously described, which extend through the whole of the seaboard region, from the extreme southern border to the great Dismal, which extends across the Virginia border. A considerable part of these areas, designated as "The Swamp Lands," is simply, as heretofore stated, covered by a peaty accumulation,—a series of true *peat bogs*, of which the peat is from 2 or 3, up to 10, 15 and even 20 feet thick. Of such peat beds there are hundreds of square miles, which must one day become an important resource for fuel as well as manure. Below are given several analyses of peats and swamp muck, &c., from different sections of the east, which will give a general notion of their several qualities and values.

	1	2	3	4	5	6	7
Silica, Insoluble,........	1.52	64.74	3.71	37.47	32.36	52.20	47.27
" Soluble,........		3.60	0.40	9.95			
Ox. of Iron and Alum.,	0.54	3.64	2.52	3.97	4.92	6.09	3.73
Lime,................	0.36	0.10	3.08	0.45	0.56	1.16	0.50
Magnesia,..............	0.14	0.29	0.05	0.58	trace	0.55	0.44
Potash,................	0.06	0.05	0.49	0.09	0.96	0.60	0.42
Soda,..................	0.13	0.03	0.84		0.26	0.00	0.90
Phosphoric Acid,......	0.06	0.06	0.05	0.22	0.45	0.34	0.12
Sulphuric Acid,........	0.00	0.21	1.40	0.10	1.30	0.65	0.85
Chlorine,..............	0.02	trace		0.03			
Organic Matter,........	87.25	22.80	87.80	41.90	59.19	38.41	46.50
Water,................	9.60	4.20		5.30			

The two first analyses represent two sorts of peaty and mucky accumulations which characterize nearly all the great tracts of "Swamp Lands" belonging to the state; the second, No. 2, from White Oak Swamp, Onslow county, E. L. Frank's, illustrating the outer rim of the swamp proper, the cultivable portion; which however might be made a valuable source of manure for all the surrounding region; No. 1 showing the character of the inner zone of the swamp which ceases to be capable of acting the part of a soil, being either covered with a stunted growth of reeds, or of scattered shrubs. Nos. 3 and 4 are examples of the peats of fresh water marshes, the former on the margin of Tar River, 1 mile above Washington; the latter, the White Marsh, in Columbus county. The former has been used to a considerable extent by Gen. Grimes, the owner, as a source of manure. There is an immense area of such marsh along this and the other tidal rivers, and it is very rapidly enlarging.

No. 7 is from one of the thousands of small local swamps, or muck beds, which are found throughout the eastern region; the specimen was obtained in a cleared and cultivated portion of such a swamp on Black River, New Hanover county, belonging to Jas. Murphy. A sample of a similar deposit analyzed for Judge Barnes, from Hertford county, not far from Murfreesboro, gave 57.85 per cent. of organic matter; and a specimen obtained from a similar bed of several acres on the farm of Elias Carr, already referred to, is of about the same composition. It has been used for manure for a generation or more, on this farm, and with very marked benefit, in connection with marl. This is one of the few farms on which a bale and a half of cotton to the acre is a common crop,—to the extent of the marled and mucked surface.

Nos. 5 and 6 are specimens of cane brake, river swamp; the first from Eagles's Island, Brunswick county, opposite Wilmington; the other, No. 6, from the famous Big Swamp, on Lumber River, in Robeson and Columbus. These deposits are capable of becoming sources of fertility for the surrounding regions, and they are inexhaustible.

It is worth while to put on record, in this connection, an analysis of another substance much relied on as a means of soil improvement in the best cotton counties of the east, Edgecombe, &c., and even used by the most intelligent farmers, who have easy access to indefinite supplies of peat and muck. I refer to what is called in cotton farming parlance "fence corner" and "ditch bank." It is the common practice to scrape together into conical heaps a few inches of the soil in the localities indicated, and after allowing time for the decay of the vegetable matter,—weeds, leaves, &c., often mixed with a little marl, to spread them upon the fields, or in the furrows. The object is, of course, mainly to procure a supply of humus. In order to demonstrate the expensiveness of such a procedure, a sample was obtained from the farm of Mr. Carr, above mentioned, who is one of the most successful and intelligent farmers of the region. It had the appearance of being of the best quality; and yet it contained but 4.10 per cent. of organic matter. The advantage of even the poorer kinds of muck over such a manure is too obvious to be insisted on.

A similar result would follow the analysis of the *woods mould*, and especially of the scrapings of worn out *old fields*, which are used for the same purpose, in the same region, under a mistaken estimate of their value. It is very important to restore the humus to these open soils, but not at such a cost; more especially where muck is accessible, or where the cow-pea will flourish.

Some other substances which are used for manurial purposes in the eastern part of the State are *salt marsh mud*, *sea mud* or *slime*, *sea weed* and *fish refuse*. The analyses below will show the composition of one specimen of each of these. And as fish offal and refuse are available in many localities along the sounds and tidal rivers, an analysis is added, which will furnish the means of estimating the manurial value of such materials.

	8	9	10	11	A
Silica, Insoluble,..........	54.42	72.70	1.55	14.48	1.33
" Soluble,............		1.92			
Ox. of Iron and Alum.,....	16.45	5.69	0.53	4.97	
Lime....................	1.18	1.39	4.03	37.57	8.67
Magnesia,.................	0.07	0.05	2.32	21.62	0.67
Potash, ...	1.18	1.82	0.31	2.89	1.54
Soda,....................	0.79	0.35	0.57	5.32	0.66
Phosphoric Acid,...........	0.25	0.13	0.30	2.80	7.78
Sulphuric Acid,.............	1.46	0.33	0.91	8.48	
Organic Matter,........... }	20.92	10.35 }	89.28		78.30
Water,.................. }		3.65 }			0.00
Oxide of Manganese,......	0.54			trace.	
Sulphide of Iron,.........	1.09	0.11			
Common Salt,............	1.63	1.71	0.20	1.87	0.95

No. 8 is a mud from the marshes of Newport river, a few miles above Beaufort, in Carteret county, previously described. This marsh, formed by the filling up of the old river channel, several miles wide, is continually enlarging at the expense of the water-surface; and similar formations, to the extent of hundreds of square miles, are accumulating in very many shallow bays and sounds and rivers near the sea, so that the quantity of such material is unlimited, and the analysis indicates how much more valuable it is for fertilizing purposes, than much of the more expensive articles in common use.

No. 9 is the sea mud or slime, which is deposited in the shoal waters of Beaufort harbor and along the sounds and estuaries of the coast. It is a fine, dark colored salt mud, formed of the silt brought down by the rivers, mixed with decaying vegetable matter, (mostly sea weed and marsh grass,) and animal remains,—of fish, mollusks and all sorts of marine organisms. This material is very abundant along shore, and continually accumulating, and widely available to the agriculture of the coast region.

No. 10 is the ash of sea weed, such as drifts ashore, at Beaufort and elsewhere in immense quantities. Its value is evident from the analysis. In Connecticut and other States north, it is largely used by the farmers, and is made the basis even of a commercial fertilizer. The ash amounts to 10.72 per cent., and its *per centage* composition is given in the next column, No. 11.

There is another valuable ingredient of this sea weed, not given in the above analysis of the mineral contents. The organic constituent includes 9.2 per cent. of nitrogenous matter, which is important as a source of ammonia.

The other column, A, of the table, gives the analysis of dried fish, from which the oil has been removed. It is from the New Jersey Geological Report, and was made for the purpose of showing the fertilizing value of this fish-refuse, which is a very important resource of the farmers within reach of the large fish-oil manufactories of the New Jersey and Long Island shores. The per centage of nitrogen is 7.72. The proportion of oil obtained from the fresh fish is 3.9 per cent. The species of fish is the same which is so abundant in the sounds of North Carolina, called here the *fat-back*,—the *menhaden* or *white fish* of the more northern coast. The analysis of the refuse and offal of the fisheries would not differ materially from this. So that here is evidently another most important and abundant source of manure to the eastern farmer, and a suggestion of profitable enterprise to the manufacturer also.

Japan Clover.—The analyses given below are inserted mainly for the purpose of showing the comparative fertilizing value of this plant, which has lately attracted much notice, both in this state and elsewhere:

	12	B	C
Silica,	1.62	0.15	0.28
Oxide of Iron and Alumina,	0.54		0.07
Lime,	0.99	1.92	1.86
Magnesia,	0.56	0.69	0.38
Potash,	0.88	1.95	1.07
Soda,	0.51	0.09	0.26
Phosphoric Acid,	0.39	0.56	0.38
Sulphuric Acid,	0.20	0.17	0.28
Chlorine,	0 02	0.21	0.30
Organic Matter,	79.78	78.05	80.75
Water,	14.30	16.00	14.30

No. 12 is an analysis of the ash of Japan clover, which might better be called Carolina clover. As this plant has been scattered very widely over the state, from the Cape Fear to the French Broad, and has supplanted to a considerable extent, the broomsedge of the old fields in many sections, it is an important question whether it has any advantage over its predecessor as an improver of the soil. As had been inferred from the fact that it is a *clover* and a deep rooting plant, it has, as the analysis shows, a high fertilizing value, and the important fact remains to be added, that of the organic component 16.6 per cent. is nitrogenons, so that it furnishes a large percentage of nitrogen, the most characteristic fertilizing constituent of the common clover. The percentage composition of the ash of the latter is given in the next column, A, for the purpose of comparison. Its percentage of ash is 5.65, that of Japan clover 5.92. It is worth while to add that the latter has a little advantage also as a forage plant in one respect, that it contains not only a greater proportion of albuminous matter, (by more than one per cent.), but also of fat,—4.15 per cent., against 3.15 for red clover. It is to be noted in the above analysis of red clover, (computed from that given in Wolff's table, as quoted by Prof. Johnson), that the silica and oxide of iron are omitted; and further, that the specimen of Japan clover analyzed, had passed the proper stage, being already in seed, and had become more woody, as well as less rich in some of its best components, from the loss of seeds, which drop in succession, as they ripen.

The third analysis, C, of the preceding table is that of the ash of pea-straw, which is seen to compare very favorably with red clover, the percentage of nitrogenous matter in each being nearly the same. The great value of this species of plant in the eastern sections of the state, whose sandy soils are not adapted to the growth of clover, is too obvious to require more than the statement.

Limestone. This mineral is not as abundant in North Carolina as in many States, constituting, as has been seen, but an insignificant proportion of the mass of its rocky strata. And yet its distribution is such, and its relations to existing and abundant means of transportation, that it is accessible to the greater portion of the state. As has been seen, that part of the eastern region south of the Neuse river is abundantly supplied with Eocene or shell limestone, and to the northern half of that section both this source of supply is open, and the oyster shell heaps of the sounds and bays round to Norfolk.

The middle region of the state lies under the disadvantage of being dependent on railroad transportarion for this most important agricultural necessity, and its source of supply is chiefly the same as for the east, together with the two narrow limestone belts described in another connection, the one extending from Gaston to Stokes, (the outcrops being intermitted between the Catawba and Yadkin), and the other lying wholly in McDowell county, so far as it appears this side of the Blue Ridge, and along the upper valley of the French Broad, beyond that range. The other outcrops, or rather ranges of outcrops, it needs only to re mention, are two; one on the lower French Broad, in Madison county, and the other across Cherokee and a part of Macon, along the course of Valley River mainly.

Analyses of some of the Triassic limestones of Orange show a per centage of 60 to 90 of lime carbonate, and similar beds are found in Chatham and Moore, some of them giving from 40 to 75 per cent. of the carbonates of lime and magnesia.

An examination of certain calcareous concretion, found on the farm of Wm. Alston, Warren county, shows the following composition:

Silica,	0.37
Alumina and Oxide of Iron,	2.17
Lime,	41.32
Magnesia,	0.90
Potash,	0.31
Soda,	0.32
Carbonic Acid,	33.46
Organic Matter,	0.27

Such concretions are common among the clays resulting from the decomposition of the dolerytic traps, and of the amphibolitic rocks of the Archæan series in this state; and they are sometimes sufficiently abundant to constitute a resource for lime, in cases where limestone is inaccessible. They are of notably frequent occurrence about Shiloh Church in Granville, in the rich earths of the Grassy Creek and Spewmarrow Creek, and common in the central (Greensboro) granite belt.

SECTION II—METALLIC ORES.

IRON ORES.

The ores of Iron are very widely distributed in this state, their occurrence being not only co-extensive with the area of the Archæan (or Azoic) rocks, but extending over a part of the Mesozoic, and even into the Quaternary. And these occurrences include all the principal kinds of ore, Magnetite, Hematite, Limonite and Siderite, and most of their varieties and modifications. But as many of these forms occur in association or close proximity, it will avoid confusion to consider them by districts,—to group them geographically. We begin with the most easterly occurrences. But for the benefit of those who are not familiar with the mineralogy of the subject, and who may not have access to authorities, it may be worth while to state that Magnetite, (*magnetic iron ore, gray ore, black ore,*) a granular, hard, dark to black, heavy mineral, contains, when pure, 72.4 per cent. of iron; Hematite, (*specular iron, red hematite, red iron ore*), 70 per cent.; Limonite, (*brown hematite, brown iron ore, brown ochre, bog iron ore, &c.,*) very nearly 60 per cent.; Siderite, *spathic ore, (carbonate of iron)*, 48.28 per cent. These ores are never found in a state of purity in workable beds, but contain various impurities, earthy or rocky, in different proportions,—alumina, silica, lime, magnesia, manganese, &c.; so that practically that is considered a good ore which yields 40 to 50 per cent. of iron in the furnace.

Limonite Ores of the East—The clayey, sandy and earthy accumulations of the eastern section, which have been previously described as Quaternary, contain in many places a rough brown ore, more or less earthy, or sandy, either in beds 2 to 3, or 4 feet in thickness, or more frequently in sheets, or layers of irregularly shaped lumps or nodules. One of the most considerable of these deposits occurs in the southern end of Nash county near the Wilson line. It is in the form of a horizontal, continuous bed, of a loose, spongy texture and rusty brown color, except in a few points, where it becomes more compact and of a submetallic lustre. It lies on the margin of Tossnot Swamp. The thickness is 2 to 3 feet, and its extent horizontally about 50 yards by 150. It is known as the Blomary Iron Mine, from the fact that iron had been made from this ore in a Catalan forge, a few miles south, during the war of 1812. Iron was also made here during the Confederate war in a furnace erected on the spot. Mr. W. H. Tappey, one of the proprietors, informed me that "the iron made was of excellent quality, soft and very strong." And there is a tradition in the neighborhood that the forge iron, previously referred to, was a sort of natural steel. The following is the analysis of what appeared to be a fair sample of the bed, selected lately:

Silica,	15.06
Alumina,	0.55
Sesquioxide of Iron,	60.74
Protoxide of Iron,	0.24
Sulphide of Iron,	0.06
Oxide of Manganese,	1.56
Lime,	1.43
Magnesia,	1.54
Sulphuric Acid,	0.03
Phosphoric Acid,	0.11
Organic Matter and Water,	15.58

Which gives Iron 42.73 per cent. This analysis places the ore among the best of its class.

A second deposit, reported to be abundant in superficial nodules and irregular lumps, is found in the southern part of Duplin county near Wallace, on the farm of D. T. Boney. The following is a partial analysis of an average specimen from a box of about 50 pounds sent to the Museum:

Silica,	7.59
Oxide of Iron,	77.03
Sulphur,	0.05
Phosphorus,	0.02; giving
Metalic Iron,	53.93

The ore is often in quite large and tolerably compact lumps, of a reddish brown color, and slightly magnetic.

Another bed of the same character and appearance, except in the size of the nodules, which are rather small, occurs in a field about 2 miles north of Rocky Point in New Hanover.

Specimens of the same sort have been frequently sent to the Museum from other points east,—Edgecombe, Pitt, Halifax and Robeson, for example; showing that this kind of ore is of common occurrence in that region.

Hematites of Halifax and Granville.—On the hills fronting the Roanoke, less than a mile below Gaston, are several outcrops of hematite ore. There are two principal beds, of which the lower only has been opened. The ore is granular, for the most part, and of the variety known as specular, but contains a considerable percentage of magnetic grains disseminated through it. On the south side of the river, the bed has been exposed for several rods on the upper slope of the hill, at an elevation of about 100 to 150 feet above the surface of the water. The ore is generally slaty, impregnating and replacing the argillaceous and quartzitic and chloritic strata which constitute the Huronian formation at the locality. This lower bed is double, another parallel outcrop appearing at the distance of about 100 yards. The strike is N. 20° E., and the dip eastward 80°. The principal bed is about 20 inches thick at the surface. There is a re-appearance of it on the other hill front about a mile distant, on the north side of the river, the ore being of the same character, but a little less slaty. It gave on analysis 63.76 per cent. of Iron, and 0.09 of phosphorus.

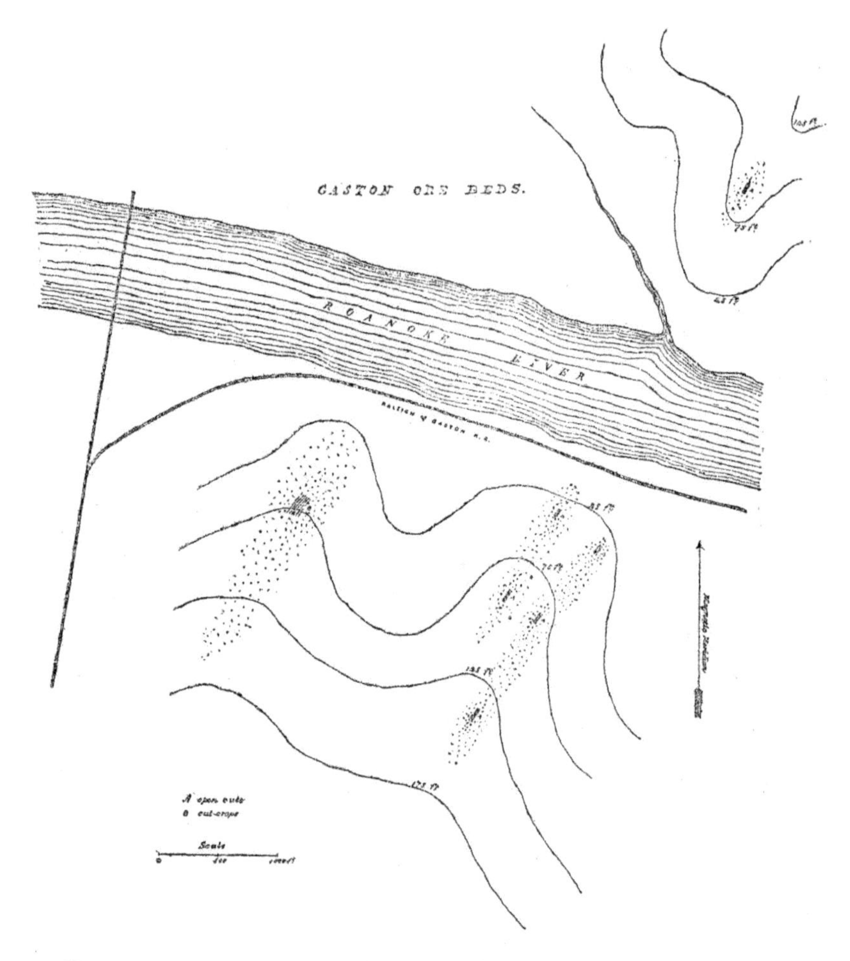

The above cut shows the relations of the different outcrops to each other and to the topography, and also a larger outcrop of another bed nearly half a mile northwest. The course of this last bed is marked by numerous surface fragments scattered quite widely. The ore, in this case, is more compact and less slaty; the inclosing rock is a gray gneissoid quartzite.

The analyses of both these beds are added below:

	3	4
Silica,	9.10	10.12
Alumina,	6.18	

Oxide of Iron,	83.96	
Lime,	0.22	
Phosphorus,	0.00	0.05
Sulphur,	0.03	0.08
Metallic Iron,	58.73	53.31

The upper bed, last described, is represented by No. 3, the lower by No. 4. These analyses were made by Mr. G. Lobdell for the owners, by whose courtesy a copy of them was obtained for this report. About 5 miles southward from the above locality the same bed makes its appearance on the farm of Mr. Hines; here, however, it is highly magnetic, fine grained and dense, although still showing the decidedly slaty structure of the first of the Gaston beds. At this point it is reported as 3 to 4 feet thick.

These ores are of conspicuous purity and obviously adapted to the manufacture of the higher grades of iron and of steel. And there is evidently a range of ore-beds here of considerable extent.

In Granville county, about a mile north of Tar River, and the same distance eastward from Fishing Creek, is an outcrop of a coarse, granular, somewhat slaty magnetic ore, having very much the appearance of that of the upper bed at Gaston. The rock is a feldspathic talco-quartzitic and chloro-quartzitic slate. This bed is revealed only by the numerous fragments scattered over the surface through the forest for several rods along the roadside. This ore is in a small triangular patch of Huronian slates, intercalated between the older rocks of the region. It is reported that there are other outcrops of iron ore near Rainey's Mill, and also in the neighborhood of Lyon's Mill, but I have not seen either of them.

Iron Ores of Johnston and Wake.—There is, according to Dr. Emmons, "a large deposit" of limonite four miles west of Smithfield; the specimens brought to the museum by Mr. Guest, owner of the land, resemble very closely the bog ore of Duplin; they are more or less sandy and earthy, irregular lumps, or nodules.

Another "bluff" of limonite is referred to by Emmons as found at Whitaker's, seven miles southwest of Raleigh, in Wake county. These last two are in the Huronian slates. And hand specimens of very coarsely crystalline magnetite of ten to fifteen pounds weight, associated with syenyte, are found within a mile of Raleigh; and compact hematite also occurs in veins in the same vicinity. These and other specimens of these species and of limonite are from different parts of the county, and are from the surface, as no openings have been made; but they indicate the very common occurrence of this mineral.

Iron Ores of Chatham and Orange.—One of the best known and most important iron mines of this region is on the borders of Harnett, the *Buckhorn Mine.* It is about seven miles below the forks of the Cape Fear, on a hill nearly 200 feet high, overlooking the river from the left bank. Its location will be easily understood from the accompanying topographical sketch. The ore occurs as a bed, capping the hill and sloping from the river, with a dip of 20° to 25° towards the northwest. It is massive at the outcrop, and breaks out in large angular blocks. The lower portion of the bed, which contains much manganese and less iron in proportion, is of a mottled gray and dull reddish color at the summit, and at the distance of two or three hundred yards along the slope, is a light colored and gray and spotted (black and dirty white,) ferriferous, manganesian slate. Occasional sheets of laminated black oxide of manganese occur, one or two inches in thickness. Some parts of the bed are slightly magnetic. The outcrop, or rather the terminal face of the bed at the opening, on the summit of the hill, is shown in the annexed diagram. The thickness is about 36 feet at this point, and diminishes to 20 at the lower quarries, 200 to 300 yards distant.

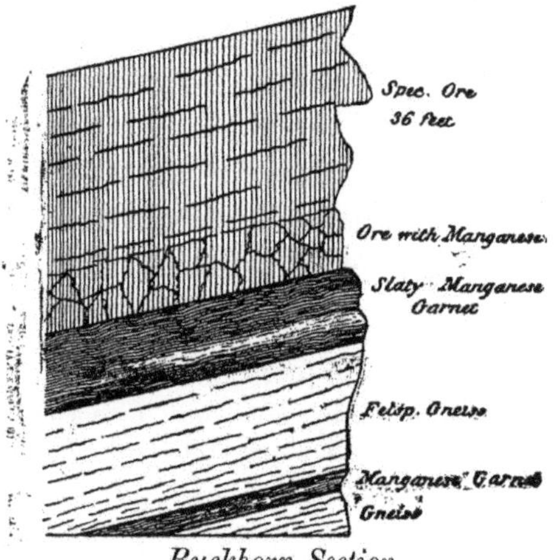

Buckhorn Section.

The ore is properly described as specular; it is of a dull, dark gray to blackish color, subcrystalline structure, and uneven fracture. The streak is dark red. Occasional fragments of the ore show a tendency to lamination, and in such cases the divisional planes are commonly coated with mica crystals. The character of this ore is very like that of the Iron Mountain, Mo., and its extent and mode of occurrence strongly suggest the Pilot-Knob. It is at least equal to either of these notable iron ore

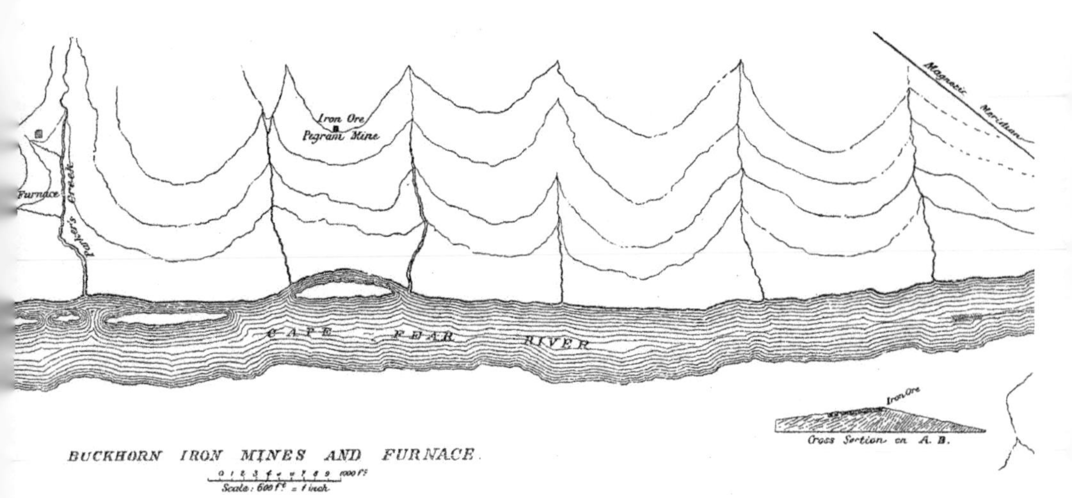

BUCKHORN IRON MINES AND FURNACE.

deposits in quantity, and is equally pure, and has the advantage of both in the presence of large percentages of manganese, and the capacity to produce *spiegeleisen* without admixture of other ores. It is not difficult to foresee that this must speedily become the nucleus of a large iron manufacturing interest; especially when the remarkable facilities for manufacturing, in the way of water power, (heretofore noted,) and the proximity of coal in abundance, are taken into account.

The rocks of this region are slaty, gray gneiss and mica slate, with occasional patches of massive light gray granite.

The rock which underlies the ore is a light-colored, felspathic slaty gneiss, which readily decomposes. The neighboring hills, at the distance of half a mile, both north and south, are reported to show many scattered fragments of the same ore on the surface; and on the right bank of the river, on nearly the same level with the Buckhorn Mine, at the distance of about one mile southwest, is the *Douglass Mine.* This is a recurrence of the Buckhorn bed, on the scale and with the features of its lower exposures, being more schistose in structure, some of the strata being in fact simply gneiss and mica slate, with disseminated grains and laminæ of hematite (and magnetite), and the lower strata passing into a slaty manganesian silicate. The thickness, not very well exposed, seems to be ten to twelve feet. Angular fragments of dark, dense, granular ore, with a black, manganese stain, are scattered over several acres of the hill top, indicating a wide extension of the bed. From the facts stated, it will be apparent that these different beds are mere remnant fragments of an ancient and very extensive deposit which has been almost entirely removed by denudation, and carried away by the erosive action of the river.

About 1 mile north of the Buckhorn mine is a small vein about 1 foot thick, of a highly magnetic ore. Its strike is N. 60° and dip eastward 30°. The gangue is an epidotic quartzite. There are two openings on the vein, called the Pegram Mine. An analysis of this ore for the owners by Mr. C. E. Buck, gave 56.57 per cent. of iron and 1.51 of titanic acid. This group of mines is worked by the American Iron and Steele Company, who have erected a charcoal furnace, the first of 8 proposed, at the Buckhorn Locks, nearly 2 miles above the ore bank. They have already expended upwards of $300,000 in opening the navigation of the river for a distance of some 40 miles above the ore bank, through the coal deposits, and they have also repaired the Endor furnace and put it in blast, and have been making a very superior car-wheel iron. The product is mostly a spiegeleisen, of which the following partial analyses by Mr. Lobdell, will show the peculiarities:

	5	6	7
Manganese,	4.573	6.50	4.88
Silicon,	0.233	0.14	0.38
Sulphur,	0.015	0.009	
Phosphorus,	0.051	0.12	0.095

The copy of these analyses was accompanied by the remark, "The above samples were made while the furnace was running on ordinary iron, no attempt having been made to produce spiegeleisen. The phosphorus and sulphur were reduced from the fluxes employed, as the Buckhorn ore used contained only very slight traces of these impurities."

The origin of this peculiar and valuable product, which was altogether accidental, will be apparent on the inspection of the analyses given below. These were made for the company in the course of their operations, by G. G. Lobdell, of the firm, and C. E. Buck, of Wilmington, Del., and by the Chemist of the Pennsylvania Steel Company.

	8	9	10	11	12
Silica,	14.45	5.65	12.80	30.50	7.50
Alumina,		0.80	5.20	19.20	8.49
Oxide of Maganese,		trace		22.80	7.52
Phosphorus,	trace		trace	0.02	0.04
Sulphur,	0.06		trace	0.03	0.02
Iron,	56.70	66.50	54.15	18.41	55.00

Of these, Nos. 8, 9 and 10 are from the upper and main portion of the Buckhorn bed, and No. 11 from the lower manganesian section. This last analysis suggests the presence, in this part of the bed, of the mineral knebelite, a characteristic ore of the most famous Swedish spiegeleisen mines. No. 12 is the Douglass ore, on the other side of the river.

Besides the localities already mentioned, a number of additional outcrops of ore have been noted, mostly magnetic; one for example, 2 miles north of Buckhorn, (at Dewer's) yielding 57.77 per cent. of iron, (no phosphorus or sulphur), and 3 or 4 others in a southwest direction, for 10 miles, to the head waters of Little River,—at McNeil's, Dallrymple's and Buchanan's; analyses as follows, respectively:

Iron,	52.90	36.47	53.25
Sulphur,	0.05	0.05	0.04
Phosphorus,	0.12	0.11	0.57

Analyses by Lobdell.

Near Haywood, in the angle formed by the junction of the Haw and Deep rivers, in the red sandstone of the Triassic, there has been opened a series of parallel beds of a red-ochreous earthy ore, on the lands of Dr. Smith. The only bed exposed at the time of my visit, was 20 to 25 inches thick, dipping southeast with the sandstone, 20° to 30°. The ore has a rough likeness to the "Clinton" or "Fossil ore" of New York, &c., and the "Dystone" of Tennessee, but has a much coarser and more irregular texture, and is composed of rounded concretionary masses of various sizes from that of the Clinton grains to ½ and ¾ inch and upward. It is commonly more or less compacted into conglomeritic masses, often of the entire thickness of the bed, but frequently it is loosely and slightly compacted, and when thrown out, crumbles to a heap of very coarse gravel. The ore is partly limonite, but seems to be largely changed to red hematite. The following analyses of samples taken from different parts of the beds, whose outcrops extend over an area of several acres, will exhibit the character of the ore:

	13	14
Silica,.		23.50
Alumina,		2.54
Sesqui Oxide of Iron,	69.73	67.50
Protoxide of Iron,	0.84	
Bisulphide of Iron,	0.17	
Phosphoric Acid,	0.10	
Lime.		0.90
Magnesia,		0.24
Water and loss,		5.03; giving
Iron,	49.56	47,25

The second of these analyses represents the ore as it occurs on the lands of Mr. Richard Smith, adjoining the preceding. This ore makes its appearance again about a mile from Sanford, some 12 miles distant, where it was opened and worked to some extent during the late war. Only one bed was exposed here, which is about 20 inches thick. The ore is easily dug and shoveled from the bed and crumbles into a heap of very coarse, reddish-brown gravel, a rough sort of *shot ore*. The preceding analyses will nearly enough represent the composition of this also.

The next ores demanding attention are the *Black Band* and *Ball ore*, or "kidney ore" of the coal measure. These are earthy and calcareous carbonates of iron, imbedded in the black carbonaceous shales which enclose the coal, or interstratified with the coal itself. These ores seem to be co-extensive with the coal on Deep River, outcropping everywhere with it, and at several places outside of its limits. Two seams are shown in the sections (pp. 143 and 144), and there is a third in the bottom shales, not penetrated at the Gulf, but shown in the Egypt section (p. 142), as accompanying the lower coal, 30 feet below the main seam.

Emmons also speaks of another seam of argillaceous carbonate as occurring at the depth of 230 feet in the shaft at Egypt, and four occurrences of it are indicated as ball ore in the Egypt section. Emmons says of this argillaceous carbonate, "It contains 33 per cent. of metallic iron; the surface ores being altered contain 50 per cent.," and he describes it as occurring "in balls, or in continuous beds." About the Gulf it occurs in rounded flattish masses, 5 or 6 to 8 or 10 inches in diameter. They are dense, uncrystalline and heavy, of a light gray to drab color, and are pretty thickly distributed in parallel layers of one to two or three feet thickness. An analysis by Prof. Schæffer, as given in Admiral Wilkes' report to the Secretary of the Navy in 1858, is as follows: protoxide of iron 40 per cent., silica 13, earthy matter 13, carbonaceous matter 34. This is evidently a black band ore. The following is an analysis (by Buck) of the ball-ore proper, as it occurs at the Gulf, and such as was used extensively and successfully as a flux during the late war:

	15
Silica,	6.04
Alumina,	0.48
Protoxide of Iron,	14.51
Sesquioxide of Iron,	1.63
Lime,	29.57
Magnesia,	6.51
Carbonic Acid,	38.30
Phosphoric Acid,	0.92
Sulphuric Acid,	0.19
Organic Matter,	1.45
Water,	0.40

Which gives 52.80 per cent. of carbonate of lime, and 13.60 of carbonate of magnesia. Its adaptation to the purposes of a flux is obvious.

There are many outcrops of ferriferous limestone in the neighborhood of Egypt (and the Endor furnace), among others this, near Dowd's Saw Mill:

Lime,............................	31.68
Magnesia,........................	0.79
Sesquioxide of Iron,.............	9.60 ; no sulphur or phosphorus.

But oyster shells from the Tertiary bluffs below Fayetteville, and limestone from the Eocene beds about Wilmington, (previously described), have been also used as fluxes in the furnaces of the region, and on account of their greater purity and abundance, and their ready accessibility and cheap transportation, will doubtless become the chief resource for fluxing.

The seam of *blackband* between the main coal beds in the Egypt shaft, is stated by Wilkes to be 16 inches, the lower one to consist of two thicknesses of 3 feet each, separated by a thin seam of coal between. He adds, "This ore is readily distinguished from a slate by its brownish black color." The analysis of this ore by Dr. Jackson, published in Emmons' report, gives

Carbon,............................	31.30
Peroxide of Iron (Protoxide ?)	47.50
Silica,............................	9.00
Volatile Matter,...................	8.81
Sulphur,...........................	3.39

Emmons adds, "The roasted ore gives sulphur 0.89 per cent." An analysis by Schæffer for Wilkes, gives only 17 per cent. of iron, and 42 of carbonaceous matter; specific gravity 2.12.

The following analyses of samples selected from a recent opening at the Gulf, represented in the section given on p. 144, have been just completed for the survey by Mr. Hanna:

	16	17	18	19
Specific Gravity,.........	2.361	3.150	2.110	2.110
Silica, ...	9.154	7.089	34.380	5.188
Alumina,..................	4.244	0.127	19.638	4.060
Protoxide of Iron,........	19.419	33.802	12.361	9.614
Sesquioxide of Iron,......	0.000	1.755	1.430	0.938
Sulphide of Iron,.........	10.485	2.145	2.023	7.146
Oxide of Manganese,.......	1.750	1.980	0.995	1.500
Lime,.....................	9.520	12.672	3.100	14.040
Magnesia,.................	1.490	1.170	1.220	0.863
Alkalies,.................	0.000	0.000	0.000	0.000

Sulphuric Acid,...........	trace,	0.170	trace,	0.152
Phosphoric Acid,..........	4.960	6.820	0.730	6.300
Volatile Matter,.............	22.065	27.215	14.913	15.009
Carbon,.................	16.213	4.726	6.562	34.473
Water,..................	0.700	0.300	2.588	0.717
	100.000	100.000	100.000	100.000
Ash, or Roasted Ore,......	60.475	72.070	76.902	48.571

Of which the composition is as follows:

	20	21	22	23
Silica,....................	15.137	9.849	44.740	10.684
Alumina,.................	7.018	0.178	25.527	8.359
Sesquioxide of Iron,........	46.360	56.562	20.922	33.252
Sulphide of Iron,..........	0.909	0.000	0.788	0.530
Oxide of Manganese,.......	2.895	2.749	1.294	3.089
Lime,....................	15.742	17.585	4.108	28.914
Magnesia,................	2.464	1.624	1.587	1.777
Sulphuric Acid,...........	1.273	1.989	0.085	0.421
Phosphoric Acid,.........	8.202	9.464	0.949	12.974
	100.000	100.000	100.000	100.000
Which give,				
Metallic Iron,.............	33.032	39.593	14.645	23.619
Sulphur,.................	0.839	0.800	0.319	.360
Phosphorus,.............	3.581	4.131	0.474	5.664

No. 1 is the lower stratum of the black-band between the coal, about 18 inches thick; No. 3 is the upper and earthy part of the same, 6 to 10 inches. No. 2 is the seam, about 12 inches, lying above the coal and separated from it by 16 inches of fire clay. This is a hard, black, slaty ore, with occasional balls still more dense. No. 4 is the stratum, about 3 feet above the coal, which consists of black, heavy, very tough, concretionary lumps of ore. The quantity of phosphorus which these beds contain is very notable, and is, of course, due to their highly fossiliferous character. And yet not only were there no fossil bones visible, as in the Egypt beds, but no identifiable organisms of any description, not even a shell. Of course the high percentage of this element excludes these ores from the manufacture of wrought iron. They must await the perfecting of the new industry of "phosphorus steel;" or the discovery of a practicable method for the elimination of this injurious ingredient. With this exception these ores are well constituted, containing the necessary amounts of carbon, of flux and of manganese, for the manufacture of iron very cheaply, by judicious mixing of the ores obtainable in the immediate neighborhood. It is not probable that this phosphatic fossiliferous character will follow the ore-beds and appear at the other outcrops in the same force; it is a character likely to be local. An investigation of these beds at other points is therefore very important and will be instituted as soon as practicable. Such ores are, however, valuable for casting. Outside of the line of outcrops of the coal, and within a few rods of it, is a bed of limonite belonging to the underlying shales. The thickness is 2 to 3 feet, and it is traceable for a considerable distance along the surface. Probably it is the result of the weathering of some of the argillaceous carbonates already described. And a similar outcrop has been noticed, and the bed partly stripped, at a point 1½ miles southeast of Egypt, on Pretty Creek, known as the McIver ore-bed. It is 20 inches thick. This is a very slaty and somewhat shaly limonite, with occasional masses of ore of considerable size, and is embedded in shales. It is obviously the result of the oxidation of one of the black-band or argillaceous carbonate seams already described, but it is in the forest, and its exact geological relations are concealed, as well by vegetation as by overlying earth. An analysis of a sample of this ore, by Buck, for the Company above referred to, gives the following result:

Metallic Iron,	47.59
Sulphur,	0.14
Phosphorus,	0.94

The Evans vein is about 6 miles north of the Gulf, on the Graham road. It is 6 feet thick. This ore is a hematite, non-crystalline, scarcely sub-metallic, hardness 6 to 6½, jaspery, non-magnetic, dark gray to bluish black, streak dark-red, fracture sub-conchoidal. The country is (Huronian) talcoid and chloritic argillite, which is a sort of spotted slate conglomerate, in the hill a few hundred yards beyond. Wilkes gives the following analysis, (by Schæffer):

Peroxide of Iron,	96.4
Silica,	2.1
Earthy Matter,	1.5

The ore is scattered abundantly in fragments over the surface of several acres. Emmons traced the vein three quarters of a mile. He speaks also of another vein of hematite (specular, crystalline,) on the neighboring farm of Mr. Glass, which was revealed only by surface fragments; and also of "a magnetic ore of fine quality on the plantation of T. Unthanks, 2 or 3 miles beyond the Evans place;" and another of the same class at Heading's, near Ore Hill. Another locality is noted by both Emmons and Wilkes as containing a bed of reddish-brown ore, which is magnetic. It is represented as 2½ feet thick at the Tysor place, and as occurring at various other points. The analysis quoted by Wilkes from Emmons, gives,

Peroxide of Iron, ...	79.72
Carbon, ...	7.37
Silica, ...	4.00
Water, ...	8.80; containing
Iron, ...	61.

But the most noted iron locality in Chatham county is known as *Ore Hill*. The accompanying plate shows the topography and general relations, and (approximately) the situation of the veins, which are numerous and lie at various angles with the meridian and with the horizon. The rock is a talco-quartzose slate, knotted and toughened with much tremolite. The ore is limonite, with the exception of one vein near the top and back of the hill, which is a hematite, (in part specular), and much resembling the Evans ore. There is much of this ore on the surface in scattered fragments, indicating a vein of considerable extent, which, however, had not been exposed. Most of the other veins have been opened, but the pits and tunnels were so much filled and fallen in that no accurate measurements could be taken at the time of my visit last year. But it was easy to see that two or three of them were very large,—10, 15 feet and upwards. The ore is very spongy, porous, scoriaceous, botryoidal, mammillary, stalactitic, tabular, foliated, dendritic, and of many fantastic and nondescript forms. The workmen state that there are large cavities (vuggs) in some parts of the veins.

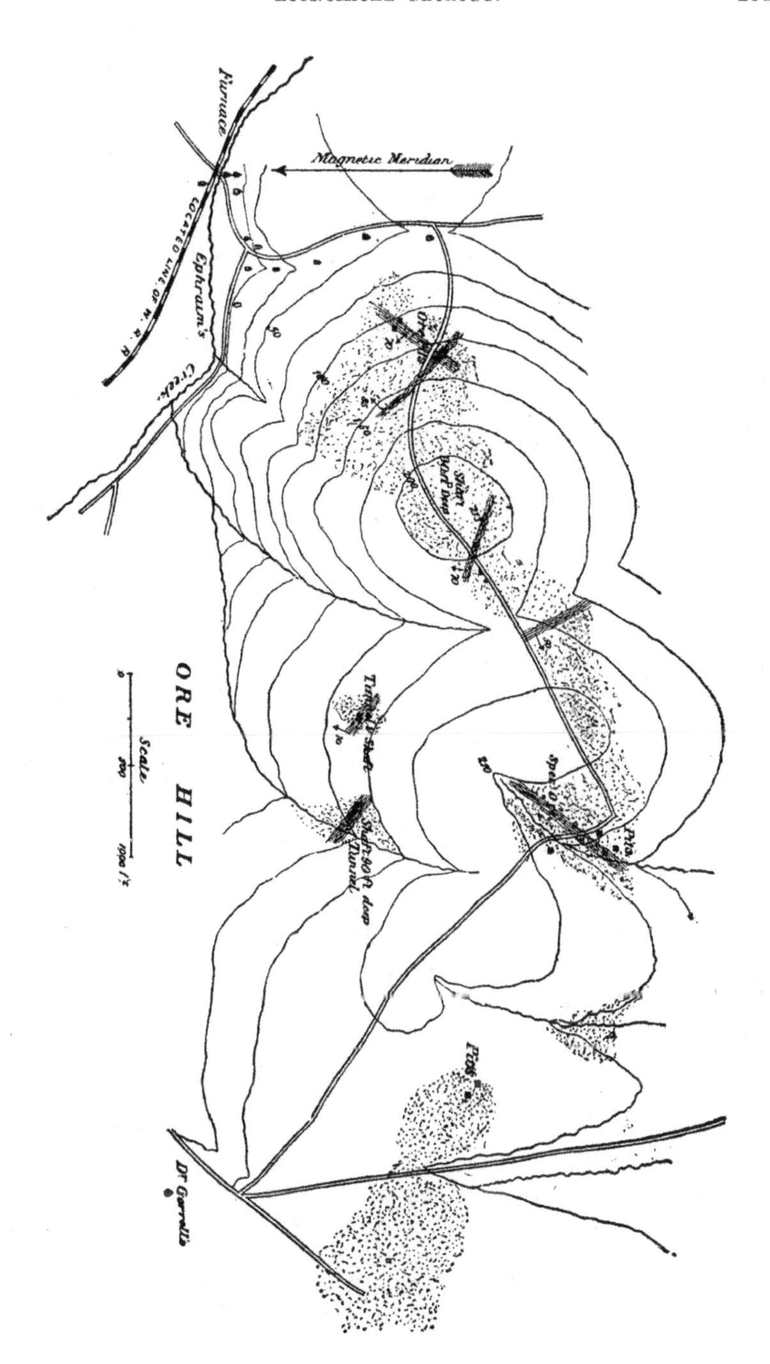
Furnace
Magnetic Meridian
Ephraim's Creek
ORE HILL
Scale
500
Dr Garrett's

The analyses below are of samples from the 90 feet shaft, nearest the hematite vein, and may be considered as fairly representative:

	24	25
Silica,...................................	1.42	3.79
Alumina,...................................		
Sesquioxide of Iron,.....................	82.02	83.69
Protoxide " "		0.11
Lime,...................................	1.19	
Magnesia,.................................	0.11	
Phosphoric Acid,.........................	0.00	trace.
Sulphuric Acid,.........................	0.00	0.77
Water,...................................	15.26	
	100.00	
Mettallic Iron,.........................	57.41	58.67

The first of these analyses was made by Chatard, for Dr. Genth, the second by Mr. Hanna. This ore was worked on a considerable scale during the American Revolution, and again during the late civil war, and the iron is reported to have been of good quality; and it is obviously an ore very readily smelted. The presence of the hematite vein and the proximity of the ball ore, which was successfully used as a flux in the last working of the furnace, furnish admirable conditions for advantageous iron manufacture. And it is gratifying to be able to state that there is a prospect of the immediate development of the property by the Philadelphia and Canadian capitalists who have lately come into possession. Negotiations for the completion of the railroad from Egypt are nearly concluded, and for the first time the needed facilities for transportation from the mines to the seaboard, and between the different ores and the fuel, are abcut to be realized.

Besides the ores above described, there are many others, of which specimens have been brought or forwarded to the Museum, from various parts of the county and region, magnetite, hematite and limonite, representing veins and deposits of whose extent I have no information. It is worth while to mention two of such specimens, one from Chatham, (between Lockville and Endor), and the other from the adjoining county of Moore, Governor's Creek, as they are almost the only examples of the species of ore called *jaspery clay iron stone* yet found in the State. The former contains 48.92 per cent. of iron, phosphorus 0.39.

A fine quality of magnetic ore, dense, mettallic and very pure, is found on the east side of Haw River and about 2 miles distant, at the foot of Tyrrell's Mountain on the farm of Mr. Snipes. The vein has not been fully exposed, but is reported to be 3 or 4 feet. It is in syenyte, and has an epidotic gangue.

The analysis (made by Lobdell) is as follows:

Silica,	1.62
Alumina,	6.60
Magnetic Oxide of Iron,	88.41
Manganese,	0.56
Lime,	trace
Magnesia,	0.85
Phosphoric Acid,	0.00
Sulphur,	0.13
Metallic Iron,	63.49

A very fine micaceous hematite is found near the mouth of Collins' Creek a few miles above, in Orange county. It has not been explored, but surface fragments are reported to be abundant.

But the most notable ore bank yet opened in this county, is that at Chapel Hill. It is a very dense, steel-gray, hematite, (specular in part), with slight magnetic indications. The accompanying diagram shows its relations. The vein is found on a hill one mile north from Chapel Hill, and more than 200 feet above the creek at its base. The rock is a gray granite and syenyte, but the vein is carried by a much-jointed, fine grained, ferruginous, slaty quartzite of several rods breadth, the iron-bearing portion of it, the vein proper, being 7 to 10 feet at the main shaft, and suddenly enlarging near the summit of the hill, just beyond the second shaft, to 25 and 30 feet. The hill top is covered with angular fragmentsof the ore of all sizes, up to more than 100 pounds weight.

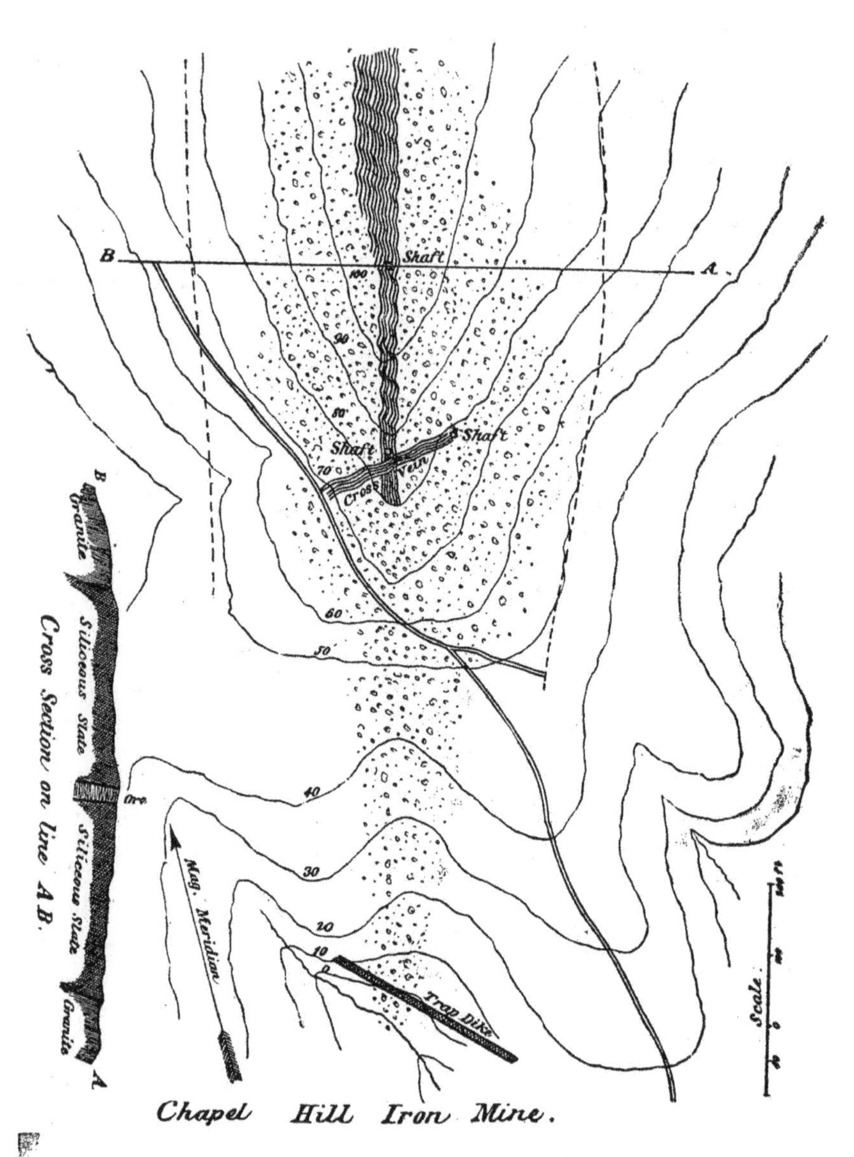

Chapel Hill Iron Mine.

The character of the ore is shown by the following analysis :

	26
Silica,	2.63
Alumina,	1.68

Protoxide of Iron,	2.45
Sesquioxide, "	91.24
Oxide of Manganese,	0.34
Lime,	0.56
Magnesia.	0.00
Phosphoric Acid,	0.04
Sulphur,	0.11
	99.05
Iron,	65.77

The ore is of notable purity, and the practical tests to which it has been subjected have confirmed the indications of the analysis, that it is an ore of high grade; and the quantity is very great. The vein, as shown in the section, has a dip to the west at an angle which is a little short of 90°. A second vein of the same character 5 or 6 feet thick, crosses the main vein near the first shaft as shown in the diagram. The ore becomes poorer as the vein is followed beyond the summit of the hill northward, until at the distance of 150 yards beyond the upper shaft, the quartzite predominates and the ore becomes poor. The distance of this mine from railroad is less than 9 miles, and the day is not distant when the superior quality of the ore will overcome this sole obstacle in the way of its profitable working.

There are surface indications on the neighboring hills, both north and south, for several miles, which show that this vein has a considerable extension; and in fact it may be considered as a continuation of the hematite veins of Deep River. And a magnetic ore makes its appearance about 20 miles northeastward, 3 miles beyond the upper forks of the Neuse River in the southeast corner of Orange county, on Knapp of Reeds Creek, on the farm of Mr. Jos. Woods. The rock here is clay slate, more or less chloritic and quartzitic, and thin bedded. The ore is slaty, and is in fact, an impregnation of the chloritic argillaceous quartzite with granular magnetite and hematite. The ore is very extensively scattered over a succession of hills, for about a mile, in a northeast direction. The ore bed outcrops at one point for a few rods, where it appears to be about 3 feet thick, and has a strike N. 40° E., and dips at an angle of 70° to the northwest. The bed seems to be duplicated towards the northeastern termination, another line of fragments marking the course of a parallel vein several rods to the east of the former. This last is associated with a bright vermillion red, and a banded, black and red jasper. The ore is of good quality, as will be seen by the following analysis by Dr. Genth:

	27	
Silica,................................	20.38	
Magnetic Oxide of Iron,..................	75.69	
Magnesia,................................	1.26	
Phosphoric Acid,.........................	0.05	
Water, &c.,..............................	2.62;	which gives
Metallic Iron,...........................	54.81	

An analysis of another sample (by a different chemist), gave iron 56.50.

Hand specimens of very fine magnetite and specular ore have been brought to the Museum from many other parts of Orange county, but no information has been received as to their quantity.

At Mt. Tirzah, in the southeast corner of Person, near the Orange line, there is a vein of hematite, (specular) from which iron was made to some extent during the war. The vein is described as about 6 feet thick. The specimen sent to the Museum indicates a very fine ore, resembling that at Buckhorn.

The ores of Montgomery and Randolph belong properly (geologically) to the Chatham range; they are found in the same great slate belt, (Huronian), that constitutes the most notable feature of the middle region of the state, both geologically and mineralogically. The best known of these ores is found near Franklinville, Randolph county. And another vein has been opened near Ashboro, both of specular hematite. Some of the strongest and most highly prized iron obtained during the war came from this locality. It was all devoted to the manufacture of shafts and other machinery for the Steam Rams (iron-clads) and the like. Dr. Emmons describes an occurrence of hematite of apparently considerable extent 7 miles southwest of Troy, in Montgomery county; he says it is free from sulphur and a very pure ore. Another occurrence of ore,—magnetite, is noted by him 4 miles north of Troy. It is found with talcose slate, and is soft and friable, and contains seams of hematite.

Iron Ores of Guilford County. One of the most remarkable and persistent ranges of iron ore in the state crosses the county of Guilford in a northeast and southwest direction, passing about 10 miles northwest of Greensboro, near Friendship. It extends from the head waters of Abbott's Creek, in Davidson county, entirely across Guilford to Haw River, in Rockingham, a distance of some 30 miles, making its appearance on nearly every plantation, and indeed almost every hillside in the range.

The ore is granular magnetite, and is every where titaniferous. It is usually rather coarse grained and frequently associated with crystals of chlorite in small seams and scattered bunches. The ore is in the form of beds, which partake of all the foldings and fractures and irregularities of bedding to be expected in a region where only the oldest metamorphic rocks are found. The deposits lie along, and just west of the line of junction of what is provisionally set down as the lower and upper Laurentian series of granitic rocks, as marked on the map. It may be here noted that in coloring the map, this line was placed a little too far north in this region. There is a second, but much more interrupted range of ore parallel to the one just described, and lying a few miles to the northwest. I visited this region in 1871, in company with Dr. F. A. Genth, who was at that time Chemist and Mineralogist to the Survey.

The entire range was taken into the tour, and specimens carefully selected from many points by Dr. G. for analysis, so as to ascertain the average character, as well as to eliminate the local peculiarities of the beds. Fortunately, an association of Pennsylvania capitalists, the North Carolina Centre Iron and Mining Company, had invested largely along this range of ores, and had recently had the beds opened by trenching, at a great many points, so as to expose very well the general features of the deposits. And still more fortunately, the Company had procured the services of Dr. J. P. Lesley, now the Director of the Pennsylvania Geological Survey; and this distinguished Geologist had recently made a very careful study of the whole range, in all its bearings. I have before me his report, and shall give some of the more important points of his results. I owe it to the courtesy of the Philosophical Society of Philadelphia, of which Dr. Lesley is Secretary, that I am able to use the plates also, which were engraved for the illustration of his very elaborate and valuable report. Whatever is found below on the subject of this range of ores, in quotation marks, is taken from this report, unless it is otherwise stated.

It is questioned by many geologists whether all our North Carolina metamorphic rocks are not altered Silurian and Devonian, like most of those of New England. I am glad to have the support of so eminent an authority in the view presented in the map published some two years ago and maintained in this report, that these azoic and crystalline rocks of Middle North Carolina are Archæan of the most ancient type and date.

"This part of North Carolina is occupied by some of the oldest rocks known; the same rocks which hold the iron ore beds of Harford county, Maryland, and Chester county, Pennsylvania, and the gold ores of Georgia, North Carolina, Virginia and Canada. The gold mines of Guilford county, N. C., are opened alongside of, and not more than ten or twelve miles distant from, the Tuscarora iron belt. Both the gold and iron range continuously, (with one break in New Jersey,) all the way from Quebec, in Canada, to Montgomery, Ala. The gold and iron bearing rocks are: granites, gneissoid sandstones and mica slates, all very much weathered and decomposed; and that to a depth of many fathoms beneath the present surface. The solid granites are decomposed least, the mica slates most. All contain iron, which has been peroxidized and hydrated, in the process of decomposition of the whole formation, and dyes the country soil with a deep red tint. The surface of the country is a smooth, soft, undulating plain, broken by gentle vales, the bottoms of which are never more than 100 feet below the plain, and commonly not more than half that depth."

GUILDFORD IRON ORE RANGE.

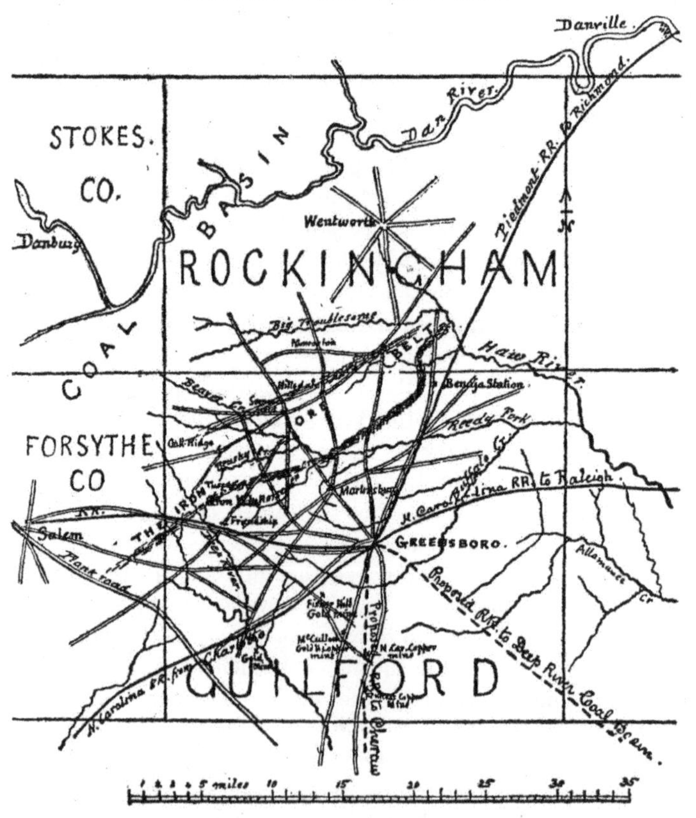

The local relations and geography of the ore belts are shown in the accompanying map.

The two following maps show the ore belt on a larger scale, giving the names of the plantations crossed by the ranges, with a scale of miles, which commences at the southwest extremity of the beds on a branch of Deep River.

Thus it is seen that the length of the outcrops, air line measure, is 28 miles.

GUILDFORD ORE BELT, NORTHERN HALF.

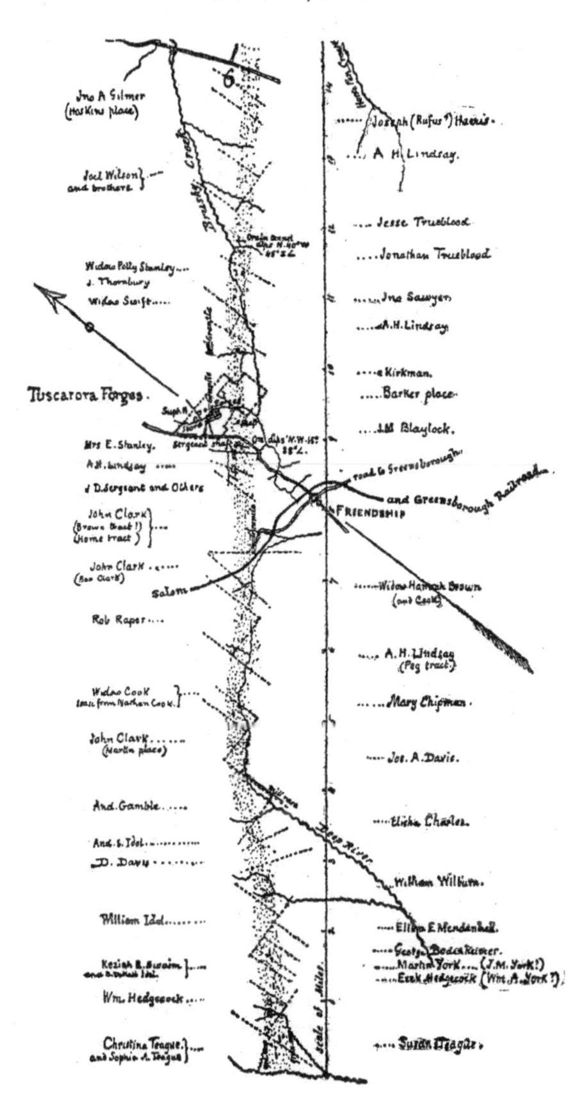

GUILDFORD ORE BELT, SOUTHERN HALF.

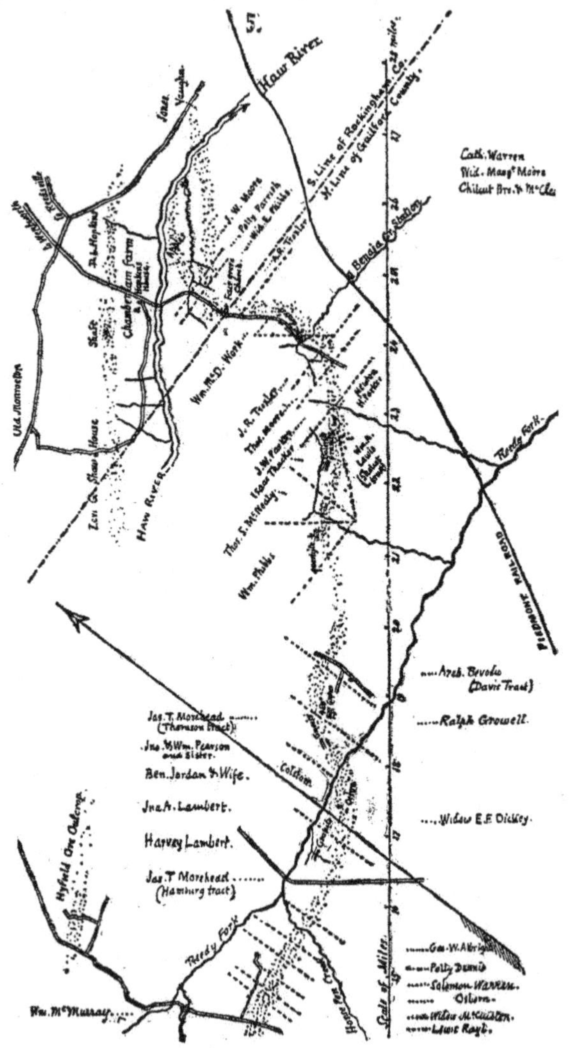

The mode of occurrence of the ore *in beds* is illustrated by Dr. L. by means of the following ideal diagram :

" The beds were deposited like the rest of the rocks in water ; deposited in the same age with the rocks which hold them; are in fact rock-deposits highly charged with iron ; and they differ from the rest of the rocks only in this respect : that they are *more highly charged with iron.* In fact all our primary (magnetic and other) iron ore beds obey this law. They are merely certain strata consisting more or less completely of peroxide of iron, with more or less intermixture of sand and mud, which when crystalized, fall into the shape of felspar, hornblende, mica, quartz, &c., &c."

" The belt of outcrop of ore-bearing rocks has a uniform breadth of several hundred yards, and I believe a uniform dip towards the northwest, or north-northwest.

The map, however, shows *another ore belt*, running parallel with the former and at a distance of three miles from it. This is called the Highfield or Shaw outcrop. Beyond Haw River the two belts approach each other, and are believed to unite in Rockingham county. This and other considerations make it almost certain that the Shaw belt is the northwest outcrop of a synclinal basin, 3 miles wide, and that the Tuscarora belt is the southeast outcrop. If so, the Tuscarora ore-beds descend with a northwest dip to a depth of a mile beneath the surface, and then rise again as ore-beds at Highfield's and Shaw's, thus :

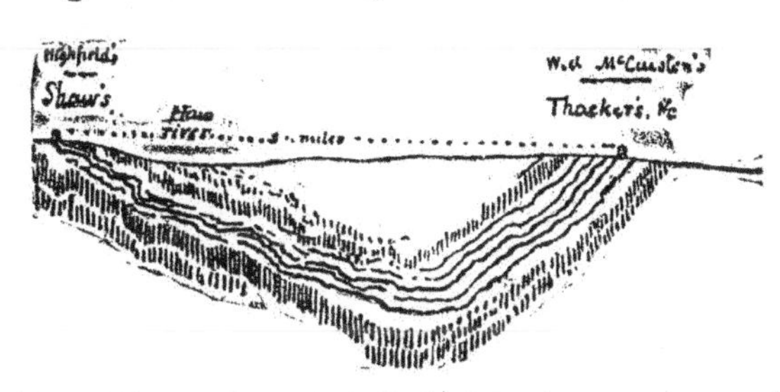

The locality of the ore beds is indicated by the occurrence of fragments of ore scattered over the surface ; and these are the indications by which nearly all iron ore deposits are discovered. Large pieces on the surface are the best evidence we can possess that the beds are of good size, for they have come from those portions of the bed, which have been destroyed in the general lowering of the surface of the country. There is no reason why the parts of the beds left under the present surface should not yield as large masses as the parts which have mouldered away."

As will be readily understood, from what has been stated above, the number of ore beds in the cross-section will be likely to vary from point to point along the range. " A large number of rock strata will become ore-beds locally. But there will always be a particular part of the formation more generally and extensively charged with great quantities of iron than the rest. In other words, the iron of the formation as a whole, is concentrated along one or more lines. This is evidently the case with the Tuscarora Ore Belt, as is shown in the almost perfect straightness of the outcrop of the Sergeant Shaft ore bed, where its outcrop has been opened for half a mile northeast of the shaft. There are two principal beds cropping out on the Teague plantation, at the (southwest) end of the belt, both vertical, and about 300 yards asunder." And not only does the number of ore beds vary, but they are often very irregular in position. This is illustrated by the following section, revealed "in a trench, cut at right angles to the outcrop, 50 feet long and 4 to 8 feet deep." It is on the widow McCawisten's plantation.

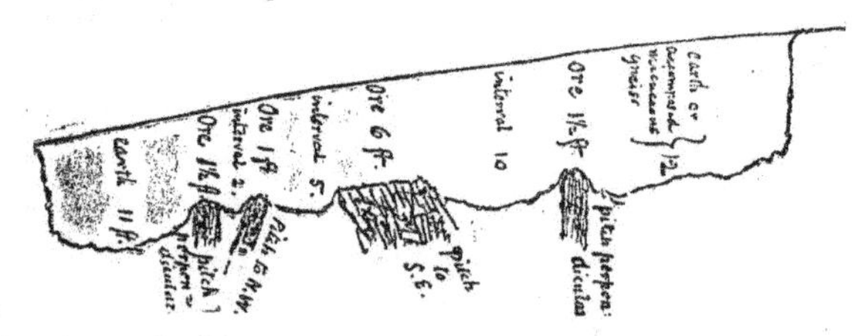

"Similar irregularities are noticeable everywhere. The miners say that the pitch of the outcrop of the ore bed worked in the Sergeant Tunnel and Shaft, was southeast for some distance down, after which it took its regular northwest dip, such as it now has in the shaft and tunnel at the depth of 100 feet. Besides which, there are in fact two beds cut in this shaft-tunnel, the smaller bed underlying the other, and with a dip which would carry the two beds together at some distance beneath the floor."

"Another instance occurs on the Trueblood plantation, where the two ore-beds appear to be only 200 yards apart at their outcrops and seem to dip different ways, which I explain by reference to the false surface dip of the Sergeant Shaft and bed. The Trueblood section is as follows :

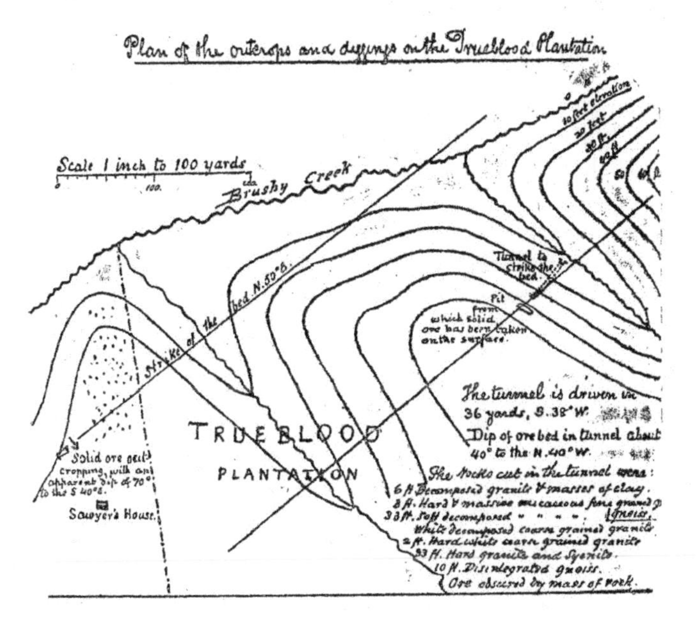

The sections made at the Shaw plantation (Shaw range) furnish a further illustration of these irregularities. "The ore-bed is full 6 feet across, solid ore,—a very green, chloritic, mica slate, rock-ore. In this run of 800 yards, there are *apparently two hundred thousand* (200,000) *tons above water level*, in the one 6 foot bed. The outcrop runs along the top of a hill about 100 feet above the bottom of Haw River Valley. There are apparent variations in the dip, some of the outcrops seeming to be vertical, whereas the principal part of the mining has already shown a distinct dip towards the southeast and south." The average dip of the ore beds of this second range was observed by Dr. Lesley to be considerably less than that of the Tuscarora beds, as is shown in the ideal section on page?

The *quantity of ore* which this remarkable range is capable of yielding is obviously immense. The number and extent of the beds have been noted. Their size varies greatly, as is shown in several of the diagrams. "They consist of strings of lens-shaped masses, continually enlarging and contracting in thickness, from a few inches to 6 and 8 feet.

The principal beds may be safely estimated on an average of four feet, and in the best mining localities, the average yield of a long gang-way may reach five feet." "It is evident that centuries of heavy mining could not exhaust it, for each of two or three principal beds may be entered and mined at fifty places."

The *kind of ore* has been stated in general terms as titaniferous magnetite. More particularly, not only titanium, but chromium and manganese are uniformly present, as will be seen from Dr. Genth's analyses, given below. "The ore belongs to the family of primary ores, the same family to which the Champlain (or Adirondack) ores, the Marqwette (Lake Superior) ores, and the ore of the Iron Mountain in Missouri, belong. It is very similar to the New Jersey ores, which are so extensively mined for the furnaces on the Lehigh river. It is a mixture of magnetic crystals and specular plates of sesquioxide of iron, with quartz, felspar and mica, in a thousand varying proportions. Sometimes the bed will be composed of heavy, tight, massive magnetite (or titaniferous magnetite), with very little quartz, &c.; at other times, of a loose, half-decomposed mica-slate, or gneiss rock, full of scattered crystals of magnetic iron. The ore is, in fact, a decomposable gneiss rock, with a varying percentage of titaniferous magnetic and specular iron ore, sometimes constituting half the mass, and sometimes almost the whole of it."

Dr. Genth, who made a special chemical and mineralogical study of these ores, says in his report, published in the *Mining Register*, "All the ores consist of mixtures of magnetic iron with titaniferous hematite, or menaccanite, probably also with rutile (titanic acid), mixed with a chloritic mineral, or a silvery micaceous one resulting from its decomposition. Some of the ores contain alumina in the form of granular corundum, in one or two places in such quantities that they become true emery ores. None of the constituents could be separated in a state of such purity that in all cases their true mineralogical character could be verified by analysis."

But besides these characteristic ores of the beds described, Dr. Lesley mentions beds of ochre of various sizes, "as one of the constituent elements of the whole formation. What the exact relationship of these ochre beds to the magnetic ore beds, I do not know. But the ochre outcrop seems to be always in the immediate vicinity of the ore beds. The largest exhibition of ochre which I saw, is on the I. Scmers plantation, on Brushy Creek. Here an ochre bed twenty feet thick rises, nearly vertical, out of a gully in a hillside covered with small pieces of fine, compact ore. The whole aspect of this place gives an impression of an abundance of ore beneath the surface, but no openings on the beds which have furnished these fragments have been made."

The following table presents the analyses of sixteen samples, collected, as stated, by Dr. Genth, along the whole length of this range of ore beds in 1871:

	28	29	30	31	32	33	34	35	36
Silicic Acid,............	0.76	5.68	0.40	1.84	1.76	1.30	12.75	1.30	26,80
Titanic Acid,..........	13.52	11.67	11.95	13.28	12.35	13.60	15.35	1.27	16.20
Mag. Ox. Iron,........	79.53	72.74	81.89	77.62	77.90	76 04	57.93	93.63	30.90
Ox. Man. and Cobalt,.	0.81	0.64	1.02	0.95	1.10	0.96	1.15	0.93	1.55
Ox. Chomium,.........	0.46	0.48	1.07	0.65	1.10	0.72	1.25	1.43	0.43
Alumina,...............	1.68	5.08	1.06	2.30	2.54	4.26	5.17	0.55	8.87
Magnesia,..............	2.79	2.61	1.99	2.01	2.41	2.33	4.14	0.75	10.30
Lime,..................	0.45	0.76	0.24	0.58	0.51	0.60	0.90	0.14	1.40
Water,................		0.34	0.38	0.77	0.79	0.18	1.36		3.55
	100.00	100.00	100.00	100.00	100.00	100.00	100.00	100.00	100.00
Metallic Iron,......	57.68	52.68	59.03	56.21	56.41	55.06	41.95	67.60	21.63

	37	38	39	40	41
Silicic Acid,..............	0.50	1.80	0.74	1.39	0.98
Titanic Acid,..............	12.27	14.46	13.92	0.78	2.42
Mag. Ox. Iron,............	79.16	74.81	76.80	42.77	46.29
Ox. Man. and Cobalt,.......	1.21	1.53	1.30	1.00	1.27
Ox. Chomium,............	0.57	0.97	1.07	0.30	trace.
Alumina,....................	3.62	2.66	3.82	52.24	44.86
Magnesia,..................	2.04	3.09	1.80	0.68	3.27
Lime,......................	0.63	0.69	0.55	0.84	0.91
Metallic Iron,.........	100.00	100.00	100.00	100.00	100.00
	57.32	54.17	55.61	30.97	33.52

The following are Dr. G.'s notes in part: "Nos. 28 and 29. K. R. Swain, Davidson county. The ores on this place are both massive and granular magnetite, with small admixtures of greenish chlorite, mostly between the fracture plants, partly altered to the above-mentioned silvery-white or brownish-white micaceous mineral, and those in which the latter forms a conspicuous constituent. Both kinds were analyzed; 28, the massive ore; 29, the micaceous.

No. 30. Elisha Charles, Guildford county. The ore is granular, iron-black, with small quantities of the silvery micaceous mineral.

No. 31. Widow Cook. The ore is similar to the last, although a little more chloritic and micaceous in little patches throughout the mass.

No. 32. John Clark. The ore closely resembles that from the Widow Cook's plantation.

No. 33. Widow Stanly, Sergeant Shaft. The ore is compact, granular, iron-black; it shows rarely octahedral crystals of magnetite, and is associated with dark green, foliated chlorite, especially on the fracture planes.

Nos. 34, 35, 36. Widow McCuisten. The greatest variety of ores exist at this plantation. They are peculiar but highly interesting and important. No. 34 is the soft micaceous ore; 35, the magnetic portion of 34; 36, the non-magnetic portion.

No. 37. W. A. Lewis. Very fine granular ore, with very little admixture of chlorite.

No. 38. Levi G. Shaw, Rockingham. Fine-grained, black, slightly micaceous; shows a somewhat stratified structure.

No. 39. P. Hopkins (Alcorn Farm), Rockingham. Very fine-grained, black, fragile ore, with little admixture of foreign substances.

No. 40. Granular, reddish ore. It has much the appearance of a granular reddish-brown garnet, for which it has been mistaken, until the analysis proved it to be not a silicate, mixed with granular magnetite, but *corundum*.

If this and the next should be found in quantity, they would be of considerable value, as a good quality of *emery*.

No. 41. Granular grayish ore. This is of a similar quality, and is found at the same locality; the minute grains of corundum have a yellowish or brownish-white color, and show in many places cleavage fractures, which give it the appearance of a felspathic mineral.

From these analyses it is seen that the average of the ten specimens of original iron ore, which represent the whole range for a distance of nearly 30 miles, is

Iron 54.61 per cent.

Titanium 8.07=13.24 per cent. of titanic acid. The ratio between titanium and iron is=1; 6.77.

All the ores were examined for sulphur and phosphorus, and were found to be entirely free from these substances."

As there seems to be an unfavorable impression of the titaniferous ores in some quarters, it is worth while to quote Dr. Lesley on the subject of the effect of titanic acid in iron ores, as there is no higher authority in this country: "This kind is difficult to smelt in the high-stack blast furnaces; but makes the best iron in the world, when smelted in the Catalan forge; and is of great value for the lining of puddling furnaces. It serves the same purpose as 'the Lake Superior ore, which is brought in large quantities to Pittsburgh and the surrounding district of Eastern Ohio and Western Pennsylvania, for lining puddling furnaces and to mix with poorer ores in the blast-furnaces.

The titaniferous magnetic ores of the Ottowa region, in Canada, are also brought by a long and expensive route to Pittsburgh, to mix with Pennsylvania ores. These Canada ores are of the same geological age, and of the same mineral character as the Tuscarora ores under consideration. There cannot be a question that these Tuscarora North Carolina ores will command a high price at the iron works of Eastern Pennsylvania.

The trial of the ore has been made by Mr. Nathan Rowland, at his works in Kensington, Philadelphia. Five tons were forwarded for trial as lining to puddling furnaces. Mr. Rowland expressed his opinion that it stood up three times as long as the Champlain ore, which he uses for that purpose. The difference is due to the superior compactness of titaniferous magnetite over that of pure crystalline magnetite. I believe that mining operations here would be successful, if they were entirely confined to this one branch of the business, so great is the demand for the best puddler's lining ores." Dr. Lesley says that these ores are "essentially like those of Northern New Jersey, as to age, situation, consistency and general composition," but unlike in this titaniferous quality. "The New Jersey ores seldom possess this property, and in any case, only in a low degree. The Canada ore and the ores of South Sweden hold large quantities of titanic acid; even as much, sometimes, as between 30 and 40 per cent. A small,—very minute quantity of titanium in pig iron, is believed to add greatly to its value, increasing its hardness and firmness, and its ability to stand wear. The Canadian ores were introduced to the Pittsburgh iron works for this end."

It has been stated above that these titaniferous ores are difficult to smelt, "requiring a much higher heat in the stack to decompose, than oxide of iron does." But they labor under another disadvantage, of suffering a loss of iron in the process of smelting; the reason of which is that "the only solvents of the titanic acid are the double silicates of *iron* and lime, or *iron* and alumina and lime, or *iron*, potash and lime, &c." And of course the more titanic acid, the greater the waste of iron in the slag. These Guildford ores therefore "have the advantage, that, while many of the Canada ores hold 25 and 30 and 35 per cent. of titanic acid," those contain less than 14, on an average. And at the same time "they have all the advantage which the presence of titanium affords: 1st. making the ore so firm that it is the best possible for lining puddling furnaces; 2nd, making the iron tougher and harder, like the best Swedish iron; and 3rd, imparting a certain quality, (the cause of which is not yet understood), which adapts the iron especially for the manufacture of *steel*." "The titanized iron is found to be exceedingly strong, and is used in Europe for armor plates, commanding three times the price of ordinary pig iron." Muchet's steel is made from titaniferous ores, for the manipulation and utilization of which, in the manufacture of steel and high grade iron, that gentleman has taken out no less than 13 patents in England, where Norwegian ores containing 41 per cent. of titanic acid are successfully employed, as stated by Dr. Lesley on the authority of Osborne.

"There is no question that titanium in iron ore favors the production of iron peculiarly suited to conversion into steel. The English steel trade has always largely depended on Swedish iron; and I believe that the titaniferous ores of the United States, (and they are far from abundant), will become annually more and more valuable, on account of the demand increasing for the best iron for steel making purposes."

Dr. Lesley refers also to the fact that the ochre-beds already described as accompanying the iron ore range, furnish a superior flux for these ores. "The ochre must become a fluid double-silicate, without robbing the ore, and will carry off the excess of titanic acid."

An analysis by A. A. Fesquet, which he gives of "this ochre, which forms large beds on the outcrops of the more ferruginous felspathic rocks," is added:

Sesquioxide of Iron,..............................	19.43
Silica,..	34.12
Alumina, ...	33.21
Water, &c., &c.,................................	13.24

So that this ochre will furnish more than enough oxide of iron for the slag, and will therefore increase the run of iron.

I add a few of Dr. Lesley's general conclusions as to the quality, quantity, uses and value of these ores.

"The quality of ore, although various and suited to at least two branches of the iron manufacture, is of the very first rate—none better in the world."

"The soft ores will smelt easily and make magnificent iron; absolutely the very best; perfectly malleable, tough and strong."

"The hard ores will command a high price for puddlers' linings; will be in demand for mixing with poorer ores of other regions," as are those of Canada and the Champlain; "and will have an especial value for the

Siemens and the Bessemer processes, and the steel manufacture generally."

"The quantity of ore is limitless."

"It would be the best policy to bring the ores to nature on the spot. Small charcoal blast-furnaces and groups of Catalan forges, are possible in a country so well provided with wood, and where any amount of labor can be got at the lowest price. The geology is all right; the mineralogy is all right; the region is a good one; population numerous; food plenty; labor abundant and cheap; railroads at hand." The range is crossed by two lines of railroad, and portions of it lie within 5 miles of a third.

Another probable advantage is the proximity of the Dan river coal. Although no satisfactory exposures of this coal have been made, yet there are good reasons for believing that it is both abundant and of good quality, from some explorations recently made by the North Carolina Centre Iron and Mining Company, about Stokesburg, and from the results of the trial of the coal from the shaft near Leaksville, during the late war.

The views of Dr. Lesley have been presented at some length, not only because, being from another state, and that a large iron manufacturing state, his opinions may be supposed to be given without bias, but chiefly because of his eminence as a geologist and especially as the highest authority in this country in everything connected with the geology, mineralogy and metallurgy of iron.

Any one who has the least knowledge of the present drift of the iron industry of the world, and of the controlling importance of high grade ores, is prepared to realize the immense value of such deposits as those just described in Guildford and in Harnett, Chatham, Orange and Halifax. For the manufacture of the common qualities of iron, England has unequalled advantages in her wonderful Cleaveland beds of fossil ore, and her clay iron stones and black band ores, mined in unlimited quantities from the same pit with the coal by which it is smelted. But for ores of the better class, adapted to the Bessemer and other processes for steel-making, and for the better kinds of iron, England is already confessedly dependent, in a large measure, on other countries. Her principal domestic resource is the Cumberland red hematites. And nothing could be more precarious than the supply from this source. This hematite is compact and mammillary, of a brick-red color, and occurs in pockets and irregular masses, of the most uncertain forms, distribution and magnitude. In fact the masses are simply the fillings of cavities of the most irregular and lawless shapes and forms which had been dissolved out the paleozoic limestones in which these ores occur. So that each mass or pocket has to be sought for and mined independently. And but for the introduction of the American Diamond Drill, it is difficult to understand how profitable mining could be carried on, after the exhaustion of the comparatively few masses which happen to make an outcrop. These ores are of very fine quality and commanded the remarkably high price of $9.00 a ton at the pit's mouth at the time of my visit in 1873. And the largest heaps of ore to be seen at the furnaces of Scotland and England, where malleable iron or steel is made, are Spanishred hematites, to procure which, English capital has penetrated by rail a hundred miles from the coast, into the province of Bilboa. I happened also to hear of a transaction of the day before, by which a Scotch firm contracted for three millions of tons of the famous hematites of the island of Elba, so popular with the old Romans, twenty centuries ago. And it is well known that English capitalists and iron associations are sending their experts and foremost iron manufacturers to investigate the iron resources of this country. The ores which fix the attention of these experienced scientific and practical Englishmen, are chiefly of the class under consideration,—the better class of iron and steel ores,—the Marquette region, the Iron Mountain, &c. It is only necessary that the numerous deposits of such ores in this state become known. If we could have a full report (such as the above) by Dr. Lesley, on each one of half a dozen iron ore ranges in the state, capital would not be long in finding a way to utilize them.

This Guilford range of ores has not been traced to its termination in either direction, and doubtless other valuable beds will be discovered; and there are already indications that there are outcrops of the same kind of ore as far northeast as Caswell county, some very fine specimens of magnetite having been brought to the Museum from that county.

There are also other iron ore localities in Rockingham, which do not belong to this range; for example, near the Virginia line, in a northeast direction from Madison; and again two miles below the mouth of Smith's river, (Morehead's Factory), there is a bed of red hematite iron ore, about ten inches thick at the outcrop. It is very dense, heavy and hard, uncrystalline, and almost jaspery, and is no doubt a good ore, judging from its appearance.

Iron Ores of Mecklenburg and Cabarrus.—No iron mines of any extent, have been worked in these counties, but ore has been found in a number of localities. Hand specimens of magnetic ore of great purity are frequenty brought to the Museum, and a systematic search would no doubt reveal workable beds. Fragments of a very heavy, black metallic ore are found in considerable quantities on the farm of Mr. Geo. Phifer, three miles from Concord, and some little search was made during the war, but not enough to reach any satisfactory conclusion. A few trenches of one or two feet depth exposed only small seams of ore, but of the best quality. Some explorations were made also in the southern part of Mecklenburg at the same time, in the Sugar Creek neighborhood. Numerous blocks of a remarkably pure granular magnetic ore were found scattered over several acres of surface of an old field, and along the public road; and several trenches were cut, which exposed two or three veins of one to three and four feet thickness. Adequate search would no doubt bring to light still larger veins, judging from the size and number of the surface fragments. Some twelve or fifteen miles north of Charlotte, in the Hopewell neighborhood, a very notable quantity of surface fragments of large size are found in an old field and skirt of woods adjacent. This is a specular ore in a gangue of quartzite, not unlike the Chapel Hill Ore. No exposures of the vein, however, have ever been attempted. Specimens of a very fine micaceous hematite have been brought from the upper end of this county also, but no information of precise locality or extent.

The ores of the southern end of this county and of Cabarrus are found in the syenyte, so prevalent in the region.

Iron Ores of Gaston, Lincoln and Catawba.—In these counties is one of the most extensive ore ranges in the State. It is also the best known and best developed of them all, and has been the principal source of our domestic supplies of iron for a hundred years. Some of the furnaces of the region were put in blast during the Revolutionary war. The ores are predominantly magnetic, with a variable percentage of hematite, and are found in the belt of talcose and quartzitic slates, (supposed Huronian), called elsewhere the King's Mountain slates. The direction of this range of ore-beds is coincident with the strike of the slates, and is about N. N. E. from King's Mountain on the southern border of the state, to Anderson Mountain, near the Catawba River, in Catawba county. These ores are also mostly of a very slaty structure, and friable. In fact they may be generally described as magnetic and specular schists, being talcose, chloritic, quartzitic or actinolitic schists impregnated with granular magnetite and hematite (itabirite). These beds have a westerly dip, with the rock strata, at a very high angle, usually nearly vertical. The general range of the beds is accompanied and indicated by a line of quartzose slaty ridges, or knobs, the quartzite lying usually to the west of the ore-beds, but occasionally on the east and sometimes on both sides. To Mr. G. B. Hanna, who has lately made an examination of many of the beds for the Survey, I am indebted for several valuable observations. He states that for a considerable part of the range there are two parallel beds, the more westerly being generally the larger and more productive, their thickness running from 4 feet (and sometimes as low as 2 feet) to 12; the interval of 12 to 20 feet between them being occupied by talcose and chloritic slates, with a littte ore in layers. The beds generally occur in lenticular masses, or flattish disks, which thicken at the middle and thin out towards the edges, having nearly the same dip with the bed; but they do not succeed each other in one plane, their edges overlapping so as to throw the upper edge of the lower behind the lower edge of the upper. The ore has been generally mined in a very rude and wasteful fashion, the operations seldom penetrating beyond water-level, 50 or 60 feet, and generally limited to surface openings. The range naturally divides itself into two groups of beds, the northern and the southern, the one lying mostly in Lincoln, and the other in Gaston. The most considerable of the Lincoln beds and the one which has been longest and most extensively wrought is known as the *Big Ore Bank.* This is situated 7 or 8 miles north of the C. C. Railroad, and, as is usual with the outcrops of these beds, is on a hill or broad ridge. There are several beds evident, but the scattered and partially filled openings do not furnish the means of arriving at a satisfactory notion of their exact relations. The quantity of ore, however, seems to be very great, the thickness of the beds at some places being estimated at about 18 feet. The surface of the hill is still covered with a coarse dark magnetic gravel, after all the large fragments have been removed, and several crops of the gravel also, as they weather out in succession. Several furnaces and a number of forges have been supplied with ore from this point for a long period. Following the compass course of the outcrops, about N. 20° E., a succession of ore beds is encountered at intervals of one or two miles, to the southeastern base of Anderson Mountain,—the Brevard Ore Bank, the Robinson Ore Bank, the Morrison Ore Bank, which last extends into Catawba county. The latter of these was not much opened until the late war, when the Stonewall furnace was erected in the neighborhood, and a considerable quantity of iron manufactured. The thickness of the beds is given by Mr. Hanna in the general statement quoted above, as ranging from 4 to 12 feet. The quality of iron manufactured from this range of ore beds has always been good; and all the furnaces on this part of the range were put in blast after the war, for the purpose of supplying a high grade charcoal-iron for the northern market.

Limestone for fluxing is found convenient, in the range of beds which accompanies these slates, one to two miles to the west, from King's Mountain to a point several miles beyond Anderson Mountain.

A few miles northwest of the last named mountain is a bed of limonite 5 or 6 feet thick, which was opened during the war, and furnished ore for a Catalan forge erected on a small stream near by.

Several miles further, in a northwesterly course,—7 miles southwest of Newton, there is a series of ore deposits, known as the Forney Ore Bank, whose mineralogical character and geological relations are entirely different from those of the ore-beds of Lincoln county. They occur in the syenytic belt which will be noted on the map, as lying in a narrow zone of 3 to 5 miles, parallel to the slate belt, across these counties, from the great bend of the Catawba River nearly to S. C. The ore is a remarkably pure magnetite, heavy, black, metallic and non-granular, for the most part. It occurs in irregular masses,—*pockets*, which seem to be scattered very disorderly through the massive syenytic rock. So that the proper way to seek for it is by the miner's compass. The iron manufactured from it in the forges of the neighborhood, particularly at Williams', was in much request before and during the war, being very malleable, tough and strong. All the blooms which could be procured at the naval works in Charlotte during the war were used for the manufacture of shafts for ironclads and bolts for the cannon of the coast forts. At a point 6 or 7 miles northeasterly from this, is the Barringer Ore Bank, which is some two miles southeast from Newton. This ore is of the same character and geological relationships as the last. Some of the ore is more granular and it is occasionally disseminated in grains in a light colored, granitic gangue. Several thousand tons of ore were mined here during the war. The openings which extend in a double line about 100 yards, did not penetrate more than 15 to 20 feet; so that no proper development of the deposit has been made. The vein is apparently nearly vertical, but it was not sufficiently exposed at any point, on account of the filling up of the pits, to give an opportunity for measurements of size or dip. But the ore is of the best quality; and the distance from railroad is only about 2 miles. There is also another deposit in Lincoln county which does not belong to the series of beds above described. It lies about two miles east of Lincolnton on the plank road, and is traceable some hundreds of yards through the forests by the surface fragments, which are widely scattered. The ore is limonite. No exposures of the deposit have ever been made, but the quantity must be considerable. Magnetic ore, no doubt belonging to the regular ranges of ore-beds, is found at other points in this county, notably on Major Graham's place, 4 or 5 miles north of the railroad, but no mining has been done here.

The lower part of the great iron range under consideration is mostly found in the southern half of Gaston, as the upper was mainly limited to the northern part of Lincoln. The ore-beds which have been opened and wrought are all found south of the South Fork of Catawba, and of its principal tributary, Long Creek, in the neighborhood of King's Moun-

31

tain and its spurs, and affiliated ridges. The rocks here are the same body of slates,—talcose, argillaceous, quartzitic (itacolumite of Lieber), which carry the ores of Lincoln. And the most prominent ore-beds of the King's Mountain region are of the same character as those of the same range already described,—granular, slaty, but with a larger admixture of hematite, and so having a decidedly red streak. These ore-beds appear to constitute a double parallel range, the divisions much more widely separated than in Lincoln. The *Yellow Ridge Ore Bank*, on the most southerly outcrop, at the western base of King's Mountain seems to belong to the eastern division. The bed here, which has been extensively wrought, and was penetrated to a depth of 120 feet, is reported by Mr. Hanna and others to be 16 feet thick (occasionally 40), with a steep westerly dip. Hanna says of the ore, "it is notably magnetic but more highly peroxidized than that class of 'gray ores' generally." It is finely disseminated in a talcose gangue, being strikingly like the ores of Lincoln county. At the western base of Crowder's Mountain, in a northeasterly course, on this range, is the Fulenwider ore-bed, on the headwaters of Crowder's Creek, and near the forge; and still further in the same direction Mr. Hanna speaks of a field which is covered thickly with fragments of ore, although no bed has been exposed.

There is also a notable succession of parallel beds of magnetiferous arenaceous slates in a nearly vertical position and with a northeast strike, on the summit of Crowder's Mountain.

The following analyses of several samples of these Crowder Mountain ores have been furnished by Hanna:

	42	43	44	45
Silica,*	11.02	23.14	9.27	2.58
Peroxide of Iron,	72.00	58.36	75.17	84.53
Protoxide of Iron,	2.03	5.40	2.68	1.30
Sulphide of Iron,	0.09	0.12	0.20	0.02
Sulphuric Acid,	0.02	0.12	0.01	0.01
Phosphoric Acid,	0.05	trace	0.02	0.07
Loss by heating,	1.65	2.78	4.02	11.88
Metallic Iron,	52.02	45.13	54.80	59.29

These analyses show a high grade of purity.

No. 42 is from the slaty beds of the Pinnacle.

*And a small percentage of Titanic Acid.

There are other beds or veins of iron ore on the east side of Crowder's Mountain, one of which, about a mile distant, a friend reports having traced two miles by its outcrops; but no openings have been made here.

There are three notable ore-beds on the western division of this part of the range, on the lands known as the "High Shoals." They are the *Ferguson*, the *Ellison* and the *Costner* ore banks. The first is the most southerly. It is a granular magnetic ore, with much iron pyrites, which has been superficially changed to limonite. This bed has been long worked, but the sulphur has always lowered, more or less, the quality of the iron made from it. The Ellison ore bank is about a mile northeasterly on the range. This has been worked for a great while, and has furnished an immense amount of ore. Its quality is very high.

The heavy iron castings for the Rolling Mills at High Shoals were made from the furnace hearth, and, after seven years use, show scarcely a sign of wear; and car wheels made of this iron were very extensively used during the late war, and were found by all the railroads which used them, "equal to the best manufactured from the Salisbury iron," as testified by the Superintendents and other officers of the most important lines, on some of which "as many as 2,000 car wheels, made principally from this iron, were in use" at one time. "In castings where strength and durability are specially required," it is pronounced by several of those officers most familiar with it, as "having no superior." This ore is a slaty granular magnetite, with much hematite, and generally has a very red streak. The slate contains actinolite, as well as some chlorite and talc. The bed has the strike of the enclosing slates, N. 20° E., and a steep westerly dip, nearly vertical, and a thickness of twelve to eighteen feet; it has been worked to a depth of more than 100 feet, and at this level is eighteen feet thick.

The *Costner Ore Bank* is about three miles in a northerly course, on the same line, and one mile east of the furnace ("Long Creek"). This has more of the seeming of a vein, from its associations and general character. The rock is granitic and syenytic, and one wall is a bed of crystalline limestone, twelve feet thick. The ore is a very dense, metallic and subcrystalline magnetite, and is very free from impurities, as will be seen from the analysis below; and the bar iron made from it is very tough and strong. The vein is ten to twelve feet thick; and it is reported by the miners who last penetrated it, at a depth of over 100 feet, to be above twenty feet thick.

There are two other important ore beds on this tract,—"High Shoals," but they do not belong to the regular range of ore beds which we have been considering, being out of their line to the west, and of a very different character. The ore nearest to the line of the deposits last described is the *Mountain Ore Bank*. It is on a high ridge, or mountain spur, (Whetstone Mountain) 2 or 300 feet above the level of the general level, and some two miles west of the Furgeson Ore Bank. It is a regular vein of limonite, fibrous, radiated, mammillary and cellular; a portion of it a dirty bluish-black, earthy mass, with a disposition to break out in small angular fragments,—evidently manganiferous and derived by decomposition from the carbonate of iron. The vein is four to eight feet thick, associated with a heavy quartz vein, in a quartzo-argillaceous slate, and has a strike N. 35° E., and which does not vary more than 1° to 5° from the vertical (towards the west). It is remarkably pure and will no doubt become valuable in the manufacture of *Spiegeleisen*. The second vein the *Ormond Ore Bank*, is in the slate belt also, and is probably a vein, (no exposures of it were visible on account of the filling up of the pits). It has been worked quite extensively before and during the late war; and the iron has a high reputation in the region. It is specially preferred for wagon tires, and is said to outlast those made from any other iron. The vein is reported to be 8 to 15 feet thick. The strike is N. 35° E. The ore is fine granular, of a dirty brownish-red color, and much of it is friable and easily falls to powder. This ore is manganiferous like the last, and is a hematite, which is partly hydrated and limonitic, (turgite ?)

The following analyses, by Dr. Genth, will show the high character of these ores:

	46	47	48	49	50
Magnetic Oxide of Iron,.....	92.18	69.64	82.14	86.66	88.56
Sesquioxide of Iron,..........		4.30			
Oxide of Manganese,........	0.28		0.53	5.12	5.17
Alumina,..................	0.44	0.96			
Magnesia,..................	2.23	1.30		0.27	0.30
Lime,......................	0.35			0.25	0.37
Silica and Actinolite,........	4.34	23.80	4.47	1.42	0.84
Water,.....................	0.18		12.86	6.28	4.76
Iron, ...	66.75	53.44	57.50	60.66	61.99

Dr. G. adds: "These ores contain neither sulphur nor phosphorus." No. 49 contains a trace of cobalt. No. 42 is the Costner ore; No. 43 the Ellison; Nos. 48 and 49 represent the fibrous limonite, and "manganiferous limonite, resulting from the decomposition of siderite," of the Mountain Mine; and No. 50 is the Ormond ore.

There are five furnaces on this range of ores, one on the High Shoals tract,—the southern part of it, and four on the northern. One of these has been in operation between 90 and 100 years, the others 80, 60 and less, down to 12 years for the last and most northern, —the Stonewall, at the base of Anderson Mountain, built during the war. These are all charcoal-furnaces, of a capacity ranging from 3 to 6 tons. And there are many Catalan forges, both in these and the adjoining counties, which have long supplied the local market, and with a much better quality of iron than could be gotten in the general iron market of the country. The belt of limestone, which forms an unfailing term of the King's Mountain slates through their course, lying generally about a mile west of the iron ore-beds, and the abundance of timber and water power have furnished the most favorable conditions for the cheap production of good iron. And the itacolumitic sandstone of the series furnishes excellent material for hearths, a "firestone" much superior in durability to any fire bricks procurable.

Iron Ores of Yadkin, Surry and Stokes.—The ores of this region occupy a relation to the Pilot and Sauratown Mts. similar to that of the Gaston and Lincoln ores to the King's Mountain range. They are found along the base and among the spurs and foot hills of the range. And like them too, these deposits divide themselves into two groups, geographically, one in Stokes and the other in Surry and Yadkin. They are all magnetic and granular, but differ, in the two groups, in their mode of occurrence. In the latter case the ore is disseminated in grains, for the most part through mica slates and gneiss rocks, and the earthy and rocky matter often bears a large proportion to the ore and requires to be separated by stamping and washing before it is sufficiently concentrated for the forge. The rock is generally decomposed to a great depth and the grains of ore are easily separated by very rude and cheap means. The ore-beds of this group have been long known, and have been used to some extent as a source of local supply of iron. They were described by Dr. Mitchell in 1842, as follows: "There is a series of beds extending in a northeasterly and southwesterly direction from the Virginia line to the Yadkin River. There are also some beds on the south side of the river." An example of this magnetiferous gneiss, and of the mode of occurrence and the method of mining, concentrating and reducing the ore is seen on Tom's Creek, in Surry county, a few miles northeast of the Pilot Mountain. The decomposed gneiss of the ore-bed has little appearance of an iron ore, and is in fact distinguishable mainly by its superior weight, the grains of magnetite merely replacing, in varying proportions, the mica and hornblende of the rock. And consequently the beds are not defined at all; the rock is worked in any direction where it is found to pay, and the excavations are made in the most irregular and undefinable fashion.

Another ore-bed and two forges (Hyatt's), are found on the west side of Ararat River, near the mouth of Bull Run Creek. This ore-bed is nearly west of the Pilot, in a light-colored slaty gneissoid sandstone. A third ore-bed, which has been worked for many years, known as Williams', is four miles northwest of Rockford. The rock is a hornblendic gneiss, and the mode of occurrence of the ore is very much as on Tom's Creek, but it is more disposed to gather into bunches and pockets and solid masses. The iron made from the ores of Surry has a good reputation in the region; they are apparently very pure. On the south side of the river, there is a series of ore-beds running from the river in a southwesterly course to Deep Creek, nearly across the county of Yadkin. There are a number of mines here, the most noted of which are the *Hobson Mines.* The ores are very much like those on Tom's Creek, but the beds are better defined, and the ore more concentrated in definite strata. The analyses below, by Dr. Genth, will show the character of the ores of this county:

	51	52	53	54	55	56	57	58
Mag. Oxide of Iron,.............	93.61	55.87	56.13	71.68	74.48	86 39	70.61	79.75
Ox. Man.,........................	0.11	0.86	trace	trace	0.04	trace	0.48	0.81
Oxide of Copper,................	0.10	0.09	0.05	0.10	0.04	0.09	0.15	0.13
Alumina,..........................	0.20	0.45	1.88	2.46	0.98	0.75	0.66	1.20
Magnesia,.........................	0.86	1.94	0.19	0.10	0.25	0.77	0.90	0.98
Lime,..............................	0.45	3.14	0.36	0.57	0.60	0.70	1.34	0.82
Silica, Actinolite, Epidote, &c,...	4.62	37.24	40.60	24.62	23.16	10.83	24.28	14.46
Phosphoric Acid,................	0.05	0.05	trace	trace	trace	0.09	0.12	0.10
Sulphur,..........................		0.02	trace	trace	trace			
Water. &c.,.......................		0.34	0.79	0.57	0.45	0.38	1.46	1.75
	67.79	40.46	40.65	51.83	53.93	62.55	51.13	57.75

The Hobson ores, several beds, are represented by Nos. 53, 54 and 57. These ores have been used in the forges of the neighborhood for many years. The ore-beds are in the northern part of the county, but others are found southward of them, and are represented by the other analyses; and the ores have also been used in the blomaries of the neighborhood for a long while. The other beds represented in the table are the Sand Bank (51), Black Bank (52), Hutchins' (55), Upper Bank (56), and Shields' (58). At East Bend also is an outcrop of magnetic ore, which is coarse, granular, and more free of rocky matter than most of the other deposits; but it has not been operated.

This range of ore-beds extends southward across the South Fork of Yadkin River into Davie county, where the ore still preserves the same characteristics as in the above mentioned counties, but of the extent of the beds and their distribution, I have no definite information.
The northern or Stokes group of the range lies on the east, (north) side of Dan River, and within 2 and 3 miles of Danbury. These are collected for the most part in a group of parallel beds, in a dark to black and greenish-black micaceous and hornblendic gneiss, the beds being very well defined, and the ore concentrated in certain definite strata, and in the case of the Rogers Ore Bank, it is aggregated into considerable masses of pure granular ore, of very coarse grain. This bed is 8 feet thick and has been worked on a considerable scale; and an excellent iron was smelted in the furnace at Danbury during the war. Another bed reported to be 10 feet thick has been opened about half a mile east of the last, and two beds, (one of them 4 feet thick, the other not opened), have been discovered at different times within 300 and 600 yards of it, on the west. The ores are all magnetites, with sometimes a small admixture of hematite. The following analyses are by Dr. Genth:

	59	60	61	62
Oxides of Iron,	92.47	85.09	79.71	67.66
Oxide of Manganese,	trace	trace	trace	trace
Alumina,	trace	0.70	2.27	0.17
Magnesia,	0.20	0.16	0.17	0.23
Lime,	0.13	0.29	0.31	0.19
Phosphoric Acid,	0.00	0.00	0.00	0.00
Actinolite, &c.,	7.20	13.76	15.66	31.75
Water,			1.88	
Metallic Iron,	65.34	61.74	57.13	49.03

The purity of these ores is conspicuous. Phosphorus is wholly wanting. Some samples contain a small percentage of pyrites. Manganese appears as only a *trace* in the analyses, but it must exist in larger proportions in some parts of the bed, as spiegeleisen is occasionally an accidental product. The above specimens of ore are all from the Rogers Ore Bank. There is also a small outcrop of limonite in the vicinity of the Rogers bed, of which Dr. Genth's analyses gives the peroxide as 31.36 per cent.; phosphoric acid 0.44. There are other outcrops of magnetic ore in the county, a notable one on the south side of the Sauratown Mountains, among the head waters of Town Fork of Dan River. It is evident that here is an important iron range which must become a centre of manufacture for the higher grades of charcoal iron whenever transportation shall have been provided, either by railroad or by the opening of the navigation of the Dan, which is very feasible. The proximity of the Dan River coal beds is another advantage, which may prove of the highest importance, whenever these beds shall be opened.

There are in the Museum several very fine specimens of magnetic ore and micaceous hematite, from (Forsythe county,) the neighborhood of Salem, south and west; which make it probable that there are valuable ore deposits in that section; but no definite information of their extent is in hand.

Iron Ores of Burke, Caldwell, &c. There are many valuable beds of limonite in a range extending in a northeast direction from the northeastern foot-hills of the South Mountains into the Brushy Mountains,—from Jacob's Fork of Catawba River, near the eastern border of Burke, across the Catawba, and by way of Gunpowder Creek, to the waters of Middle Little River near the eastern border of Caldwell; and beyond, near Rocky Creek, in Alexander, and even on the northern slopes of the Brushy Mountains in Wilkes, the same ores occur, being undistinguishable in appearance, and of identical lithological relations. These ores are associated with the peculiar kyanitic hydro-mica schists, and purplish paragonite schists, which characterize the region.

There is a bed near the town of Hickory, reported to be 5 or 6 feet thick; and 3 miles west, at Propst's, are a number of pits from which a quantity of ore was obtained during the war; and at the distance of 6 miles, on the lands of Mrs. Townsend, a bed was opened some thirty years ago, and the ore, in considerable quantities, smelted in the Shuford furnace in the neighborhood. The beds are not exposed in either of these cases, the pits being filled up. The ore was mixed with the magnetite obtained from the Barringer Mine near Newton (already referred to), and the iron so made is reported to have been of good quality.

Iron was also made on Gunpowder Creek, Caldwell county, 30 or 40 years ago, from a similar series of limonite beds. The quantity of ore is reported as large. The beds on Middle Little River, 12 miles southeast of Lenoir, were worked nearly 50 years ago, and the ore hauled 7 miles to Beard's furnace, on the Catawba River. The outcrops are traceable on the slopes of McIntyre's Mountain and Bald Mountain, near Mr. White's, on Miry Branch, for a distance of 2 to 3 miles, the outcrop on the former being about 3 or 4 feet, and on the latter 8 or 10; and it is reported that at some points the thickness is more than double the above figure. There is every surface evidence of abundance of ore. Being a mountainous region, timber for fuel is abundant, and water power also; and the proximity of magnetites and hematites, to be presently mentioned, completes a very favorable combination of circumstances for the establishment of iron manufactures.

Specimens of magnetic ore are of frequent occurrence in Burke county, and the western part of Catawba, of which there are several very fine examples in the Museum,—sent, one from a point near Hickory, and another from near Morganton, &c., but nothing is known to me of the quantity or special mode of occurrence. On Steele's Creek also in the northwestern part of Burke county, there is an outcrop of magnetic and hematite ore of the best quality. The bed or vein has not been exposed, and the quantity cannot be safely conjectured. It occurs on a spur of Brown Mountain on the land of Mr. Estes. Limonite also occurs in Brindletown, among the spurs of the South Mountains.

A bed of superior magnetic ore occurs on Warrior Creek, not far from Patterson, Caldwell county, and within a mile of the bend of the Yadkin River. It is traceable hundreds of yards by large surface fragments of a fine grained heavy metallic ore, remarkably free from rocky admixtures; and a similar ore is reported as occurring in large mass a few miles west on Mulberry Creek. Another very fine ore, a shining metallic, slaty hematite, of great purity, is found a few miles above on the spurs of the Blue Ridge, flanking the Yadkin River, in a cove known as Richlands. The smooth faces of the slaty masses of ore, as well as of the walling slates, are sprinkled quite thickly with small shining octahedral crystals of magnetite, many of which have been converted into hematite, constituting a fine example of *martite* schist. The bed at this point outcrops only a few inches in thickness, among the thin bedded and shaly, argillaceous and arenaceous micaceous slates of Linville, which show themselves in force along the flanks of the Blue Ridge in this section. The analysis of this ore, by Hanna, is as follows:

	63
Sesquioxide of Iron,	96.14
Sulphide of Iron,	0.08
Sulphuric Acid,	0.01
Phosphoric Acid,	0.00
Manganese,	trace
Silica,	2.25
Alumina,	0.87
Water, &c.,	.85
Metallic Iron,	67.32

In the same neighborhood, on the farm of Mr. J. Curtis, on the banks of the Yadkin River, 7 or 8 miles above Patterson, is a heavy ledge of titaniferous iron ore in a massive, granular, talco-chloritic gneiss of a light greenish-gray color. The ledge is exposed in a cliff rising sheer out the river, and again in the steep face of a hill 150 yards distant. The exposure is not less than 12 to 15 feet thick, and the surface is covered with heaps of angular fragments of all sizes, up to a hundred pounds and more. The bed also contains a small proportion of sesquioxide of chromium, amounting, according to Hanna, to 0.10 per cent.

Some 10 or 12 miles northeast of this point, on the flanks of the Blue Ridge, near Cook's Gap, in the edge of Watauga county, occurs another outcrop of the specular (martite) schist of Richlands. The bed at this locality, which is called Bull Ruffin, is reported to be 3 or 4 feet thick at the outcrop, and the neighboring and enclosing rocks, granular quartzose schists and other characteristic schists and slates of the Linville belt, are often impregnated, as well as the ore schist itself, with fine to coarse crystals of magnetite and martite. The ore so exactly resembles that at Richlands that it is impossible to distinguish them. There is also an outcrop of limonite near the same point, of which the Museum contains a specimen, but I have no information of its extent. The quality of this ore is so high as to justify an exploration of this promising outcrop, and indeed of the whole range; which however does not stop at this point, but follows the line of the Blue Ridge for a distance of 75 miles, showing itself in the notable magnetiferous and martitic schists of Fisher's Peak, near the Virginia line, on the Surry-Alleghany border.

In McDowell county there are several beds of limonite. These are mostly aggregated along the top of Linville Mountain, southern part, and the western slope, near the foot, and in the spurs of the southern end. One of these ore-beds was worked by Mr. Conolly twenty-five or thirty years ago. Another bed, Fleming's, was opened also, 2 or 3 miles south of Linville, on the slope of Graveyard Mountain; the thickness appeared to be 2 to 3 feet. These Linville limonites made an inferior iron when worked alone; but mixed with the magnetites and hematites of the region, they would become available for the manufacture of good metal. There are ores of the last named species in the Linville River region, of which however, I have seen hand specimens only.

The limestone beds of the same belt, in North Cove and along the flanks of Linville, are conveniently located for furnishing a flux, and the forests of these mountains will furnish indefinite quantities of fuel.

Ore Mountain, one mile west of Swannanoa Gap, (and therefore just over the Buncombe line), is named from the occurrence on its flanks of a bed of limonite, which doubtless belongs to the iron ore range of Linville. The bed is not well exposed, but 3 or 4 feet of thickness are visible on the steep escarpment, and large masses which have broken off, are fallen down to a lower point on the slope.

Iron Ores of Mitchell and Ashe.—In Mitchell county is found one of the most remarkable iron-ore deposits in North America. It lies on the western slope of the Iron Mountain, (a part of the Great Smoky range), in the northeast corner of the county, 3 miles from the Tennessee line, and about a mile from the rapid torrent of Elk River, the principal affluent of the Watauga. It has been long known as the Cranberry Ore Bank, from Cranberry Creek, which flows at the foot of the steep mountain spurs, on which it outcrops. The prevalent and characteristic rock of the mountains in this locality is hornblende slate and syenyte, and it is on the northern margin of a mountainous ledge of such rocks, that the ore-bed occurs, gray gneisses and gneissoid slates coming in beyond in immediate succession and association, in part.

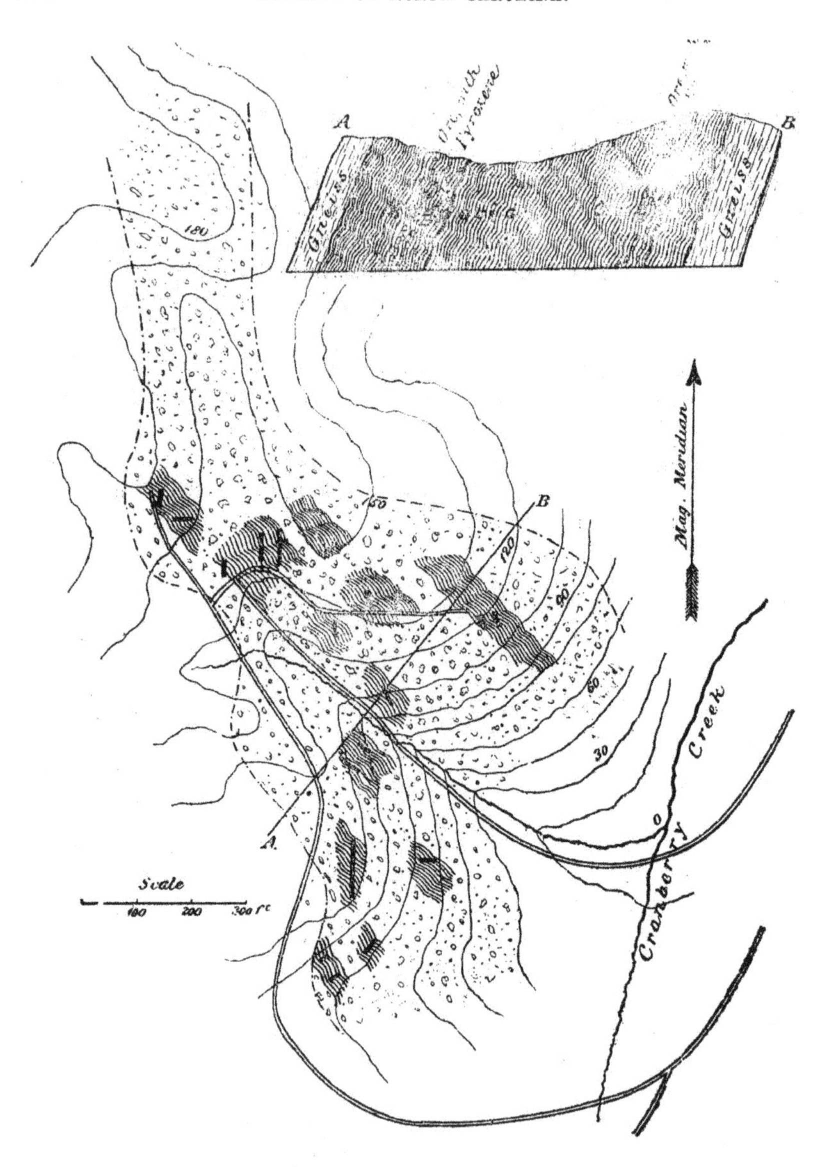

Cranberry Ore Bank

The ore is a pure magnetite, massive and generally coarse-granular, and exhibits strong polarity. It is associated with pyroxene and epidote, in certain parts of the bed, as shown in the appended diagram. The steep slope of the mountain gorge and ridges which the bed occupies, are covered with blocks of ore, often of hundreds of pounds weight, and in many places, bare vertical walls of massive ore, 10 and 15 feet thick, are exposed, and the trenches and open diggings, which are scattered, without order, over many acres of surface, every where reach the solid ore within a few feet of the surface. The length of the outcrop is about 1500 feet and the breadth 200 to 800,—600 in the section given in the diagram. A large quantity of ore has been quarried and smelted here during the last two or three generations, but no *mining* has been done, the loose and partly decomposed and disintegrated masses of ore and magnetic gravel mixed with the surface earth, having been preferred by the ore diggers, as being more easily obtained, and much more readily stamped and granulated for the forge fire. The quality of the ore will best be seen by reference to the following analyses:

	64	65	66	67	68
Magnetic Oxide of Iron,......	94.37	91.45	85.59	80.77	91.89
Oxide of Manganese,.........	0.26	0.06	0.24	1.42	0.32
Alumina,.....	0.42	0.77	0.11	0.52	1.03
Lime,....................	0.43	1.01	0.72		1.06
Magnesia,...................	0.36	0.53	0.33		0.23
Water, ...		0.44	1.53	8.21*	1.15
Silica, Pyroxene, &c.,........	4.16	5.74	11.48	9.08	4.02
Sulphur,....................					0.25
Phosphoric Acid,............					trace
	100.00	100.00	100.00	100.00	99.95
Metallic Iron,...........	68.34	66.22	61.98	58.49	66.53

The first four of these analyses are by Dr. Genth, who says "the first three samples contain neither titanic acid, nor phosphorus and sulphur, the fourth contains a trace of phosphoric acid."

No. 68 was made in 1869, by Prof. Chandler, of Columbia College, New York city, who remarks: "This is the best iron ore I have ever analyzed. It is very rich in iron and very free from sulphur and phosphorus." The smiths and farmers of the region will use no other iron, if the Cranberry can be had, and they willingly pay fifty per cent. more for it than any other in the market. The softness and toughness of this iron is very remarkable, and its tensile strength, as tested by the United States Ordnance Department, ranks with that of the best irons known. The blooms from the Cranberry forges have been extensively used in

Baltimore for boiler iron, and commanded fifteen dollars a ton above the market. In quality it is unsurpassed by any iron in the world. And in regard to quantity, the bed much exceeds the great deposits of Missouri and Michigan, and at least equals anything in the Champlain region. So that it has not probably an equal in this country. It has been recently sold to one of the leading iron manufacturing companies of Pennsylvania, for $175,000, and when they shall have completed the branch railroad, thirty miles in length, from the ore to the East Tennessee & Virginia Railroad, no doubt the iron world will begin to hear of the deposit in a practical way.

The topographical sketch of this ore-bed was taken rapidly and roughly, with a mountain level and pocket barometer, and of course lacks accuracy of detail, but the main features and measurements are approximately exact. The epidote is not entirely confined to a single stratum, or part of the bed, being mixed to some extent with the pyroxenic rocky gangue which most abounds towards the western side of the vein.

There are other magnetic ore-beds in the neighborhood of less extent. One is said to occur along the face of the same (Iron) mountain between one and two miles eastward; and several others at the distance of six to ten miles in a southeast direction. Northwestward also, beyond the State line and within a few miles of it is a number of ore-beds, mostly magnetic—one limonite; indeed it is evident that there is an extensive range of iron ores in this region, which are of the highest quality, and must one day attract a large capital for their development. Deposits of ore are also found in other parts of the county; but like the last named, they are known only by their outcrops. One of these is a bed of magnetite, on the lower slope of Little Yellow Mountain, at Flat Rock. The ore is quite like the Cranberry, of equal purity apparently, and strongly polaric. Some large blocks are found on the surface, weighing several hundred pounds, but no vein or bed of more than one or two feet, has been exposed by the slight effort at trenching recently made. Frequent specimens of menaccanite are also found at the same locality.

A bed of limonite occurs three or four miles northwest of Flat Rock, recognizable by a profusion of surface fragments, but no explorations have been made. On Rock Creek, beyond Bakersville, at the foot of the great Roan Mountain, are also several beds of magnetic ore, of which hand specimens resemble the Cranberry ore, and the geological associations are also the same. Of the size of the beds I have no definite information, except in regard to one near the mouth of Big Rock Creek, where a little trenching has been done, and a few small veins or beds of irregular shape, and one or two feet thickness, were touched. The rock is gneiss, syenite and doleryte, much decomposed superficially. Other larger deposits are said to exist near the head of the same stream. Near Bakersville, also, I have seen small outcrops of limonite.

In Ashe county, in the northwest corner of the State, there are some important ore deposits, on the waters of North Fork of New River. They lie chiefly north and northeast of Jefferson, on Horse Creek, and Helton Creek. On the former creek there are two beds of ore, both coarse, granular, highly magnetic and polaric, in gneiss and syenyte. The gangue is largely pyroxene and epidote. One is on a high mountainous ridge, some 500 feet above, and on the west side of the creek, and two miles from the river, at Hampton's; the other on the east side, at Graybill's. Both are traceable many rods by numerous surface fragments which indicate beds of considerable extent.

On Helton, six or eight miles east of the last, are still larger deposits, of very pure magnetic ore, which has been long used in the forges of the neighborhood. The ore is a coarse-grained and very pure magnetite, one of the beds of which is reported to be eighteen feet in thickness and another nine feet. This is manifestly an iron region, and worthy of a thorough investigation.

There are many other localities in this region from which hand specimens have been brought to the Museum; as for example, Cove Creek in Watanga, which has furnished both magnetite and limonite, and the neighborhood of Flat Top Mountain, where a titaniferous ore is found.

Iron Ores of the French Broad.—There are several localities on the western slopes of the Black Mountain, on the head waters of Ivy, in the eastern edge of Madison where magnetite is found in considerable surface masses, though no explorations have been made. A bed also of titaniferous iron occurs here near the public road, and about midway between Ashville and Burnsville. The prevalent rock of the region is gneiss, with much hornblende slate and syenyte. There are many fragments of this ore of considerable size along the steep slope of a mountain spur. It is very hard, lustre resinous, color black, fracture subconchoidal. The analysis is as follows (Hanna):

Titanic Acid,	37.88
Protoxide of Iron,	37.06
Sesquioxide,	11.03
Sesquioxide of Manganese,	0.89
Alumina,	9.51
Lime,	2.57
Magnesia,	0.93

Sulphur,..	0.09
Phosphoric Acid,..	trace
Water,..	0.15
Silica,..	0.83
	100.94

On Bear Creek below Marshall, near the French Broad, there are surface fragments of magnetite in hornblende slate, but no vein or bed has been exposed. On the eastern fork of Big Laurel there is a large outcrop of a slaty granular magnetite at Mrs. Norton's, and near Jewel Hill a bed or vein of specular hematite in a reddish felspathic gneiss, the ore said to be abundant. About 5 miles west of Ashville a bed of limonite of several feet thickness has been opened. There are hand specimens of magnetic ore in the Museum, brought from the eastern part of Buncombe county, but no outcrop has been reported to me. There is a range of limonite ore-beds associated with the limestones of this county, which follow them from Cane Creek across and up the French Broad into Transylvania.

In *Haywood* county, there is a larger massive outcrop of granular magnetite; it is in the northeastern part of the county on Wilkins' Creek. The bed is no doubt large, from the boldness of the outcrop, which projects in large masses above the surface.

There are also magnetites and hematites in various localities of Jackson and Macon counties, some of which are represented in the Museum by very fine specimens, and the deposits are reported to be extensive, but as no iron has been made in those counties, there has been no occasion for their development. Mr. Smith has some observations on the ores of this section in the Appendix, p. 115 et seq., to which the reader is referred.

Iron Ores of Cherokee.—There is no other county in the state which contains so much iron ore as Cherokee. It is all however of one species, limonite. The marble beds of Valley River and Notteley River are everywhere accompanied by beds of this ore. There seem to be generally 2, 3 and 4 parallel beds of it, one or two of which are frequently slaty and micaceous,—a limonitic mica slate, and the others cellular concretionary, &c., and (the most western, generally) ochreous. The breadth of this iron and marble range is 2 to more than 3 miles. The trough which has been scooped out by the rivers, in a northeasterly and southwesterly direction, owes its existence to the destructible beds of limestone and their associated soft mica-schists and hydro-mica slates and shales, which occupy this tract. The direct valley range is about 24 miles in length; and there is bifurcation of it, at a point 6 or 8 miles above Murphy, one branch pursuing a more southerly course, by way of Peachtree Creek and Brasstown Creek, making the whole iron range of the county above 30 miles.

The most common and characteristic terms of the series, in cross section, are, counting from the northwest, slaty gneiss and mica schist, limonite, steatyte, marble, limonite, slaty quartzyte, slaty limonite, mica-schist and slaty gneiss.

At several points there are two or three reduplications of the marble, and there are commonly intercalations of mica schists and hydro-mica slates between the different terms of the series. The section at Valleytown shows two parallel beds of limonite on the slope of the mountains to the south, these beds being sometimes not more than 100 to 200 yards apart; the marble lies in the valley, and the slaty talc beds to the north side of the valley, and a bed of ochre north of that, outcropping in Paint Creek, 6 to 10 feet wide. There are here two or three parallel beds of marble. Lower down, at the Parker Mine (gold), and across by the Taylor place, are, first, the 2 beds of limonite, some 200 yards apart; then the valley, with its marble and steatyte, with an outcrop of limonite to the north. This is nearly half way between Valleytown and Murphy. At Colbert's, the quartzyte ridge appears with iron beds on both flanks. This is 6 to 7 miles above Murphy, where some rude mining has been done for iron ore quite recently, and much more and more systematic mining in ancient times, by no one knows whom or for what purpose. There are still visible shafts more than a hundred feet deep, which are said to have been approached by drifts, of which some signs of the entrance still remain. The marble here comes next the iron, to the northwest, and then the steatyte. The latter appears of unusually fine quality in a large bed near by, at Mrs. Leatherwoods. At Mrs. Hayes', the quartzyte appears with its northern bed of limonite, followed by the marble, talc and another bed of limonite. At several points between this and Murphy the same terms of the series are discoverable. About one mile north of Murphy the quartzyte forms a high ridge, having the two beds of limonite, one on either flank, that on the northwest very fine and 25 feet thick. From this point much one has been obtained for the supply of the neighborhood forges, chiefly the one on Hanging Dog Creek. The iron was reputed of very good quality. Beyond this bed of ore in the same section, is the marble and talc of "No. 6."

At one-half mile below Murphy there seem to be four limonite beds with a small outcrop of the quartzyte, the marble occupying the middle term of the section. One of these beds may be seen in the streets of

Murphy; but half a mile below, are two fine outcrops, indicating the presence of immense quantities of ore. Taking the course of the Notteley to the southwestward, the two limonite beds, with intervening quartzyte, appear near the Ducktown road about 5 miles from Murphy, and there is a large outcrop also at the bridge, 6 miles from Murphy. There is a large quarry of steatyte within the same distance. Ascending the Hiwassee from Murphy, on the south bank, at the distance of about 2 miles, and after passing a heavy bed of slaty gneissoid quartzyte, is a large bed of limonite; and beyond this, other quartzose gneisses, much-veined; then a second bed of the ore, after which come hydro-mica slates, and at 3 miles, (Martin's), white marble. Half a mile beyond is a fine bed of limonite 10 to 12 feet thick, which has been worked to some extent, and a few hundred yards further, is a bed of blue marble, which is reported to occur also on Brasstown Creek. The steatyte does not show itself in this section, being concealed by superficial deposits, but in another section a little north (less than 2 miles,) it comes in as a brown spongy decomposed massive talcose rock just west of Garrison's, the marble and iron ore appearing on both sides of it at Garrison's, and west of the ledge; this last being an ocherous bed, associated with quartzyte. Eastward of Garrison's, on this section, at Williams', the marble appears, and at Southard's, both marble and limonite; and the marble and iron are reported as outcropping again at Coleman's, on Little Brasstown Creek, the marble here having a greater thickness than at any other point, many hundreds of feet. The last outcrop in this direction of the marble and limonite is near Peachtree Creek, between 7 and 8 miles from Murphy. So that here the beds must have suffered much and rapid folding or faulting.

These beds of ore are traceable northwards to within two miles of the Valley River beds near Mrs. Hayes'. The quantity of ore in this county is therefore immense, and very widely distributed, and the forests of the mountain slopes furnish unlimited supplies of fuel, while the marble is at hand everywhere for fluxing. The quality of the ore may be inferred from the following analysis by (Chatard for) Genth, of a large mass obtained from the open cut a mile north of Murphy:

Sesquioxide of Iron,	85.69
Silica,	1.50
Water,	12.81
Metallic Iron,	59.98

The above description of the Cherokee ore beds is made from the abbreviated notes of a hurried exploration made several years ago. These fine ore ranges are eminently worthy of detailed study and mapping; and it is hoped that before long some additional investigation may be made. Prof. Bradley has recently published some very interesting notes of observations and measurements on different parts of the range, in the American Journal of Science, and it is hoped he will pursue the subject.

This completes the description of the North Carolina iron ores, as far as my investigations and information have gone. There remains much to do to complete the chapter; there are many blanks to fill, and whole counties, of which little is known, except that they contain iron ores. My work has been necessarily limited to the study of such ore beds as have happened to be opened, and of course these are but a small proportion of the whole, in a region always wholly devoted to agriculture and studiously eschewing all sorts of manufacturing. A map of the iron ore deposits of the State, as far as known, is a desideratum which it is hoped will be supplied in the next volume.

It may be worth while to add here, as a sort of appendix to the chapter, an analysis by Dr. Genth, of a sample of spathic iron from Conrad Hill, Davidson county:

Oxide of Iron,	47.70
Oxide of Manganese,	2.06
Magnesia,	10.77
Lime,	0.63
Carbonic Acid, Water &c.,	38.84

Metallic Iron,	37.10

This spathic ore, (siderite), is found in many of the mines of Cabarrus, Rowan and Davidson, and in some of them in large quantities. At the Cosby Mine in Cabarrus, an immense heap of it has been thrown out in mining for copper, and it is contaminated by the presence of copper pyrites.

2. Copper Ores.

For obvious reasons, there has been little mining done in North Carolina since the war, and so but little has been done in the way of re-opening old or discovering new copper mines. Dr. Emmons brought down the description of enterprise in this direction pretty nearly to the date of the war; and as few of the mines which he described have been worked since, there is no need to go over the ground. To this remark there are a few exceptions. One of the mines of Guildford county, the old Gardiner Hill Mine, was re-opened and worked down below 300 feet. The ore was still very fine copper pyrites, and the vein is reported as holding out well, but for some reason, the working has been abandoned. The Emmons' Mine also, more recently called the Davidson Mine, was re-opened and worked for several years by a Baltimore company, but has been abandoned for several years, no doubt because it did not pay. This vein is on the same line with Gold Hill, in the argillaceous and chloritic and talcoid slates of the western border of the great central Huronian belt. It was worked down to a considerable depth and very complete works for the concentration of the ore were erected, and much ore shipped to Baltimore. But for two or three years they have been idle.

The Clegg Mine also, in Chatham, was re-opened since the war by a northern company and extensive works were erected, and the vein followed down to 200 feet, but everything has been abandoned for some reason, for these two years.

The vein is quartz, with copper pyrites in talco-argillaceous and talco-quartzitic slates. Much of the veinstone, in depth, is a talco-siliceous and argillaceous breccia, of a gray and bluish mottled appearance, together with a dark blue jaspery quartzitic rock. The vein is traceable for hundreds of yards through the forests by large outcrops of white quartz. The thickness of it in the workings was reported as ranging from three, or four to six feet. Calcspar, in hexagonal prisms, occurs in the vein, and also in curved plates, enclosing masses of bituminous coal. The mine has also furnished fine specimens of azurite.

I had never an opportunity to explore any of these veins, while operations were going on, although such opportunity was sought, and so I do not venture to give any detailed descriptions, which would be only at second hand. There are, however, several copper mines in the western section of the State, which although opened before the war, are not mentioned by Emmons. The chief of these are in two ranges, one in Jackson and Haywood counties, the other in Ashe and Alleghany. Those of the former I visited shortly after the war, when, of course, little was to be seen. The copper belt occupies the middle portion of Jackson county, from the headwaters of Tuckasege river northward to Scott's creek and Savannah creek, a region which is characterized, geologically, by the prevalence of hornblende slates, and gneisses and syenytes. The principal points where mining operations have been carried on are Waryhut, Cullowhee and Savannah, although work has been done and symptoms of the presence of copper discovered at many other places, as Shell Ridge, Scott's Creek, Sugarloaf, Panther Knob, Wolf Creek, &c. The first named of the above mines, Waryhut, had been opened by a shaft said to have been 100 feet deep. The mine is on Waryhut creek, about six miles southeast of Webster; the vein was described as five to eight feet thick, the ore copper pyrites, with the usual carbonates and silicates near the surface. The rock is a tough, grayish syenytic gneiss. The Cullowhee mine is on Cullowhee mountain, southwest of the former, and at an elevation of several hundred feet above it. The rock is a gray gneiss, with hornblende in immediate association with the vein. The thickness of the latter is estimated to be about eight feet. The ore is copper pyrites, but too much weathered to allow an estimate of its richness. The vein was not well exposed, and so no minute examination could be made. A similar remark may be made in regard to the Savannah Mine, nine miles west of Webster, on Savannah Creek. The rock here is a massive coarse garnetiferous syenyte, and the vein about nine feet thick. The ore is copper pyrites, but no fresh surfaces were exposed, and therefore no good specimens could be procured for analysis. My impression of the Cullowhee and Savannah Mines was that they are very promising and well worthy of the attention of capitalists. Of the Waryhut I could form no opinion, because it was not accessible. There is in the northern part of Haywood county a copper mine, near Wilkins' Creek, where two shafts have been sunk and a drift of 75 feet cut; but the vein was not accessible. There was however a very formidable outcrop of *gossan*, indicating a large vein. For further information of this mine, as well as of others belonging to this range, I refer to Mr. Smith's paper in the Appendix, p. 112.

Of the other copper range, in Ashe and Alleghany, one of the most notable localities is Elk Knob and its spurs, within a radius of three or four miles. The prevalent and characteristic rock of this mountain and region is garnetiferous hornblende slate, with gray gneiss. The Elk Knob Mine is on the northwest slope of the mountain, at an elevation of some 4000 feet above the sea. The vein which cropped out in a deep ravine, was insufficiently exposed; but it is evidently not less than six or seven feet thick. The rock is a dark gray gneiss. The ore at the surface was mostly iron pyrites with a moderate admixture of copper pyrites. At the southern base of the mountain the Miller Mine had been opened, and a shaft sunk 60 feet, and some fine specimens of calcho-pyrite were still obtainable among the rubbish, but nothing can be stated as of my own observation, as to the character or size of the vein. At other points on the slope of the mountain are promising outcrops of gossan, but no explorations of them had been made.

The Peach Bottom Mine is in the western part of Alleghany county on Elk Creek, and not far from New River. This mine had been opened before the war to a depth of 150 feet, and works erected for the preparation of the ore for market; and during the war several hundred barrels of fine ore were sent to Petersburg. The shaft was full of water at the time of my visit. The cre is calchopyrite, with a little galenite. The rock is a gray soft decomposable gneiss.

Gap Creek Mine is situated in Watauga county, near the southern border of Ashe, and about 3 miles from Deep Gap. This is a quartz vein, or rather a group of them; the principal one carrying variegated copper, with a little chalcopyrite, malachite, chrysocolla, specular iron, pyrite, together with visible free gold and silver. The vein is in a large body of hornblende slate, though the prevalent rock of the section is a gray gneiss, with a strike N. 60° E., and dip southeast 40°. The vein is a true fissure, with a direction N. 35° W., dip northeast 45°. Dr. Emmons, who visited the mine when it was open, says: "This is a true vein, and has a perfect regularity in direction as well as in its walls." "The width is variable, being 18 inches at the surface, and from 12 to 24 inches at different depths below ground." The ore was analyzed by Mr. Manross, who reported "gold 1¾ ounces and silver 18 ounces per ton of mixed ore and rock."

The most remarkable vein however in this range, and indeed in the state, is at Ore Knob in the southeast corner of Ashe, near the top of the Blue Ridge, and about 2 miles from New River. This mine was opened before the war, but not explored to any depth or with any system, and its real character was not developed until about two years ago, when it was purchased by the present owners, the Messrs. Clayton & Co., of Baltimore. These gentlemen have opened the vein by a series of shafts and tunnels, and have been repaid by the discovery of a body of ore which is not equalled at any mine I know of outside of Ducktown. The accompanying topographical chart and section will show the relations of things and the extent of the operations better than any description. The chart was made from observations taken last autumn with a Locke's level and pocket barometer and compass, and the section is a copy kindly made for me from the working section in the office, by a young civil engineer, Mr. Raht, of the Rensselaer Polytechnic School, who happened to be present.

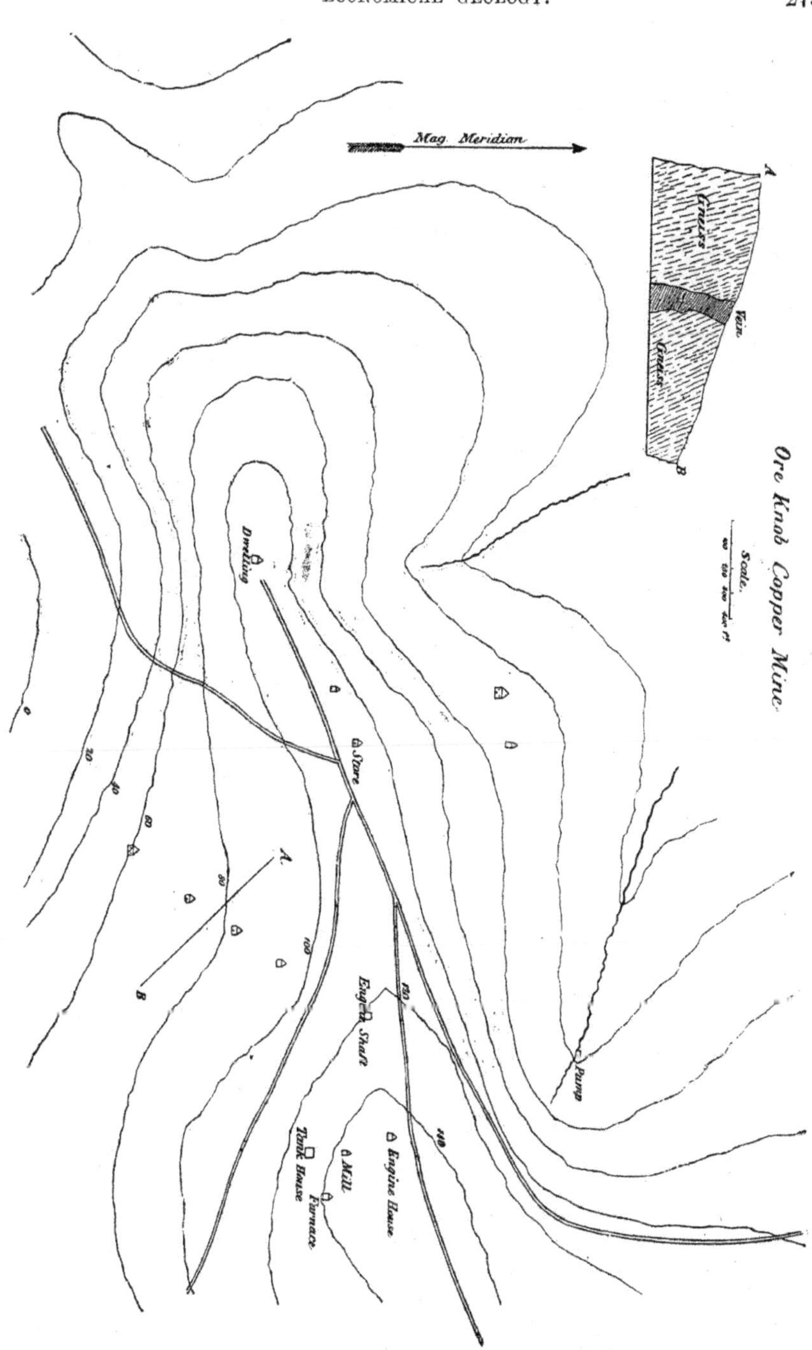
Mag. Meridian
Ore Knob Copper Mine
Scale.
Gneiss
Vein
Gneiss
Dwelling
Store
Engine Shaft
Pump
Engine House
Mill
Tank House
Furnace
A.
B

The rock of the region is a gray (and usually) thin-bedded gneiss, with mica schists and slates. These have a prevalent strike a little east of northeast, and dip east at a tolerably high angle; though both dip and strike are subject to considerable variation. The walls of the copper vein are micaceous gneiss and mica slates, with a strike N. 57° E., and dipping southeast at an angle of 40° to 45°. The copper vein is coincident in strike with the rocks, but is vertical, cutting across the strata in dip, so that it is a true fissure vein, and not bedded, like those at Ducktown. It is traceable by an outcrop of *gossan* for more than a mile, and has been proved by trial shafts and trenches for nearly 2,000 feet. The breadth of the lode varies from about 6 feet to 15 feet, (is stated to measure 20 in some cases), averaging about 10 probably. Seven shafts have been sunk vertically in the vein, and levels driven, at the depths of 90 and 150 feet, these shafts and drifts often not touching either wall; so that the vein is opened for a linear distance of 650 feet. There is, properly speaking, no gangue stone, the whole breadth of the fissure being filled with ore. The gossan, which is decomposed oxydised ore, extends to an average depth of over 50 feet in the different shafts, the lower half containing however a valuable percentage of copper in the form of oxyd and malachite. Below this level of oxydation, the ore is sulphuret of copper. The quantity of ore removed in the mere process of opening the mine is very great, (estimated at over 3,500 tons), as there was no loss of work, every foot of excavation being represented by its equivalent of ore on the surface. Some parts of the vein contain small portions of magnetite, quartz and garnet. Dr. T. S. Hunt had examined the mine a few weeks before my visit, and I give his analyses of the ores. He says: "Two samples of the gossan, taken at distances of two or three feet above the sulphurets, yielded respectively 14 and 22 per cent. of copper. It is evident that a large proportion of this gossan can be treated advantageously for copper." Of the unaltered portion of the vein, he says: "Some parts of the vein are filled with copper pyrites, mixed with more or less magnetite, and yielding in different specimens 17 to 22 per cent. of copper, while a larger portion consists chiefly of an impure variegated ore, giving in different assays, 35, 39 and 45 per cent. of copper." "An average sample of fresh and undried ore from a large pile gave 25 per cent., and another from a large pile, chiefly of iron-black ore gave 36 per cent. of copper." The average of the ores which were undergoing reduction in August, 1874, was estimated by Mr. Clayton to range between 12 and 20 per cent.

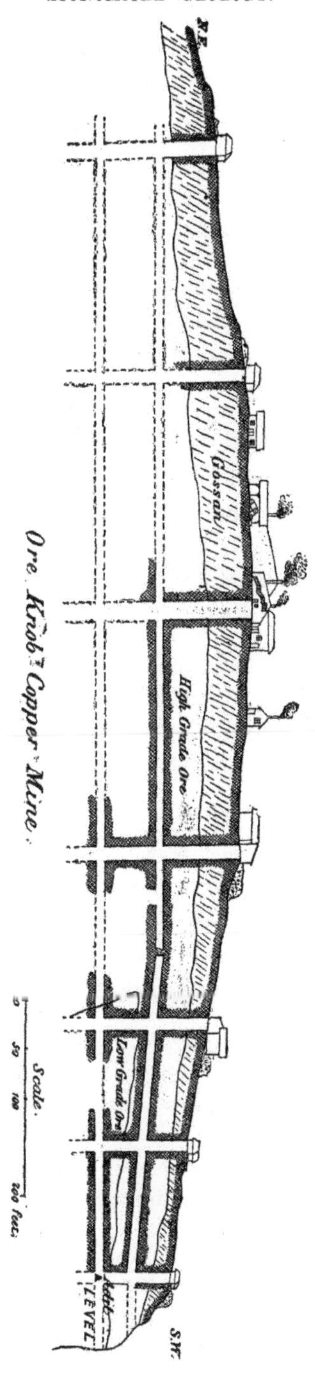
Ore Knob Copper Mine.
N.E.
Gossan
High Grade Ore
Low Grade Ore
Scale.
0 50 100 200 feet.
Adit LEVEL
S.W.

The mine being situated at the distance of 40 miles from the nearest railroad depot, (Marion, Va.), it was desirable to reduce the ores on the spot. For this purpose the process of precipitation, by the method of Hunt & Douglass, has been adopted, and the works were turning out daily 2½ tons of "cement copper," yielding 75 to 80 per cent. of the metal. Preparations were making to erect furnaces for smelting the cement copper, and thus saving an additional item of cost of transport, by hauling only the pure pig copper to the railroad. The furnaces I am informed have been erected and all the operations of reduction are completed on the ground. Preparations were also making to double the capacity of the reducing works, which when completed will place Ore Knob among the leading copper mines of the world. To carry on these large operations, which is done by the employment of the labor which the region itself furnishes, a considerable town has already sprung up in the wilderness, and a market has been created for all that the region can produce.

The intelligence, skill and energy displayed in the rapid and successful development of this magnificent property are beyond all praise, and have well merited the splendid results which are already more than in sight.

It is very unfortunate that a proposition from the same enterprising gentlemen, the Messrs. Clayton, father and son, was not accepted by the owners of the Elk Knob Mine. The whole region, and the state even, would feel the impulse of this activity and reap the most direct and varied benefits.

It is not improbable that this very decided success may lead to further investments in the great copper range which extends, with interruptions, from Ore Knob to Ducktown, including Elk Knob and the promising veins above mentioned in Jackson and Haywood.

I add some general notes by Dr. Genth, which were published in the Journal of the Franklin Institute, Philadelphia, in 1872. They are the result of extensive observations made by this eminent minerolagist, both while he was assisting in the Geological Survey in 1871, and during several years of residence and exploration in the mining districts of the state in former years, when mining operations were carried on very widely and on a large scale in all directions: so that his opportunities for intimate and extensive acquaintance with the history of mining among us, and with the range and character and peculiarities of the mineral veins and ore deposits of the state, are unsurpassed.

Copper.—" Copper ores have been found in many localities throughout the state, in the veins of the old gneissoid rocks, as well as in the more recent slates, and even in the triassic formation.

The principal ore is chalcopyrite or copper pyrites; and there is every reason to believe that many of the mines require only a fuller development to enable them to furnish large quantities of valuable ores.

Many of the gold veins are associated with pyritic ores, and in fact almost all the North Carolina copper mines in the central counties have first been worked for gold, and there are hardly any mines in Guilford, Cabarrus and Mecklenburg Counties occurring in the gneissoid and syenitic rocks, which do not show strong indications of copper ores.

When mining operations receive a new impetus, it is to be hoped that this very important fact will be borne in mind, and that no mine should be started without sufficient means to develop it at once to such a depth that a workable body of copper ores may be reached.

The general character of these mines is that about at water level, the so-called brown gold ores are replaced by quartz richly charged with iron pyrites more or less mixed with copper pyrites, the latter increasing as the mine deepens, and in many places becoming the only, or the predominating ore, and forming a regular copper vein.

The ores either became poor in gold or the latter could not be extracted by the ordinary process, then chiefly in use in North Carolina—Chilian mills and arastra—therefore many valuable mines were abandoned, mostly before a larger and paying quantity of copper ores had been reached.

In this formation there is not at present a single copper mine in operation, although many look favorable for further development.

The principal mines which promised to change into copper mines are in Guilford county, the Fisher Hill, the North Carolina, the McCulloh, Lindsay, Gardner Hill, Twin Mines, etc.; in Cabarrus county, the Ludowick, Boger, Hill, Phœnix, Orchard, Vanderburg, Pioneer Mills, etc., and in Mecklenburg the McGinn, Hopewell, Rudesill, Cathay Mines, etc.

The cupreous minerals observed in the mines are, near the surface, small quantities of native copper and cuprite, the latter sometimes in beautiful needles, the so-called chalcotrichite, malachite, rarely azurite, chrysocolla and pseudo-malachite, and in some of the mines chalcocite and barnhardtite; all resulting from the decomposition of chalcopyrite or copper pyrites, which forms the principal ore. Siderite or carbonate of iron often forms an important gangue rock."

3. Gold.

The same influences which have prevented mining operations in other directions, account also for the fact that but few of the gold mines of the state have been re-opened since the war. A few of the more noted mines, however, have claimed the attention of capitalists, and work has been resumed in several quarters. The King's Mountain Mine, for example, was unwatered and a California battery of 20 stamps started within two or three years after the war; and it has passed into the hands of a strong company, who have imported the latest forms of machinery for the elimination of the metal from its ores. It is worth while to mention that the gold is found here in a bluish talco-argillaceous slate and in a gray and bluish *limestone* which constitutes one of the series of the King's Mountain slates, described elsewhere. The gold is found disseminated through a large part of the thickness of the bed (above 60 feet), some strata, however, being much richer than others. The mine has been worked to a depth of 200 feet, and is said to have yielded, in the aggregate, more than $1,000,000.

The Rhodes' mine, also in Gaston county, on the South Fork of the Catawba, near Dallas, was worked by a Montana compay a few years ago on a considerable scale; but the ores were found too poor to justify the expense of separating the metal. The mine is peculiar in that the gold is found not in a vein, but in a bed of ferruginous, decomposed, slaty, micaceous gneiss.

The famous Gold Hill Mine in Rowan county has also been re-opened, and work has been carried on almost continuously ever since the close of the war. Experiments have recently been tried here with new processes for the reduction of sulphuret ores, and with new machinery; but with what result I am not informed. The mine is described by Emmons.

A mine was opened up in Cleaveland county by the Mountain Mining Company a few miles south of Shelby, a year or two after the war, but was soon abandoned because too poor. This is mentioned because the mode of occurrence of the gold is peculiar. There is no vein, but, as in the case of the Rhodes' Mine, the gold occurs in the rock, which here is a brown and purplish, decomposed, garnetiferous hydro-mica-schist, the gold-bearing strata being more than 100 feet thick.

Some mining has been done in several of the placer or gravel deposits of the state, within the past few years. In the neighborhood of the famous old Reid Mine, some fine nuggets have been recently found, of the value of several hundred dollars, and in one case of two thousand dollars.

A good deal of work has also been done at the old Portis Mine in Nash and Franklin counties, and at other localities in the neighborhood, where there are extensive gold-bearing gravel-beds.

The Montgomery beds have also been worked on a small scale in a number of localities, but with no striking results. Something has also been done towards the re-opening of some of the numerous vein mines of this and the neighboring counties, Moore, Randolph, &c., but the absence of capital is still too seriously felt to permit the development of so expensive an industry.

In the South Mountains, however, a considerable amount of mining has been done, operations having been resumed in a multitude of gravel deposits of this region, where are found by far the most extensive placer diggings in the State. For a description of the character and origin of these deposits, see page 156. The area over which these are spread in the counties of Burke, McDowell and Rutherford, can hardly be less than 200 square miles. The gold-bearing drift, or "gravel" is accumulated along the beds of the streams, on the benches and in all the various situations which in California have given rise to the terms *river*, *hill*, *bench*, *flat and gulch* "*diggings*." An immense quantity of gold has been obtained from the mines of this section since their opening about 1829, probably between two and three millions of dollars. The most noted localities,—the richest and most extensive beds of auriferous gravel lie on the head waters of Silver Creek, Muddy Creek and First Broad and Second Broad rivers,—Brindletown, Brackettown, Whiteside and Jeanstown. As much as ten dollars a day to the hand has often been made in the early workings of these deposits, and I am informed by some of the older citizens, that just before the California gold deposits began to attract attention, as many as 3000 hands might have been seen at work on one of the streams above named.

There is still a large amount of gold in the beds which remain untouched, as well as in those which have been rudely and carelessly worked over, some of them more than once. Indeed, some of the richest of these deposits have remained unworked on account of the difficulty of bringing a supply of water to their level, being situated considerably above the neighboring streams, or the higher slopes and benches of the foot hills of the mountains. In one of these cases, on the upper waters of Silver Creek, water has recently been brought from a distance of several miles, and an attack made upon some of these more elevated deposits; and the result is that they are found to be very rich and the working highly remunerative. This enterprise has been inaugurated by Col. J. C. Mills, who owns a very large acreage of such detrital beds, some of them 20 to 25 and even 30 feet deep.

Vein mining has never been found profitable in this section; in fact there are no veins of size discoverable. The gold seems to have been contained in mere strings and thin sheets of quartz intercalated between the beds of decomposable mica schists and micaceous gneisses of the Archæan formation. And among the gravel beds are frequently found fragments of quartz with strings and plates and crystals of native gold, these fragments evidently representing the entire thickness of the vein from which they were weathered. And in a few localities the minute veins and gold-bearing laminæ of quartz are so abundant in the decomposed mass of rock as to make it profitable, where water is abundant, to wash down large masses and breasts of such earth. Col. Mills has made this interesting and successful experiment. But the drift-beds, where nature has already performed this preliminary and expensive part of the work, furnish as yet, more profitable working.

There is also a series of gold-bearing gravel-beds in Caldwell county, chiefly on Lower Creek and its tributaries, mostly those on the north side. In this region, on John's River, are two vein mines of some note, the Baker Mine and the Michaux Mine. In the latter the veins are very much scattered and subdivided into threads and strings. The country rock is gneiss and mica schist, much decomposed. The Baker Mine is a little higher up the river, near the mouth of Wilson's Creek. The vein is enclosed between a heavy bed of serpentine and a body of felspathic slaty gneiss. A large quartz vein, which meets this, nearly at right angles, is auriferous, and contains argentiferous galena, in minute quantities.

In Polk county also, near the foot of the Blue Ridge, there are several gold "diggings" at Sandy Plains, and on Pacolet (Pactolus?) River. The gold is found in the "gravel" from the debris of the neighboring denuded hills of mica schist. These deposits are found along the streams, over an area of several miles.

Beyond the Blue Ridge are several gold mining localities, some of which at one time attracted considerable attention. In Watauga county a limited area of gold-gravel is found on Howard's Creek, which was worked on a small scale some years before the war. Indications of gold have been found on Cane Creek, in Buncombe county, and on Boylston in Transylvania, but no deposits or veins of importance have been discovered.

There are two other "gold regions" in the mountain section, one in Cherokee, the other in Jackson.

The gold of Jackson county is also obtained almost entirely from placers or detrital beds. These are situated chiefly along southern slopes of the Blue Ridge, near Hogback and Chimney Top Mountains. The most important locality is Fairfield Valley, where Georgetown Creek, one of the head streams of the Toxaway, is said to have yielded between two and three hundred thousand dollars. The deposits extend several miles along these elevated basins and have by no means been exhausted.

The origin of the gold here is doubtless to be sought in veins in the Blue Ridge, which rises as a precipitous wall of gray gneiss, sheer up from the valley 7 or 800 feet, on the north and east; and it is along the base of this wall, where Georgetown Creek has cut a deep channel across it, that the gold is principally obtained. The deposits in Transylvania county east of the Blue Ridge, on the head waters of French Broad, will probably be found to have the same origin, and are evidently a continuation of the same belt.

The gold belt of Cherokee is in the same body of soft slates and schists which carry the limestone and iron. It is found both in veins and superficial deposits. The sands of Valley River yield profitably through a large part of its course, and some very rich "washings" have been found along its tributary streams on the north side. The origin of this gold is very near the limestone. A remarkably rich vein has been opened near the town of Murphy, known as No. 6, which immediately underlies the marble. This is a silver-lead quartz vein, in which is embedded a large percentage of free gold. There is a strong probability of other similar veins having furnished the golden sands of the river and streams above mentioned.

On the southeast af the limestones is also a series of "diggings" along the lower slopes of the mountains, from near Valleytown to Vengeance Creek, a distance of 12 to 15 miles. The gold is found here in the drift which covers the lower spurs and terminal ridges of the mountains lying south of Valley River. The drift beds have a depth of 10 to 20 feet and an elevation above the river of 150 to 200 feet, and are remarkable for the great size of their quartz boulders and their very large and abundant staurotide crystals. These last indicate, with a good degree of probability, that the gold here is derived from the talco-micaceous slates, (several miles to the southeast), where these crystals are found in place.

At one point, the Parker Mine, extensive arrangements had been completed at the opening of the war for working these deposits by the hydraulic process. For this purpose water was conveyed three or four miles along the face of the mountain in canals and aqueducts so as to gain the necessary elevation.

The continuation of this gold belt southwestward across the country is rendered probable by the existence of several mines in this direction beyond the Hiwassee, as the Warren Mine, on Brasstown Creek, and others on Nottleley River, in the edge of Georgia.

The following general observations are added from the paper by Dr. Genth, already mentioned:

Gold. "According to the earliest records, the first piece of gold found in North Carolina was picked up in 1799, in a little branch at the Reid plantation, Cabarrus county. It weighed between three and four lbs., and was kept several years without its real character being suspected; subsequently it was sold to a jeweller, in Fayetteville, for $3.50. When its true character became known, search was made for more, and fourteen lumps, weighing in the aggregate 153 lbs. troy, were obtained at the same locality.

The gold veins and gravel deposits were afterwards discovered; and for a considerable time gold operations were conducted in many localities on a comparatively large scale. The discoveries of gold in California, where a far richer harvest was promised. led to the abandonment of many of those enterprises; other causes have also influenced in the same direction, as, for example, the difficulties connected with deep vein mining, and the impossibility of extracting the gold by the imperfect and slow machinery then principally in use, the Chilian Mill and Arastra, etc., from heavy ores like pyrite, &c., which nature has not already decomposed. With the exception of minute quantities of telluride, in the *very rare* mineral nagyagite, at the King's mountain mine, gold in North Car olina is always found in the metallic state. It is rarely quite pure, but generally alloyed with more or less silver. It occurs in crystals or crystalline masses, in thin plates or laminæ, between the foliation of the slates or through associated minerals, such as quartz, pyrite, galenite, zincblende, etc., in such a fine state of division that it is generally invisible to the eye.

It has been observed in four different geological positions:

1st. It is met with in the *mass* of the gneissoid, granitic and hornblendic rocks.

2. In quartz veins, often associated with pyrite, chalcopyrite, galenite tetradymite and other minerals.

3. In ore beds, cotemporary with the strata of rocks in which they are found, as in chloritic and talcose slates, argillites, quartzites, etc.

4. Loosely in the soil and decomposed rocks, especially in gravel deposits, resulting from the destruction of the above first three formations. One of the most remarkable features peculiar to the rocks of the Southern States is their rapid disintegration.

In some of the auriferous regions of North Carolina, quartz veins are very numerous; in others, they are less frequently met with.

Most of them are exceedingly small, varying in width from the thickness of a knife's blade to a few inches, and often extending in depth but a few feet; some bulge out and form nests and pockets in the rocks, while others again are of enormous size, and are known to exist as deep as they have been developed, which, in a few rare instances, is down to 200—300 feet.

Many of these quartz veins are in reality beds, as they coincide in strike and dip with the stratification, whilst an equally great number run in every conceivable direction, and dip just as irregularly.

The greater portion of these quartz veins contain *no* gold, or only such a small quantity that they could not be profitably worked, especially the large veins of vitreous and milky quartz.

Many of the small veins, principally those which contain granular or saccharoidal quartz, are rich in gold.

Some of the large veins, especially those containing much cellular quartz, have frequently been found to be the most productive. This cellular quartz results from the decomposition of pyrite, which once occupied the now empty spaces; leaving them either occasionally quite free from iron, or more generally rusty and more or less filled with limonite. These, the so called brown gold ores, are the best and most easily worked. At a greater depth of the veins, where the pyrite is not decomposed, the gold is so much mixed with heavy sulphurous ores that, with the present system of operations, it cannot be extracted with profit; in many cases the gold disappears entirely.

Most of these gold veins in North Carolina were abandoned, when the iron and copper pyrites increased too largely, and before they had been wrought deep enough to contain copper ores in paying quantities.

The gold in these mines is not evenly distributed through the mass of the gangue; the veins often contain entirely barren portions alternating with rich ones, the latter called shoots of ore or chimneys.

Such shoots are in reality veins inside of a vein, and are frequently quite regular in their dip; the ores at the foot wall are generally richer than those at the hanging wall.

Many gold mines of this description have formerly been worked, and many of them undoubtedly are still of great value.

Many of the quartz veins in the slates, differing in strike and dip from the inclosing slate, carry gold, especially those which contain cellular and cavernous quartz, associated with limonite, hematite, siderite, pyrite, chalcopyrite, etc.

The gold deposits, which are cotemporary with the slates themselves, are of far greater importance than the true gold veins.

The talcose, chloritic, micaceous or arenaceous slates in which they occur, contain portions which are more or less charged with gold. The gold in these slate beds, like the slates themselves, is derived from the destruction of the older rocks, and has been deposited simultaneously.

The width of these auriferous beds varies from a few inches to from 60 to 70 feet.

The gold in them is often found without any admixture, and the auriferous strata show no line of demarcation, and cannot be distinguished from the barren layers; but, generally, and subsequently to its deposition, it has been acted upon by chemical agencies, dissolved and precipitated again, and has assumed a crystalline structure; it has accumulated in strings which sometimes form lenticular and more highly auriferous masses in the beds, and is associated with crystalline quartz, pyrite, chalcopyrite, galenite, blende, mispickel, etc.

These are often parallel with the slates, and so close together that they can be worked by the same operation, especially where the slates between are also auriferous.

To this class belong the mines at Gold Hill, in Rowan County, which have already produced not less than $2,000,000, and have reached a depth of 750 feet. Although this appears to be a very large production, I do not hesitate to say that perhaps four-fifths of all the gold in the ore, which is a talco-micaceous or chloritic slate, intermixed with pyrite, magnetite, and a little quartz, has been lost in the tailings, on account of the very imperfect process used for the extraction of the same.

The King's Mountain Mine, of Gaston County, also belongs to this class. The gold is, to a great extent, contained in a quartzose limestone, and is associated with very small quantities of pyrite, galenite, chalcopyrite, but also with the very rare tellurides of lead, altaite, and with nagyagite, a telluride of gold and lead.

In gold mining operations, the deposits which result from the disintegration of the rocks, and subsequent denudation, are undoubtedly of the greatest importance; there the gold which was contained in the rocks and in the small auriferous veins (which have been broken up into fragments) has been concentrated by nature, and in many places has been deposited, with the remnants of the veins, in the gravel beds which I have already mentioned.

Those gravel beds occur to a greater or less extent throughout the whole gold region; the oldest gneissoid rocks as well as the slate formation contain them.

The quartz in general is not water-worn, only the sharp edges are rounded. Many pieces still present the shape and thickness of the veins whence they came.

The most extensive gravel deposits exist in the South Mountains, on the headwaters of the first and second Broad River, Muddy Creek and Silver Creek, in the counties of Rutherford, McDowell, Burke, Caldwell, also in Polk and Cleaveland; embracing an area of over 200 square miles.

They appear to cover the greater part of the land, rise often to a considerable height on the slope of the hills, but are naturally more concentrated in the bottom and flat lands. The gravel beds in this region vary in thickness from a few inches to thirty feet, and are covered with soil and clay, which is also more or less auriferous, although much poorer than the gravel beds below.

These deposits have been worked since 1830, and before gold was known in California many thousands of hands were at work digging and washing in a rude way, yet many millions of dollars were produced without the knowledge of a proper use of water.

Since that time very little has been done; in some instances the old gravel was worked over again, and has made fair returns to the adventurers.

Very large tracts of land, containing extensive and valuable deposits, have never been touched, and, by the introduction of the Californian hydraulic system of operations, a safe and very profitable business could be carried on.

The gold is rarely found in nuggets; generally as fine dust and in small grains. Its fineness averages about 825 thousandths. It is associated with numerous interesting minerals, such as platinum, diamond, zircon, xenotime, monazite, and many others.

Experiments with vein-mining in this region have not proved successful; the rich veins are too narrow in width, and of too limited extent in depth, and the large veins do not contain enough gold to be advantageously worked.

A small region of valuable gravel beds exists in the gneissoid rocks and micaceous slates of Franklin and Nash counties, in the eastern part of the state. It has been most extensively prospected at the Portis Mine, where it is very rich, and has been worked since about 50 years, having produced, it is said, over $1,000,000.

The productive gravel is here the result of the disintegration of numerous small granular or sugary quartz veins, and very fine specimens of gold in such quartz are frequently met with.

The fineness of the Portis Mine gold was generally about 985 thousandths.

There are enormous gravel piles at the mine—the remnants of former operations.

The gold in the gravel deposits, principally, is the *loose* gold, which had existed in the rocks and between their laminæ, or that from the *small* quartz veins, whilst the large veins are mostly *barren*. In a region which contains many small veins, the gravel deposits are generally valuable, even if the bulk of the beds has been made up from the destruction of large ones.

There are several highly important gravel deposits in Montgomery county, in the slate formation, some of which have produced a large amount of gold; the gold is mostly crystalline, in flat pieces, often covered with octahedral crystals, and in large nuggets; very little fine-grained gold has been found.

The best known deposit, which has produced large returns, but which is still, so to say, barely touched, is the so called Christian mine.

The Swift Creek mine, about seven miles distant, produces gold of similar appearance.

West of the Blue Ridge several gravel deposits have been worked, to a greater or lesser extent, in Cherokee and Jackson counties, also at Howard's Creek, in Watauga, and on the French Broad and New Rivers.

Throughout the whole gold region, every stream, branch and rivulet contains gold; and, as the washing of these is the most convenient way to obtain the precious metal on a small scale, there is hardly one which is not more or less worked, many of them up to their source."

Platinum.

"Only a few grains have been found in North Carolina, associated with gold in Rutherford and Burke counties; and there is no prospect that it ever will be found in large quantities."

Silver, Lead, Zinc.

"I shall consider those three metals under one head, as they are always associated.

Silver is a rare metal in North Carolina. With the exception of the silver alloyed with gold, varying from 1 or 2 to about 20 per cent., in the gold from veins and gravel deposits of the granitic and gneissoid rocks, very little silver has been found in the veins of these strata.

The only localities which came under my notice were at the Baker mine, in Caldwell, and at Scott's Hill, in Burke county. There it occurs but rarely, in veins of auriferous quartz. At the latter place it is only observed after burning the ore, and a little fragment which I have seen makes me feel confident that it is present as cerargyite, or chloride of silver.

Small quantities of argentiferous galenite and pyromorphite are associated with it.

Native silver has been observed with chalcocite or copper glauce at Gap Creek mine, in Wilkes county, and at the Asbury vein in Gaston county.

The only real silver mines of North Carolina are ore beds of zinc blende, mixed with galenite, in the argillaceous and talcose slates. The type of these is the old Washington mine, now Silver Hill, in Davidson county, which was discovered in 1838. Near the surface it formed a bed of carbonate of lead, having in many places films and plates of metallic silver disseminated through the mass of the ore. These ores were easily reduced, and produced handsome returns to the owners. This was, however, but of short duration. The undecomposed ores, which were a very fine-grained mixture of brown zinc-blende and argentiferous galenite, were soon reached, and presented great difficulties in the extraction of the precious metals.

When I was at the mine, about 22 years ago, an analysis of an average sample of between 2000—3000 tons of ore gave me about 45 per cent. of zinc, 21 per cent. of lead, about 8 ounces of silver per ton, with minute quantities of copper and gold. If the Philadelphia owners had abided by my advice, viz., to work the ores for zinc, and extract silver, copper and lead from the residues, they would probably still be in possession of this valuable mine.

The ore bed is large, and in one place has had a thickness of about 60 feet.

Occasionally it contains very rich spots, with native silver in lumps and filiform masses, or disseminated through the ore with argentite or highly argentiferous galenite; and besides these minerals this mine has furnished the most magnificent cabinet specimens of cerusite, pyromorphite, etc.

The mine is now 650 feet deep, and the ore is greatly mixed with slate. The purer masses are kept separate; the slaty ore is crushed and separated by buddles, etc., and the buddled ore is roasted and shipped to New York for the manufacture of the so called Bartletts' white lead. The production of this mine is now about 400 — 500 tons per month.

Very similar ore is found about six miles northeast of Silver Hill. The vein has not been developed, and the work done at Silver Valley has not been productive.

The Hoover mine, about six miles from Silver Hill, contains galenite, in a more coarsely crystalline variety, in a calcareous veinstone, and the Boss mine, two miles distant, has furnished handsome cabinet specimens of galenite in quartz.

The McMakin mine, about 1½ mile southeast from Gold Hill, is a very interesting one; the principal vein is a large vein of zinc-blende in talcose and argillaceous slates; it contains native silver, argentite, argentiferous galenite, and highly argentiferous tetrahedrite. The latter contains, according to my analysis, 10.53 per cent. of silver, and an average sample of ore of a 5′ vein, at 80 feet depth, which was sent to me about 11 years ago, yielded 246 ounces of silver per ton, worth about $334. The mine is not worked, but looks favorable enough to deserve fresh attention.

The Troutman mine, also in the neighborhood of Gold Hill, and one mile southeast of it, has been opened as a gold mine. It consisted of porous quartz, and yielded near the surface very rich ores, worth $50 per bushel; at the depth of 100 feet, where the sulphides are undecomposed, the ores yielded only $1, and contained a string of ash grey zinc-blende with pyrite, from 2 to 6 inches in width, which had increased to 18 inches when abandoned at a depth of 160 feet. These ores are well worthy of a fuller investigation, as they may be rich in gold.

I have already mentioned, when speaking of gold, the beds and veins of gold ore in Union and Montgomery counties, as being frequently associated with zinc blende. The string veins of the Steele mine principally consist of these and galenite.

At the Long (or Monroe) mine, in Union county, the quartz veins in the slates are richly charged with argentiferous galenite; but the veins have not been sufficiently explored to know whether it will increase in depth.

At the Lemmond (Marion) mine, a very remarkable vein or bed has been worked; it is irregular in size, sometimes widening out from a few inches to six feet. It consists of quartz, richly charged with brown zinc-blende and galenite, with small quantities of arsenopyrite, chalcopyrite, often intermixed with grains of electrum, a highly argentiferous variety of gold. Both the galenite and the zinc-blende are very rich. I have examined a *pure* specimen of galenite which did not show any admixture of *free* gold to the eye, but which yielded at the rate of nearly 30 oz. of gold and 86½ oz. ef silver to the ton; and pure brown zinc-blende gave me about 32 oz. of siver and gold, nearly half of which was gold. This vein appears to have a considerable longitudinal extension, and passes into the Steward mine property, formerly owned in Philadelphia.

At the latter mine, and at various other localities in this region, similar ores have been found, but the war has stopped all operations, and it will require capital and skill to develop this highly important mining district.

Galenite and zinc-blende occur at several other mines, associated with gold ores, as at the King's mountain, the Cansler and Shuford, and the Long Creek mines in Gaston county, etc.

At Cedar Cove, McDowell county, in the limestones of the so-called

Taconic slates, at the Dobson mine, there is found an accumulation of yellow and yellowish brown zinc-blende mixed with lime. I have not, however, seen anything from there which looks encouraging.

Galenite and zinc-blende is associated with the gold ores at Murphy, Cherokee county. Highly argentiferous galenite occurs at several localities on Beech mountain, Watauga; argentiferous and auriferous galenite have been discovered at Flint Knob in Wilkes county, and I have seen specimens of it from Marshall, Madison county, Clayton, Johnston county, and Elkin Creek, Surry county, and also in several of the copper mines throughout the state, but I have no knowledge of any deposit of sufficient magnitude to be worked advantageously."

TIN.

"No tin ore has been found in North Carolina as yet. Traces of this metal have been found in the tungstates of Cabarrus county, and in a micaceous slate in Gaston county, associated with garnet and columnar topaz (pycnite)."

ARSENIC, ANTIMONY AND BISMUTH.

"Only a few ores of arsenic and antimony have been noticed in North Carolina. Amongst these is very rare native antimony, of which a small piece was submitted to my examination by Dr. Hunter, of Cottage Home, Lincoln county. It has been found in a small vein in Burke county. An examination proved it to be quite pure.

Both arsenic and antimony are found in combination with other metals; arsenic at a few localities in Union and Gaston counties, in small quantities, as arsenopyrite or mispickel, associated with gold ores; and both arsenic and antimony in the highly argentiferous tetrahedrite of the McMakin, and the tetrahedrite of the Ludowick mines in Cabarrus county.

Bismuth has been observed as bismuthinite in minute particles associated with the gold and copper ores of the Barnhardt vein at Gold Hill, and by Dr. Asbury as bismuthite with gold ores at the Asbury mine in Gaston county; also as bismite, or teroxide of bismuth, in the same mine, and in combination with copper, lead and sulphur at Col. White's mine in Cabarrus county, probably as aikinite. The most interesting ores are the telluride of bismuth (tetradymite) and the tellurate of bismuth (montanite)—both found associated with gold ores in numerous localities—in Davidson, Cabarrus, Gaston, McDowell and Burke counties. The bismuthic gold mentioned by Shepard as coming from Rutherford, is probably an artificial product resultlng from the simultaneous amalgamation of gold and tetradymite."

COBALT AND NICKEL.

"Small quantities of these two metals have been observed in the manganese gossans of several mines in Gaston county, but thus far no regular workable deposits have been found."

MANGANESE.

Pyrolusite, psilomelane and wad are found in small quantities in many places in this state, but no where in abundance, so far as known. They are generally associated with iron, gold and silver ores. There is a very promising vein, or bed of psilomelane in Caldwell county, 5 miles west of Lenoir. It is found in irregular and rounded masses, embedded in light-colored gneissic slates, some of the masses being 10, 15 and 20 inches thick, and occupying a breadth of three or four feet of the strata. There is also a small seam in the town of Danbury, Stokes county, and laminated masses of ½ to 1 inch thick occur in the Buckhorn iron ore-beds, and there are hand specimens in the Museum from Nash county and several other points.

A specimen of manganese ore recently sent from Jackson county gives

Silica,	12.25
Alumina and Sesquiox of Iron,	14.10
Protosesquiox of Manganese,	74.45

It is probably braunite, variety marceline. A similar specimen from Chatham was probably the same mineral. Manganese is found associated with the iron ores in various parts of the state, as has been seen. At Buckhorn it is found as a silicate and probably in the form of Knebelite, as stated in another connection. Beds of Manganese garnet are of common occurrence and often of great thickness. There is a series of such beds associated with the King's Mountain slates of Gaston, Lincoln and Catawba, which are superficially changed to black oxide. A slaty specimen from Major Graham's place gave

Silica,	47.93
Protoxide of Manganese,	12.86
Binoxide " "	5.60
Alumina and Sesquiox. of Iron,	30.44

This has been used in a neighboring furnace as a flux, and with very good results.

CHROMIC IRON.

Small quantities of chrome are found associated with some of the iron ores of the state, the lead which crosses Guildford county for example. But it is also found as chromic iron, in coarsely crystalline masses, often of considerable size and in the form of very irregular veins, or pockets in the chrysolyte beds of Jackson, Yancey, Mitchell and Watauga counties. The most considerable deposits are two, one near Webster, and the other 5 miles from Burnsville, on Jack's Creek, at Hampton's. An analysis of the former by Genth gave,

Chromic Oxide,	63.32
Ferrous "	25.04
Magnesia,	0.85
Lime,	1.32
Silica and Alumina,	9.47

There have been no openings at either of these points, but the outcrops are such as to justify experiments at both, whenever the facilities for transportation shall be sufficiently improved.

SECTION III. USEFUL MINERALS, NOT ORES.

COAL.

The general facts in regard to the occurrence of mineral fuel in this state have been given in a previous chapter. It will be remembered that the principal coal beds are found on Deep River, in Chatham and Moore counties. The area of this coal fie d is given by Emmons as about 900 square miles. The quality of the coal is also discussed by him and by Admiral Wilkes, and various analyses are published; the three following by the latter, of samples from different parts of the field:

Carbon,	60.7	59.25	84.56
Volatile Matter,	32.7	30.50	7.42
Ash,	5.3	10.21	7.89
Sulphur,	1.3		
	100.0	99.99	99.87
Specific Gravity,	1.28	1.41	1.49

The first analysis (by Schæffer) represents the coal at the Egypt shaft, the second by Prof. Johnson, the outcrop at Farmersville, and the third, by she same, the Wilcox seam. Wilkes says, in his report to the U. S. Government, "The three upper seams of the bituminous coal are well adapted for fuel, cooking, gas and oil. It is a shining and clear coal, resembling the best specimens of Cumberland. It ignites easily and burns with a bright, clear combustion, and leaves a very little purplish grey ash. It swells and agglutinates, making a hollow fire." "It yields a shining and very porous coke, and is an excellent coal for making gas or for burning." "The dry or debituminized coal" exists in "but small quantities in the basin," and "contains less than one quarter of the volatile matter that the bituminous coal contains."

The following analyses by Dr. Genth were made for the Survey, of specimens selected by myself three or four years ago from large heaps newly mined.

Fixed Carbon,	63.28	70.48
Volatile Matter,	25.74	21.90
Ash,	10.14	6.46
Moisture,	0.84	1.16
	100.00	100.00
Sulphur,	1.35	1.02

It will be seen that these are good coals; they contain very small percentage of sulphur, much less than many of the coals of Ohio and the West, which are largely used in the reduction of iron ores. The former analysis represents the Egypt coal and the latter that at the Gulf, the Gulf specimens being obtained within 15 feet of the surface.

In regard to the value of the Chatham coal for gas making, I have received the following testimony from the Messrs. Peters, of Portsmouth, as to the result of a trial in the gas works of Norfolk and Portsmouth, of a lot mined some three years ago: "Their (the Superintendents') reports are highly favorable to the Chatham coal, both as to the quality of the gas produced and the quantity which a given amount of the coal yielded." And Mr. C. S. Allman, President of the Norfolk Gas Works, says: "Our Superintendent thinks it about equal to the best Clover Hill coal, giving of 14 candle gas, $3\frac{3}{4}$ cubic feet per pound. I have no doubt that fresh mined lump would give much better results."

A sample of a thin seam of coal, which was struck last year in Anson county, in Boggan's Cut, gave, on analysis, (by Hanna),

Fixed Carbon,	63.76
Volatile,	23.13
Ash,	2.47
Moisture,	9.95
	99.31
Sulphur,	0.75

The seam exposed in the cut was only two or three inches thick; but it represents the Chatham coal in its continuation southwestward. There have been no explorations here to determine whether larger seams exist.

The lignite bed on Tar river, near Oxford, in Granville county, is the continuation of the Chatham coal formation in the opposite direction. The thickness of the seam is reported about five or six inches; but no explorations have been made to ascertain either its horizontal or vertical extent.

It is worth while to mention here also the *bituminous shales*, which show themselves in so strong force above the coal in the Egypt section. Dr. Emmons estimated the thickness of the oil-bearing strata at seventy feet, and pronounced them capable of yielding thirty per cent. of their weight in kerosene oil. So that here is an inexhaustible resource for fuel, over and above that furnished by the coal seams.

The other coal in the valley of Dan River, is much less known; but it was mined at Leaksville during the late war, and the coal acquired a very high reputation as a fuel. It is semi-bituminous. The thickness of the only seam explored at this point is about three feet. The longitudinal extent of this deposit is as great as that of the Chatham beds, but it is probably narrower. As stated elsewhere, some recent openings by the Iron Company operating in Guilford, seems to show a succession of parallel beds more numerous and of greater thickness in places than those on Deep River. These explorations were made four years ago, near Stokesburg. Two analyses by Dr. Genth, of samples of different seams opened here gave, respectively, 75.96 and 76.56 per cent. of fixed carbon, 11.44 and 13.56 per cent. of ash, the volatile matter being about 12 per cent. in each. The development of these deposits is a matter of sufficient interest to the state to justify an exploration of the whole length of both these coal areas; and the diamond drill offers a ready and cheap means of tracing out the boundaries and ascertaining accurately the depth, thickness, and all the conditions which will determine their value. And I do not think a few thousand dollars could be more profitably expended.

GRAPHITE.

This mineral is quite widely distributed in North Carolina, both in the Huronian and Laurentian formations. There are very fine hand specimens in the Museum from a number of counties, Person, Yancey, Catawba, Cleaveland, Burke and others; and there are beds of a more or less impure, slaty and earthy variety, in several sections of the State, the principal of which are two: one in Gaston, Lincoln and Catawba, as a constant associate of the argillaceous and talcose slates and shales which belong to the King's Mountain slates; and the other in Wake county. The former may be seen at various points crossing the public roads and cropping out in the gullies. At Sigmond's, not far from Catawba Station, in Catawba county, the bed was opened many years ago, and several barrels mined; and within the last year or two a considerable amount of trenching and exploration has been made, and several parallel beds are reported, three feet and more in thickness. In Cleaveland county there are several outcrops also, of a thin seam of a few inches; one of them is near McBrier's Spring.

But the Wake county beds are the most extensive, as well as the best known graphite beds in the State. They extend in a northeast and southwest direction for a distance of sixteen or eighteen miles, passing two and a half miles west of Raleigh. There are two beds apparently, forming a sharp antichinal. The thickness is two to three, and occasionally four, feet. The eastern (and longitudinally the most extensive) bed is nearly vertical, dipping sometimes east, but mostly west, at an angle of 70° to 90°; it was opened at a number of points many years ago, and is wrought to a considerable extent at present. It is a bed of quartzitic and talco-argillaceous slates and shales, which are more or less graphitic—from about twenty or thirty to sixty per cent.

A large bed of a similar character is reported from Alleghany county, and a sample sent, which shows 12.38 per cent. of graphite.

Many of the Archæan gneisses of the middle and western regions of the state contain graphite, along with, or replacing the mica. Specimens of this description may be seen in the Museum from Forsythe, Ashe and other counties.

Crystallized graphite like that at Ticonderoga, N. Y., is rare in this state, although there are a few (small) such specimens in the Museum, from different localities.

KAOLIN, FIRE CLAY, &c.

From what has been said under the head of general geology, it will be readily inferred that there must be an abundance of clay of all sorts in the state. The vast Tertiary and Quaternary tracts of the eastern section abound in beds of potter's clay, fire clay, &c. And among the older formations also, are numerous seams and beds of kaolin resulting from the decomposition of the felspathic rocks. One of the largest of these beds is found near Greensboro, a few miles south. It is white and fine—grained and is reported to cover several acres; and other smaller beds of the same region are represented in the Museum. One of these on a partial analysis, gives 82 per cent of silica, the residue being mostly alumina. Another sample of the same sort, a white, almost impalpable dust, from Johnston county, near Clayton, gave silica 67 per cent. Both of these and many other specimens, from a number of counties, Chatham, Wake, Guilford, &c., have the appearance of what is called sometimes "mountain meal." Other specimens of very fine hydrows silicates are often brought to the Museum for meerschaum. One of these, from Burke county, gave water 15.9 per cent., alumina 44, magnesia 3.8.

The following analyses of *clays* were made for the Survey by Dr. Genth and Mr. Chatard, his assistant:

Silicic Acid and Quartz,	56.63	60.93	72.25	86.47
Alumina,	26.22	26.58	11.28	6.73
Sesquioxide of Iron,	5.93	1.71	3.62	
Magnesia,	0.00	0.35	1.75	0.47
Lime,	0.30	0.99	0.00	0.17
Water,	10.92	9.44	11.10	6.16

The first is from Harnett county, and represents a large bed of fine, purplish clay, at Spout Spring on the Western Railroad. The second is from a bed said to be large, near Shoe Heel Depot, Robeson county; fine and white. The other two are from a bed of fine whitish, ash-colored clay, called Dirt-eater's Clay, on Major Blount's farm, in Lenoir county.

Under this head may be placed the beds of argillite, or pyrophyllite slate,—*agalmatolite*, in the southwest corner of Chatham. This is a large deposit belonging to the Huronian series, which has a quite extensive range; occurring in Montgomery and other parts of Chatham. It is popularly called soapstone, and has the soapy feel of that mineral, but contains only 3.02 per cent. of magnesia. This substance has been an article of trade to New York, on a large scale and for many years. It is used in the manufacture of paper,—wall-paper especially, soaps, cosmetics, pencils, &c., and for various adulterations.

Soapstone.

This is a very common mineral in North Carolina, both in the form of the impure, greenish, massive, or slaty rock, (potstone), used for grave stones, and for chimney and furnace hearths and linings, and in the form of a pure massive white steatyte. The most extensive beds of this mineral are found in Cherokee and Macon, in immediate association with the marble range previously described, and accompanying it throughout its whole extent, on Nantehaleh River, Valley River and Notteley. An analysis of this rock, as it occurs at Jarrett's, on Nantehaleh, gave 23.71 per cent. of magnesia, which is about the percentage for pyrallolite. The variety rensselaerite is found in Forsythe county, and probably also in the south mountains, in Burke county.

Serpentine.

This mineral is found in large masses in many portions of the state. A noted locality in Wake county, was long ago described by Dr. Mitchell. The finest beds of it are those near Patterson, in Caldwell county. It is dark, almost black, and fine-grained, and polishes well. It is beautifully seamed with minute veinlets of amianthus. Serpentine of fine quality, sometimes approaching precious serpentine, is found in the chrysolite beds of the west, as a result of their alteration.

Asbestos.

This is one of the commonest associates also of the chrysolite beds just mentioned, and it occurs also quite widely in the Laurentian rocks of the middle and western parts of the state. One of the best known localities in the state, is that near Bakersville, in Mitchell county; in fact it occurs in two or three places in that vicinity. It is long, fibrous, white and readily reduced to a pulp, or mass of fine lint. An equally fine article is brought from the southern part of Jackson county. It is also found near Tryon mountain, in Polk county. Another well known locality is in Caldwell county, near the Baker mine. This is associated, like many others, with a serpentine rock. Specimens have been brought to the Museum also from Ashe county, and from Yancey. There is considerable inquiry for this mineral from various quarters, for sundry new uses and manufactures, and it is likely to become very soon an article of commerce of considerable value.

CORUNDUM.

Attention has been called in another connection to the emery beds associated with the Guildford range of iron ores; and an analysis by Genth was given. But the region to which attention has been of late largely drawn as a source of emery, or corundum proper, lies west of the Blue Ridge; and as elsewhere pointed out, it is there associated with the chrysolyte beds throughout the whole of their extent, so far as any examination has been made. The richest localities however, thus far discovered, are found in Macon county, near Franklin, and in Clay county on Buck Creek. For a fuller account of these localities, see the paper of Mr. Smith in the appendix. This gentleman also calls attention to other localities in this range, and Dr. Genth has published an elaborate paper on the associated minerals of the whole series of chrysolyte beds; Prof. Shepard also, and Dr. J. Lawrence Smith have published interesting investigations on the same subject. There are in the Museum specimens from several other places, one in the southern extremity of Jackson county, south of the Blue Ridge, another on Ivy River in Madison county, where I procured very handsome specimens in 1867, and a third 1½ miles from Bakersville, within 200 yards of the asbestos above described, at which point, in company with Mr. Irby, I found several specimens last fall. There are also hexagonal crystals of corundum in the Museum, from Crowder's Mountain in Gaston county, and some large sized ones from Forsythe. A friend has lately written me from Iredell, that he has some crystals found in that section. So that it is evidently a mineral of very wide distribution in the state.

MICA.

The mining of this mineral is a comparatively new industry in North Carolina, having been inaugurated only 4 or 5 years ago. And it is still chiefly limited to some half a dozen counties, mostly beyond the Blue Ridge. The marketable mica is obtained from the great ledges (veins?) of very coarse granite, elsewhere described, which characterize the middle region of the mountain plateau, a little southeastward of, and parallel to the great hornblendic and chrysolytic ranges described in a previous chapter. The most noted localities are in Mitchell and Yancey, on the waters of the Nolechucky, between the Black Mountain and the Roan. In this basin are a great many enormous ledges of the granite above referred to, and scores of mines have been opened within a few years, some of which have proved very profitable. The mineral is taken out in large lumps (rude crystals), of 30 or 50 pounds weight up to several hundred, and even a thousand occasionally. These are readily fissile into laminæ of any desired thickness; and sheets are sometimes found three feet in diameter and upwards, and will often cut 16 by 20 inches. The most common sizes however, are much smaller, ranging from 2 by 3 inches to 4 by 6, occasionally a little larger. Last September, I saw in one heap, about 200 tons of rough mica, that had just been quarried from a pit near Bakersville. The mica nodules are accumulated along certain planes or ranges in a quartz, or felspar, or quartz felspar matrix. A large proportion of the mineral obtained is rejected, either on account of a want of transparency, or because it is gnarled, the plates being so interlocked as not to be separable.

The largest business in this line has been carried on by Messrs. Heap and Clapp, near Bakersville, who have opened and operated several mines. Mr. Irby also has operated quite largely in the same neighborhood. Mr. D. G. Ray, however, was one of the earliest in the new enterprise. He opened an extensive and very profitable mine on the northern slope of the Black Mountain, within two miles of Burnsville. Other mines have been and are now operated in Haywood, on Richland Creek for example, and in Jackson and Macon at several points. In Ashe county also are a number of mines, near Jefferson. Wilkes county on this side of the Blue Ridge, and Burke, Cleaveland and Catawba have entered to some extent into the mica-getting business. And if the market were sufficient, a large number of other counties could contribute to its supply. I believe there are no larger sheets obtained anywhere, not even in Siberia, than in the mountains of this state, and no finer qualities; and probably nowhere has the business received so great a development. The largest and finest sheets seen at Vienna, were from the Ray Mine, Yancey county.

There is a point of great interest connected with the history of mica-mining in this State, which it is worth while to refer to in this connection. This industry is not really new here, it is only revived. The present shafts and tunnels are continually cutting into ancient shafts and tunnels; and hundreds of spurs and ridges of the mountains, all over Mitchell county (especially), are found to be honey-combed with ancient workings of great extent, of which no one knows the date or history. In 1868 my attention was first called to the existence of old "mine holes," as they are called, in the region. Being invited to visit some *old Spanish silver mines* a few miles southwest of Bakersville, I found, as stated in the report for 1868, a dozen or more "open pits forty to fifty feet wide, by seventy-five to one hundred long, filled up to fifteen or twenty feet of depth, disposed along the sloping crest of a long terminal ridge or spur of a neighboring mountain. The excavated earth was piled in huge heaps about the margins of the pits, and the whole overgrown with the heaviest forest trees, oaks and chestnut, some of them three feet and more in diameter, and some of the largest belonging to a former generation of forest growth, fallen and decayed; facts, which indicate a minimum of not less than three hundred years." I added the remark as to the probable origin of these pits, "There is no appearance of a mineral vein and no clue to the object of these extensive works, unless it was to obtain the large plates of mica, or crystals of kyanite, both of which abound in the coarse granite rock." about two years afterwards in a conversation with Col. Whittlesey, and subsequently in numerous publications on the subject of the mounds of the northwest, I learned that mica was of common occurrence in the tumuli of the Mound Builders, among the utensils and ornaments which such rude people are in the habit of inhuming with their dead owners. And upon further inquiry I ascertained that cut forms, similar to those found in the mounds were occasionally discovered among the rubbish and refuse heaps about, and in the old pits. These circumstances revealed unmistakably the purpose and the date of these works, and showed them to be cotemporary with the extensive copper mining operations of Lake Superior.

Since the development of mica-mining on a large scale in Mitchell and the adjoining counties, it has been ascertained that there are hundreds of old pits and connecting tunnels among the spurs and knobs and ridges of this rugged region; and there remains no doubt that mining was carried on here for ages, and in a very systematic and skillful way; for among all the scores of mines recently opened, I am informed that scarcely one has turned out profitably which did not follow the old workings, and strike the ledges wrought by those ancient miners. The pits are always open "diggings," never regular shafts; and the earth and debris often amounts to enormous heaps.

One of the most profitable of all the modern mines, (on Cane Creek), is one which is marked by the greatest of the old excavations and the largest earth heaps about its margins, in the whole region, showing that this was the richest of the ancient diggings. The tunnels are notable as being much smaller than such workings in modern mining, being generally only three to three and a half feet in height and considerably less in width. Some of these tunnels have been followed for fifty and a hundred feet and upwards. It is asserted by the miners that distinct tool-marks are often found along the walls of these tunnels, resembling the stroke of a pick or chisel. It is also noticed that the best parts of the veins were often abandoned by the old workers, evidently on account of the hardness of the rock; they do not seem to have been able to penetrate the unweathered and more solid portions of the ledges in any case, a circumstance which shows the inferiority of their tools.

As to the uses to which this mineral is put, the principal one seems to be to furnish windows for parlor stoves. But it is also manufactured into lamp-chimneys and shades, and it is also latterly used, to some extent, already, as among the ancients, for purposes of personal ornaments of women—another illustration of the periodicity of fashions. The mechanical uses are multiplying, so that ere long the demand will no doubt overtake the supply, and when that happens, a large field of profitable industry will be open to many counties of the State.

Building Stones.

From what has been said under the head of general geology, it will be apparent that there exists the greatest abundance of material for architectural and engineering uses, over a large part of the state. Granite and gneiss are among the commonest rocks throughout its whole length, except in the coastward region, where it is overlaid by the Tertiary and Cretaceous beds. And the sandstones of the Triassic, red and gray, as well as those of the Huronian, are available over considerable areas; while the shell-limestones of the Eocene furnish a very fair building material to the sandy and alluvial coast region; and the crystalline limestones and marbles of the west supply an ornamental building stone of great variety and beauty.

Granites.—The capitol is built of the light colored gray gneiss which is so abundant in the Laurentian formation of the state, and in the Penitentiary, which is in process of building, the same material is used. An analysis by Mr. Hanna shows the composition of this rock. It is as follows:

Silica,	69.28
Alumina,	17.44
Sesquioxide of Iron,	1.08
Protoxide of Iron,	1.22
Manganese Oxide,	0.16
Lime,	2.30
Magnesia,	0.27
Potassa,	2.76
Soda,	3.64

It will be noted that felspar is the predominant element, and that this belongs mainly to the soda section,—probably oligoclase. The rock is evidently capable of resisting the action of the climate indefinitely, as there is no visible effect of erosion, in the case of the capitol, in 40 years. Other quarries have been opened in the neighborhood of Raleigh, in which the gneiss shows the same general characteristics, with differences of color, grain, &c. The Henderson Quarry, in Granville county, furnishes a harder and more quartzose rock, of a darker gray color. There are several quarries as far east as Edgecombe and Wilson, near the Wilmington and Weldon Railroad. The former of these was used for the foundation courses of the U. S. Post Office in Raleigh, and likewise in various structures along the railroad. It is of a slightly greenish-gray color, quite hard, and doubtless durable.

A fine light colored feldspathic granite, specked with a small percentage of black mica, is quarried in Warren county. Extensive quarries have been wrought also near Salisbury, at Dunn's Mountain. And recently a very light colored, almost white granite is obtained from the same locality, and has been adopted for the superstructure of the post office building already mentioned. It is a beautiful stone, of fine and uniform grain, dresses well and resembles marble at a little distance. It is marred by the occurrence in certain parts of the mass, of minute octohedral crystals of magnetite, which under the action of the lime of the cement, gives it a slight ferruginous stain in patches; but it is not probable that they will affect the durability of the stone. This is a true granite, and the ledge is of great extent. The predominant ingredient here also is feldspar, partly, at least, of the soda section. A very coarse porphyritic granite with large crystals of orthoclose, has been mentioned elsewhere as common along the western side of the central granite belt, passing a few miles west of Salisbury, across the southern end of Iredell county, and reappearing in large force on Long Creek, in the middle of Gaston. In places this is a good building stone, while in others, as the first named locality, it weathers too readily. A granite of the same general description, that is, coarse and porphyritic, occurs on the lower Yadkin (Pedee), in Richmond and Anson. This is of a slightly greenish color, contains oligoclase or albite instead of orthoclase, at least in part, and forms a very fine and durable building stone. Quarries have been opened in many places in the gneiss and granite ledges of the piedmont and mountain sections, more especially along the railroads where such material is in demand for various engineering structures. The mountainous ledges of porphyroidal gneiss (augen-gneiss), heretofore described, so abundant and conspicuous in Henderson county, about Flat Rock, Hendersonville and Hickory Nut Gap; in Hickory Nut Mountain, McDowell county, in the spurs of the Blue Ridge, among the head waters of the Catawba, and again on the turnpike road, just below Blowing Rock, in Caldwell county, furnish numerous quarries of a very good building stone. There are also very notable, bare ledges of light gray granite of great extent, near Mt. Airy, in Surry county. But it would be tedious and needless to particularize, as granite and gneiss are everywhere.

Sandstone.—The Red or Brown Sandstone of the Triassic has been already described, and its extent and general characteristics indicated. It is found in two tracts,—narrow zones, one lying along the valley of Dan River, near and almost parallel to the northern boundary of the State, as may be seen by reference to the map. The other lies in a northeast and southwest direction, nearly across the eastern side of the middle division of the State. A considerable part of this formation consists of sandstone—red, gray and variously colored, and of various grain and texture. These afford many quarries of fine building stone. One of the best yet opened is near Wadesboro, in Anson county. It is reddish brown to buff colored, and of fine and very uniform grain. I have seen nothing from Portland, Conn., or on Fifth Avenue, superior to it. Quarries have been long opened in most of the other counties along the line of its outcrops; in Chatham, for example, near Egypt, above and below, on the river and on the railroad. Other quarries of note are found on the North Carolina Railroad, near Durham, in Orange. Stone from this locality has been long used for building in Raleigh. Two specimens examined lately with reference to constitution and probable durability, showed that the cementing material of the quartz sand consisted mainly of iron oxide and clay, each about four and a half per cent. in one, which is of a dark-reddish brown color, and two per cent. in the other, which is light gray. The former also contained one and three-quarter per cent. of lime, an equal quantity of magnesia, and eight-tenths per cent. of soluble silica; the latter respectively three-quarters and nine-tenths per cent. of the same substances. These, however, did not appear to have much cementing effect. The samples were taken from large blocks, fresh from the quarries, and may be regarded as giving a fair representation of these sand-stones, in their general character.

Marble. As elsewhere stated, there are several ranges of beds of crystalline limestone in the middle and western regions. The first belonging to the King's Mountain belt, contains so far as yet known, very little marble, that may be considered as available for the purposes of ornamental architecture, or regarded as better than other common building stones. In the extreme west, however, in Macon and Cherokee, the limestone range, both on Nantehaleh and Valley River, contains beds of very fine marble of various colors, white, pink (or flesh-colored), black, gray, drab and mottled. It is capable of a very fine polish, and will one day, (when the difficulties of transportation shall be overcome), acquire a high value in architecture, as well as in other ornamental arts. In this last connection some of the *serpentine* beds may be mentioned as likely to come into use, and so to acquire a market value.

Millstone and Grindstone Grits, &c.

The sandstone just described are, in many places, well adapted to the purposes of grindstones, and during the war, while the foreign supply was cut off, they were largely so used. The Anson county quarries furnish a very fine grindstone and whetstone grit.

The conglomerates of the Triassic series, which are associated with and replace the sandstones above mentioned have been long and widely used for millstones. They have been principally obtained from Moore county, on McLennan's Creek, where they are obtained of excellent quality; and they have been distributed from this point, over a large number of the intervening counties, to the Blue Ridge. Some of these stones have been in use for 50 years; and they are occasionally found to be nearly equal to the French buhr-stone.

The coarse porphyroidal granites and gneisses which are scattered over so large a part of the State, are however the most common material for mill-stones. And in the eastern section, the shell rock is often partly or wholly silicified, forming a sort of buhr-stone, as in Georgia, and is well adapted to the same uses. In Madison county, in the Huronian slates on Laurel River, there is an irregularly laminated whitish quartz, occurring in large veins, which is used for millstones, which are reported to be a good substitute for buhr-stone.

Whetstone. Among the silicious argillytes so abundant in the Huronian strata, there are frequent beds of novaculite or whetstone. One of the best localities is a few miles west of Chapel Hill, from which these stones have been carried in all directions. Other quarries are found in Person county, near Roxboro, in Anson, not far from Wadesboro, in Montgomery and adjoining counties, on the great Huronian belt, and in fact almost every section of the State has its own quarries, which either do or might supply the local demand, at least in part, and as to articles of the commoner grades.

DIAMOND.

Dr. Genth has given all that is known on the subject of the occurrence of diamonds in North Carolina on p. 57 of the Appendix. All the specimens hitherto found, were discovered by accident, and in washing for gold. Doubtless an intelligent search, by persons trained to recognize the gem in the rough state would have brought to light scores of them in the extensive gold diggings of the state.

AGATE.

Rough specimens of this form of quartz are very common, for example, in Cabarrus, near Harrisburg and near Concord, and in Mecklenburg; and occasionally a handsome gem has been found amongst them; but a year or two ago some very fine specimens of moss-agate were discovered near Hillsboro, which were at last accounts in the hands of Col. Whitford.

OPAL.

A number of gems of this species have been found in the state. Within the last twelve months a large number have been picked up in Concord, Cabarrus county, some of them of much beauty and high market value.

SECTION V. MISCELLANEOUS.

MINERAL WATERS.

Both Chalybeate and Sulphur waters are of common occurrence in the tate and in all sections of it, the former eminently so. Alum waters are also of frequent occurrence. In the eastern section, the abundance of peat and muck insures the prevalence of carbonated waters, which are continually dissolving the iron oxides from the ferruginous Quaternary earths, and in their issue in springs at the foot of the slopes and in the ravines, they come charged with this element, which is deposited in a flocculent ochreous precipitate, along the course of the streams. In the granitic and slaty regions of the middle and west, the presence of iron and alum is due to the decomposition of the iron pyrites, so widely diffused in the gneisses, granites and slates.

Many of the springs of these sections have become noted places of resort.

No general investigation of the subject has been yet attempted, and so no general discussion will be entered on here. But a great many partial analyses have been made, of waters from every section, of which a few examples will be given.

The figures represent the number of grains of the different substances found in a United States standard gallon.

	1	2	3	4	5	6	7
Organic and Vol. Matter,	5.16	5.79	1.23	1.79	1.02	3.95	1.23
Silicic Acid,........	1.65	3.76	0.62	1.60	2.10	1.01	1.15
Oxide of Iron,...... } Alumina, ... }	3 80	0.86	0.74	0.92	0.60 } 0.18 }	0.14	0.11 0.11
Lime, ...	4.80	1.17	0.49	1.72	1.62	1.74	0.19
Magnesia, ...	0.49	0.06	0.12	0.25	0.42	0.75	0.10
Soda,.........					0.27	1.09	0.89
Sulphuric Acid,.......	0.25	1.23	0.12	0.74	0.12	0.40	0.08
Chlorine,.............	0.92	0.18	0.37	0.37	0.42	2.62	0.17
Carbonic Acid,........			23.40	32.22	large.	0.82	0.54
Phosphoric Acid.......						1.00	
Solid Matter,.....	17.07	13.05	3.69	7.69	6.75	12.70	4.03*

No. 1 is the famous "Alum Spring," Onslow county, described on page 12. The water issues, clear and strong, from an aperture in the limestone of about the diameter of a flour barrel, and discharges, at a rough estimate, 2,000 gallons per minute. There is a decided smell of sulphur in the air about the spring, discernible at the distance of several rods; but this ingredient, being in gaseous form, is evanescent, and hence does not appear in the analysis. There is a ochreous precipitate for some distance along the brook below.

No. 2 is a similar spring, not so large, but still very bold and copious, situated some four miles north of Washington, known as "Cowhead Spring." The temperature is 60°. This also gives an iron precipitate.

No. 3 is one mile above Morganton, on the railroad.

No. 4 is called "Glen Alpine Spring," some ten miles south of Morganton, in the South Mountains.

No. 5 is a spring near Greensboro, analyzed for Dr. Duffy.

*Add .21 grain of sulphur, in the form of sulphides.

No. 6 is a well at Thomasville, (of Mr. Thomas). This is notable as containing a grain of phosphoric acid to the gallon. The analysis also showed minute quantities of nitric acid and of the sulphides. The presence of these substances furnishes ground of suspicion of contamination.

No. 7 is from Warrenton, analyzed at the request of the mayor. It is a sulphur water, otherwise very pure, containing only four grains of solid matter to the gallon.

It will be observed that the amount of solid matter does not reach twenty grains in any of these samples, all of which are popularly considered *mineral waters*. But an ordinary potable water may, and often does, contain even more than that amount. Some of the wells of Raleigh contain much more. A few examples will show the range of solid matters in drinkable waters, in grains per gallon:

Cochituate, Boston,	3.11
Croton, New York,	4.78
Ridgewood, Brooklyn,	3.92
Fairmount, Philadelphia,	3.50
Lake Michigan, Chicago,	6.68
Genesee River, Rochester,	13.25
Thames, London,	18.50
Kent, "	26.50
Seine, Paris,	8.83
Rhine, Basle,	11.80
Loch Katrine, Glasgow,	2.30
Distilled Water,	0.10

Absolutely pure water is unknown, outside of the laboratory of the chemist.

No spring, or well, or lake water is pure. And it is generally considered that a certain (small) per centage of mineral matter improves not only the taste, but the wholesomeness, of drinking water. Lime carbonate, one of the most common impurities, does not impair its healthfulness, until the quantity passes twelve or fifteen grains, but sulphate of lime, magnesia salts, and whatever communicates permanent *hardness* to waters, are reckoned injurious, even when existing in small proportions. Organic matter is commonly set down as injurious, if found in quantities above one grain to the gallon.

But whether a larger proportion is hurtful, depends altogether on the nature and (especially) the source of it. If derived from the putrid decomposition of vegetable, or (especially) animal matter, it is injurious in all proportions; but the brown humous acids, from peat and muck beds, do not seem to be deleterious even when amounting to saturation. Sea-going vessels are said to prefer the brown, wine-colored waters of the Dismal Swamp and other such peaty waters of the coast.

Suspended matters in drinking water are usually unwholesome, and a frequent source of disease.

Nitric acid, ammonia, phosphoric acid and chlorine are commonly in dications of pollution, especially the three last named, and waters so contaminated are dangerous to health. The greatest total amount of solid matter per gallon in potable waters should not exceed 30, or at most, 40 grains; the carbonate of lime should not constitute more than one third of that; the organic matter should not pass one grain, and sulphate of lime and magnesia salts should be absent, or if present, only in minute quantities.

Lake and River waters are generally purer than that from spring and wells, and for obvious reasons. All waters come from the ocean by evaporation, and fall in the form of rain in a state of comparative purity, absorbing from the atmosphere, besides the gases of which it is composed, the animal, vegetable and mineral dust which floats every where in it, and also a minute portion of ammonia, nitric acid, and other matters (sulphurous acid, &c.), thrown into it by the combustion of coal, &c. A part of this water, after reaching the surface of the earth, passes directly into the rivers and lakes; another portion penetrates the crevices of the rocks, or the porous earth, and makes its way, by a slow underground circulation, to the sources of springs, or is tapped by wells, and so comes to the air again, charged with whatever soluble mineral matters there may have been in the rocks and earths through which it has percolated, so that the character of the water so issuing, is determined by that of the rocks. Other things being equal, the water is purer in regions characterized by the older, crystalline formations, granites, gneisses, &c.

Mineral waters are simply those which contain either an excess of those mineral matters usually found in spring and well water, or (and more commonly) such rare substances as are supposed to have valuable medicinal properties. The following analyses will convey a general notion of the composition of such waters. It will be seen that sea water is a most conspicuous example of mineral water.

	grs. pr. gal.
Ocean Water,..	2,408.00
Dead Sea "	13,488.10

Salt Lake "	15,203.00
Congress Spring, Saratoga,	700.89
U. S. " "	331.84
Spouting Well, "	991.55
Ballston Artesian Well, Ballston,	1,233.25
Greenbrier White Sulphur Springs, Va.	16.21
Rockbridge Alum, Va.,	5.85
Buffalo Springs, Va.,	98.38
Warm Springs, N. C.,	9.81
Hot Springs, Ark.,	8.50
Vichy, France,	38.99
Kissingen, Germany,	65.52
Louisville Artesian Well, (2,086 feet deep),	113.96
Charleston " " (1,250 feet deep),	16.96

The waters of some of the public wells of the city of Newbern have been analyzed, at the request of Col. J. D. Whitford, and the result is given below, as furnishing a fair example of the potable waters of the seaboard region:

	1	2	3	4	5	6	7
Silica,	7.87	4.43	5.42	9.15	6.93	3.79	0.69
Organic Matter,	5.07	9.33	2.68	7.05	3.67	1.34	1.85
Alumina,	0.29	0.46	0.29	trace	0.17	0.35	0.01
Oxide of Iron,	0.29	0.29	0.58	trace	0.64	0.11	0.01
Lime,	4.08	8.22	1.51	6.12	2.04	3.26	0.47
Magnesia,	0.93	0.58	0.64	1.22	0.64	0.64	0.11
Sodium,	2.68	7.75	2.39	7.75	2.09	3.03	0.38
Phosphoric Acid,	trace	trace	0.17	0.17	0.17	0.51	0.15
Sulphuric Acid,	0.93	2.21	0.47	2.68	0.58	0.64	
Chlorine,	2.79	5.83	trace	0.81	trace	trace	0.30
Solid Matter,	24.93	39.10	14.14	34.95	16.93	13.67	3.97
Depth, (in feet),	37	15*	15*	69	15*	22	
Temperature,	63°	68°	67°	69°	68°	55°**	

*Not more than 15 feet.

**Temperature taken in January.

No. 1 is from the Whitehurst pump.
No. 2 is from Manly's pump.
No. 3 is from the Gildersleeve pump.
No. 4 is from the Episcopal Church pump.
No. 5 is from the Lane pump.
No. 6 is from H. J. B. Clark's, 9 miles from Newbern.
No. 7 is from T. S. Howard's, 1½ miles north of Newbern.

It will be observed that the *solid matter* about reaches the limit of potability in two cases. These are the second and fourth. And it will also be obserbed that much of the excess in both cases is common salt, (chlorine and sodium), which exists in much greater proportion in these wells than in any of the others. This is explained by the fact that they both penetrate to a level below the surface of the Neuse River, whose waters are brackish, and the former is only 200 feet distant from it. These waters also contain a larger proportion of lime and organic matter than the others. Their temperature is also highest, indicating a more direct communication with waters having the surface temperature, so that they cannot be recommended as wholesome drinking water, although they are within the allowed limits of potability. The quantity of silica found in all these waters is very considerable; but there is nothing specially injurious to health in this mineral, beyond the fact that it is so much added *solid matter*. The organic matter is also large in all of the samples, and in several of them, notably so. The Whitehurst, for example, comes next to the Episcopal Church well in this respect. This is doubtless due to the source of the water, which is to be sought in the peaty swamps and rivers further inland, from which these waters are derived through their communication with the subterraneous streams. A considerable additional part of the solid matter of this water is evidently derived from the river, as indicated by the large proportion of chlorine, sodium and magnesia. The temperature of this well shows, however, as well as its structure, that the main sources of its supplies are distant and deep,—that they are a part of the subterraneous circulation peculiar to this section, and arising from its special geological features, explained elsewhere.

Of course those wells are the safest sources of water for drinking and other domestic uses, which reach this underground circulation, provided of course they do not also communicate with brackish or other undrinkable waters. The shallower wells,—those which stop short of this stratum, that is, which derive their supplies directly from the rainfall by percolation through the superficial porous, sandy strata, which characterize most of the eastern section, will ever be liable to pollution from various sources; and the dangers of such pollution are greater, and are continually augmenting, especially in cities, as the sewage and decaying animal and vegetable matters are continually descending, and will sooner or later reach the sources of such shallow wells.

It will be noted that Nos. 3, 4, 5 and 6 contain an appreciable amount of phosphoric acid, especially the last; this is always objectionable and suspicious, even in the smallest quantities. No. 7 is an exceptionally pure water. The following analyses of polluted and unwholesome waters are added, as an illustration of the effect of sewage and manure heaps and other animal and vegetable filth, which, without proper sanitary precautions, will accumulate in all cities, and even about private houses. They are from the last Journal of the Royal Agricultural Society of England, and were made by Voelker.

	1	2	3
Organic Matter,	0.56	1.56	2.68
Phosphoric Acid, Oxide of Iron and Alumina,	}	0.98	0.17
Phosphate of Lime,	0.42		0.95
Sulphate of Lime,	18.14	20.67	96.71
Carbonate of Lime,	5.41	11.21	
Carbonate of Magnesia,		12.81	
Nitrate of Magnesia,	8.21	0.19	13.93
Sulphate of Magnesia,			34.83
Nitrate of Lime,	8.97		
Sulphate of Soda,			3.96
Chloride of Sodium,	13.53	20.44	45.35
Alkaline Carbonates,	2.72	1.58	17.86
Silica,	0.84	1.40	1.82
Solid Matter,	58.80	70.84	218.26

No. 1 was taken from a public pump in the suburbs of London. Dr. V. found on inquiry that there was a burial ground in the vicinity, and he had no doubt that the drainage from thence reached the well and rendered it "unwholesome and totally unfit for drinking purposes."

No. 2 is a sample of water from a well used by a family that had been attacked by typhoid fever. Dr. V. says the sample is "contaminated with drainage products, which fully accounts for the outbreak of typhoid fever in the family."

No. 3 is a sample of water from a well in Lincolnshire, that had proved fatal to two farm animals. Dr. V. to whom the suspected water was sent for analysis, says that the water was free from smell, but was colored slightly yellow, and he adds, "unquestionably the water was charged with a large proportion of injurious organic impurities, and much contaminated with saline and earthy compounds, which were derived from yard drainage, sewage, or similar objectionable liquids. In consequence of these impurities the water was positively poisonous and probably produced the death of the two beasts."

These cases are given, out of hundreds, in order to fix attention upon a subject of the last importance, both to cities, and to individuals and to society at large, and this because it has been almost wholly neglected among us, even in our largest towns and cities, whose death rates have doubtless often responded sadly to this public ignorance and private and official negligence.

METEORITES.

In addition to what Dr. Genth has said on this head, page 56 of the Appendix, I add the following.

The Rockingham Meteorite, referred to by Dr. G., I obtained in 1866, from Mr. Peters, who found it a few years earlier, and who lived near the point where it was picked up. It was found in an old field which had not been cultivated for about 20 years, on the top of high hill (Smith's Mountain), and near the site of a former dwelling; so that its fall probably occurred within 20 years. The mass is very compact and almost as hard as steel. The original weight was within one ounce of eleven pounds. It was coated with rust. Dr. Genth's analysis of a small fragment sent him, gave

Iron,	90.41	
Nickel and Cobalt,	8.74	
Nickel,	0.33	Phosphide.
Iron,	0.27	
Phosphorus,	0.14	
Copper,	0.11	

He says: "It consists of a mixture of several Iron-Nickel alloys, intermixed with phosphide of Nickel-Iron." "The iron contains besides, pyrites, and probably quartz, or a silicate in minute quantity." "This meteoric iron is undoubtedly one of the most interesting in existence."

He also notes the point that it contains chloride of iron, a substance rarely found in meteorites.

Dr. J. Lawrence Smith, for whom I was able with much difficulty to sever a larger fragment, also made a minute investigation of it. His analysis is as follows:

Iron,	90.88
Nickel,	8.02
Cobalt,	0.05
Copper,	0.03
Phosphorus,	0.03

The fragment analysed was selected so as to be "free from any schreibersite visible to the eye." "Its specific gravity was 7.78." "Its structure is highly crystalline, and when polished and either heated or acted on by nitric acid, develops remarkably fine Widmanstætian figures with delicate markings on the inside of the figures." "I discovered some of the chloride of iron, enough to test its nature and leave a small fragment' that is now in the Garden of Plants, Paris."

The Nash County Meteorite.—On May 14th, 1874, at 2½ P. M., there fell near Castalia, in Nash county, a shower of meteorites. Dr. King has given me the particulars of the fall. He says there were "rumbling explosions as of fire arms in battle a few miles off, which continued for four minutes." Four fragments have been picked up, one of 12 pounds, one of 6, and two smaller, of between one and two pounds, which I was so fortunate as to obtain from the finders through their courtesy and by favor of Hon. J. J. Davis. The specimens all have a thin black coating, and are of a light to dark gray color inside.

Dr. Smith, to whom I forwarded a fragment, has made an analysis and report, from which I make the following abstract: "The principal cause of the dark color is doubtless the large amount of Nickeliferous iron, and in the lighter portions there are some white spots of a mineral which is doubtless enstatite. The specific gravity is 3,061." The composition is as follows:

Nickeliferous Iron,	15.21
Earthy Minerals,	84.79

The former is composed of

Iron,	92.12

Nickel,	6.20
Cobalt,	0.41

The latter consists of "bronzite and olivine with small particles of auorthite, and it will be seen from this statement that its composition is a common one."

ERRATA.

Page 40, line 9, for 46,000,000, read 46,000,000,000.

" 71, " 27, column *Y'rs of Obs.*, for 11½, read 1½.

" 71, " 28, " " " for 8, read 18.

" 71, " 16, for 4,000,000, read 40,000,000.

" 107, " —3, for Fohiated, read Foliated.

" 122, " 13, for ieda, read idea.

" 126, lines 7 and 8, strike out "in the vertical and overhanging cliffs on the Turnpike, just below Blowing Rock, in Caldwell," and insert at line 23, page 135, after *Blue Ridge*.

Page 127, line 13, for Chorite, read Chlorite.

" 130, " 16, for n, read In.

" 135, " —5, for hydra- read hydro-

" 146, " —8, for Triossic, read Triassic.

" 159, top, for p. 195, read 159.

" 189, line 22, for glanconite, read glauconite.

" 217, line 26, for section II, read section III.

" 250, line 6, for Spanishred, read Spanish red.

" 293, line 20, for section III, read section IV.

Appendix, page 14, line 2, for Exoyra, read Exogyra.

Appendix, page 24, line 18 from bottom, strike out *is*, after ostrea sellæformis.

Appendix, page 27, heading Callicardia, add *Cardium Bechei*, Adams and Reeve.

Appendix, page 105, line 3 from bottom, for moles, read makes.

In the map, at the beginning, there is an obvious blunder in the marking and coloration of the section, *Hiwassee to Catawba*, at the junction of the Huronian and Laurentian.

Professor Conrad wishes to add the following note to appendix A:

"I have inadvertently given precedence to the name *Busycon*, quoting *Sycotypus* as a subgenus of the same, but the latter has priority of date, and should stand for the genus while *Busycon* represents the subgenus Two well defined groups are met with in this genus, which, culminating in the Miocene, contains no doubtful species as to which section it appertains; *Busycon* being always without a channel about the suture, and when armed, it is always with spines; whereas, the subgenus *Sycotypus*, has invariably a channel and tubercles in place of spines. Such a marked difference between the two sections might constitute two genera, but the arrangement in genus and subgenus is quite as convenient, leaving the generic question to be solved by the anatomist."

INDEX.

A

B

C

D

E

F

G

H

I

PAGE.

N

O

P

Q

R

S

V

W

Y

Z

APPENDIX.

APPENDIX A.

DESCRIPTIONS OF

NEW GENERA AND SPECIES OF FOSSIL SHELLS

OF NORTH CAROLINA,

IN THE STATE CABINET AT RALEIGH.

By T. A. CONRAD.

The Cretaceous fossils described in this paper represent the Ripley group of that formation, so named from the town of Ripley, Mississippi. Some of the species of Ripley are identical with Carolina shells, and others with those of Eufala, Georgia, and Haddonfield, New Jersey. Not only this identity of several species, but the mineral character of the beds in which they are found is the same, and also the state of preservation of the fossils, proving not only a simultaneous deposit, but a similar depth of water, not in an estuary, but in a marine basin. Oyster shells are very rare and so far only one estuary shell, a Neritina, has been found, and that in Mississippi. I conclude, therefore, that the Ripley ocean extended over most of the Southern States, bordered on the north by the Triassic, Carboniferous and older rocks, and that the materials which drifted into the Cretaceous sea, were derived in all localities from a similar source, since the marl is a fine, brown sand, holding minute grains of transparent quartz, which constitutes a friable, incoherent earth, from which the most delicate hinges of the bivalves are easily cleared. This marl is destitute of green sand in the localities referred to above. The Ripley group constitutes the great bulk of the Cretaceous strata, east of the Mississippi, and it corresponds most nearly in age with the Senonian stage of d'Orbigny, or that part of the Cretaceous series, which underlies and most nearly approaches in age to the chalk.

All the species, except two, herein described, are from Snow Hill, Greene county.

BIVALVES.

ANOMIA. *Lin.*

A. *linifera*, pl. 1, fig. 1. Shell rounded, convex, thin in substance, with numerous radiating irregular acute lines minutely tuberculated.

This shell is extremely rare, while *A. argentea*, Morton, is abundant.

A. *lintea*. Shell having the larger valve, ventricose, and scuptured with reticulated lines, radiating lines alternated, waved.

Locality: The Barn, Cape Fear river.

RADULA. *Klein. Lima.*

R. *oxypleura*, pl. 1, fig. 5. Shell ovate, oblique, inflated; ribs 19, compressed, acute; umbo inflated; anterior extremity angular and situated above the middle of the valves.

Common in a particular part of the bed, which is exposed only to the depth of about 5 feet, but very rare in other places. It is almost always pressed out ot its true shape, but otherwise the shell is in excellent preservation, though very friable.

TRIGONOARCA. *Conrad.*

This genus is very characteristic of the Ripley group of America and the Senonian of Southern India, where its development reaches its climax. It is a well defined genus, characterized by an exterior resemblance in form and sculpture to CUCULLÆA, and in the marginal plate of the posterior cicatrix, while it has the oblique descending series of teeth, somewhat resembling those of AXINÆA. There is no trace ot this genus in the older Eocene and none apparently in the chalk. The area between the beaks in the American species is long anteriorly and very short behind the beaks.

T. *triquetra*, pl. 1, fig. 7. Shell triangular, inequilateral, cuneiform posteriorly; umbonal slope nearly straight, very oblique, angular; disk flattened anterior to the umbonal slope; posterior slope profoundly depressed; interior radiately striated.

This species is rare and is the only one I have seen without radiating lines on the disk.

SUBGENUS BREVIARCA. *Conrad.*

Shell comparatively short; hinge area minutely striated across, hinge line straight in the middle, descending towards the ends; cardinal teeth minute, crowded; sculpture, minute radiating lines.

This subgenus allies TRIGONOARCA with AXINÆA, and may readily be distinguished from either by its minute close teeth.

T. *umbonata*, pl. 1, fig. 8. Shell triangular, direct, equilateral, with a very prominent broad umbo and a terminal umbonal slope which is rounded; posterior slope very small and almost at right angles with the disk; lower half of disk flattened on the posterior side; scupture minute cancellated lines.

T. *perovalis*, pl. 1, fig. 3. Shell oval, compressed, subequilateral, thin in substance; margins rounded; base mediately truncated; umbonal slope obtusely rounded; 2 or 3 minute plications near the beak on the anterior submargin; inner margin entire.

T. *Carolinensis*, pl. 1, fig. 4. Shell subtriangular, inequilateral, ventricose, posterior margin subtruncated; umbonal slope undefined; inner margin entire.

This species is shorter and more ventricose than the preceding.

T. *congesta*, pl. 1, fig. 2. Shell rounded, ventricose, slightly oblique, inequilateral, umbonal slope undefined, margins rounded; cardinal series long, inner margin entire.

This is perhaps the most abundant bivalve at Snow Hill, and yet in almost every instance consists of separated valves, while in the genus CYCLOTHYRIS whole shells are not uncommon.

T. *Saffordii*, Gabb, is a member of this subgenus.

NEMODON. *Conrad.*

This genus differs widely from the Jurassic MACRODON in having a very slender cardinal plate except towards the extremities, in having a few oblique linear teeth under the anterior side of the beaks, and in having the anterior teeth parallel with the hinge margin. It differs from CUCULLARIA, *Deshayes*, as represented by *Arca heterodonta*, in having a simpler form of hinge character and a straight hinge margin. It comprises two forms of extremely thin shells, punctato-radiate on the exterior.

N. *brevifrons*, pl. 1, fig. 15. Shell subrhomboidal, umbonal slope inflated, very oblique, rounded, much curved on the umbo which is broad and the summit obtuse; cardinal line short, posterior margin very oblique, slightly curved; anterior side very short, obtusely rounded; hinge line slightly sinuous, sculpture very fine, almost obsolete, cancellated lines punctate at the intersection.

Of this extremely thin shell I obtained 3 valves, showing the hinge in perfection. It is widely distinct from *N. Eufalensis*, Gabb, which is found associated with it at Snow Hill.

In the American Journal of Conchology it is stated that *Arca heterodonta* is a species of this genus, when I meant exactly the reverse—the word *not* having been omitted by the printer.

BARBATIA. *Gray.*

SUBGENUS PLAGIARCA. *Conrad.*

Shell, with a straight hinge margin terminating in an angle, narrow cardinal area, having minute close angulated lines; cardinal teeth very oblique without angles towards the interior margin; short; anterior series with one or two teeth comparatively large, slightly angulated in the middle and very oblique.

B. *Carolinensis*, pl. 1, fig. 11. Shell trapezoidal, ventricose, very inequilateral, umbonal slope acutely rounded above, undefined below, anterior margin truncated; posterior end emarginate below the hinge extremity; disk with numerous prominent unequal closely-arranged, very narrow ribs, crenulated and with a few intermediate lines.

SUBGENUS POLYNEMA. *Conrad.*

Shell with the hinge line slightly descending, the teeth on both sides very oblique, those of the posterior side elongated, striated, the series suddenly terminating in a few short teeth; cardinal margin straight, angulated at the ends; cardinal area extremely narrow with two profound lines angulated under the beaks.

B. *lintea*, pl. 1, fig. 12. Shell trapezoidal, subulated posteriorly; umbonal slope inflated, rounded; disk cancellated with very numerous close lines, the radii most prominent, acute.

This is a thin, rare shell allied in subgeneric characters to *Arca Edwardsii* and *A. distans*, Deshayes.

ARCOPERNA. *Conrad.*

A. *Carolinensis*, pl. 1, fig. 6. Shell suboval, inflated, beak prominent terminal, hinge and ventral margins parallel; posterior end rounded.

INOPERNA. *Conrad.*

Shell profoundly elongated, of a mytiloid form; hinge entire? concentrically plaited on one side and longitudinally striated on the other or basal half of the valves; hinge and ventral margins subparallel; posterior end rounded.

This is an extremely thin shell, very pearly, and having undulated ribs or plaits very like those of many species of INOCERAMUS. I have had only a partial view of the hinge, and therefore cannot state its character with certainty. The substance of the shell is fibrous like that of INOCERAMUS to which it is nearly allied.

To this genus I refer *Modiola plicata*, Sowerby; *M. flagellifera*, Forbes, and *Inoceramus siliqua*, Matheron.

I. *Carolinensis*, pl. 1, fig. 22. Shell slightly arcuate towards the posterior end, much compressed, gradually expanding to the posterior extremity, which is rounded.

The shorter outline and larger ribs distinguish this species from the allied forms. The compression of the valves may be owing to pressure, one valve being perfectly flat.

MYTILUS. *Lin.*

M. *condecoratus*, pl. 1, fig. 10. Shell small, ventricose, slightly incurved; disk undulato-plicate concentrically; substance pearly; beaks oblique, prominent, acute.

I found only one valve of this beautiful shell.

M. *nasutus*, pl. 1, fig. 9. Shell broadly triangular, suddenly depressed anteriorly, incurved, rostrated; beaks acute and very oblique.

Very rare. One specimen has concentric plicæ near the beaks.

ETEA. *Conrad.*

Shell equivalved; right valve with one primary cardinal triangular bifid direct tooth under the apex and a pit on each side; 2 lateral teeth, anterior, one approximate, robust; a broad cavity between it and the hinge margin, posterior lateral tooth distant; left valve with two widely diverging cardinal teeth, posterior one bifid and very oblique; lateral teeth profoundly developed, pallial line with a small sinus, straight or truncated.

E. *Carolinensis*, pl. 1, fig. 14. Shell oblong-ovate, slightly ventricose, very inequilateral; umbonal slope carinated; posterior side elongated, cuneiform, contracted anterior to umbonal slope; cardinal margin nearly straight, long and oblique; posterior end obliquely truncated, extremity angular; disk entire.

A common and graceful shell, of what family remains in doubt.

BRACHYMERIS. *Conrad.*

Shell equivalved, inequilateral; hinge with two cardinal teeth and a deep pit between them; anterior tooth of right valve bifid; one lateral tooth anteriorly and remote from the apex; muscular impressions large, submarginal pallial line entire, posterior tooth of left valve bifid.

B. *alta*, pl. 1, fig. 16, and pl. 2, fig. 23. Shell ovate, slightly ventricose, height rather more than length; posterior side short, subtruncated, extremity angular, umbonal slope rounded; beaks situated rather posterior to the middle of the valves.

CRASSATELLA. *Lam.*

SUBGENUS PACHYTHÆRUS. *Conrad.*

C. *Carolinensis*, pl. 2, fig. 24. Shell suboval, short, equilateral, compressed with distinct lines of growth; posterior end truncated, nearly direct.

This rare species occurs in New Jersey, where I found one valve, and one only at Snow Hill.

C. *pteropsis*, pl. 1, fig. 25. Young shell of this species?

ARENE. *Conrad.*

Shell equivalved; hinge of right valve with two cardinal teeth, anterior one bifid, direct; a large deep channel on the anterior side of the hinge, with a short lateral tooth at the anterior end of it.

A. *Carolinensis*, pl. 2, fig. 19. Shell rounded, thin in substance, ventricose, smooth; posterior slope suddenly depressed; umbonal slope angular; posterior end truncated.

LUCINA. *Brug.*

L. *glebula*, pl. 1, fig. 18. Shell rounded oval, convex, concentrically laminated; anterior end truncated, direct; posterior end emarginate; posterior slope suddenly depressed.

One valve only was found.

CARDIUM. *Lin.*

SUBGENUS TRACHYCARDIUM.

C. *Carolinensis*, pl. 2, fig. 1. Shell elevated, slightly oblique, ventricose; ribs about thirty to the umbonal slope, convex, little prominent, close, the intervening spaces linear, ribs transversely rugose; ribs on posterior slope large, angular, subcarinated; cardinal and lateral teeth prominent; cardinal teeth equal in length.

Rare. The ribs are closer than represented in the outline figure.

PROTOCARDIA. *Beyrich.*

P. *Carolinensis*, pl. 2, fig. 21. Shell rounded, direct, equilateral, ventricose; umbo broad, summit prominent; umbonal slope undefined; posterior slope slightly impressed or concave, with eight rather wide, little prominent, flattened ribs; disk with minute, close, concentric, impressed lines, largest towards the base; anterior lateral tooth distant, very prominent; posterior tooth small.

Only one valve has been obtained. It differs from *P. Hillanum*, Sowerby in having larger and much fewer ribs posteriorly.

APHRODINA. *Conrad.*

When I defined this genus I knew one species only, but my visit to Snow Hill revealed a much larger and better characterised species, and fully justifies the separation of a group of Cretaceous shells from CYTHERIEA, MERETRIX, CARYATIS or VENUS do not occur in American Cretaceous strata.

A. *regia*, pl. 2, fig. 7. Shell ovato-triangular, very inequilateral, ventricose, thick in substance, umbo oblique, lunule lanceolate, defined by a minute impressed line; margins rounded; disk with a few concentric furrows and strong lines of growth; anterior lateral tooth narrow, elongated, parallel with the hinge margin above it, and rough with tuberculiform striæ.

A common species, the largest of which found entire measures three and a half inches in length. Others much larger could only be obtained in fragments.

CYCLOTHYRIS. *Conrad.*

Shell rounded, inequilateral; hinge with four cardinal teeth in the right valve, three of which are united above; hinge of left valve with three widely diverging cardinal teeth, posterior tooth linear, very oblique and with a broad, flattened, triangular pit between it and the middle tooth; fulcrum long, broad, obtuse; pallial sinus profoundly angular, ascending, lunule undefined.

C. *Carolinensis*, pl. 2, fig. 3. Shell rounded, ventricose; length slightly exceeding the height; dorsal margin posteriorly very oblique, slightly curved; end margin subtruncated; disk with concentric unequal lines obsolete on the middle of the disk.

A very common shell, often found entire with united valves.

C. *alta*, pl. 2, fig. 4. Shell short ovate from ventral margin to beak, equilateral; margins regulary rounded; disk polished, lines of growth distinct.

TENEA. *Conrad.*

T. *parilis*, pl. 2, fig. 25. American Journal of Conch. vol. 6, p. 74, pl. 3, fig. 12.

Dosinia —— Conrad. Journ. Acad. Nat. Sciences, vol. 4, 2d series, pl. 46, fig. 16.

BARODA. *Stoliczka.*

B. *Carolinensis*, pl. 2, fig. 10. Shell oblong, very inequilateral, convex, with a few slightly impressed concentric furrows; posterior cardinal margin long straight, oblique; margins rounded; umbonal slope undefined and regularly convex with post-umbonal slope.

This is the first species found in America and represents an interesting exclusively Cretaceous genus. The hinge fortunately can be obtained in perfection at Snow Hill. The genus is common to the Senonian strata in America, Europe and Southern India.

ŒNE. *Conrad.*

Shell with the hinge of the left valve having one long oblique cardinal tooth projecting below the hinge margin, and a minute tooth posteriorly; right valve unknown.

Œ. *plana*, pl. 1, fig. 17. Shell subtriangular, slightly folded; right valve flat, umbonal slope subangular, post-umbonal slope with minute radiating lines granulated behind the umbo and on the submargin; disk sculptured with very minute concentric close impressed lines; basal margin subrectilinear. (*Tellinidæ.*)

LINEARIA. *Conrad.*

SUBGENUS LIOTHYRIS.

Valves smooth, slightly bent.

L. *Carolinensis*, pl. 1, fig. 20, 23, 24. Shell subovate, convex; beaks situated behind the middle; umbonal slope undefined; anterior end acutely rounded, posterior end truncated, direct.

Although the exterior of this shell is very unlike that of the typical sculptured species of LINEARIA, the hinge character is identical. (*Tellinidæ.*)

VALEDA. *Conrad.*

V. *lintea*, pl. 1, fig. 26. Large and perfect specimens of this shell enabled me to distinguish the difference between this genus and CYMBOPHORA, Gabb (*Mactridæ.*)

CYPRIMERIA. *Conrad.*

C. *depressa.* Conrad. Single valves of this shell are exceedingly abundant at Snow Hill. They are generally more or less water-worn, but perfect specimens, with united valves occur sparingly. All the shells of this deposit indicate an open ocean with a shore at no great distance where weathered beach shells were abundantly deposited among a comparatively few living specimens. The genus is eminently characteristic of the Ripley group and next to *Axinæa congesta*, the present species is the most common shell at Snow Hill.

HERCODON. *Conrad.*

Shell equivalved, hinge of left valve with two small cardinal teeth, anterior one bifid, posterior one linear; right valve with two diverging teeth, anterior one angular and excavated or angulated below the middle, long and very oblique; cartilage pit deeply impressed; anterior cardinal plate slightly furrowed longitudinally; pallial line with a deep, regularly rounded, broad sinus.

H. *ellipticus*, pl. 2, fig. 2, 8. Shell elliptical, inequilateral, convex, disk entire; beaks remote from anterior end which is acutely rounded, posterior end rounded; umbonal slope undefined; post-umbonal slope convex; ventral margin regularly curved.

The smaller outline figure represents what I suppose to be a young shell of this species, and is very abundant, while the large specimens are very rare. The largest found measures 3½ inches in length.

CYMELLA. *Meek.*

Shell equivalved, thin in substance, gaping posteriorly; hinge of right valve with a thin transverse tooth parallel to the shell's length and approximate to, and below the cardinal margin, flat on the upper side and a curved pit above it; fulcrum prominent, acute, straight; left valve with a minute cardinal tooth anterior to the apex, approximate to the cardinal margin, and a much larger tooth under the apex, with a pit above it; teeth all directed the same way.

C. *bella*, pl. 2, fig. 9. Shell ovate, inequilateral, profoundly ventricose; substance extremely thin; umbo broad and prominent; disk sculptured with concentric furrows and acute radiating ribs interrupted at the furrows, anterior side nearly or quite destitute of radii and occasionally exhibiting minute raised points; basal and posterior margins rounded.

This genus appears to be very distinct from Poromya, Forbes, although the external outline is very similar. The species is very beautiful and pearly, as thin as paper, and therefore I found only one entire small valve.

The hinge of *Pholadomya infrequens*, as figured by Zittel, has a close resemblance to that of Cymella the principal difference being the absence of the anterior cardinal tooth which is a prominent character in Cymella.

CORBULA. *Lam.*

In a small group of Cretaceous Corbulæ the beaks of both valves are spiral as in Mr. Gabb's genus Pachydon, but they differ from all Eocene and latter species described not only in the above mentioned character, but in having the umbo directed obliquely towards the posterior end. The only exception I know of is a species figured by Deshayes. So slight a variation from the type of a genus, as the spiral beaks and peculiar obliquity, when it marks a group of species peculiar to a formation, has a significance which entitles it to notice, and especially when one believes that all life was destroyed at the close of the Cretaceous era. In all the Eocene species the smaller valve has involute and concealed beaks, and in all the later fossil and recent species this character is preserved, except in the Tertiary genus PACHYDON, Gabb, which name must be retained to designate Mr. Gabb's genus, as PACHYODON, Stuchbury is superseded by THALLASSIDES, Bergner. In this group the umbo when oblique points towards the anterior end or in the opposite direction to that of the Cretaceous group. *Corbula obliquata* Desh. is a small shell which has a very slight obliquity, exaggerated in the enlarged figure, if the small outline is correct.

C. *Carolinensis*, pl. 2, fig. 15. Shell oblique; right valve ventricose, the left inflated, concentrically striated, posterior side very short, suddenly contracted; end of left valve obliquely truncated, reflexed, submargin minutely carinated.

Common, generally with separated valves, not water-worn. I found one specimen with connected valves.

C. *perbrevis*, pl. 2, fig. 5. Shell elevated, with a short, truncated wing and concentrically marked with prominent striæ; posterior submargin carinated from beak to posterior extremity; summit prominent.

C. *subgibbosa*, pl. 2, fig. 12. Shell triangular, equilateral, rostrated, obliquely truncated at the posterior end; disk with concentric obsolete lines; ventral margin gibbous; valves carinated from beak to posterior extremity, submargin deeply impressed.

C. *oxynema*. Shell ovate acute, inequilateral, ventricose; posterior side cuneiform, compressed; disk delicately sculptured with fine, close, sharp equal lines.

Locality: Cape Fear river.

C. *bisulcata*, pl. 2, fig. 13, 14. Shell ovate-acute, equilateral, concentrically striated, with two or three distant large concentric furrows; posterior extremity acute.

UNIVALVES.

DIPLOCONCHA. *Conrad.*

Shell composed of two adhering tubes, one resting in a furrow on the side of the opposite tube.

D. *cretacea*, pl. 2, fig. 26. Shell having sinuous tubes, minutely striated across, and with acute distant ridges; tubes separating towards the apex.

This singular shell is not uncommon, but owing to its fragility has not been seen entire.

Of several specimens of this shell none was found attached to shells or other substances, and no wood was seen accompanying them, but that might readily have disappeared, and the shell be allied to TEREDO.

CALLONEMA. *Conrad.*

Conoidal, with spiral prominent lines, sutural space channelled, columella direct, thin, reflexed, projecting over the subbase and rounded at base, labrum thin.

C. *tuba? bella*, Conrad, is a representative of this genus which is probably allied to LITTORINA, but the above generic diagnosis will distinguish the two genera from each other.

Turritella ventricosa Forbes is probably a species of this genus.

C. *Carolinensis*, pl. 2, fig. 27. Shell with a prominent conoidal spire; suture of last volution margined by a carinated line which disappears on the back of the shell; spiral lines equal, prominent, 14 on last volution, 5 on penultimate volution, 3 first volutions entire.

Smaller and proportionally shorter than *C. bella.* Being the only perfect specimen of the genus known to me, it is regarded as the type.

ANCHURA. *Conrad.*

A. *rostrata*, Morton, pl. 2, fig. 28. Shell with a broad, expanded labrum, acute at the apex and sinuous inferiorly; beak straight, rather short, acuminate, labrum ridged on the back; ribs longitudinal, acute, curved.

Rostellaria rostrata, (Morton.) Gabb. Journ. Acad. Nat. Sci., second series, vol. 4, p. 390, pl. 68, fig. 7.

This species is common in New Jersey in the form of imperfect casts, but at Snow Hill the shell is preserved.

It bears considerable resemblance to *Alaria glandina*, Stoliczka, except in the notched margin of the labrum.

LIODERMA. *Conrad.*

L. *thoracica*, pl. 2, fig. 30. Shell subpyriform, volutions of the spire contracted or widely channelled; canal slightly sinuous; 2 folds on the columella, upper one obsolete, the lower one ridging the margin of the columella to the extremity; labrum distinctly emarginate at the summit.

Only one entire specimen was found, differing from the type L. *lioderma* in the contracted volutions and elongated fold. This genus is not found in the Eocene.

LUNATIA. *Gray.*

L. *Carolinensis*, pl. 2, fig. 29. Shell with 5 volutions, the apicial one minute indistinct; spire short, conical; volutions convex; suture canaliculate; length greater than the breadth; umbilicus moderate.

SYNOPSIS OF THE CRETACEOUS MOLLUSCA OF NORTH CAROLINA.

BY T. A. CONRAD.

CONCHIFERA.

Anomiidæ.

Anomia argentaria, *Morton.* Synopsis of the Cretaceous formation of the United States, p. 61, pl. 5, fig. 10.

A. *tellinoides*, Morton, ib., fig. 11.

A. linifera, *Conrad..* Geolog. Survey of North Carolina.

A. lintea, *Conrad.* ib. ib.

Ostreiidæ.

Exoyra costata, *Say.* American Journal of Science, vol. II, p. 43, 1820.
Ostrea Americana, Deshayes. Encyclopedie Methodique, vol. II, p. 304, 1830.
O. torosa, Morton. Synopsis, p. 52, pl. 3, fig. 9.
O. plumosa, *Morton.* ib. p. 51, pl. 3, fig. 9.

Spondylidæ.

Plicatula urticosa, *Morton.* Synopsis, p. 62, pl. 10, fig. 2.

Radulidæ.

Radula oxypleura, *Courad.* Geological Survey of North Carolina.
R. denticulaticosta, *Gabb.* Proceedings of the Academy ot Natural Sciences, 1861, p. 327.

Pectinidæ.

Camptonectes bellistriatus, *Conrad.* American Journal of Conchology, vol. 5, p. 99, pl. 9, fig. 11.

Nuculidæ.

Nucula percrassa, *Conrad.* Journal of the Academy of Natural Sciences, vol. 3, 2d series, p. 327, pl. 35, fig. 4.
Perrisonota protexta, *Conrad.* American Journal of Conchology, vol. 5, p. 98, pl. 9, fig. 24.

Arcidæ.

Idonearca Tippana, *Conrad.* Journal Acad. Nat. Sciences, vol. 3, p. 328, pl. 35, fig. 1.
Trigonoarca, (Breviarca) umbouata, *Conrad.* Geolog. Survey of North Carolina.
T. (Breviarca) perovalis, *Conrad.* ib. ib.
T. (Breviarca) congesta, *Conrad.* ib. ib.
T. (Breviarca) Carolinensis, *Conrad.* ib. ib.
T. passa, *Conrad.* American Journal Conchology, vol. 5, p. 43, pl. 1, fig. 17.
T. *cuneiformis,* *Conrad.* ib.
Nemodon brevifrons, Geolog. Survey of North Carolina.

N. Eufalense, *Gabb*, (Arca) Journal Acad. Nat. Science.
Barbatia (Plagiarca) Carolinensis, *Conrad*. Geolog. Survey of North Carolina.
B. (Polynema) lintea, *Conrad*. Geolog. Survey of North Carolina.

Trigoniidæ.

Trigonia thoaaccica, *Morton*. Synopsis, p. 65, pl. 15, fig. 13.

Aviculidæ.

Arcoperna Carolinensis, *Conrad*. Geolog. Survey of North Carolina.
Avicula——inedited.
Gervillia ensiformis, Journal Acad. Nat. Sciences, Second Series, vol. 3, p. 328, pl. 34, fig. 10.
Inoperna prolixa, *Conrad*. Geolog. Survey of North Carolina.
Mytilus condecoratus, *Conrad*. ib. ib.
M. nasutus, *Conrad*. ib. ib.
Perna cretacea, *Conrad*. ib. ib.

Crassatellidæ.

Crassatella (Pachythærus,) Carolinensis, *Conrad*. Geolog. Survey of North Carolina.
Etea Carolinensis, *Conrad*. Geolog. Survey of North Carolina.
Brachymeris alta, *Conrad*. ib. ib.
Arene Carolinensis, *Conrad*. ib. ib.

Lucinidæ.

Lucina cretacea, *Conrad*. Geolog. Survey of North Carolina.
L. laminifera, *Conrad*. American Journal of Conchology, vol. 5, pl. 9, fig. 11.

Cardiidæ.

Cardium (Trachycardium) pervetum, *Conrad*. Geolog. Survey of North Carolina.
C. (Trachycardium) Eufalense, *Gabb*. Journal of the Acad. Natural Sciences, vol. 4, p. 282, pl. 46, fig. 12.
Criocardium dumosum, *Conrad*. American Journal of Conchology, vol. 6, p. 75.
Protocardia Carolinensis, *Conrad*. Geolog. Survey of North Carolina.

Veneridæ.

Aphrodina regia, *Conrad.* Geolog. of North Carolina.
Cyclothyris alta, *Conrad.* ib. ib.
C. Carolinensis, *Conrad.* ib. ib.
Baroda Carolinensis, *Conrad* ib. ib.

Cyprinidæ.

Venilia Conradi, *Morton.* Synopsis, p. 66, pl. 9, fig. 3.

Tellinidæ.

Cyprimeria depressa, *Conrad.* Journal Nat. Sciences, Second Series, vol 4, p. 278, pl. 46, fig. 6.
Hercodon ellipticus, *Conrad.* Geolog. of Survey of North Carolina.
Æne plana, *Conrad.* ib. ib.
Linearia metastriata, *Conrad.* Journal of Acad. Nat. Sciences, Second Series, vol. 4, p. 279, pl. 46, fig. 7.
L. (Liothyris,) Carolinensis, *Conrad.* Geolog. Survey of North Carolina.

Anatinidæ.

Periplomya applicata, *Conrad.* (Periploma) Journal Acad. Natural Sciences, Second Series, vol. 4, pl. 46, fig. 1.

Myadæ.

Cymella bella, *Conrad.* Geolog. Survey of North Carolina.

Corbulidæ.

Corbula Carolinensis, *Conrad.* Geolog. Survey of North Carolina.
C. perbrevis, *Conrad.* ib. ib.
C. oxynema, *Conrad.* ib. ib.
C. subgibbosa, *Conrad.* ib. ib.
C. crassiplicata, *Gabb.* Journal Acad. Nat. Sciences, vol. 4, Second Series, p. 394, pl. 68, fig. 24.

Solenidæ.

Legumen appressus, *Cornad.* Journ. Acad. Nat. Sciences, Second Series, vol. 3, p. 325, pl. 34, fig. 19.

GASTEROPODA.

Serpulidæ.

Hamulus sqamosus, Gabb. Proceedings of the Academy of Natural Sciences, 1859, p. 1: Journal Acad. Nat. Sciences, Second Series, vol 4, p. 398, pl. 68, fig. 45.
Diploconcha cretacea, *Conrad.* Geolog. Survey of North Carolina.

Strombidæ.

Anchura rostrata, (*Morton.*) *Gabb.* Journal of Acad. Natural Sciences, Second Series, vol. 4, pl. 68, fig. 7.

Volutidæ.

Lioderma gularis, *Conrad.* Geolog. Survey of North Carolina.
L. lioderma, *Conrad.* Journal Acad. Nat. Sciences, Second series, vol. 4. (VOLUTILITHES.)

Littorinidæ.

Callonema alveata, *Conrad.* Geolog. Survey of North Carolina.

Naticidæ.

Lunatia Carolinensis, *Conrad.* Geolog. Survey of North Carolina.
Gyrodes alveata, *Conrad.* Journal Acad. Nat. Sciences, Second Series, vol. 4, p. 289, pl. 46, fig. 45.

Purpuridæ.

Morea cancellata, *Conrad.* Journal Acad. Natural Sciences, Second Series, p. 290, pl. 46, fig. 30.

Family—?

Thylacus cretaceus, *Conrad.* Journal Acad. Nat. Sciences, Second Series, vol. 4, p. 290, pl. 46, fig. 23.

Ammonitudæ.

Ammonites placenta, *Dekay.* Annals of Lyceum of Nat. Hist. of New York, vol. 2, pl. 5, fig. 2. *Morton.* Synopsis, pl. 2, fig. 1.

Eocene.

TEREBRATULA.

T. demissirostra, pl. 3, fig. 1. Shell ovate, inflated, with five short plications, lateral plicæ widest; valves nearly equally ventricose, the smaller valve least so and regularly arched in outline; tip of the beak of larger valve acute and curved downwards nearly to the summit of the opposite valve; foraminal area very oblique.

Local. Wilmington, N. C. Prof. Kerr.

Prof. Kerr informs me that this species was found imbedded in a whitish Eocene limestone near Wilmington. The pendent angle of the rostrum is a striking character of the shell.

PECTEN. *Lin.*

P. anisopleura. Shell ovate, ventricose, ribs about 25, very unequal, crossed by arched squamose lines. Length 3 inches; height 3¾ inches.

In the intervals of the large ribs there are 2 smaller ribs in some, one in others.

Found by Dr. Yarrow, 40 miles from Beaufort, N. C.

P. Carolinensis, pl. 3, fig. 2. Shell ovate, convex, ribs numerous, narrow, densely and minutely crenulated, rounded, alternating with2 smaller, interstitial radii which are also crenulated.

The upper figure represents the lower valve, the outline figure 2 the upper valve.

Miocene.

LIROPECTEN. *Conrad.*

L. Carolinensis. Shell rounded, lower valve slightly convex or nearly flat, ribbs 11 or 12, convex on the back, angular on the sides, subnodose; disk undulated concentrically; interstices of the ribs with minute radiating lines crossed by minute squamose lines, ears large, sinus rather deep with a rounded margin; height 3 inches; length 3 3-8 inches.

OSTREA. *Lin.*

O. perlirata. Shell elevated, pointed towards the apex, fan-shaped, very thick in substance, with profoundly elevated divaricating ribs laterally compressed. Height 6 inches.

Locality. Neuse river, 10 miles above Newbern.

PLACUNOMIA. *Broderip.*

P. fragosa. Subrotund, compressed, surface of disk very irregular or uneven with small radiating irregular closely-arranged interrupted ribs, having a very rugose appearance; cardinal process thick and broad, rib prominent. Length 1¾ inches.

Locality. 20 miles north of Wilmington, Cape Fear River.

RAETA. *Gray.*

R. alta, pl. 3, fig. 3. Shell elevated, subtrigonal, inflated, rudely lineal concentrically; umbo plicated, beaks nearer the posterior than the anterior end; posterior end regular.

R. erecta. Shell subtriangular, thin in substance, inflated anteriorly, umbo not oblique, sculptured with prominent subacute slightly waved concentric folds or ribs, which on the rest of the valve are less prominent, where it is sculptured with fine hieroglyphic wrinkles; anterior end obtuse; cartilage pit large; length 2¼ inches; height 2 inches.

Locality. Goldsboro', N. C.

The species differs from *R. canaliculata* in being proportionally higher, and without obliquity of umbo, while the ribs on the lower half of the valve are less prominent and regular. The cartilage pit is proportionally much larger than that of the allied species.

ABRA. *Leach.*

A. bella, pl. 3, fig. 4, 6. Triangular, solid, and sculptured with close, very numerous fine reticulated striæ, the concentric lines sharp and more prominent than the radii, which are flattened; fold distinct; beak situated behind the middle of the valve; cardinal and lateral teeth prominent.

Locality. Wilmington, N. C. Prof. Kerr.

A. Holmesii, pl. 3, fig. 8. Shell oval, convex with numerous concentric lines, beaks nearest the posterior end; margin rounded; posterior end obtusely rounded.

Syndosmya carinata, Tuomey and Holmes (not Conrad) Plio. Foss. S. C. pl. 25, fig. 2.

NOETIA. *Gray.*

N. protexta, pl. 3, fig. 5. Rhomboidal, ventricose about the umbonal slope, which is angular; disks widely contracted or impressed from beak to base; ribs 31 or 32, bifid on the post-umbonal slope, which is impressed or concave, interstices of the ribs with a minute line, on the post-umbonal slope these lines are larger and more prominent; fine concentric lines crenulate the ribs.

N. filosa, pl. 4, fig. 3. Rhomboidal, comparatively short, ventricose; ribs 30, slightly grooved, two or three about the umbonal slope more distinctly grooved; posterior margin behind the beak and umbo much curved; umbonal slope angular, posterior slope slightly impressed; end margin nearly straight.

The figure represents a young specimen. The adult measures 1⅞ inch. in length; height 1½ inches. The posterior margin of the figure is incorrectly represented as emarginate, but it has a slight outward curve.

MERCENARIA. *Schum.*

M. Carolinensis. Shell subtriangular, elongated, very inequilateral, slightly ventricose, disk with coarse, flattened, uneven, imbricated ridges on the middle and posterior side, the lines disposed to be ramose; on the anterior side and posterior slope they are sharp, prominent, rugose, imbricated lines; lunule large, cordate. Length 5 inches; height 4 inches.

Locality. Cape Fear river.

LEPTOTHYRIS. *Conrad.*

Shell equivalved, thin; cardinal teeth compressed, diverging from the apex with equal obliquity, one towards the anterior and the other towards the posterior; anterior cardinal margin passing the apex and ending in an expansion or dentiform projection; fulcrum excavated, which excavation extends behind the expanded cardinal termination under the apex; pallial sinus extending rather beyond the middle of the valves, slightly ascending and truncated at the inner end.

L. parilis, pl. 3, fig. 9. Shell oval, ventricose, equilateral, summit prominent; base truncated medially, umbonal slope subangular; post-umbonal slope flattened, much depressed; disk with obscure concentric slightly impressed broad furrows; posterior end truncated.

There is but one valve of this shell in the State Cabinet, but the hinge is so peculiar that I could not refer it to any genus known to me.

CARDIUM.

Subgenus TRACHYCARDIUM.

T. bellum. Shell slightly oblique, suboval, profoundly vetricose, ribs profoundly elevated, narrow, slightly oblique or turned towards the anterior side, about as wide as the interstices, 30 in number, with arched scales turned towards the anterior end; anterior area with scales of a different pattern, funnel-shaped on very close ribs; posterior margin slightly rounded or curved, direct anterior margin truncated obliquely inwards. Length 1 3-4 inches; height nearly 2 inches, or about one-sixteenth less.

MYSIA. *Leach.*

M. Carolinensis, pl. 4, fig. 5. Rounded, inflated, thin, equilateral, slightly oblique, posterior end obtusely rounded; cardinal teeth are one direct, situated under the apex, and the other very oblique; left valve with a very oblique bifid tooth; anterior margin carinated and suddenly turned up to the apex.

PLEUROMERIS. *Conrad.*

P. decemcostata. Conrad. A larger specimen of this species than I have heretofore seen is in the State cabinet at Raleigh. The hinge character approaches that of WOODIA, *Desh.* but the large triangular tooth of the right valve is not subcanaliculate like that of *Woodia*, but deeply and angularly grooved the whole width of the tooth, leaving sharp angles on the margin; and there is a small anterior lateral tooth in the left valve, an elongated posterior cardinal tooth, also, and profound ribs on the exterior, and a deeply-impressed small lunule, in which character it differs from the allied genus. The crenulations of the inner margin have none of the obliquity of WOODIA. A fine exotic example of this genus is the *Cardita Kicxsii*, Nyst. Other species are *C omaliana*, Nyst, C. *scalaris*, Sowerby and *C. orbicularis*, Sowerby, *C. chamæformis*, Sowerby, *C. analis*, Phillippi. The genus can be easily recognized by external characters, such as its small size, elevated triangular outline, and granulated, radiating ribs. It has more the general outline of CRASSINA than of CARDITA.

PTERORHYTIS. *Conrad.*

This genus, related to the above, comprises 2 small species of the Atlantic Miocene compressed triangular short shells, with prominent, radiating ribs. The left valve has two diverging bifid teeth, with an intermediate triangular pit, the posterior cardinal tooth being profoundly divided; above the posterior muscular impression is a long, narrow, accessory one. I have not seen the right valve of either species.

SAXICAVA. *Bellevue.*

S protexta, pl. 4, fig. 6. Shell elongatod, very inequilateral, contracted from beak to base; posterior hinge margin parallel with the ventral; beak prominent, and margins rounded.

Locality.

ZIZYPHINUS. *Gray.* CALLIOSTOMA. *Swains.*

Z. Virginicus, pl. 4, fig. 4. Trochiform; spire and last volution equal in height; 2 prominent revolving lines on last volution immediately above the aperture, the upper one having a slight channel where it joins the volution, another line near the suture and only two lines on each of the other volutions at top and base; sutnre carinated; base with four large revolving lines or ribs and other unequal finer lines subumbilicated.

Locality: Suffolk, Virginia.

I found the specimen, from which the description was made, in a marl bank in the yard of a dwelling and the main street of the village, near the Nansemond river, where many fine specimens of *Mulinea congesta* and other fossils may be collected.

TURRITELLA. *Lam.*

T. perexilis, pl. 4, fig. 9. Shell slender, volutions convex, 3 acute prominent revolving ribs on each, a prominent line below the suture, and fine revolving lines between the ribs; obscure, oblique longitudinal plications which subintercalate the ribs; sutural area deeply impressed.

Locality. Wilmington, N. C.

T. Carolinensis, pl. 4, fig. 8. Shell elongated, broad and angular at base; volutions with their sides very slightly convex and obsoletely contracted below the suture which is deeply impressed; revolving lines fine, slightly prominent, alternated, 11 on the penultimate volution; aperture large, subquadrangular.

Locality.

FISSURELLA. *Lam.*

F. Carolinensis, pl. 4, fig. 1. Shell suboval, sides compressed, 39 very prominent flat sided ribs, rugoso—crenulated. Fissure oblong, narrow.

LITTORINA. *Feruassac.*

L. Carolinensis, pl. 4, fig. 11. Ovate-acute, volutions 5 or 6, those of spire slightly convex, revolving lines prominent subequal; not alternated, rugose, 8 on the penultimate volution and 22 on last volution; suture deeply impressed.

L. Caroliuensis. Conrad. Proceed. of the Acad. Nat. Sci. vol. 14, p. 567.

L. irrorata. Tuomey and Holmes, (not Say.)

L. Carolinensis, Var. pl. 4, fig. 10. Shell elongated, volutions convex, revolving lines large, 8 on penultimate, and 16 on last volution.

BUSYCON. *Bolten. Subgenus* SYCOTYPUS. *Browne.*

B. Kerrii, pl. 4, fig. 2. Shell pyriform, thick, elongated; last volution long and comparatively narrow; spire scalariform, volutions flat on the top, angle carinated slightly on the spire, conspicuously on the last volution, and subtubercated and subacute; a wide contraction of the volution forms a concave furrow round it beneath the carina; revolving lines coarse and wrinkled; canal long and wide, slightly oblique.

This large species measures 9 inches to the top of the penultimate volution, where the spire is broken. There is no canal around the suture in this large specimen, and it differs from Busycon only in wanting spines. I think, therefore, that Sycotypus is a subgenus of Busycon. It is probably tubercated in young specimens, the traces of which are observed on the summit of the large volution.

It was found by Prof. Kerr at James King's marl pit, Sampson county. A comparatively young specimen has been found which shows a slightly impressed canal, and the top of last volution sloping obliquely inwards.

B. amœnum. Shell pyriform, spire scalariform; sides of volutions straight, direct, angle acute, with longitudinal tubercles, top of large volution flat, canal slightly impressed, obsolete on the spire which is acutely pointed, the two first volutions smooth; spiral lines rather fine, unequal, columellar fold prominent and the furrow above it rather deeply impressed.

Locality. Walker's Bluff, Cape Fear river. Allied to *canaliculatum*, but distinguished by its slight canal and absence of a carinated line bordering the suture and angle of last volution.

B. concinnum. Shell pyriform, with unequal very distinct prominent spiral lines; volutions prominently carinated, those of the spire tuberculated; tubercles obsolete on the angle of last volution; beneath this angle and on the slight contraction of the 3 inferior volutions are very fine equal spiral lines; summit of volutions oblique and concave; canal wide, moderately impressed.

Locality. Mr. King's marl.

This species is the most nearly allied to *B. canaliculatum* of any Miocene species. Compared with a specimen of the latter nearly of the same size it has smaller and more numerous tubercles, a wider and less deeply impressed canal, narrower body volution, a shorter siphonal canal and larger revolving lines. The fine lines beneath the carina are wanting in *B. canaliculatum.*

It is a generally received opinion that some species of Miocene shells escaped the destruction of the general fauna, and however unaccountable this may seem to be, yet the small amount of variation, and in a few species none at all, seems to indicate that some few kinds of shells are now living which originated in the Miocene period. Dr. Yarrow, who was stationed at Beaufort, N. C., has collected great numbers of the marine and estuary shells of the adjacent coast, which prove that many of the existing Testacea of the West India coasts, as well as of the Atlantic and Gulf coasts of Florida, are now living in the waters about Beaufort. Among these shells, *Oliva litterata*, Lam, is very abundant, a shell which lives in myriads in Tampa Bay, whilst there is a Miocene Oliva equally abundant in the bank of Cape Fear river, which, when compared with the *litterata*, offers no character by which to distinguish it from that species. It is found associated with many extinct shells, and therefore the bed containing it cannot be confounded with the Post Pliocene, which contains no extinct species, and does not occur nearly so far up Cape Fear river. Even a trace of the colored marking of the fossil in question corresponds with that of the recent shell. This fact, as well as the absolute identity of characters between the fossil *Marginella limatula*, Conrad, and a species living on the coast of South Carolina, leads me to believe that other recent shells have lived in the Miocene era. I therefore suggest that the following species of that formation may be now living, viz: Anomia ephippium, *Lin.*, Lucina divaricata, *Lam.*, L. Conradii *d'Orb.*) Tellina flexuosa, *Say*, crepidula unguiformis, Lam., and C. fornicata, *Say.* In a future Report on the Geological Survey of North Carolina I will make a more extended list of such species as appear to be both recent and fossil.

Remarks on the Tertiary formations of the Atlantic slope.

The study of the Tertiary fossils of North Carolina has confirmed my opinion of the Miocene age of all those strata of sand and clay which border the Atlantic from Cumberland county, New Jersey, to the middle of

South Carolina. It was one contemporaneous sea bottom, holding living individuals of certain species throughout its entire length, and which is characterized by some of its species closely resembling existing ones, but many more having no affinity with American shells. In it culminated the genera BUSYCON and MERCENRIA, species of which characterize it in almost every locality. The Post-Pliocene above it is easily recognized by having none but existing species of shells. The Tertiary formations in North America are admirably distinguished by definite boundaries and a vast difference in their groups of organic remains. The formation which immediately preceded the Miocene is what I have named Oligocene, to distinguish it from the Eocene below and the Miocene above it. Some writers object to the name Oligocene, I fear from want of knowledge of the fossils it contains, for if a unique fauna entitles a group of strata to a separate and independent name, none is more worthy of it than the Vicksburg Group, which contains not one species of any animal, shell or coral in common with either the Eocene or Miocene. The corresponding beds in Europe are named Oligocene by Beyrich and Older Miocene by Lyell; but the affinities of the Vicksburg shells are with the Eocene forms and are widely different from the Miocene, and therefore I protest against the term Miocene being applied to the Vicksburg group. It has a higher claim to be named Upper Eocene, but it is far better to follow what we observe in Nature and classify it by a name which has no reference to other formations, with which it holds no species in common.

In the Eocene Check list, published by the Smithsonian Institution, I made the error of including *Ostrea sellæformis* is in the Older Eocene. It should be in the Claiborne or Newer Eocene group, and the bottom of the bed which holds it is the line of division between Older and Newer Eocene. This latter group has a strictly marine fauna, and when it was elevated so that lagoons were formed, the *Ostrea sellæformis* made its first appearance, and continued its existence into the Claiborne sands but sparingly, and soon disappeared. It continued to live while a deposition of 70 feet of clay was deposited with scarcely any associated shells of other species, and then a gradual sinking of the deposit occurred, restoring sea water with its vast abundance of marine shells, and forming a new epoch in the Eocene series. *O. sellæformis* is very rare in North Carolina, but it is not uncommon in Virginia and South Carolina.

The Claiborne Group I regard as Newer Eocene; the Jackson Group as Older Oligocene, and the Vicksburg Group as Newer Oligocene. The surveys and explorations in North America have been continued so long, that we may fairly assume the above divisions or formations to represent the succession of the groups, without supposing intermediate formations to have been deposited and swept away without leaving a trace behind.

REMARKS ON SOME GENERA OF SHELLS.

T. A. CONRAD.

PROTOCARDIA. *Beyrich.*

The type of this genus is *P. Hillana*, Sowerby, a cretaceous fossil, and strictly defined, the genus first appears in the LIAS, in one species, P. Phillipsii, *Conrad*, (*P. striatula*, Phillips, not Sowerby). The Carboniferous allied forms are *Cardium dissimilis* and *C. striatulum*, Sowerby, which I exclude from the genus.

PROTOCARDIA proper consists of vetricose shells which are scuptured with concentric lines ending at the angle of the umbonal slope, and having entire radiating ribs on the post-umbonal slope; umbonal slope slightly incurved.

The above diagnosis applies only to the Cretaceous species and excludes *Cardium bisectum*, Forbes, which Stoliczka includes in the group.

Eocene Group.

Shell having fine radiating lines; post umbonal slope with acute tubercles on the ribs.

The aberrant forms are *P. difficile*, Deshayes, *P. Plumsteadiana*, Sowerby, and *P. nitens*, Sowerby, which have smooth posterior ribs, but radiating lines on the disk.

Older Oligocene Group. (Jackson Group.)

Agree in scupture with the Eocene species.

Newer Oligocene Group. (Vicksburg Group.)

Decussated striæ; entire radiating lines on the post-umbonal slope.

Recent.

Decussated striæ; short spines on the post-umbonal slope.

Subgenus CALLICARDIA, *Conrad:*

Of this elegant species, Dr. Gray remarks, that 2 odd valves have been dredged up from deep water, one valve in the Sooloo seas and the other in the Yellow Sea. If the fossil species had the same kind of station we might infer that they indicated deep water in the ocean where they lived.

PACHYCARDIUM, *Conrad*, is very different from this genus, being more elevated, with prominent summits, direct, and having no angle to the umbonal slope limiting the radiating lines to the post-umbonal slope, but the radiating lines are on part of the disk. Unlike PROTOCARDIA there is no form nearly related to it in a Tertiary formation.

CYPRIMERIA.

The many perfect valves found at Snow Hill enable me to give the following diagnosis of this genus:

Shell inequivalved, bent to the right, dorsal area excavated, hinge of right valve with 3 cardinal teeth, and a wide triangular pit under the apex, which is ridged or uneven; left valve with 3 cardinal teeth, the posterior one very oblique, narrow, lobed or bifid, the lobes linear; pallial line with a slight sinus.

The above generic character excludes from this genus *obesa* d'Orbigny, *Oldhamiana*, Stoliczka, and *analoga*, Forbes, which are referred to it by Stoliczka, and indeed I do not find recorded in his Palæontology of Southern India a single species of CYPRIMERIA. His species, whatever the hinge may be, are all without fold and equivalve. *Arcopagia numismalis* and *A. rotundata*, d'Orbigny, are typical species. *Lucina discus*, Matheron, is a fine species, well figured by Dr. Zittell, under the name of *Circe discus*. *C. densata*, Conrad, a large species from New Jersey, figured in vol 3, of Journal of Acad. Nat. Sciences, Second Series, is very different from the species of the same name in vol. 2, which may be named *C. alta*.

VENILIA. *Morton.*

Stoliczka repudiates this name and substitutes one of his own. There is no recognized name of VENILIA in Conchology, except that given by Morton. Stoliczka has described some shells which he places in this genus, which, however, belong to another, and all the species which he refers to CYPRINA are true species of VENILIA.

IDONEARCA. *Conrad.*

This genus is limited to Cretaceous strata. The following shells are exotic species of it: *Arca Japetica*, Forbes; *Arca disparilis*, d'Orbigny; *Arca Marceana*, d'Orbigny; *Cucullæa glabra*, Sowerby; *C. carinata*, Sowerby: *C. oblonga*, Miller. American species—*I. Tippana*, Conrad.

LATIARCA. *Conrad.*

Differs from the above genus in being without the internal plate.

L. idonea. Less elevated than *L. ononcheila*, Rogers, with a more depressed or shorter post-umbonal slope; posterior side more cuneiform in shape, substance thick; margin of posterior cicatrix thick, prominent, acute. Length 3½ inches.

LIOPISTHA. *Meek.*

This genus was founded on external characters. Mr. Gabb has published as my opinion that the hinge resembles that of PAPYRIA, but I have no recollection of telling him so, nor of having seen the hinge, though I may have had a partial view of it. However I have now cleared it from the matrix of three valves from Mississippi, and give the following diagnosis:

Right valve—2 cardinal teeth just anterior to apex, anterior one short, conical, erect, very small, the other oblique, bent or angulated and directed anteriorly; left valve—one very small tooth under the apex, triangular or pyramidal, erect, flat on top, acute.

L. protexta, Conrad, (Cardium). The ribs are angular and acute, shell extremely thin in substance; the few ribs on the post-umbonal slope are minutely punctate, and the smooth part minutely granulated. Casts are common in New Jersey, but it is only near Ripley, Mississippi, that the shell has been found.

Cardium subdininense, d'Orbigny and *C. cornuelianum*, d'Orbigny, are species of this genus.

APPENDIX B.

SYNOPSIS OF THE VERTEBRATA WHOSE REMAINS HAVE BEEN PRESERVED IN THE FORMATIONS OF NORTH CAROLINA.

BY PROFESSOR EDWARD D. COPE.

ELASMOBRANCHII.

AETOBATIS ARCUATUS *Agass.* Miocene.
MYLIOBATIS sp. Miocene.
ZYGOBATIS sp.
NOTIDANUS PRIMIGENIUS. *Agass.* Miocene.
GALEOCERDO LATIDENS. *Agass.* Miocene.
ADUNCUS. *Agass.* Miocene.
CONTORTUS. *Gibbes.* Miocene.
EGERTONI. *Agass.* Miocene.
ZYGÆNA PRISCA. *Agass.* (*Sphyrna.*) Miocene.
HEMIPRISTIS SERRA. *Agass.* Miocene.
CARCHARODON ANGUSTIDENS. *Agass.* Miocene.
MEGALODON.' *Agass.* Miocene.
OTODUS OBLIQUUS. *Agass.* Miocene.
APPENDICULATUS. Miocene.
OXYRHINA XIPHODON. *Agass.* Miocene.
HASTALIS. *Agass.* Miocene.
DESORII. *Gibbes.* Miocene.
SILLIMANII. *Gibbes.* Miocene.
MINUTA. *Agass.* Miocene.
LAMNA ELEGANS. *Agass.* Miocene.
CUSPIDATA. *Agass.* Miocene.
PRISTIS BRACHYODON. *Cope.* Proc. Boston Soc. Nat. Hist. 1869, 312 Miocene.

PRISTIS ATTENUATUS. *Cope.*

Tooth slender, width at base less than one-sixth length, thick and straight. Posterior face straight, with a wide groove, anterior curved backwards, obtuse, with a faint median longitudinal groove. Posterior face at the tip of the tooth oblique; no striae.

Length 26.7 lines; width 4.5 lines; depth at base 3 lines.

This species is much more slender than the P. agassizii, *Gibbes*, the only species which resembles it. Found by Prof. W. C. Kerr, State Geologist of North Carolina, at Flowers' marlpit, Duplin county, North Carolina.

ACTINOPTERI.

AMBLYPTERUS ORNATUS. *Emmons*, N. Amer. Geol. 44, fig. 16. Trias.

RHABDOLEPIS SPECIOSUS. *Emmons*, l. c. 45, fig. 17. Triassic beds.

PYCNODUS CAROLINENSIS. *Emmons*, Geol. North Carolina, 1856. Miocene, Duplin county.

PNEUMATOSTEUS. *Cope.*

This genus is established on a caudal vertebra of a fish nearly allied to the gars of North America. It is opisthocoelian, and without trace of suture of either neural or haemal arches. The elements constituting the haemal arch appear to be diapophyses; they are divergent, and probably do not unite distally; they are directed more posteriorly than anteriorly. Their proximal boundary is apparently indicated by an indistinct elevation, perhaps the position of the original suture. The neural arch is split above by a deep median anterior fissure, on each side of which the narrow zygapophyses diverge. There is no zygantrum. The base of the broken neural spine is very small, and is as long as wide; it may probably have had but little elevation.

The structure of the bone is exceedingly light, and the external osseous layer very dense. In order to reduce the weight consistently with the size, the lateral and inferior faces are excavated by deep concavities terminating in pits. There are two on each side separated by a longitudinal ridge-like septum, which is plane with the expanded rims of the cup and ball. The superior pits are beneath the base of the neural spine, and nearly meet under the floor of the neural canal. The inferior concavity is very large, and extends from rim of cup to ball, and is divided longitudinally by a thin laminar hypapophysis. The bases of the diapophyses are wide, and extend from the base of the ball three-fourths the distance on each side to the rim of the cup.

The form of the vertebra is compressed. The ball is more convex transversely than vertically, and presents a slightly double convexity in profile. This is produced by a slight transverse contraction of the inferior fourth of the vertical diameter. The floor of the neural canal is raised to the superior margin of the ball.

This vertebra resembles the fourth in advance of the first bearing chevron bone in Lepidosteus. It differs from it generically, solely in the completeness of the neural arch above, since it is longitudinally fissured in the existing genus.

PNEUMATOSTEUS NAHUNTICUS. *Cope.*

The specific characters of this fossil are as follows: The cup is a vertical oval, slightly truncate below, and openly concave truncate above. Its form is not unlike that seen in some of the Pythonomorpha. The neural arch is much contracted tranversely opposite the neural spine. The surface of the bone is very smooth, except a few slight rugae near the rim of the cup.

MEASUREMENTS.

	In.	Lin.
Length of centrum,	1.	0
Width " " (between lateral septa)		7.1
Depth of cup,		8.4
Width of cup,		7.9
Depth of ball,		8.5
Length of base ?pleurapophysis,		6.8
" " " neurapophysis,		7.
Width neural canal (external, front,)		5.2
" " " (internal, behind.)		2.8

The large cells are exposed by the fractures of portions of the bone. The largest are at the posterior base of the haemal arch and at the sides of the former 1.5 line in diameter. These measurements indicate a gar of six feet in length, if of usual proportions.

The specimen on which this species is established was found by the writer on a pile of Miocene marl on the plantation of Nathan Edgerton, in Wayne county, North Carolina. Its interstices are filled with a hard clay matrix, similar to that which adheres to Cetacean remains in the hard stratum in the lower part of the Miocene shell bed of that region The color is black.

DIODON ANTIQUUS. *Leidy, Proc. Acad. Nat. Sciences.*

Superior and inferior jaws from the Miocene. This fish was described from transported and much worn specimens from the Ashley River,

South Carolina. The present specimens are unworn, and display the characters of the species. These are very much like those of the recent D. filamentosus. The species appears also to pertain to the horizon of the Miocene.

PORTHEUS ANGULATUS. *Cope.*

The crown of the tooth which indicates this species is slender, compressed and curved backwards and a little inwards. The circumference is divided by two edges, the anterior acute, the posterior obtuse; the convex faces separated by these are not equal, that towards which the crown is curved laterally, *i. e.* the inner, being somewhat more extensive, and considerably more convex.

Enamel smooth, without sculpture. Cutting edge without curvations, more curved backwards than the posterior, which has but little curvature. Inward curvature slight.

	Lines
Diameter (antero-posterior) at middle crown,	5
Diameter (transverse) at middle crown,	4
Diameter (transverse) near tip,	3
Diameter (antero-posterior) near tip,	2

Discovered by Prof. W. C. Kerr, State Geologist of North Carolina, in the Miocene marl, Duplin county, N. C., with Polygonodon rectus, and Ischyrhiza antiqua. *Leidy.*

ISCHYRHIZA ANTIQUA. Leidy, Proced. Acad. Nat. Sci. Phila. 1856, 256. Emmons' N. C. Geol. Survey, 1856, figs. 47, 48.

The Miocene of Sampson, Duplin and other counties.

The teeth of this genus bears a very close resemblance to those of the genus Esox at present existing in the fresh waters of the northern hemisphere.

BATRACHIA.

PARIOSTEGUS MYOPS. *Cope.* Trans. Am. Philos. Soc. 1869, p. 10.
Trias. of Chatham Co.

DICTYOCEPHALUS ELEGANS. Leidy, Proc. Ac. Nat. Sci. Phil. 1856, 256. Emmons' N. C. Geol. Survey, 1856. N. Amer. Geology 59, fig. 31, 32.
Trias. of Chatham Co.

REPTILIA.

CROCODILIA.

THECACHAMPSA sp. Sampson county, N. C.
Vertebræ in the State collection at Raleigh.

THECACHAMPSA RUGOSA. *Emmons.*

Polyptychodon rugosus. Emmons, Geol. Surv. North Carolina.
Emmons' figure of this species is not distinguishable from a worn canine of a *Basilosaurus*, and as such I regarded it on a former occasion. An examination of a specimen received from Prof. Kerr, shows that its affinities are Crocodilian, and its structure similar to that of *Thecachampsa*, Cope. It is more strongly rugose-striate than in any of the known species but is approached in rugosity by *Thecachampsa squankensis*, Marsh. The range of the genus is thus extended to North Carolina.

PLIOGONODON PRISCUS. Leidy, Proc. Acad. Nat. Sci. Phil. 1856, 255, *P. nobilis Leidy.* Emmons' Geolog. Survey N. C., 1858, p. 223, figs. 43, 44.

POLYDECTES. *Cope.*

Proceed. Amer. Philos. Society, 1870, 271.
This genus is indicated by one, perhaps more teeth, which resembles in some respects those of the Crocodilian genus Thecachampsa. Crown or dense concentric dentinal layers, with small pulp cavity. Enamel with two prominent ridges separating inner from outer aspects, but approximated on the inner face, which thus included, is but one third the circumference of the tooth. Ridges extending from tip to near base of crown, with a sulcus along the inner side of each. Crown acuminate, a little swollen at the base and above the middle, section circular.

POLYDECTES BITURGIDUS. *Cope.*

Crown, a slender cone slightly curved near the base. Middle portion constricted, its surface marked with narrow obscure facets. On the inner face, a shallow groove within each of the bounding sulci, the two separated by an indistinct groove. The enamel is smooth and worn, and leaves no traces of other sculpture.

	Lines
Length of crown,	30
Diameter at base of crown,	10
Diameter at middle,	6
Diameter above middle,	6.5

From the marl pits of James King, Sampson county, N. C. Discovered by Prof. W. C. Kerr, director of the Geological Survey of North Carolina.

TESTUDINATA.

TRIONYX BUIEI. *Cope.* Trans. Amer. Philos. Society, 1869, 153.
From greensand of Duplin county, N. C.
TRIONYX sp.
Miocene marl of Sampson county.
TAPHROSPHYS STRENUUS. *Cope*, Var.
Trans. Amer. Philos. Soc. 1869, 168.
Intrusive in Miocene marl in Sampson county.

THECODONTIA.

BELODON CAROLINENSIS. Emmons. *Rhytidodon carolinensis.* Emmons' (*Rutiodon*) N. C. Geol. Survey, 1856. North American Geology, 82. Manual of Geology 179, fig. 157. *Belodon*, Cope. Proceed. Ac. Nat. Sci., Phila., 1866, 249. ? *Palaeosaurus sulcatus*, Emmons, *l. c.* ? *Centæmodon sulcatus*, Lea. ? *Omosaurus perplexus*, Leidy, Pr. A. N. S., Phil. 1856. Coal strata of the Kemper Trias, of Chatham and Moore counties.

Teeth of both the smooth and fluted types were found in Anson county. The latter (*B. carolinensis*, Emm.) appear also to occur in Wheatley's collection, from the Trias of Phoenexville, Penna. Three successive forms of the maxillary teeth of *B. priscus* are figured.

BELODON PRISCUS.

Clepsysaurus pennsylvanicus, in part of Emmons' N. C. Geol. Survey, 1856. N. Amer. Geology and Manual of Geology. ? *Palæosaurus carolinensis*, Emmons, ibidem. ? *Compsosaurus priscus.* Leidy, Proc. Ac. Nat. Sci., Phil., 1856.

Trias of Chatham, Moore and Montgomery counties.

The examination of a portion of the specimens described by Prof. Emmons, from Montgomery county, prove it to be also a Belodon, differing from the last in its rather shorter vertebræ and larger size. Portions of the cranium exhibiting the angle and symphysis of the mandible with a tooth, and part of the nasal bones, point out conclusively its Belodont affinities.

Belodon leaii. Emmons. *Clepsysaurus laeii.* Emmons' N. C. Geological Survey. N. Amer. Geology. Manual of Geology.

Triassic coal bed of the Dan River region, North Carolina.

Of this speceies I have only seen casts of the conical vertebrae figured by Emmons. The evidence to be deduced from the descriptions and figures of this author, is in favor of its reference to the Belodonts, rather than to the Dinosauria.

DINOSAURIA.

Clepsysaurus pennsylvanicus. Lea, Jour. Acad. Nat. Sci. Phila. II. Emmons' Geol. N. C., 1868, in part.

Teeth of this genus are very rare, one only having been observed by Dr. Lea. Prof. Emmons believed that he had discovered two species in the Trias of North Carolina, *C. Pennsylvanicus* and *C. leai.* The greater part of the remains on which these were based I have shown to be Belodonts, but one tooth figured by Emmons N. C. Geol. Surv., Pl. V. f. 3, may belong to this genus.

Prof. Kerr's collection contains two teeth which are identical with that associated with the *C. pennsylvanicus* by Lea, one of them nearly perfect, the other the basal portion only. They exhibit two minutely denticulated cutting edges, separated by one-third of the circumference. This third is nearly flat, the remaining portion being very convex. One cutting edge extends to the base of the crown, the other occupies only the distal two-thirds. The section of the tooth would be round at the base were it not for the projection of the cutting edge. The enamel is minutely striats under the glass. The base of the larger tooth measures .75 of an inch in diameter. The figure of Emmons leaves something to be desired, as he does not represent the long cutting edge of the crown. His discriptions of the tooth appears to refer to this genus. Kerr's specimens are conclusive as to the extent of this formidable genus of carnivorous Dinosauria to N. Carolina. They were obtained in Anson county.

ZATOMUS *Cope.*

This genus embraces reptiles whose teeth are discribed and figured by Prof. Emmons, American Geology, Pt. VI. p. 62, fig. 34. He found them associated with radiate osseous plates (probably dermal) which he found on one occasion in connection with the cranium of the supposed Labyrinthodont, *Dictyocephalus* elegans, Leidy. Both the plates and teeth are too large to be associated with the latter, and the teeth especially remind one of the *Dinosauria*. Emmons describes a tooth in the following language:

"It is compressed, curved, finely serrate posteriorly, which appears to point to the apex, when seen so as to bring into view a slight wrinkle or groove at the base of each tooth. Its enamel covers the whole crown, or all above the part implanted or inserted. The enamel is finely or mine utely wrinkled and at the posterior edge, at the junction of the plates at each side, a faint groove remains; and the serrae appear like a double rows but near the apex they entirely disappear; the convex or anterior edge is smooth. 'The tooth appears much like the tooth of a *Megalosaurus* in miniature, though it is less curved. I have found only two teeth of this kind; the smallest is half the size of the one figured." This size is .022 m. in length; diameter at base .012.

In the section given by Emmons, one side of this tooth is a little more convex than the others.

The affinities of this genus appear to be to *Teratosaurus* and *Lœlaps*. From both of these, as well as from *Megalosaurus*, it differs in the absence of serration from the anterior margin, and in the groove in the posterior cutting edge dividing it into two appressed serrate edges which disappear near the apex. The species may be called

ZATOMUS SARCOPHAGUS. *Cope.*

Its size about equalled large specimens of the Southern Alligator.

HYPSIBEMA. *Cope.*

Char. gen. Proportions of limbs and feet much as in Hadrosaurus. The caudal vertebrae elongate and depressed, in the median part of the series.

The elongate depressed form of caudal vertebrae, distinguishes this genus from Hadrosaurus. The latter possesses elongate vertebrae near the extremity of the series, but anterior to this point, they are first subquadrate in profile, then proximally much narrowed. The form exhibited by the known species of this genus is more like that of Hylæosaurus Mant.

HYPSIBEMA CRASSICAUDA. *Cope.*

The remains on which this species is founded consist of the distal extremity of the right humerus, a portion of the shaft of the left tibia, a a portion of the fibula, the right internal metatarsus somewhat broken, and a caudal vertebra. There are other uncharacteristic fragments, and a piece which may be a dermal bone.

Associated with them are several coprolites of large animals.

These species indicate an animal of about the size of the Hadrosaurus foulkei, Leidy, and with a similar disproportion in the lengths of the limbs. This is readily appreciated on comparison of the huge metatarsus with the light humerus. The medullary cavity of the tibia is large; that of the humerus small.

The portion of the humerus preserved is injured, and the condyles are worn. Its relation to that of H. foulkei is readily determined, and on comparison the following marked differences appear: The ridge connecting the external condyle with the shaft posteriorly is acute; it is rounded in H. foulkei. External distal face is flat or slightly concave; in H. foulkei somewhat rounded. It is at right angles to the plane of the anterior face, and forms with it rather less than a right angle; in H. foulkei this region is rounded. Distally the shaft is much flattened in H. crassicauda.

Measurements.

	Lines
Antero-posterior diameter of shaft, just above condyles,	20.5
Width external face distally,	24
" olecranar fossa,	16
" condyles, (estimated)	64

The anterior face at over three inches above the condyles is slightly concave. About 4.5 inches above the articular face of the external condyle, the acute ridge dividing the posterior and external faces disappears, and the surface becomes regularly rounded.

The portion of the tibia is from the shaft of that of the left side, just below the superior antero-posterior expansion. Therefore the inner face is the most extensive, and the posterior the least so. It differs from the same part in H. foulkei, in its less angularity, especially in the more rounded, and less defined posterior face. The internal face narrows downwards, and while the greatest diameter of the fragment above is antero-posterior, below it is diagonal, the anterior point being the inner.

Measurements.

	Lines.
Antero-posterior diameter above,	48
Transverse " "	22.5
" " medullary cavity,	20.5

The portion of fibula is the distal, and resembles that of Hadrosaurus foulkei, in being slightly expanded near the extremity, and cylindric in the lower part of the shaft. In both genera and Ornithotarsus, Cope, the distal extremity of the fibula is less attenuated than in Iguanodon.

	Lines.
Transverse distal diameter,	40.5
do. five inches above.	30

The right internal metatarsus also bears considerable resemblance to that of H. foulkei. Its proximal extremity is much more convex in its inner outline than in that species. The inner proximal face is plane and longitudinally wrinkled. The proximal or tarsal articular face is concave anteriorly; its plane is at right angles to the axis of the shaft of the bone It is strongly oblique in Hadrosaurus foulkei, and a rib-like prominence of the outer face crosses the latter obliquely and at right angles to the proximal extremity. No such rib exists in the present casecause, be the weight was supported by the shaft bone, directly and not obliquely as in Hadrosaurus. Thus the Hypsibemæ walked more exactly on the toes than did the Hadrosauri.

The posterior margin is thinner, and as in H. foulkei, presents a rather small median protuberance. The distal condyle is broken away, but the twist of the distal portion of the shaft shows that it was directed away from the adjoining metatarsal, posteriorly.

Measurements.

	In.	Lin.
Length from antero-superior to postero-inferior extremity (inferior articular face worn away),	10	10
Transverse diameter proximally,	3	
" " medially,	2	3.5
Antero-posterior do. do.,	3	6

The diameters of the shaft are somewhat larger than in the H. foulkei given by Leidy.

The caudal vertebra is of large size and peculiar form. The centrum is considerably wider than deep, and considerably longer than wide. The posterior chevron articulations are small, and each is connected with each anterior by a strong rounded angulation. Between the latter the space is wide and slightly concave in transverse section, least so medially. A marked peculiarity is seen in the strong longitudinal ridge which divides the lateral surface of the vertebrae into two nearly equal faces, The neural arch is elongate, the neural canal small, in section a short very tical ellipse. The articular face of the zygaphophyses makes an angle of about thirty-five degrees to the perpendicular. The crest of the arch rises a half inch behind these into the very stout basis of the neural spine, the greater part of which, with the posterior zygapophyses, is broken off. The inclination of the base is at about 65° to the vertical diameter of the bone

The articular faces are both slightly concave, as are the lateral faces which are separated by the lateral ridge.

	In.	Lin.
Length of centrum,	4	6
" " basis neural arch,	2	9
Width posterior articular face,	4	
Depth do. medially,	2	8
" " laterally,	3	3
" basis neural spine,		12
Transverse diameter neural canal behind,		10
Width between latero-inferior ridges,	1	9
" vertical, of face of zygapophyses,		11

There is a light rugose protuberance in the position of the diapophysis.

The peculiarities of this vertebra indicate most strikingly the generic distinctness of this great reptile from the Hadrosaurus. It is true it presents some similarity in form to the terminal caudals of that genus, and if it could be referred to that portion of the series, would indicate merely another and larger species of Hadrosaurus. It differs in form from these vertebrae, in its depressed instead of compressed form, and its lateral angulation. That it belongs to a more anterior position in the tail is evident from the very large size of the basis of the neural spine, and general greater development of the neural arch and zygapophyses, and the trace of diapophysis. Further, it is over four times the size of the terminal caudal, of H. foulkei, while the remaining elemements do not indicate any such extraordinary dimensions. A position a little behind the middle of the series would relate well to the other proportions.

A worn bone found with the metatarsus, has the proportions of some of the dermal bones of certain Dinosauria Its large size is appropriate to the present species. Its base is flat with rounded outlines, and does not exhibit any superficial dense layer; the texture of the interior bone is rather dense. The mass of the bone rises as a short thick cone turned abruptly to one side, the middle and apex strongly compressed, so much so that the section presents an acute angle on that side to which the apex curves. The bone is not entirely symmetrical, one side near the posterior keel being more concave than the other. The structure of the bone is rather dense. Its exact posoition is somewhat uncertain.

	In.
Diameter at base,	3
Greatest height (apex broken),	2 5

This is another of those remarable forms which the reptilian type developed in past ages. That it was herbivorous, and relied less on its tail for support than Hadrosaurus, appears probable. Large coprolites of the character of those of herbivorous animals accompanied the bones. They resemble somewhat those of the hog; one has a diameter of four inches one way, and 2½ inches the other; extremity broad, obtuse. The probable form of the ungual phalanges, points also to the same habit. The proprietor of the pit told the writer that he had more than once seen large "hoofs" and "wide toe-joints" taken out during the excavation.

This species is different from the Ornithotarsus immanis, Cope, and belongs to a different genus. The shaft of the tibia in the latter is filled with cancellous tissue; in the present animal it is entirely hollow.

From the marl pits of James King.

HADROSAURUS. *Leidy.*

HADROSAURUS TRIPOS. *Cope.*

At a point about ten miles distant from the marl pit in which the Hypsibema was found, Prof. Kerr discovered a caudal vertebra of a colossal reptile, whose affinities are evidently near to the Hadrosaurus foulkei.

This vertebra is one of the distal, as evidenced by the entire absence of any trace of diapophysis, and its subquadrate longitudinal section, as well as by the small size of the neural arch and spine. At first sight it would appear to occupy a position between the thirtieth and thirty-sixth of the series; the former in H. foulkei has, however, rudiments of a diapophysis. Both its articular faces are distinctly biconcave. The large size of the chevron articular face is as in the thirtieth, and the concavity of its lateral faces as in the twenty-sixth; in the thirty sixth the sides are entirely plane. The round form of the neural canal, as well as the lack of diapophyses, are points of resemblance to the thirty-sixth, but it is more than twice as long as that vertebrae in the H. foulkei. In the thirteenth the neural is somewhat depressed and becomes more so as we advance towards the proximal part of the series. The small antero-posterior extent of the neural arch is much as in the thirtieth in H. foulkei, but the basis of the neural spine, which is broken off in this, as well as the old species, is much more slight. It is so very thin and weak as to indicate either a comparatively slight development of the spine, or a very posterior position in the series. A weak lateral ridge marks the side of the centrum, which is below the middle line. It holds the same position in the thirty-sixth in H. foulkei, but is above the middle in the thirtieth and those anterior.

Measurements.	*In.*	*Lin.*
Depth centrum to summit chevron articulation,	5	
do. from neural canal without chevron face,	4	
Greatest width do.,	4	9
Length centrum,	4	3
do. neurapophysis,	2	6
Width between anterior zygapophyses,	1	3
do. of arch above,	1	6
do. neural canal,		10
Depth do. do.,		10
do. basis nural spine,		5

This specimen was procured from the marl pit of W. J. Thompson, Sampson county, North Carolina.

A second and much smaller vertebra from the pit that furnished the remains of Hypsibema crassicauda, belonged to a third individual, and possibly to this species. Its proportions would point to a position near the end of the tail, and its form is less elongate and compressed than those in that position in H. foulkei. Its neural arch is not co-ossified. The extremities are slightly concave, the general form subquadrate.

	Lines.
Length of centrum,	20.5
Diameter extremity, (vertical)	18.
" " (transverse)	21.5
" middle,	15.

The first named vertebra pertained to an immense species, perhaps double the Hadrosaurus foulkei in weight and bulk, should the general proportions of the two have been at all similar. In that case the length of the femur would be sixty-two and a quarter inches.

PYTHONOMORPHA.

?POLYGONODON RECTUS. Leidy. Emmons' Geol. Survey N. C. 1856, 218.

Duplin county and Cape Fear River.

LIODON sp. *Macrosaurus* sp. Emmons l. c.

MOSASAURUS CRASSIDENS, Marsh in Cope's Synopsis Bat. Rept. N. Am. Trans. Soc. Philos. 1869, 198.

AVES.

CATARRHACTES ANTIQUUS, Marsh Sill. Amer. Journ. Sci. Arts, 1870, 213. Tarboro', Edgecombe county, N. C.

MAMMALIA.

Cetacea.

ESCHRICHTIUS MYSTICETOIDES. Emmons. (*Balaena.*) Emmons' No. Ca. Geol. Surv. 1856, p. 204, fig. 26. Leidy Mamm. Dak. Nebr. 1869.

ESCHRICHTIUS POLYPORUS. *Cope.*

Species Nova.

Character. Ramus mandibuli with coronoid process but little elevated; form compressed with narrow acute superior margin, which is not flattened posteriorly. On its inner face a wide shallow groove in which the inner series of foramina lie. Foramina of outer series large, numerous. Size large.

Description. This whale, from the form of the ramus mandibulli, is a finner, and from the slightly developed coronoid process, allied to the humpbacks. The coronoid, the anterior position of the dental foramen, and the angular process, confirm these relationships. Whether it be a Megaptera or an Eschrichtius I am not prepared to state. Ear bullae of the forms of both these genera occur in the strata in which the present species was found, and future investigation must determine which are referable to the latter. Such a bulla of the form of and probably belonging to, Megaptera, has been named *Balaena mysticetoides* by Emmons', (North Carolina Geol. Survey Tab.)

The fragment on which the present species is based, is the proximal two-fifths the left ramus mandibuli, with a considerable part of the condyle. The direction of the shaft from a short distance anterior to the coronoid process, is decurved. The inferior margin is slightly contracted below the coronoid process, and is for a short distance convex and narrowed into a ridge; anteriorly it is more obtuse or convex transversely. The inner face is plane at the coronoid process, the outer convex. Anterior to this point the convexity is strong; at the distal end of the fragment, much marked.

The angular process has extended beyond the line of the condyle; its extremity is broken away. A wide groove separates it from the base of the ramus. The surface of the condyle is transverse to the plane of the ramus, and is strikingly elevated above the portion of the ramus anterior to it, being as high as the tip of the coronoid process. A low knob projects on the inner face of the ramus beneath its anterior part, and below the groove. The dental foramen is large and is overhung by the thin incurved superior margin of the ramus. Its anterior margin terminates just behind the posterior part of the base of the coronoid process.

The pores of the inner series are small and numerous; the last one is a little anterior to the base of the coronoid process (34 lines). They are situated in a wide shallow groove which occupies a portion of the inner face of the ramus below the upper edge. Their interspaces are noquite equal; thus twenty lines separates two, and four are included in thirty-six lines. The foramina of the external series are more numerous than in any of the other species from the Miocene of our Eastern States. As in others the last pairs are less spaced than the anterior. In a space of six inches and twenty lines there are six foramina, the third from behind nine lines below the superior margin. Thirty-four lines separates the anterior pair; twenty-two of the posterior. The last foramen is about a half inch anterior to the place of the last one of the inner side.

	Feet.	Lines.
Length of fragment,	2	42
Depth just behind coronoid,		56
" " in front of "		66
" at fourth inner foramen,		62
Diameter " " "		27

This ramus chiefly resembles that of Eschr. cephalus from Maryland. It is less compressed, though crushed, and less attenuated on the upper margin near coronoid process; the coronoid process considerably smaller Outer series of pores most numerous and extending farther back, inner in a marked groove which is wanting in E. cephalus. Outer wall of angular region more everted. Inferior wall of dental or mandibular canal descending from margin of foramen in E. cephalus, ascending in E. polyporus.

From the Miocene marl of Edgecombe county, N. C. Obtained by the writer under the auspices of the North Carolina State Geological Survey, under Prof. W. C. Kerr, director.

Vertebræ which as to size and structure would accord with the present species, are not uncommon in the same deposit; their description is reserved for a future occasion.

MESOTERAS. *Cope.*

Genus novum

Character. Orbital process of frontal narrower, exceedingly thick and massive at the extremity. Posterior lumbars and anterior caudals with short antero-posterior diameter. Premaxillary and maxillary bones depressed, the latter thin, horizontal, narrow. Otic bulla depressed.

This genus is allied to Balaena in the form of its vertebra, and to some extent in that of its frontal bone. The flatness of the maxillary and premaxillary is rather that of Balaenoptera. The extraordinary mass of the superciliary portion of the frontal is peculiar to the species which forms the type of the genus, so far as known.

MESOTERAS KERRIANUS. *Cope.*

Species nova.

This species was discovered by Prof. W. C. Kerr, Director of the Geological Survey of North Carolina, in a bed of miocene marl, at a point where it was cut by Quanky creek, a tributary of the Roanoke river, in Halifax county, N. C. A portion of the cranium had been noticed for some years projecting from the steep bank or wall of the small cañon of the creek at about thirty feet below the surface of the ground. Prof. Kerr, with the aid of a number of men, dug from its bed and elevated to the surface of the ground a large fragment of the cranium, including the greater part of the left maxillary and premaxillary bones, with a large part of the frontal. A large fragment of the right ramus of the mandible; an otic bulla, several lumbar and caudal vertebra, with several broken ribs, were also obtained.

These remains indicate not only a species, but a genus new to science, and the largest extinct Balaenoid yet discovered.

The principal mass includes from the posterior margin of the transverse process of the frontal, to within four or five feet of the end of the muzzle. The mass measures eleven feet six inches in length. The fragment of the ramus mandibuli measures thirteen feet; five feet are probably lost distally, and there is no trace of coronoid process at the point where it is broken off proximally. The length of the restored cranium would not be less than eighteen feet. This gives for the total length, estimating on the basis of Megaptera, seventy-five to eighty feet.

The orbital process is nearly in line with the maxillary, probably in consequence of pressure when lying in an oblique position. The whole cranium has been injured from the same cause, and the matrix usually soft, formed a solid investment of carbonate of lime from the carbonic acid liberated during decomposition, which required several days labor to remove. The parietal, occipital, and other bones of the brain-case proper, were not recovered.

Description. The upper surface of the muzzle is but little decurved anteriorly. A portion of its outer margin, at the posterior part, is preserved, so that its width is known. The maxillary forms a rather thin lamina, and does not present any great median decurvature, as though the vomer was not prominent below. Perhaps this peculiar flatness is partly due to pressure, but the *premaxillary* presents a similar character, which is evidently normal. This element forms one margin of the mass, and the question as to whether the exposed face were the outer of the right, or the inner of the left bone, required some care for its solution. Anteriorly it is three inches in depth, near the posterior extremity, two inches. The greatest width near the middle, six inches. The margin next the remainder of the mass, is rather the more elevated; the external somewhat prominent and rounded. Beneath it a deep groove marks apparently the exit of a foramen. A groove in the same line is seen at various points throughout its length where exposed. This bone is thus much flatter than in any of the Finner whales, and resembles more that of the right whales. The outer face being nearly plane, it can scarcely be the vomerine face, which is concave, especially so in Balaena, for the accommodation of the cartilaginous axis. The foramina and grooves equally present in boththese genera, are on the external side; I therefore conclude that the external side of the right premaxillary is the one exposed, and that the width of the muzzle includes the left premaxillary and maxillary. The suture between the latter is not distinct, owing to the presence of longitudinal fractures. The width of the maxillary after the premaxillary is deducted, is not great, and is intermediate between that seen in Balaena and Megaptera. The right premaxillary may be traced for six feet two inches. Behind it a portion of the superficies of the cranium slopes towards the position formerly occupied as a blowhole.

The margin of the *maxillary* is horizontal, and rather thin. It becomes thicker posteriorly where it has been crushed back on the lateral orbital process of the frontal. Its accuminated extremity is seen lying on the latter.

The orbital process of the *frontal* is remarkably massive, and might at first be taken for the squamosal. Its posterior margin is free to within a foot of the probable position of the blowholes. This fact, in connection with its deep postero-inferior concavity in cross section, is conclusive as to its relations. The form is not horizontally expanded as in Megaptera, nor attenuated as in Balaena, but has rather the proportions seen in Reinhardt's figure of the young Balaena mysticetus: (Om Nordhvalen pl III.) That is, it has subparallel anterior and posterior sides; the extremity a little widened by the production backwards of the posterior portion. The anterior portion also somewhat, though less, protuberant. The whole extremity truncate and remarkably thickened. Thus it is nineteen inches long, the anterior tuberosity seventeen inches deep, the inferior outline nearly straight. The orbital concavity, which is continuous with the optic foramen, opens behind the posterior tuberosity and is defined exteriorly by the expanded posterior margin of the bone. Thus the great tuberosity which gives character to the bone was above and in front of the eye.

The portion of the *mandible* preserved presents marked characters. The inner face is slightly concave, or plane, the external, strongly convex. The inferior edge is narrowed, and the superior scarcely less so; the inner face rounds a little to the former, and to a wide groove just below the latter. This groove is one inch wide near the middle of the ramus, and is marked by a series of many small foramina. These are closer together in the anterior, and regularly more widely spaced to the posterior portion. Thus anteriorly they are 2.5 inches apart; posteriorly four inches separate them, and near the extremity of the series, six inches. I failed to find any foramina on the external face of the ramus. It is difficult, however, to believe that they are totally absent; it may be that they are confined to the anterior portion, which has not been preserved. This peculiarity, if entirely established, marks the species as quite distinct from any heretofore known from characters of the mandible. The depth in this species at the first point where the foramina are four inches apart, is fourteen inches.

There are some other pieces apparently belonging to the cranium, whose exact positions I cannot now assign. One of these looks like a segment of a ramus of the lower jaw, but the contraction of the superior and inferior outlines is too great. One face is plano-concave, the other convex flattened, with oblique superior and inferior faces, the latter the widest. Depth of plane, ten inches; depth exterior flattened face, 7.75 inches. Depth six inches from same point, 7.5 inches. The second uncertain fragment is long and with parallel margins. The outer face is strongly convex; the inner, at one extremity concave, so that a section would be half a crescent (the lower portion being lost.) The inner face gradually becomes convex, though not strongly so, and the long diameter is transverse, while it is vertical at the anterior end. The former is seven inches; the latter eight inches. The fragment looks like the extremity of a premaxillary bone, possibly a maxillary, but it is scarcely appropriate to the premaxillary already described.

The periotic bones of the left side were preserved almost entire. The bulla has the flat inferior face of the genus Balaena, and the periotic processes are exceedingly short, shorter even than those of the species of Balaena (B. mystictus and B. cisarctica.) The external process is not longer than the posterior, and is compressed and deeply grooved longitudinally below. The posterior process is at right angles to the exterior, and as broad as long. It bears a sublongitudinal ridge near the middle of its inferior face; anterior to it, separated by an interval, a transverse ridge occurs to which the edge of the thin lip of the bulla is attached. The anterior process contains the usual foramina, and is broader than long. The superior face of these bones is quite rugose. The bulla is more flattened, *i. e.* has a shorter vertical diameter, than either that of Balaena mysticetus or B. cisarctica. The circumference is not a sharp edge as in B. cisarctica, but is truncate and rugose, at the inner extremity most so. At the external extremity the face gives way to a rounded edge. The inferior face is coarsely impressed punctate, and has a curved depression inside the anterior margin. The posterior margin is marked by the usual three grooves with intervening inflations. The general outline, viewed from below is hexagonal, with the length of the sides as follows, beginning with the longest; posterior, anterior, interior, postero and antero-exterior equal, antero-interior very short. The bulla of B. cisarctica exhibits a long posterior and long interior side, connected by an arched outline.

The vertebræ are those of the genus Balaena. The general form of the centra of anterior lumbars and caudals, is abbreviated, especially the latter. The diapophyses of the former are thick at the base; one of those preserved may be a posterior dorsal, but the ends of the diapophyses are not preserved. In a caudal with very short diapophyses, which are a little nearer the bases of the chevrons than that of the neural arch, a small foramen penetrates the centrum from a point three inches above the base of the diapophyses, and issues at a point 2.5 inches below it. The articular faces are convex; there is a small rugose central area, and an external annular space with coarse, concentric ridges.

Measurements.

	Ft.	In.	Lin.
Length of fragment of o. maxillare to extremity which reposes on frontal,	9.	8	

	Ft.	In.
Width of same (?with left premaxillary) at 42 inches from extremity,	16	
Transverse diameter periotic bulla,	5	8.7
Longitudinal,	4	9.5
Vertical,	3	1.5
Length external periotic process,	1	9.5
" posterior " "	2	2
" centrum anteriorlumbar no. 1,	10	7.5
Vertical and transverse diameter do. each,	12	
Width neural canal	5	
Length diapophysis,	17	
Width " at base,	7	
" " middle,	6	
Length centrum lumbar no. 2,	10.5	
Both diameters of articular face,	13	
Width neural canal,	5.5	
" (antero-posterior,) neural spine,	5	
Length centrum of a caudal,	6.5	
Diameter articular face, (vertical)	14.	6
" " (transverse)	14.	
" neural canal,	1.5	
" inter-chevron groove,	3	

As compared with the described species, the characters of the Mesoteras kerrianus are well marked. Thus the earbone is totally different from that of Eschrichtius cephalus and E. mysticetoides (*Balaena* Emmons, Leidy) and the mandibular ramus is not flattened above as in E. priscus and E. expansus. The paucity or absence of external foramina distinguished it from the E. polyporus. Finally, E. leptocentrus presents generic characters in its known cervical vertebræ which will not probably be found in the present whale. Though these vertebræ of Mesoteras have not been found, I anticipate that they will present more nearly the characters of the genus Balaena, in accordance with the remainder of the structure. They are probably entirely different from those of Palæocetus of Seeley.

It has been known to geologists and others for some time, that a skeleton of some kind had been exposed by the erosive action of the waters of a creek in Eastern North Carolina, and was to be seen lying in its bed diagonally across it. The writer recently visited the spot, and found the stream to be some fifty feet in width, containing water of from three to five feet in depth. The direction and extent of the skeleton was indicated by the proprietor, Jesse W. Parker, since the water concealed it from view. It would appear to extend very nearly across the creek, and have a length of 50 to 60 feet. Some of the vertebrae could be distinguished by feeling with a rod. When the waters are low towards the end of the summer, its length is exposed, and it can be used as a foot log by the traveller. The only notice of this fossil is that given by Timothy A. Conrad in the "Miocene Shells of North America." On the bank near the this skeleton were four portions of the skeleton of an adult finner whale of some sixty feet in length.

Prof. Kerr, director of the survey, succeeded in obtaining one or two of the lumbosacral vertebrae of the specimen, which is above noticed. These were submitted to me at Raleigh. They belong to a right whale, or one nearer to Balaena than Balaenoptera. They are in fact identical in character with those of the species Mesoteras kerrianus, and belong probably to it. The following is a description of one of them from the posterior dorsal anterior lumbar region.

Median line below, obtusely keeled, sides a little concave. Articular face with a large median elevated area, which is coarsely obsoletely rugose; the marginal area exhibits fine concentric rugosities.

Measurements.

			Inches.
Length	centrum,		7
"	basis of diapophysis,		4.5
Depth	"	"	3.25
"	articular face,		8.5
Width	"	"	9
Thickness of epiphysis,			0.75

The epiphyses are free and the individual is young. A vertebraof similar character to, and rather larger size than any here described, was obtained by the writer near Nahunta, Wayne county, N. C. The species would not appear to be rare.

This whale is named for Prof. W. C. Kerr, of Raleigh, who has vitalized the State Survey and is prosecuting it with great advantage to all the branches of science that lie within its scope.

BALAENOPTERA sp. Otolites of whale. Emmon's N. C. Geol. Survey, 1856, 205 fig. 27.

DELPHINAPTERUS ORCINUS. *Cope*, sp. nov.

Established on a portion of the ramus of the mandible containing alveoli for four teeth, and exhibiting a considerable part of the symphysis mandibuli; several cervical, dorsal, and lumbar vertebrae, with fragments of ribs and other bones. They were found by the writer near together on the surface of a rather small pile of marl of the Miocene of Wayne County.

The mandibular ramus is rather slender, but thick, and the symphysis is short. Though the extremity is broken away on the inner side. The distal surface appears on the outer side. The alveoli are large, circular in section, separated by rather weak septa, and are but slightly oblique. Their form, size and position are quite similar to that seen in the genus Orca.

The cervical vertebrae from the fifth posteriorly, are separate. The fourth or fifth of the series, is round in the section of the entrum; and of very small fore and aft diameter. The vertebral canal is not quite enclosed by well developed, flat diandparapophyses. The lumbro sacral vertabrae are not elongate, but intermediate as in the Delphinapteri (*Belugas.*) The diapophyses are flat. Diameter of centra, two inches; length a little greater. Diameter of centrum of cervical, two inches. Depth of ramus at fourth alveolus from distal extremity 18 lines. Epiphyses all co-ossified.

The large separation of the cervical vertebrae, distinguishes this Delphinoid as allied to Delphinapterus, or the Belugas of the colder regions of the modern ocean, though the anterior may be found hereafter to be more consolidated than in them. The character of the dentition is more powerful than in the existing species, and approaches that of Orca, though weaker than most of the known species of that genus. Its size was probably that of the average of the white whales, about thirteen feet. It might be mentioned in this connection, that I have recently become acquainted with an Orca, probably from the warmer parts of the American Atlantic coasts in which, only four cervical centra have coossified centra, and the fifth is attached by the neural arch only. The cranium measures 32 inches in length.

PHYSETER VETUS. Leidy. *Physeter antiquus*, Leidy, not Gervais. *Catodon vetus*, Leidy, Extinct Mamm. Dakota and Nebraska.

Miocene.

ORYCTEROCETUS CORNUTIDENS. Leidy. Synopsis N. Am. Mamm. in Ext. Mamm. Dakota and Nebraska. Proc. A. N. Sci. Phil. 1856, 225. Emmons Geol. Surv., N. C. 1856 210–1 figs. *O. quadratidens*, Leidy l. c. Emmons l. c. Miocene, Pitt Co., and Cape Fear River.

Sirenia.

ONTOCETUS EMMONSII. Leidy. Emmons Geol. Surv. N. C., 1856. Miocene.

Proboscidia.

TRILOPHODON OHIOTICUS. Blum. *Mastodon giganteus, ohioticus et americanus* auctorum.

Postpliocene, various localities.

MASTODON OBSCURUS. Leidy Journ. Acad. Nat. Sci. Phil. 1869, p. 396 Tab. xxvii 13–15–16.

Miocene, Edgecombe and Pitt Counties.

ELEPHAS AMERICANUS. Leidy l. c. p. 397, Postpliocene.

Insectivora.

DROMATHERIUM SYLVESTRE. Emmons' N. C. Geol. Survey 1856. N. Amer. Geology pt. VI p. 93, fig. 66.

Triassic coal measures, Chatham County.

TOTAL NUMBER SPECIES OF VERTEBRATA.

Mammalia,	12
Aves,	1
Reptilia,	15
Batrachia,	2
Teleostei,	2
Ganoidei,	4
Elasmobranchii,	24
	60

EXPLANATION OF PLATES.

Plate 5—*Hypsibema crassicauda.*

Fig. 1. Caudal vertebra of Hadrosaurus tripos, side ; 1a. articular face.

Fig. 2. do. young? a. end ; b. below.

Fig. 3. Eschrichtius polyporus, side. 3a. above.

Plate 6—*Hypsibema crassicauda.*

Eig. 1. Humerus, distal portion, from below ; 1a. from end.

Fig. 2. Tibia shaft, from the side; 2a. from end.

Fig. 3. Caudal vertebra.

Fig. 4. Coprolite fragment.

Plate 7—*Hadrosaurus tripos. Eschrichtius polyporus.*

Fig. 1. Fibula, lower portion; a. proximal end of do.

Fig. 2. Outer metatarsal, inner side; 2a. proximal end of do.

Plate 8—*Mesoteras kerrianus. Clepsysaurus pennsylvanicus. Thecachampsa rugosa. Polydectes biturgidus. Belodon priscus. Diodon antiquus.*

Fig. 1. *Mesoteras kerrianus,* periotic bones. 1a. interior view; 1b. end view.

Fig. 2. *Polydectes biturgidus,* crown of tooth, side; 2a. inner view.

Fig. 3. *Thecachampsa rugosa,* crown of tooth, inner view.

Fig. 4. *Clepsysaurus,* tooth, inside view ; 4a. posterior view ; 4b. section base ; 4c. do near extremity ; 4d. base of larger sp.

Fig. 5. *Belodon? priscus,* anterior tooth ; 5a. posterior view of another ; 5b. lateral view ot a posterior tooth ; 5c. edge of do.

Fig. 6. *Diodon antiquus,* upper jaw, front ; 6a. do. from below ; 6b. lower jaw from front ; 6c. do. from above.

APPENDIX C.

PROF. W. C. KERR,

State Geologist of North Carolina:

SIR:—I beg to submit the following preliminary report on the minerals found in the State of North Carolina. The time allotted to me for the preparation of the same having been very short, and most of the principal localities of minerals being at present inaccessible, my list necessarily must be very imperfect; it shows, however, a variety of highly interesting and commercially important minerals and ores, which is *greater than that of any other State in the Union.* It is to be hoped that the wisdom of your Legislature will order the continuation of the geological survey, which has already given such important results to the State, and that a more liberal appropriation may enable you to continue the work on a larger scale. The materials collected for the mineralogical report can in the meantime be worked up, the various ores and minerals be analyzed and the results be presented in a more finished shape.

I am under obligations to several gentlemen for the assistance which they have given in the preparation of the list of the North Carolina minerals, especially to General Clingman, of Asheville, Dr. Hunter, of Cottage Home, Lincoln county, Dr. Asbury, of Charlotte, Rev. C. D. Smith, of Franklin, Macon county, and many others. Many promises of assistance have been made, but, unfortunately, nearly as many have been forgotten, and it is to be hoped that those, who made them will in the future show a more lively interest in the work, which we are doing, by sending to the Museum, at Raleigh, everything in their immediate neighborhood, which which may be of interest, so that it can be described and preserved.

Although it might have been more convenient to adopt in this preliminary report another plan and to put the different ores of one metal under one head, etc., I preferred to give at once a scientific arrangement, which must be the basis of a subsequent and fuller report, and I have therefore selected "Dana's System of Mineralogy" as the best and most in use in this country and Europe.

I. Native Elements;

II. Compounds:—the more negative element an element belonging to the Arsenic or Sulphur group;

1. Binary: Sulphids and Tellurids of metals of the sulphur and arsenic groups;

2. Binary: Sulphids, Tellurids, Arsenids, etc. of metals of the gold, iron and tin groups;
3. Ternary: Sulpharsenids, Sulphantimonids and Sulphobismuthids:

III. Compounds:—the more negative element an element of the group consisting of chlorine, bromine, iodine, fluorine and oxygen;
1. Chlorids, Bromids and Iodids;

IV. Compounds:—the more negative element fluorine;
1. Fluorids;

V. Compounds:—the more negative element oxygen;
1. Binary: Oxides;
2. Ternary: 1. Silicates; 2. Columbates, Tentalates; 3. Phosphates, Arsenates, Antimonates, Nitrates; 4. Borates; 5. Tungstates, Molybdates; 6. Sulphates, Chromates, Tellurates; 7. Carbonates; 8. Oxalates.

VI. Organic Compounds.

I. NATIVE ELEMENTS.

1. Gold.

Gold occurs in numerous localities throughout the State, generally in quartzveins of the gneissoid, granitic and dioritic rocks, also in those of the talcose, chloritic and argillaceous slates, and in beds of the slates themselves, and in gravel deposits, the debris of the decomposed rocks and veins. The principal counties, in which it has been found in sufficient quantity for exploitation are: Franklin, Nash, Guilford, Davidson, Randolph, Montgomery, Stanly, Union, Cabarrus, Rowan, Mecklenburg, Lincoln, Gaston, Catawba, Caldwell, Burke, McDowell, Rutherford, Polk, Cleaveland, Cherokee, Jackson and Watauga.

It is generally more or less alloyed with silver, varying from pure gold on the one side to pure silver on the other. It is associated with limonite and at a greater depth of the deposits with pyrite, chalcopyrite, galenite, zincblende, tetradymite, arsenopyrite, rarely with altaite and nagyagite. Specimens of gold, remarkable for their size, have been found at the Reid Mine, in Cabarrus county, the Crumpp Mine and the Swift Island Mine in Montgomery county (at the latter place in plates covered with octahedral crystals) at the Cansler & Shuford Mine, in Gaston county, and the Little John Mine, in Caldwell county. Very beautiful arborescent gold has been obtained from the Shemwell vein in Rutherford county. The variety, "electrum," containing [from 36 to 40 per ct. of silver, has been met with in octahedral crystals at Ward's Mine in Davidson county; also, in Union county, at the Pewter Mine, and associated with galenite and zincblende at the Stewart and Lemmon Mines, and in the neighborhood of Gold Hill.

According to Dr. Asbury, very interesting specimens have been found at Silver Hill, when the mine was first opened, consisting of specimens of several inches in length, one end of which was pure gold, while the other was pure silver. None of them have been preserved.

2. Silver.

This is on the whole a rare mineral in North Carolina. It has been obtained in considerable quantities at Silver Hill, in its native state, foliated and in plates in cerussite, also associated with argentite, galenite, zincblende, in small lumps, and arborescent and filifirm masses; it has also been found in small plates and reticulated masses, associated with tetrahedrite and zincblende, at the McMakin Mine* in Cabarrus county; two specimens of laminated silver have been observed by Dr. Asbury at the Asbury Mine in Gaston county; it has also been found by Hon. C. J. Cowles, of the Charlotte Mint, associated with chalcocite, at Gap Creek Mine, Ashe county.

3. Platinum.

The occurrence of grains of platinum among the sands of goldwashings of Rutherford and Burke counties, was first brought to notice by General Clingman, who sent half a dozen grains from a mine, near Jeanestown, to Prof. C. U. Shepard. It has also been found on Brown Mountain, in Burke, according to the information received from Mr. E. Bissell. It is reported as having been found near Burnsville, Yancey county.

4. Palladium.

General Clingman sent a specimen to Prof. C. U. Shepard, which came probably from Burke or Rutherford county, which the latter pronounced "native palladium."

5. Copper.

It has been found in small quantities in several mines, principally near the surface, so in minute distorted crystals with limonite at the McCulloh Mine, in Guilford county, arborescent and in crystalline plates at the Union Copper Mine, in Cabarrus county, near Gold Hill; one lump of copper, about two inches in size, much resembling that from the Cliff Mine, Lake Superior, said to have been found in Stokes county, is in the Museum at Raleigh; it also occurs in quartz and epidote-rock at Harris mountain, one-half mile east of Gillis Mine, Person county. A very interesting association is that of native copper in quartz crystals from lower Mecklenburg county, as observed by Mr. E. Bissell.

6. Iron.

No terrestrial native iron has been observed in North Carolina, but a great number of highly interesting meteoric masses have been found in the State; many of them have been preserved through the industrious perseverance of General Clingman, and were described by Prof. Shepard. The meteorites found were both irons and stones. They are:

1. The Asheville iron, described 1839 by Shepard, weight about thirty pounds; found six miles north of Asheville;

2. The Hominy Creek iron, near the base of Pisgah Mountain, ten miles west of Asheville; also described by Shepard;

3. The Black Mountain iron, from the head of the Swannanoa river, fifteen miles east of Asheville; described by Shepard;

3. The Guilford County iron, described by Shepard;

5. The Randolph County iron, found 1822, and described by Shepard;

6. The Caswell County iron, which fell January 7th, 1810, and weighed three pounds; described by Madison;

7. The Madison County iron, from Jewel Hill; described by J. L. Smith;

8. The Haywood County iron, which weighed only 1-8 of an ounce; described by Shepherd;

9. The Rockingham County iron, from Smith Mountain, where a farmer picked it up in 1866, on an old field, grown up with pines, but cultivated ten or fifteen years previously. It fell probably during the time in which the field was not in cultivation. A preliminary analysis, which I have made of this iron, leaves no doubt of its meteoric origin; (in the Museum at Raleigh.)

10. The Cabarrus County stone; described by Shepard;

11. A peculiar substance, consisting principally of iron and silicon, supposed to be of meteoric origin, has been found near Rutherfordton. Shepard described it and called it "ferrosilicine."

7. LEAD.

A few small irregular lumps of what has been alleged to be "native lead," were received from Messrs. Bechtler, of Morganton. They were said to have been dug up four miles north of Morganton, in making a road near the Catawba river.

8. ANTIMONY.

A small piece of native antimony was received from Dr. Hunter. It is quite pure and free from arsenic, but coated with a crust of antimonic oxide. From a small vein in Burke county.

9. SULPHUR.

It is frequently met with in minute crystals in cellular quartz, filling the cavities formerly occupied by pyrite, in Cabarrus, Mecklenburg, Gaston, Caldwell and Stokes counties; it also occurs diffused through the interstices of a white quartzose sandrock in Lincoln county.

10. DIAMOND.

This rare gem has been repeatedly found in North Carolina, and the following occurrences have been well established. In every instance it was found associated with gold and zircons, sometimes with monazite and other rare minerals in gravelbeds, resulting from gneissoid rocks, but it has never been observed in the North Carolina *itacolumite* or any debris resulting from its disintegration. The first diamond was found in 1843 by Dr. M. F Stephenson, of Gainesville, Georgia, at the ford of Brindletown creek. It was an octahedron, valued at about one hundred dollars. Another from the same neighborhood came into possession of Prof. Featherstonehough, while acting as United States Geologist.

The third diamond, at Twitty's Mine, Rutherford county, was observed in 1846, by General Clingman in D. J. Twitty's collection, and has been described by Prof. Shepard. Its form is a distorted hexoctahedron, and its color yellowish.

The fourth came from near Cottage Home, in Lincoln county, where it was discovered in the spring of 1852, and was recognized by Dr. C. L. Hunter. It is greenish and in form similar to the last, but more elongated.

A very beautiful diamond was found in the summer of 1852 in Todd's branch, Mecklenburg county. It was nearly of the first water and a perfect crystal. It was in possession of the late Dr. Andrews, of Charlotte. Dr. Andrews informed me that a very beautiful diamond of considerable size, like a small chinkapin, and of black color, had been found at the same locality, by three persons, while washing for gold. In their ignorance, believing that it could not be broken, they smashed it to pieces. Dr. Andrews tested the hardness of a fragment, which scratched corrundum with facility, proving it to be a diamond. A very beautiful octahedral diamond of first water has been found many years ago at the Portis' Mine, Franklin coounty. There is a report that a second one has been found at the same locality.

11. Graphite.

Graphite has been found at numerous localities. It forms large beds in the gneissoid and micaceous schists; sometimes very minute scales are disseminated thaough the micaceous rocks. In most places' it is yet too impure and gritty, at others purer, and better varieties have been obtained. The largest beds occur in Wake county, others in Lincoln, Cleaveland, Catawba, Alexander, Stokes, Surry, Wilkes, Person and Yancey counties.

II. COMPOUNDS.

1. *Sulphids and Tellurids of metals of the sulphur and arsenic groups.*

12. Bismuthinite.

In very minute crystals and specks in the chloritic slate associated with gold, chalcopyrite and pyrite at the Barnhardt vein of Gold HIll, Rowan county.

13. Tetradymite, var 2. sulphurous.

This rare mineral has been found associated with gold in quartz at David Beck's Mine, five miles west of Silver Hill, in Davidson county; also, in minute scales in Cabarrus county, at the Phœnix Mine, Boger Mine, Cullen's Mine, at the Asbury vein, in Gaston county, at Capt. Mills' Mine,* in Burke county, and Capt. Kirksey's*, McDowell county.

14. Molybdenite.

In granite and quartzveins, in fine scales in the neighborhood of the

Pioneer Mills Mine, Cabarrus county; also, in Guilford county, and in many places west of the Blue Ridge.

2. *Sulphids &c. of metals of the iron, gold and tin groups.*

15. Argentite.

In small grains, associated with native silver, in the ores of Silver Hill, Davidson county, and the McMakin Mine*, in Cabarrus county, also in slates of Montgomery county. (Emmons.)

16. Galenite.

At Silver Hill sometimes in highly argentiferous, crystalline blueish grey masses, also coarsely and finely granular. In coarse grained masses at the Hoover Mine and Boss Mine, in Davidson county, and the McMakin Mine, Cabarrus county, in small quantities at Miller's Mine, Baker Mine and Little John Mine, in Caldwell county, at Pax Hill, in Burke county, in Alexander county, at Cansler & Shuford Mine, the Asbury Mine and King's Mountain Mine,* in Gaston county, highly auriferous and argentiferous galenite occurs at the Stewart Mine, Lemmond Mine and Long Mine, in Union county; with copper ores it is found at the Clegg's* and Williams' Mines, in Chatham county; the Peach Bottom Mine,* in Alleghany county; at Marshall, in Madison county, with gold at Murphy, Cherokee county. Specimens of fine grained galenite have also been obtained from Beech Mountain,* in Watauga, and on Elk creek,* Wilkes county.

17. Altaite.

This exceedingly rare mineral occurs associated with gold, nagyagite, galenite, etc., at King's Mountain Mine,* Gaston county.

18. Bornite or variegated copper ore.

I have crystalline specimens of bornite from Guilford county, probably from the Gardner Hill Mine; it is of somewhat rare occurrence in North Carolina, but has been found with other copper ores at Clegg's Mine, in Chatham county, Marshall, in Madison county, Peach Bottom, Alleghany county, and the Gap Creek Mine, Wilkes county.

19. Sphalerite or Zincblende.

This mineral occurs in quantities sufficient for exploitation only at a few mines. The principal localities are Silver Hill* and Silver Valley, in Davidson connty, and the McMakin Mine,* in Cabarrus county, where it is found associated with silver ores; associated with gold ores at Stewart, Lemmond, Long and Moore Mines, and rarely at the Union Mine, in Union county; in limestone at Dobson's Mine,* Cedar Cove, McDowell county, and in Macon county; in small quantities with other ores at King's Mountain Mine,* in Gaston county; at Clayton, in Johnston county, near Marshall, in Madison county, and on Uwharrie river, Davidson county.

20. Chalcocite.

This is also a copper ore, but rarely met with in the State. The massive variety has been found at the Ore Knob Mine, in Ashe county; also, associated with bornite at Gap Creek Mine, Ashe connty, the Waryhut* and Wolf Creek* Mines in Jackson county, the Gillis Mine* in Person county; also, at the Pioneer Mills Mine in Cabarrus, and in Guilford county, as a product of the alteration of other copper ores, rarely with silver ores at Silver Hill.

21. Pyrrhotite.

Compact pyrrhotite is found at the bottom of the Asbury shaft in Gaston county, also associated with chalcopyrite at the Elk Knob Mine,* Ashe county.

22. Rhadbite.

This mineral of meteoric origin has been observed in minute quanratic prisms of great brilliancy in the meteoric iron of Smith's Mountain*, Rockingham county.

23. Pyrite.

Pyrite is one of the most common minerals of North Carolina. It is not only found in globular crystalline masses in many of the marlbeds of the eastern counties, but many of the genissoid rocks and slates contain it in considerable quantities, and besides it is found in almost every mine of the State, In the gold mines the associated pyrite is generally auriferous. Cubical crystals occur at Hickory, Catawba county, Asbury Mine,

Gaston county, Soapstone Quarry, twelve miles' northeast of Statesville, Silver Hill, Gold Hill and many other localities. Combinations of cubes and octahedra are found at Clegg's Mine, Chatham county, and in the Guilford county gold and copper mines; the pyritohedron, often in combination with cubical and octrahedral planes, is found at the Stewart Mine, in Union county, Cambridge Mine, Guilford county, Long Creek Mine, Gaston county, udesill Mine, Mecklenburg county, etc. Large veins of compact pyrite occur in Gaston county.

24. Chalcopyrite.

This is very abundant, and indeed is the only reliable copper ore of North Carolina. It has been found in fine crystals at the Gardener Hill Mine, probably also at other copper mines of Guilford county. It is the ore of all the gold mines, which in depth change into copper mines in Guilford, Cabarrus and Mecklenburg counties; also at the Clegg's Mine* in Chatham county, the Conrad Hill and Emmons Mine* in Davidson county; Peach Bottom, Alleghany county; the copper mines of Macon* and Jackson* counties; at many other localities it is found associated with other ores.

25. Barnhardtite.

A peculiar and rich copper ore, first noticed on Daniel Barnhardt's land, and then at the Pioneer Mills Mine in Cabarrus county. It also occurs at the Cambridge Mine, in Guilford county, and the Wilson Mine and the McGinn Mine, in Mecklenburg county. The true barnhardtite contains forty-eight per cent. of copper; there is another copper ore, sometimes associated with it, which contains forty-eight per cent. of copper. It appears to be uniform and does not look like a mixture. Its true character is not yet established.

26. Marcasite.

According to the information received from Dr. Asbury, of Charlotte, this mineral occurs in Iredell county.

27. Leucopyrite.

It has been observed by Dr. Asbury at the Asbury Mine, in Gaston county.

28. Arsenopyrite or Mispickel.

It occurs sparingly in North Carolina, and has been observed in minute crystals, associated with gold ores, at the Lemmond and Stewart Mines, Union county, and at the Barringer Mine, in Cabarrus county. It has been found by General Clingman, in Cleaveland county, and by Dr. Asbury, at Ore Knob Mine, in Ashe county, the Honeycutt vein at Gold Hill, and highly auriferous at the Asbury Mine, in Gaston county. It also occurs near Cooke's Gap, Watauga county, in fine crystalline particles, disseminated through siliceous rock.

29. Nagyagite.

This exceedingly rare mineral, which heretofore has been known only from Transylvania, in Hungary, occurs sparingly in minute crystals and foliated particles at the King's Mountain Mine, where it is associated with altaite, gold, etc.

30. Covellite.

Resulting from the decomposition of chalcopyrite and associated with it, covellite occurs at several of the North Carolina copper mines, for instance at the Phœnix Mine, etc , in Cabarrus county ; in fine scales at the Gillis Mine,* in Person county.

3. *Sulpharsenids, Sulphantimonids, etc.*

31. Proustite (?)

Microscopic crystals of a bright aurora red color occur with talc, rhodochrosite, etc. at the McMakin Mine. As they are rich in silver they are probably proustite.

32. Aikinite (?)

A mineral, containing sulphur, bismuth, lead and copper, and therefore probably aikinite, has been observed in small particles in quartz associated with chalcopyrite at Col. White's Mine, Cabarrus county.

33. Tetrahedrite.

Two varieties of Tetrahedrite are found in North Carolina, the highly argentiferous (Freibergite,) containing ten and a half per cent. of silver; it is associated with silver, zincblende, galenite, talc, magnesite, etc., at the McMakin Mine, Cabarrus county; the other, which contains little or no silver, at George Ludwick's Mine, in the same county. It is associated with chalcopyrite, scorodite, arsenosiderite etc. in a quartz vein. There is probably an occasional small admixture of argentiferous tetrahedrite with the minerals associated with the native silver of Silver Hill, as they give before the blowpipe incrustations of antimony.

III. COMPOUNDS OF CHLORINE, ETC.

34. Halite or Common Salt.

Found in the waters of the Atlantic Ocean, from which it can be obtained by evaporation, and in wells and springs at several points in the Triassic beds, e. g. in Chatham, Orange and Rockingham.

35. Cerargyrite.

In some of the gold ores of Scott's Hill, in Burke county, silver is found after roasting; a specimen, which I had an opportunity to examine, makes it probable that the silver is present as chloride of silver or cerargyrite.

IV. FLUORINE COMPOUNDS.

36. Fluorite.

According to General Clingman, fluorite occurs at Brown Mountain, Burke county, also in Watauga, and with barite below Marshal, Madison county.

37. Yttrocerite (?)

A few minute deep violet blue spots were observed in association with pyrochlore, black tourmaline, orthoclase, quartz, etc. at Ray's Mica Mine, Hurricane Mountain, Yancey county.

V. OXYGEN COMPOUNDS.

1. *Oxides.*

38. Cuprite.

Cuprite or the red oxide of copper occurs in some of the copper mines near the surface. It is rarely found in small crystals at Cullen's Mine and upon native copper at the Union Company Copper Mine, in Cabarrus county. It has also been observed at Clegg's Mine, Chatham county, at Silver Hill, at the Harris Mine, in Person county, in Caldwell county, and upon the gossan of the Waryhut Mine, Jackson county. At the McGinn Mine, in Mecklenburg county, and several of the Guilford county copper mines, cuprite in acicular and capillary crystals (so-called chalcotritchite) was formerly found in beautiful specimens.

39. Melaconite.

It is found occasionally as a black coating or a powder associated with cuprite at the McGinn Mine, and with zincblende, etc., sparingly at Silver Hill.

40. Corundum.

Several varieties of this mineral have been found in North Carolina. It has lately been discovered near Franklin*, Macon county, where it occurs in the most beautiful varieties and in very large masses. Some are red and semi-transparent, in small fragments even transparent, and form a fair ruby, other specimens of gray and reddish corundum have disseminated through the mass the most beautifully colored azure blue sapphire. Unfortunately the particles of the red and the blue are too small to have any value as gems. The greater portion is found in granular or cleavable masses, also in small crystals. A large mass of dark blue corundum weighing nearly one hundred pounds, was found in the spring of 1847 three miles below Marshall, in Madison county, General Clingman's attention having been called to it, he searched for more and obtained in the summer of 1848 a second piece of about half the size. It has lately been found in Jackson county* and in Yancey,* and Buncombe,* in small red and white grains with gold in Rutherford, McDowell and Burke counties. A blueish variety, sometimes in crystals, partly altered into margarite, occurs at Crowder's* and Clubb Mountain. and a reddish variety in Polk county; it is associated with cyanite in Wilkes county. The granular variety, "Emery," has been found at Crowder's Mountain, and lately in the titanifereus iron ore belt, near Friendship, in Guilford county.

41. Hematite.

Red oxide of iron or hematite is one of the most important iron ores of North Carolina. The compact ore, sometimes more or less mixed with the specular variety, forms large beds in Chatham county, at Evans' and Kelley's ore beds, Ore Hill,* etc.; also, in Moore county,* twelve miles east of Carthage, and in Orange county, at Chapel Hill,* extending northeast towards Red Mountain. Foliated and micaceous hematite occurs at Buckhorn,* Ore Hill,* seven miles west of Lockville, in Chatham county, Snow creek, Stokes* county, near Gudger's, nine miles below Marshall, on the French Broad river. A very fine variety of slaty hematite with crystals of magnetite is found at Cooke's Gap, Watauga county. Other localities are: Smith's river,* two miles east of Morehead's factory, in Rockingham county; a granular variety one mile east of Gaston;* at House's mill, Cabarrus county; at Hickory,* Catawba county,* in Lincoln,* Gaston* and Mecklenburg counties, etc. The ochreous variety has been observed in Buncombe county,* four to five miles west of Asheville, at Valley Town* and on Peachtree creek, Cherokee county.

42. Menaccanite.

Many of the titaniferous iron ores are mixtures of true magnetite and menaccanite, others belong to this species and others again are really magnetites, in which a portion of the iron is replaced by titanium. Our present knowledge of these ores is too limited to put all the varieties, occurring in the State, with certainty at the place where they belong. Those from the following localities, appear to belong under this head: Big Laurel, in Madison county, on Ivy, Yancey county, Crab Orchard, Cane Creek,* and Flat Rock, in Mitchell county, Old Harris Mine, twelve miles southeast of Charlotte, south end of Crowder's Mountain, Yadkin river, near Patterson, in Caldwell county,* and the neighborhood of Raleigh. Iserite is frequent in the gold sands of Rutherford, Burke, and McDowell counties, etc.

43. Gahnite.

Gahnite, or Automolite, is mentioned by General Clingman as occurring in Cleaveland county.

44. Magnetite.

This is the most abundant and most valuable iron ore in North Carolina. It occurs in small octahedral crystals in the slates at Fisher's Peak* and Chestnut Mountain* in Surry county, also at Bull's Head, in Alleghany county, in quartzose sand rock at Cooke's Gap,* Watauga county, at Capp's Hill, in Mecklenburg county, and Fisher Hill, in Guilford. It occurs in its granular variety, mixed with muscovite, manganiferous garnet, etc. at Buckhorn,* in Chatham county, and mixed with menaccanite and occasionally with corundum, in a succession of beds, passing through the gneissoid rocks of Davidson, Guilford, Forsythe and Rockingham counties*. There appear to be several isolated outcrops northwest of this band and betweeen it and the Dan river, and also in Randolph and Montgomery counties. A band of granular magnetite, free from titanic acid, mixed with actinolite, tremolite and a little epidote, passes from near Danbury,* in Stokes county, and also from Surry county, through Yadkin,* Forsythe, Davie, Lincoln, and Gaston counties.* It contains some of the most valuable ore beds. It is also found in large beds near Newton, in Catawba county,* also in Mecklenburg and Cabarrus counties. Some very valuable ore beds of crystalline magnetite occur in Mitchell county, the most extensive probably at Cranberry.* A bed of granular ore, similar to the ores of Surry county, is worked at the north fork of New river, near the mouth of Hilton creek,* in Ashe county. There are several other localities, from which I have seen magnetite, but they are of less importance than those enumerated.

45. Chromite.

Occurs in the chrysolite beds, which form lenticular masses in the hornblende slates, etc., in minute octahedral crystals and granular masses near Franklin,* in Macon county, Webster, in Jackson county, Mining creek,* near Hampton's, in Yancey county, in small quantities near Bakersville,* Mitchell county, and on South Toe river,* and on Rich Mountain,* Watauga county. Where it is found in abundance, it may become a valuable ore, when it can be brought to market. A small admixture of chromite is found in the titaniferous magnetite belt of Guilford, Rockingham, etc., counties.

46. CHRYSOBERYL(?).

Observed in greenish yellow rhombic, striated crystals between muscovite, at Ray's Mica Mine, Hurricane Mountain, Yancey county.

47. RUTILE.

In beautiful crystals at Crowder's and Clubb Mountains, Gaston county; also granular at the same localities; in acicular crystals, sometimes over one inch in length, near Beattie's Ford, Mecklenburg county; in long crystals in quartz on a hill near Buckhorn Falls,* in Chatham county; in needles in amethyst at the head of Honey creek, in Wilkes county, as observed by Mr. Cowles, of the Charlotte Mint, also in Mitchell county,* Rutherford county, and Burke county.

48. BROOKITE.

According to General Clingman and Professor Shepard, found in the gold sands of Rutherford and Burke counties.

49. PYROLUSITE.

It is found near Murphy,* Cherokee county, then two miles north of Hickory, Catawba county, and with silver ores, at the McMakin Mine, Cabarrus county, also in fine crystalline masses at Beck's ore bank, three miles from Ellison's ore bank, also near Danbury,* in Stokes county, and near Webster,* in Jackson county. No large deposits have yet been discovered in North Carolina.

50. DISAPORE.

General Clingman observed this rare mineral associated with blue corundum from near Marshall, Madison county. I have not been able to distinguish it with certainty from any of the other corundum localities.

51. GOETHITE AND LIMONITE.

I put these two species of hydrated sesquioxide of iron together, as I have had no time yet to examine the various specimens, in the museum, in order to ascertain to which they belong. Large beds of hydrated sesquioxide of iron are found at Ore Hill,* in Chatham county, on the High Shoals,* in Gaston county, in Lincoln and Catawba counties, and near Murphy,* in Cherokee county. Brown hematites accompany in small quantities many of the magnetite and hematite beds, and form the upper part of many of the gold and copper mines; they are often the result of the alteration of siderite and pyrite, and show frequently the form of the original mineral, for instance, at Conrad Hill, in Davidson county, Cabarrus county, Guilford county, Gaston county, etc.

52. Psilomelane.

It is often an associate of gold and iron ores in coatings of the quartz at Scot's Hill, Burke county, together with pyrolusite at Beck's ore bank, on the High Shoals, Gaston county, and in botryoidal masses in a vein, said to be four feet wide, near Lenoir, in Caldwell county,* and in Chatham.* In Gaston county, at the Long Creek Mine, on Cross Mountain, Ormond Ore Bank, etc., a variety occurs, which contains a small quantity of cobalt and nickel.

53. Wad.

There is often an imperceptible change from pyrolusite into psilomelane and wad, that without analysis it is often difficult to know to which a specimen may belong. The earthy varieties are generally called wad. A brownish, black earthy wad occurs near Murphy,* Cherokee county, also near Franklin,* in Macon county, and Webster,* in Jackson county.

54. Senarmontite or Valentinite.

The incrustation of the native antimony of Burke county, which does not show any crystalline planes, belongs to either one or the other of these species.

55. Bismite.

An earthy greenish yellow and straw yellow mineral has been observed at the King's Mountain Mine and the Asbury vein, in Gaston county. It is probably Bismite.

56. Molybdite.

Found associated with molybdenite as a yellow earthy powder, near Pioneer Mills, Cabarrus county.

57. Quartz.

As a constituent of most of the rocks of North Carolina and the gangue of almost every vein, it occurs nearly everywhere throughout the State. Several of its varieties are quite interesting. Good spiecimens of *Rock crystal* have been found in Rutherford county,* also near Hickory,* in Caldwell county, near Morganton, in Burke county, Alexander county,* Mountain Mine,* in Cleaveland county, at Hampton's,* Mining creek, Yancey county, Stokesburg,* in Stokes county, Rich Mountain, head of Cove creek, in Guilford and Wilkes counties; *Radiated quartz* occurs at Dilahay's Gold Mine,* in Person county; very fine crystals and clusters of crystals of *Amethyst* of good violet and pink, but mostly of a dark smoky color, at Randleman's, Lincoln county, also at the lead mine, in Alexander county,* at Hickory,* in Catawba, and in Rutherford, Chatham* and Wake* counties;* amethyst, with inclosed rutile, at the head of Honey creek, in Wilkes county. I have found *Rose quartz* near Concord, in Cabarrus county; *Smoky quartz* is found three miles from Taylorsville,* in Alexander county, and at the mouth of Beaver Dam creek; *Milky quartz*, at the forks of the Laurel, Madison county, and at War Hill,* Surry county; *Opalescent quartz*, at Dan river, in Stokes county; *Quartz pseudomorphous*, after calcite, both crystallized and fibrous, is found two or three miles northwest of Rutherfordton, in Rutherford county, the fragment often containing water inclosed. Similar pseudomorphs occur in Alexander county.* *Chalcedony* has been found at Franklin,* in Macon county, in Jackson county, near Webster,* at Hampton's,* Mining creek, in Yancey county, and at Martin's lime quarries,* in Stokes county. *Hornstone* is found at the same locality;* also, near Asheville, in Buncombe county, and in Madison county. *Itacolumite* or flexible sandstone forms a stratum in the quartzite at Linville,* Burke county, Sauratown Mountains,* in Stokes county, and Bending Rock Mountain,* in Wilkes county. *Fossil wood* is abundant near Germanton,* in Stokes county, near Cheek's creek,* in Montgomery county, and in the marl beds near Goldsboro',* and in Johnston* county, etc.

58. Opal.

2. *Ternary Oxygen Compounds.*

1. *Silicates.* *A. Anhydrous Silicates.*

59. Enstatite.

In coarsely granular masses with chrysolite, at Webster, Jackson county, also in small crystalline particles, disseminated through chrysolite, at Hampton's, Mining Creek, Yancey county, and two and a half miles south of Bakersville, in Mitchell county.

60. Pyroxene.

Black and brownish black, cleaveable masses, with magnetite, at Cranberry,* Mitchell county; green coccolite, in calcite, two or three miles from the mouth of Bear creek*, and in marble, at Walnut creek,* one mile from French Broad river, Madison county.

61. Amphibole.

Amphibole is represented in North Carolina by numerous varieties. We find white and gray *tremolite*, associated with talc, at Marble creek* and Murphy,* Cherokee county, also on the Tennessee creek,* Jackson county, in talc and chrysolite, at Webster,* Jackson county, the White-side Mountains,* Sugartown,* eight and a half miles from Franklin, Macon county, two and a half miles south of Bakersville,* in Mitchell county, and at Hampton's, Mining Creek*, Yancey county. on Toe river,* gap of Black Mountain, and the southeast slope of the Three top Mountain,* in Ashe county; grey and brownish *grammatite* occurs near the Tennessee creek*; *actinolite* has been observed at Shooting creek,* Clay county, Swannanoa river,* near Asheville, and with chrysolite at Webster,* Jackson county, Hampton's, Mining Creek,* in Yancey county, two and a half miles south of Bakersville,* Mitchell county, in talcose rocks, near Tennessee creek,* on the east fork of Tuckasege, one and a half miles from its mouth, Rich Mountain,* Watauga, Franklin,* in Macon county, at Bolejack's Limestone Quarry,* in Stokes county, at Rogers' Ore Bank,* near Danbury, in Stokes county, and Ellison's in Gaston county. *Asbestos* has been found at Webster,* on Sugartown creek,* near Franklin, at the Nantehaleh river,* in Macon county, the Brushy Moun tains, in Wilkes county, at Hampton's,* Mining Creek, in Yancey county, Buchanan's* and Cane Creek,* near Bakersville, in Mitchell county. *Black* and *greenish black hornblende* is abundant throughout the State in the hornblenke slates, hornblende rock, syenite and diorite. It has been found in rather large cleavage pieces, twenty-three miles below Franklin,* on the Swannanoa river,* near Asheville, at the Cullowhee* and Savannah Mines,* in Jackson county, at Jarrett's,* on the Nantehaleh, at Polecat creek, and near Greensboro', in Guilford county.

62. Beryl.

In six-sided prisms, sometimes doubly terminated, from about half an inch to four inches in thickness, and from one to six inches in length. Their color is yellowish and bluеish green, small pieces of the latter color are sometimes transparent, and might be cut for gems (aquamarine ;) associated with orthoclase, muscovite, tourmaline, etc. at Ray's Mine,* on Hurricane Mountain, Yancey county; one imperfert yellowish green crystal, of about one and a half inches in length, has been found at Buchanan's* Mica Mine, three and a half miles east of Bakersville, in Mitchell county; one blueish green crystal, implanted in quartz, has been found at Captain Mills' gold mine,* in Burke county.

63. Chrysolite.

This is one of the most interesting minerals of North Carolina, where it forms large beds between the hornblende and granitic rocks. It is generally of a yellowish green color, but also greenish white, grey and brownish green, mostly finely granular, rarely foliated, occasionally in larger grains. Associated wish chromite, enstatite, actinolite, tremolite, asbestos, talc, chromite, and rarely with corundum, near Franklin,* Macon county, Webster," in Jackson county, Hampton's,* Mining Creek, in Yancey county, two and a half miles south of Bakersville,* in Mitchell county, Shooting Creek*, Clay county, South Toe River,* seven miles from Burnsville, and at Rich Mountain, Watauga* county.

64. Garnet.

Widely distributed through the State, and a constant constituent of many of the mica and hornblende slates, in which it occurs in minute dodecahedral and trapezohedral crystals of a brownish or brownish red color; it also occurs in many of the talcose and chloritic slates; larger trapezohedral crystals of a brownish red color are frequently met with in the mica mines of Mitchell* and Yancey* counties; imperfect dodecahedral crystals at Weaver's*, Jeanestown, Rutherford county, and in talcose slate, in Rockingham* and Cherokee* counties. The most beautiful and perfect crystals are large trapezohedra, of a brownish red color, from Burke, Caldwell and Catawba* counties. Some of these are transparent and, when cut, show a peculiar play of colors. Large crystals and crystalline masses of a reddish brown garnet, are found near Franklin,* Macon county, and on Toe river. Mitchell county. *Pyrope*, of good color, has been observed in the sands from gold washings in Burke* and McDowell counties. The massive *maganese garnet* is abundant at Jeanestown,* Rutherford county, at Buckhorn,* Chatham countr, near Moore's* Mills, Stokes county, near Gold Hill, in Cabarrus county, near Brevard's Forge, one and a half miles from the Vesuvius Furnace,* and near Macpelah Church, Lincoln county, near High Shoals, Gaston county, and near Madison,* Rockingham county.

65. ZIRCON.

Abundant with the gold sands of Burke,* McDowell,* Rutherford, Caldwell,* Mecklenburg, and other counties, in very minute yellowish brown and brownish white, sometimes amethystine, pink and blue crystals with many planes; large greyish brown crystals of zircons are found so abundant on the south side of the Blue Ridge, near Green river,* that General Clingman easily obtained, in a few weeks, in 1869, one thousand pounds of crystals. It is rarely found associated with chrysoberyl,* at Ray's Mine, Hurricane Mountain, Yancey county.

66. VESUVIANITE.

A mineral, resembling vesuvianite, occurs in brownish green indistinct crystalline masses, intermixed with quartz, and associated with reddish brown garnet, in Macon county.

67. EPIDOTE.

Epidote is found abundantly in North Carolina, although fine crystals are exceedingly rare. The finest specimen, which I have seen, is a crystal, in my cabinet, from the gold washings of Rutherford county; it is strongly pleochroic, like the so-called "Puschkinite," from the auriferous sands of Katharineberg, in the Ural Mountains. Yellowish and brownish green crystalline masses, sometimes with indistinct crystals, have been found near White's Mill,* Gaston county, and near Franklin, Macon county. Epidote of olive green or greyish and brownish green color occurs massive as a frequent admixture of hornblende slate, or diorite, sometimes forming pure masses of epidosite. It has been met with in many of the magnetic iron ore beds.

68. Zoisite (?)

About half a mile southwest of Silver Hill. About twenty-one years ago a greyish white foliated and columnar mineral was found, when searching for the continuation of the vein, which had the appearance of zoisite. No further examination was made, and there is now probably no specimen preserved.

69. Phlogopite.

Small brownish scales of it have been found in the granular limestone of Bolejack's quarry,* near Germanton, and at Martin's quary* on Snow creek, Stokes county, on Walnut creek,* one mile from the French Broad river, on Valley river, in Cherokee county, and at Judge Pearson's,* near the Yadkin river.

70. Biotite.

Biotite is a constituent of many of the granites, gneisses and micaschists of North Carolina. It is found only in small black or brownish black plates or scales. The localities are too numerous for mentioning any particular one, as no fine specimens have as yet been observed.

71. Muscovite.

The mica of the gneiss and micaschist is mostly muscovite, hence it is one of the commonest minerals of North Carolina. In a few localities it is found in beautiful crystals, for instance, with magnetite, at Buckhorn,* in Chatham county, with quartz, at Hickory,* Catawba county, and with pyrite, in Stokes county. Since the year 1867, it has been mined in many places and has been obtained in large plates, at times over three feet in diameter, generally of a brownish color, or in crystalline masses or small crystals, associated with grey granular quartz, orthoclase, etc., in several localities in Mitchell,* Yancey*, Burke, Caldwell, Catawba, Lincoln and Cleaveland counties.

72. LEPIDOLITE.

This mineral is mentioned by Emmons as occurring in the granites of Gaston, Lincoln and Catawba counties. There is a pink colored, somewhat scaly mineral found associated with orthoclase, etc., at Ray's Mine,* on Hurricane Mountain, Yancey county, which may be lepidolite. It has not yet been analyzed.

73. LABRADORITE.

It has been found in grey granular cleavable masses, but only at a few localities. Near the road, six miles north of Burnsville,* it is associated with mica, garnet, etc., as one of the constituents of a stratified rock ; it occurs in diorite, near the Tuckasegee ford,* half a mile from the Catawba river, on the road to Charlotte, also at Shiloh church,* in Person county. The latter locality furnishes specimens, which show slightly the play of blueish colors.

74. ALBITE.

Small white granular cleavable, also compact masses have been found at the Steel Mine, Montgomery county, associated with prochlorite, blende, galenite, gold, etc. Some of the granite rocks, three miles west of Leasburg,* Caswell county, contain small grains of a triclinic feldspar, which may be albite. It is a rare mineral in North Carolina.

75. ORTHOCLASE.

This is the most widely distributed minerals in the State, forming an essential constituent of all the granite, gneiss, etc. It is found in beautiful crystals in a band of porphyritic granite, near Salisbury,* Rowan county, the High Shoals, White's Mill,* in Gaston county, and on Hitchcock creek,* and elsewhere in Richmond county, also in the "Chesterlite" form at Silver Hill, associated with pyromorphite and quartz. Large lamellar masses of a white, greyish or reddish color, occur at Ray's Mine,* Yancey county, at Flat Rock,* Blalock's,* and near Bakersville,* in Mitchell county, also in Caldwell* county, at Hampton's,* Mining Creek, near Burnsville, Sugartown* Turnpike, ten miles from Franklin and the Whiteside* Mountains, and on French Broad river, in Madison county. The peculiar compact variety of orthoclase, which is spotted with hydrated sesquioxide of manganese, the so-called "leopardite," is found near Charlotte, Mecklenburg* county, and also in Gaston county.

76. Tourmaline.

The tourmalines, found in many localities in North Carolina, are mostly the black varieties. Crystals of from one to two inches in size, have been found near Mountain Mine,* Cleaveland county, at Hanging Dog creek,* in Cherokee, in Rutherford county, Mecklenburg county. In slender black crystals, often radiating, and of needle-like shape, frequently flattened between the plates of muscovite; it is found at Ray's Mine,* near Burnsville, where also a greenish and yellowish green, fibrous and finely columnar variety occurs. It is frequently and in large masses associated with the corundum of Franklin, in Macon county. A large outcrop of fibrous and granular tourmaline, with quartz, is found about two hundred yards northeast of the Ellison Mine,* on the High Shoal property, in Gaston county, and a peculiar finely striated variety, with quartz, at Clubb Mountain; similar finely fibrous wood-like masses occur at Leasburg,* Caswell county, and in Wake.* It has also been observed in the gold sands from Burke* county. Tourmaline rock and slate has been noticed at Kernersville,* Guilford county, at Bee Rock,* head of Turkey creek, in McDowell county, and at Jeanstown,* Rutherford county.

77. Cyanite.

This is one of the characteristic accessories in many of the mica and hornblende schists of Macon,* Yancey,* Mitchell,* Caldwell,* Catawba,* Gaston* and other counties, and is generally of a greyish white or grey color, and in imperfect crystals. Fine crystals occur at Clubb Mountain; coarsely bladed masses of a blue and greenish blue color at Swannanoa Gap,* also near Ray's Mica Mine,* Yancey county; in Wilkes* county, in Stokes county,* six miles east of Danbury, at Davidson College,* in Mecklenburg county, at Crowder's Mountain,* in Gaston county. A greyish white, radiating cyanite is found at Ararat river,* four miles southeast of Mount Airy, in Surry county, and a white cyanite at the foot of Barnett's Mountain,* in Person county.

78. Topaz.

Topaz is reported as occurring at Crowder's Mountain, but it is very doubtful; crystals from there, which were considered topaz, were cyanite. The variety, *pycnite*, occurs in finely columnar aggregations of a yellowish and brownish yellow color, associated with garnets, near White's Mill,* Gaston county.

79. Enclase.

General Clingman mentions a very handsome crystal of this rare mineral from the gold mine of the late Morril Mills, in the eastern part of Polk county.

80. Titanite.

General Clingman mentions titanite, or sphene, as occurring in Buncombe county. I have observed it at Morganton Springs* in minute brown crystals, in hornblende slate and in granite at White's Mills,* in Gaston county, and at Rogers' Ore Bank, near Danbury, in Stokes county. To this species probably belong two of Prof. Shepard's very doubtful species, the *Xanthitane*, from Green river, in Henderson county, and the *Pyromelane*, from the gold washings of McDowell county.

81. Staurolite.

Very large, brownish red crystals, from two and a half to three inches in length, and one to one and a half inches wide, single individuals as well as twins, at the Parker Mine,* in Cherokee county. There are many other localities in Cherokee and Macon counties, where it occurs abundantly in argillaceous and talcose slates.

B. Hydrous Silicates.

82. Chrysocolla.

Inferior specimens, generally much mixed with other copper ores, have been observed at the copper mines, for instance, at the Gardner Hill and Cambridge Mines, in Guilford county, the Pioneer Mills, in Cabarrus county, the Hopewell,* in Mecklenburg county, the Clegg's* Mine, in Chatham county, the Gap Creek Mine,* in Watauga, and many others.

83. Calamine.

The only specimen of calamine, which I have observed, came from Silver Hill, Davidson county, where it occurs sparingly as an incrustation of fibrous and radiating structure upon argentiferous galenite.

84. TALC.

Foliated talc, of a white or greenish white color, is found in many of the chrysolite beds, west of the Blue Ridge, at Shooting Creek,* Clay county, Franklin,* Macon county, Webster,* Jackson county, Hampton's,* Mining Creek, Yancey county, Bakersville,* Mitchell county, and other localities ;* in sheets of three quarters to one inch in thickness and of a somewhat columnar structure, near Pilot Mountain, Surry county; fibrous talc, with silky lustre, and of a white or green color, also compact, crystalline white talc, with a splintery structure on Valley river,* Cherokee county, and also in Macon* county. Talc slate and coarse soapstone is found in many localities throughout the State.

85. PYROPHYLLITE.

In white, yellowish, greenish and brownish white, stellate aggregations, fibrous and radiated masses at Cotton Stone Mountain,* Montgomery county, Pilot Knob,* Randolph county, Hillsboro',* Orange county, Crowder's* and Clubb Mountains, in Gaston county, and on Linville Mountain,* McDowell county. The slaty variety forms large beds of yellowish white or greenish color in Chatham* and Moore* counties.

86. STILPNOMELANE (?)

A mineral, similar to Stilpnomelane has been found in compact greenish black masses at the Cosby Mine, Cabarrus county.

87. GLAUCONITE.

The green grains, forming one of the constituents of the many so-called marl beds, in the eastern part of the State, are glauconite.

88. SERPENTINE.

The massive are found in many localities. The best appears to come from the neighborhood of Patterson, Caldwell county. It has a dark, greenish black color, and contains fine veins of the yellowish green fibrous and silky *chrysotile*, and admits of a fine polish ; greenish grey massive serpentine, also with seams of greenish and greyish white chrysotile is found at the Baker Mine, in Caldwell county, at which place is also found the variety *picrolite*. Dark green serpentine has been observed in the neighborhood of Asheville,* in Forsythe,* and Wake counties. A greyish or yellowish green serpentine occurs in the chrysolite beds of Macon,* Jackson,* Yancey,* Mitchell* and other counties; it results from the decomposition of the chrysolite.

89. Deweylite.

This mineral is found in all the chrysolite beds of the Western counties, in which yellowish and greenish masses, in their veins or seams, through the decomposed rocks.

90. Kaolinite.

Snow white kaoline is found as the result of the decomposition of orthoclase at Blalock's Mica Mine,* near Toe river, also near Bakersville,* in Mitchell county; in small quantities at Ray's Mine,* in Yancey county; good qualities are found six or seven miles from Newton,* Catawba county, also in Lincoln, Burke,* Macon and other counties. *Clay* for firebricks and earthenware in many localities throughout the State.

91. Damourite.

Very fine white and yellowish white pearly scales are found with the cyanite at Crowder's Mountain, which are probably damourite.

92. Peninite.

The variety Kaemmererite, in violet and peach-blossom red scales, is associated with chromite at Franklin, Webster,* Hampton's,* Mining Creek, Rich Mountain,* Watauga county, etc.; three-sided and six-sided plated crystals of a dark, greenish and purplish color, associated with talc, etc., in the chrysolite beds at the same localities;* also, at Bakersville,* Mitchell county.

93. Prochlorite (and Chlorite.)

Fine grained scaly prochlorite, of a dark, green color; is found associated with an albitic rock, from the alteration of which it has resulted, at the Steele Mine, Montgomery county; foliated chlorite is a frequent associate of the other species in the Western chrysolite beds; chlorite in scales and scaly aggregations is found in many of the gold and copper mines in the State, and chloritic slate at many localities throughout the whole slate belt.

94. CORUNDOPHILITE.

Probably the greater portion of the dark green foliated mineral, which is associated with the corundum, from Madison, Macon and Buncombe counties, belong to these species.

(These greenish, chloritic minerals, found in the State, viz: Penninite, Ripidolite, Prochlorite, Corundophilite, etc., require fuller investigation, before in all cases their true character and place in the system can be decided.)

95 CHLORITOID (?)

Small scales of a greenish black mineral are disseminated through the slaty pyrophyllite, from Evans' Mill,* in Chatham county, which appear to belong to this species.

96. MARGARITE.

In small foliated masses of silver white color and pearly lustre, some of the folia showing planes of crystals, associated with the corundum at Corundum Hill,* near Franklin, also about eight miles from Franklin, with pink corundum. It has also been observed with the blue corundum from Madison county. In small scaly aggregations, with the corundum of Crowder's* and Clubb Mountains, where it also occurs cryptocrystalline and in pseudomorphs after corundum.

2. *Columbates, Etc.*

97. PYROCHLORE.

Microscopic brownish yellow or honey yellow grains and crystals, which appear to be octahedra, with dodecahedral planes, are associated with orthoclase, tourmaline, etc., at Ray's Mica Mine,* on Hurricane Mountain, Yancey county.

98. COLUMBITE.

This mineral also occurs at Ray's Mica Mine* in imperfect crystals and grains, associated with garnet, beryl, etc., in orthoclase and muscovite. The few crystals, which have been found, were not perfect enough for measurement, but their appearance and association leave very little doubt that they are columbite. General Clingman reports this mineral as being found in the soil of several localities.

99. Yttrotantalite.

According to General Clingman, grains of this mineral have been found in several localities.

100. Samarskite.

Grains of it have been observed in several counties, as stated by Gen. Clingman.

101. Rutherfordite.

In crystals and grains, associated with rutile, brookite, zircon, monazite, etc., in the gold mines of Rutherford and Burke counties.

3. *Phosphates, Arsenates, Etc.*

102. Xenotime.

In minute crystals, in the sands, from gold washings in McDowell, Burke and Rutherford counties.

103. Apatite.

This is a rather rare mineral in this State. I have observed it in imperfect crystals of a greyish and reddish green color in orthoclase, etc., at Ray's Mine,* Hurricane Mountain, Yancey county, and in small granular patches of a greenish color. in granite, found three miles south of the Blue Ridge,* sixteen to seventeen miles from Jefferson, on the road to Wilkesboro'.

104. Pyromorphite.

This is one of the most beautiful minerals found in North Carolina, and formerly has been quite abundant at the Silver Hill Mine, which furnished very handsome specimens of hexagonal prisms and crystalline aggregations of different shades from colorless almost to black, also honey and wax yellow, green, brown, etc.; less abundant, and mostly of a yellowish green color, it is found at Silver Valley, Davidson county. In green and yellowish green crystals, at the Troutman and McMakin Mines, in Cabarrus county; also, at the Stewart Mine, in Union county, and in minute green crystals in the gold veins of the Baker* and Miller* Mines, Caldwell county.

105. Monazite.

It has been reported from the gold sands of Rutherford, Burke and McDowell counties; also, from the neighborhood of Crowder's Mountain. The only localities, from which I have seen it, are Todd's Branch, in Mecklenburg county, where it has been found in association with diamond, zircon, etc., and Col. Mills' Gold Mine, in Burke county.

106. Olivenite.

Minute green crystals and brownish green fibrous masses, associated with tetrahedrite, scorodite, etc., at George Ludwick's Mine, in Cabarrus county, appears to belong to this species.

107. Pseudomalachite.

In reniform and fibrous masses, of a dark emerald green color, at the McGinn and Wilson Mines, in Mecklenburg county, Cullen's Mine, in Cabarrus county, Fisher Hill Mine, in Guilford, at Clegg's Mine,* in Chatham county, and about one mile from the Soapstone Quarry, in Moore county;* also, at the Peach Bottom Mine,* in Alleghany county.

108. Lazulite.

In dark blue crystals and crystalline masses, in quartz, and associated with cyanite and margarite at Crowder's and Clubb's Mountains, in Gaston county; also, in quartz, and very little margarite, at Coffee Gap, in the Sauratown Mountains, Stokes county.

109. Scorodite.

In small leekgreen and yellowish green crystals, associated with tetrahedrite, quartz, etc., at George Ludwick's Mine, in Cabarrus county.

110. Wavellite.

Globular and hemispherical aggregations of white and greyish white wavellite, associated with silver, galenite, pyrite, etc., are rarely met with at Silver Hill, Davidson county.

111. Pharmacosiderite.

Exceedingly minute crystals of this mineral, of a brownish green color, are associated with the scorodite of George Ludwick's Mine, Cabarrus county.

112. Dufrenite.

It is rarely met with in greyish green tufts of silky lustre, with the so-called "black band" iron at Egypt, Chatham county.

113. Torbernite.

General Clingman reports Uranite (Torbenite or Antunitel) (?) from Mitchell county, and other places.

114. Nitre.

Crystalline crusts on mica slate at Nantehaleh river,* in Cherokee county.

5. *Tungstates, Molybdates, Etc.*

115. Wolframite.

In laminated masses with cuproscheelite and sheelite at the Cosby Mine,* and with barite, at the Flowe Mine, both in Cabarrus county; also, according to General Clingman, frequent in Rutherford and Burke counties.

116. Rhombic Tungstate of Lime.

Associated with wolframite, in barite, at the Flowe Mine, in Cabarrus county, in small crystals and laminated masses of a yellowish and greyish color.

117. Scheelite.

Orange colored quadratic octahedra are found at the Flowe Mine; yellowish brown and greyish, imperfect crystalline masses at the Cosby Mine, also at the Cullen's Mine, Cabarrus county, in rounded granular patches of a greyish yellow color, with auriferous pyrite in quartz.

118. Cuproscheelite.

This mineral was first observed and distinguished by me at the Cosby Mine, Cabarrus county, where it occurs in pulverulent masses of a pistacchio-green color, with sheelite and wolfram.

119. Stolzite.

A few small quadratic octahedra of a blueish grey color and one greyish yellow, somewhat barrel-shaped crystal of this very rare mineral has been found in one specimen of quartz, associated with brown zincblende, at Silver Hill, Davidson county.

6. *Sulphates, Chromates, Etc.*

120. Barite.

In small white tabular crystals, with pyromorphite and manganese ores at the McMakin Mine, Cabarrus county. The laminated and coarsely granular white variety at the Cosby Mine* and orchard vein, in Cabarrus county; a vein of the coarsely laminated, greyish white barite, at the Latta Mine,* near Hillsboro', Orange county. It occurs coarsely granular, and has the appearance of white marble, at Colonel Walkup's,* Union county. A vein of very white compact and granular barite of from seven to eight feet in width, has been found at Crowder's Mountain; west of the Blue Ridge, a vein of eight feet in width, of the white granular variety, exists at Chandlers',* nine miles below Marshall, in Madison county, where it is white and greyish white, and of a granular structure, with small patches of laminated barite, and again on Elkin creek,* Wilkes county.

121. Anglesite.

In small tabular rhombic prisms, with very few additional planes in the brown granular zincblende of Silver Hill, Davidson; also, according to General Clingman, at the Baker Mine, in Caldwell county.

122. Crocoite.

I have observed this rare animal in small cavities of saccharoidal quartz, from Nash county, associated with gold and small quantities of galenite in very minute dark hyacinth red crystals.

123. Melanterite.

As the result of the decomposition of pyrite, disseminated through many of the mica slates, etc., of Rutherford, Cleaveland and other counties, melanterite or copperas is formed, but no good crystallized specimens have come to my notice.

124. Goslarite.

In the water of the Silver Hill Mine, also in fine fibrous crystalline masses, formerly at the McMakin Mine, Cabarrus county.

125. Chalcanthite.

Very fine crystals, granular and fibrous crystalline masses of sulphate of copper, were formerly obtained from the upper works of the Silver Hill Mine, principally at the sixty feet level.

126. Alunogen.

I have once seen a beautiful specimen of fibrous, silky alunogen of the western counties, but could not learn the exact locality, from which it came. It is found abundantly associated with melanterite, in Rutherford, Cleaveland and other counties, but not in good specimens; also in Iredell county and in Catawba.*

127. Jarosite.

The impure variety generally called "Misy," has been observed in association with galenite and pyrite, at Flint Knob.*

128. Montanite.

This very rare tellurate of bismuth has been found with tetradymite at David Beck's Mine, in Davidson county, and at Captain Mills' Mine, in

Burke county. The yellow oxide of bismuth, observed by Dr. Asbury, at the Asbury vein, in Gaston county, may belong to this species.

7. *Carbonates.*

129. Calcite.

I have not seen any crystallized calcite from this State. It occurs coarsely granular in a vein at Hoover's Mine, about six miles from Silver Hill, at Moore's Mine, ten miles southeast of Lexington, and rarely at Silver Hill, and the Steele Mine, Montgomery county. Small quantities of granular calcite were found in digging a well at Morrisville,* Wake county. The granular varieties, which constitute marble, are sometimes found associated with the compact varieties of limestone in the band, which passes through North Carolina, from Stokes county, through Catawba, Lincoln and Gaston counties, so, for instance, at the quarries of Martin* on Snow creek, Bolejack,* near Germanton, Pfaff, in Forsythe, Hooper* in Catawba and Stowe* in Lincoln counties, and in the Eocene limestone of New Hanover county. A veined grey and white marble is found at Powell's Quarry, near Catawba Station. Very beautiful varieties of white, pink and grey marble are found abundantly at the Nantahaleh river,* Marble creek,* Valley river* and other places in Cherokee county. A band of compact limestone, sometimes finely granular is found at Turkey Cove,* and Cedar Cove,* in McDowell county, also in Transylvania* and Henderson* counties. It is also found in small seams and crystalline grains, replacing in part the orthoclase of a massive granitoid gneiss in Harnett county.

130. Dolomite.

Granular dolomite of a greyish white color, resembling marble, is found on Valley river,* ten miles from Murphy, Cherokee county.

131. Magnesite.

The lamellar white and greyish variety, from which distinct cleavage crystals can be obtained, is found at McMakin's Mine,* Cabarrus county; also, with chrysolite at Webster,* Jackson county, and Hampton's,* Mining Creek,* Yancey county. At the latter locality is also found the white compact, and at Webster,* the white earthy and pulverulent variety.

132. Siderite.

In fine rhombohedral crystals, formerly at the McCulloch, the North Carolina, and several other mines in Guilford county, where it occurred in considerable masses in the vein. In the same manner it is of frequent occurence in many of the gold veins of the State, especially in those which carry copper. It often forms almost the whole mass of the veins, frequently, however, decomposed into limonite, which still retains its rhombohedral form, for instance, at Conrad Hill, in Davidson county, and Gaston county, at some of the mines in Randolph county, and the Cosby Mine,* in Cabarrus county. In smaller quantities it has been observed in Stokes county, and some of the mines in Mecklenburg county. A white cleavable variety occurs at the Rudesill Mine, near Charlotte. The earthy and argillaceous varieties of siderite from large beds in the triassic coal strata of Chatham county,* and constitute the so-called black band or ball ore at Farmville, Egypt,* the Gulf,* etc., in Chatham county.

133. Rhodochrosite.

In small globular pink and rosered concretions, with earthy manganese near Franklin, Macon county, also mixed with magnesite, talc, etc., in compact and granular masses at the McMakin Mine, Cabarrus county.

134. Cerussite.

The most beautiful crystallizations, single individuals as well as twins, have been found at Silver Hill, immediately after the discovery of the mine, also white, yellowish and greenish white, compact varieties, frequently highly argentiferous. A very interesting occurrence at the same mine is cerussite, pseudomorphous after pyrite. Yellowish white columnar cerussite occurs in Gaston county. Rhombic prisms with octahedral planes, together with imperfect crystalizations and earthy masses, are found at Clegg's Mine, Chatham county. At Elk creek, in Wilkes county, earthy cerussite has been observed coating galenite. It is also found at the Baker Mine,* in Caldwell county, and at Murphy, Cherokee county.

135. Malachite.

Malachite, in its varieties, fibrous, compact and earthy, being the result of the decomposition of other copper ores, is found in association with the latter in almost every copper mine in the State. The Guilford, Cabarrus and Mecklenburg county copper mines contain it. I have observed the fibrous variety at Silver Hill and Conrad Hill, in Davidson county, the Gillis Mine,* in Person county, the Cheek Mine, in Moore county, and both the fibrous and earthy malachite at Clegg's Mine,* in Chatham county. It has been found in the Brushy Mountains,* Alexander county, the Peach Bottom Mine,* Alleghany county, the Ore Knob Mine, in Ashe county, the Gap Creek Mine,* in Watauga county, the Cullowhee,* Savannah,* and Waryhut* Mines, in Jackson county, and many other localities too numerous to be mentioned. Pseudomorphs of malachite, after cubical cuprite have been found at Cullen's Mine, Cabarrus county.

136. AZURITE.

This variety of carbonate of copper is far less frequently met with. Small but very beautiful and perfect cryrtals are found at Clegg's Mine,* in Chatham county, and at the Cheek Mine, in Moore county. It is rare at the Cullen and Boger Mine, in Cabarrus county, and the Wilson Mine, in Mecklenburg county.

137. BISMUTITE.

In yellowish white concretions, often of a pearly lustre or white incrustations upon gold-bearing quartz, at the Asbury Mine, in Gaston county, where it has been discovered by Dr. Asbury.

Mineral Coal.

138. ANTHRACITE.

A very interesting occurrence of anthracite is that of masses with conchoidal fracture in the vein rock at the Clegg Mine*. The bituminous coal, both of the Deep and Dan rivers, is frequently, especially near trap-dykes, almost deprived of its hydrocarbons, approaching often true anthracite.

139. BITUMINOUS COAL.

The greater portion of the coal in the Deep river beds is bituminous coal, the volatile matter varying from about eight to thirty-two per cent. The Dan river coal, which I had an opportunity to examine, is so-called semi-bituminous coal, that from some recent developments, near Stokesburg, Stokes county, containing about ten per cent of volatile matter.

140. Lignite or Brown Coal.

Frequently met with in the marl beds of the eastern counties, and in Trias of Granville county,* on Tar river.

This completes the list of minerals thus far found in the State of North Carolina, which necessarily form only the basis of a more complete work on the Mineralogy of the State.

Many of the species, which are mentioned in the above, were determined by qualitative, chemical analysis, the nature of others can be accurately established only by very minute quantitative analysis and crystallographic determinations, both of which, you are aware, consume much time. However imperfect the above work may be, I believe it to be sufficient to show the very great richness of both interesting and useful minerals and ores, and that their development will place North Carolina in the first rank of the mineral producing States.

All of which is respectfully submitted,

F. A. GENTH.

December 15th, 1871.

*Specimens in the Museum at Raleigh. W. C. K.

ERRATA,

[IN APPENDIX C.]

On page 53, line 27, strike out one "which."
On page 54, line 12, read "Tantalates" instead of "Tentalates."
On page 56, line 22, read "4" instead of "3."
On page 57, line 4, read "Morganton" instead of "Norganton."
On page 58, line 6, read "corundum" instead of "corrundum."
On page 58, line 7, begin a new line with "A very beautiful * * * "
On page 58, line 9, read "county" instead of "coounty."
On page 58, line 22, read "Hill" instead of "Hlll."
On page 59, line 32, read "Ashe" instead of "Wilkes."
On page 60, lines 11 and 12, read "at the Steele Mine, Montgomery," instead of "Davidson."
On page 60, line 31, read "gneissoid" instead of "genissoid."
On page 61, line 5, read "octahedral" instead of "octrahedral."
On page 61, line 7, read "Rudesill" instead of "udesill."
On page 61, line 25, read "forty" instead of "forty-eight."
On page 61, line 29, read "information" instead of "infermation."
On page 62, line 18, read "Guilford" instead of "Cabarrus."
On page 64, line 12, read "trichite" instead of "tritchite."
On page 69, line 13, read "mine" instead of "mtne."
On page 72, line 11, read "manganese" instead of "maganese."
On page 72, line 35, read "Katharinenburg" instead of "Katharineberg."
On page 74, line 17, read "Steele" instead of "Steel."
On page 76, line 1, read "Euclase" instead of "Enclase."
On page 78, line 19, read "Penninite" instead of "Peninite."
On page 82, line 13, read "Torbernite or Autunite" instead of "Torbenite or Antunitel."
On page 82, line 20, read "scheelite" instead of "sheelite."
On page 83, line 9, read "scheelite" instead of "sheelite."
On page 83, line 19, read "Orchard" instead of "orchard."
On page 86, line 13, read "form" instead of "from."

12

APPENDIX D.

CORUNDUM AND ITS ASSOCIATED ROCKS.

BY REV. C. D. SMITH.

I propose, in this paper, to discuss that rare and valuable mineral, Corundum. The discovery of it in the United States is of comparatively recent date. Its discovery and development in quantity sufficient to render the mining of it an object, and to give to it a commercial and economic value amongst the resources of North Carolina, is of very recent date. Its geological and lithological relations and character are matters of scientific interest, and claim for it a place in the official report for the State. The probable introduction of its use into the arts, and the consequent demand for it in quantity, will necessarily make it an important article in our resources.

The geological formation to which the outcrops that bear Corundum belong, is of the Azoic time or age. The principal mass of the Blue Ridge, as it tends southwards from the Grandfather Mountain, is Granite and granitic Gneiss. These rocks are quite crystalline and have a large per cent. of Feldspar in their composition. They are the oldest rocks upon the continent, perhaps in the world, and are, in the proper sense of the term, primordial. The rocks, of which the main mass of this part of the Blue Ridge is composed, bear very little evidence of being disturbed since the upheaval.

There is, however, a zone of gneissic rocks on the northwest side of the ridge, which has been much disturbed since the main mass was folded up. At this point, where the Corundum is found, this zone lies about ten miles from the summit of the Blue Ridge, though as it tends northeastward, it diverges further and further from the principal elevation until it crosses the French Broad Valley, when, owing to the curvature of the ridge to the northward, it approaches nearer and nearer the main elevation, and so passes directly into the angle, where the Blue Ridge and Iron Mountain separate. Along the entire length of this zone from Cane creek, in Mitchell county, to Choeestoee, in Union county, Georgia, and perhaps still further south, there is a system of dike fissures through which, at intervals, Chrysolite and Serpentine have been protruded. The

Gneiss, which encloses these Chrysolite and Serpentine beds, is somewhat peculiar and deserves a more special description. It bears evidence of having been much affected by heat from the dike fissures which traverse it. It is consequently hard and crystalline in a high degree. This rock is charged with grains and partial crystals of a rose color, sometimes sparcely distributed, and at others predominating. I have heretofore classified this rose colored material as a species of Garnet, and see no good reason for changing my opinion. The Mica in the composition of this rock is usually of a brownish black color, while the Feldspar is quite white. This contrast in color, of the component minerals, gives to well selected specimens a very handsome appearance.

The mineral silicates found in this rock are almost entirely anhydrous silicates of Alumina, such as Kyanite, Tourmaline, Garnet, Epidote, etc. It is also charged with metalic sulphurets of Iron and Copper, and very sparsely with sulphurets of Lead and Zinc. It is in this zone that the copper mines of Jackson county are located.

Along this belt there are numerous out-crops and beds of Syenite. In this distribution of the Hornblend there is a fact worthy of special note, because it has a special bearing upon the question under consideration. In traversing the Chrysolite out-crops from Corundum Hill, in Macon county, north-eastwards, the Geologist cannot fail to observe a gradual decrease in the approximate out-crops of Hornblend to the Chrysolite, and an increase of Feldspar, usually decomposed, forming a species of Kaolin. This is especially true up to the Yancey county line. From Corundum Hill, as the zone crosses the Tennessee valley in a south-west direction, the fissures scatter, until instead of being from one to two miles across the zone, it is some eight miles across it in the Tennessee valley. Some observations upon the facts here stated led me to suspect some important change in the axis of the disturbing force, and after such examinations as I have been able to make, I am satisfied that the axis of disturbance, which had maintained a uniform line from Mitchell county to this point, here terminated against the most southern and massive part of the Nanteeyalee mountain. This is a transverse chain that intersects the Blue Ridge at the head of the Tennessee river, Nanteeyalee river and Talula. Here the Blue Ridge curves around the head of Tennessee river and runs several miles north, until it forms a junction with the Nanteeyalee, and then tends off again to the south-west. Had the line of disturbance continued in its regular course, it would have passed directly through this great mass at the point of intersection between the Blue Ridge and the Nanteeyalee, and from that point south-westward, the dikes and out-crops would have traversed the main crest of the ridge. The axis of disturbance, however, was here shifted to the north-west, so that when it re-appears on the west side of the Nanteeyalee chain, it is with its relative distance from the summit of the Blue Ridge.

The out-crop of Chrysolite at this point, on Buck creek, a tributary of the Nanteeyalee river, is the boldest I have seen at any point on the zone. Here, too, and lying on the south and upon the Chrysolite, is the heaviest bed of Syenite I have ever seen. It is at least ten thousand feet thick. It sets in rather abruptly, and from this point south-westward is very persistent, constituting a distinguishing feature with all the Chrysolite outcrops as far as I have traversed the belt.

I have been somewhat particular in describing the immediate geology of this zone, because it has a significance in reference to the occurrence of Corundum, as will be seen in the sequel. I am sure the reader will not regret this description of the rocks and their relations, when he comes to consider that it is not only certain classes of rocks, but the special condition and associations of such rocks that produce any given class of minerals.

The Chrysolite bears decided marks of its igneous origin. Its general crystalline texture, together with disseminated octahedral crystals of Magnetite and Chrome Iron, speak of its igneous origin. It is a laminated rock, but the strike of its laminæ seldom conforms to the strike of the enclosing rocks. It appears to have been protruded or lifted through the fissures and laid at various angles across the enclosing gneiss. It cannot, therefore, be regarded as a regular interfoliation, nor as an intercalation with the enclosing beds. It differs from them, as already stated, in its strike, and generally in its inclination. These facts all point to it as an igneous rock.

These Chrysolite beds are traversed by numerous seams or veins of Chlorite—mostly the species Corundopholite, Leuchtenbergite, and probably Rhodopholite, together with Talc, Asbetus and Chalcedony. I now speak more particularly of Corundum Hill or the Culsagee mine. There also occurs here, in connection with the Chryoslite, what I have named Anthophyllite rock. This rock is composed of Talc, green Chlonite and Anthophyllite, with disseminated crystals of Chrome Iron—the Anthophyllite, however, largely predominating. There exists also in these veins or seams of Chlorite, massive black Tourmaline. This is sometimes wrapt up in apparently geodes of Chlorite. I have occasionally seen specimens of it which possessed regular tables, resembling in shape the tabular pieces of Corundum often found in the Chlorite. On these grounds are also found Actinolite Tremolite, Chrome ore and what is perhaps a species of Pyropholite.

In these Chloritic veins the Corundum chiefly occurs. The Chlorite seems to have been first crystalized, and then the Alumina, of which the Corundum is composed, was evidently in a state of solution and must have permeated the Chlorite either in thermal waters or steam. This theory is sustained by facts patent to every careful observer. Plates or scales of Chlorite are often enclosed in the Corundum. It is, moreover, not uncommon to find Corundum that conforms in its faces and general shapes to the Chlorite that is present.

One of these veins carries massive Tourmaline, which is associated very intimately with the Corundum. Occasional specimens have been found in which it appears that the Corundum and Tourmaline crystalized at the same time and mutually penetrated each other. On one part of the hill there are considerable masses in which it appears that the Corundum was first crystalized in small coarse hexagonal prisms and then disseminated through the Tourmaline while it was in a plastic state, and hardening, the Tourmaline encloses and holds the Corundum. Another of the veins upon this hill is composed of decomposed Feldspar, a little soft Chlorite and occasional small fragments of Emerylite, but the Feldspar predominates largely. Through this mass or gang Corundum is distributed in small imperfect crystals, in grains and even as mere Corundum sand. When the soft and lighter material are washed away, which is easily done, the Corundum obtained is very pure and in a favorable condition to be crushed for use in the arts. This vein promises to be valuable in its yield of Corundum as an article of commerce. These associations demonstrate that Corundum does not occur alone or by itself, but always in the most intimate relations with some other mineral having kindred elements. This remark will apply not only to this locality, but to others also, as we shall hereafter see. What has been said of Corundum as found at the Culsagee mine, is true of all the localities where it has been found in the same neighborhood.

After the scattering and termination of the lines of disturbance as heretofore described, it re-appears on the west side of the Nauteeyalee mountains, on Buck creek. Here is the largest out-crop of Chrysolite to be found at any point along the zone for a distance of a hundred and ninety miles. The bed covers an area of at least three hundred acres. The Chrysolite here does not carry so much of the Corundopholite as at Corundum Hill. Most of the Chlorite that exists at this locality is soft and of a dark silvery color. This variety has none of that rigid and crystalline structure that characterizes the deep green variety. Indeed, much of it that is of a green shade is not compact, but rather friable, being a loose aggregation of small scales. I have seen upon these grounds but little white foliated Talc, such as occurs at the Culsagee mine and in its vicinity. This out-crop is comparatively barren in Chalcedony, although occasional pieces are met with. I have not yet found so much as a single specimen of Tourmaline at this locality. At every other point east of this, and at Gainesville, Ga., where I recently discovered Corundum, Tourmaline is present. Its absence here is a distinguishing feature between the Buck creek and Culsagee localities. Nor does Anthophyllite abound here as it does at Corundum Hill. There it exists as large massive rocks; here I have not found even a good hand specimen. Another characteristic of this out-crop is the sparcity of Chromium, There is not an appreciable amount of Chrome sand present to interfere with the process of washing Corundum from the dirt. There is much more Actinolite here than at the Culsagee locality, and Tremolite is somewhat abundant with Actinolite. Amianthus also occurs here of a very fine quality, and Picrolite exists in seams or apparent veins in the Chrysolite rocks. Beautiful specimens of it may be had at this point. I have here found Chrysolite attached as an enveloping matter to considerable masses of Corundum; and I also found a white silky fibrous mineral. which I have classified as Marmolite. This also envelopes Corundum.

The most marked characteristic of the Buck creek out-crop is the occurrence of Feldspars differing from those heretofore found in the general geology of this section. I have not found anything like them at any other point in Western Carolina. One variety is found in masses upon the surface resembling in shape the masses of Corundum found in close proximity to the Feldspar. Some of these lumps will weigh from eighty to a hundred pounds. Some of them when broken are very white and are massive in their structure, having very seldom any of the usual facel angles of common Feldspar. I have a specimen in which it seems to run imperceptably into Corundum. This may prove to be a pseudomorph, a question I am anxious to have examined by the most profound anylitical chemistry. These Feldspathic masses differ from Corundum in specific gravity, hardness and the usual crystalline faces. Some of this variety more translucent than that just described and having the faces, luster and hardness of Feldspar is penetrated through and through with crystals of black Hornblend. This is probably Orthoclase.

On another part of the out-crop there occurs large masses of apparently another variety of Feldspar. Seams running through some of these masses are filled with a rather granular Actinolite of a most beautiful green color. Grains of this Actinolite sometimes penetrate the Feldspar, which often has a greenish and blueish green color. In this variety, there occurs, sometimes amongst the Actinolite, and then again in the

Feldspar, small fragments of beautiful pink and ruby colored Corundum. I have not however discovered any blue or gray Corundum in these rocks. This variety is probably Labradorite.

The principal question, however, to be discussed touching this wonderful out-crop with its great variety of minerals is the main veins in which the great body of the Corundum occurs—for it evidently occurs in veins here. The manner of its distribution upon the surface and the minerals with which it is associated in mass give evidence of veins. These veins probably occupy subfissures in the Chrysolite rocks. This opinion is based upon the existence of Hornblend, and yet another and in this geology unusual variety of Feldspar in connection with Corundum. This Feldspar I have classified as Couzeranite. The crystals are long and vertically striated, and generally of a grayish and yellowish gray color. There is also in this associated mass frequently Emerylite of a fine quality. When split into moderately thin plates it is almost entirely transparent. I had a small pit dug while upon the grounds and found this vein stone or mass apparently in place only two or three feet below the surface. Here I found one mass sticking in the surface, principally Corundum, which I suppose will weigh nearly or quite five hundred pounds. All that I saw and turned over during one day's exploration, I suppose would amount to two thousand pounds. There is abundant evidence of veins of this character at different points upon the out-crop.

The difference in the associated minerals here and at the Culsagee mine, will at once suggest to the scientific reader a probable difference in the crystalline structure of the Corundum. There is a marked difference —a difference too that suggests, as I have already intimated, the probable existence of pseudomorphism at this locality. At Corundum Hill, (Culsagee mine,) the general form of the Corundum is tabular. These tabular faces are striated both ways or at right angles. They appear to have been laid off with mathematical precision for an infinite number of small cubes. Cleavage is often obtained with great perfection following the lines of striation. There appears at the Culsagee locality a strong tendency in the Corundum to regular crystalization. Small hexagonal prisms are common, and even in the larger masses it is not uncommon to find two or three faces of a hexagon. One crystal having all the faces of a hexagon well defined, has been found, which approximates closely three hundred pounds in weight. The prevailing colors here are the Sapphire, Ruby and Gray—rarely opalescent in small crystals

At the Buck creek locality the principal part of the Corundum is more massive in its structure, and when faces exist a general interlocking of them appears. This structure gives to these masses great toughness, and renders fracture very difficult to obtain. Some masses, however, are tabular in their structure and striated, but the striæ are not at right angles but cross each other obliquely, giving, when cleavage is obtained, rhomboidal faces and angles similar to that of common Feldspar. Cleavage in some specimens is eminently perfect. The prevailing color of the Corundum at this locality is gray and blueish gray, with much less of the regular Sapphire, than at Corundum Hill. This Corundum is very hard, and usually gives extremely sharp cutting angles. It is a superior stone for use in the arts.

The pink and ruby colored Corundum found at this locality is distinct from that described. It occurs in a different matrix, and so far as my observation extends, is wholly unconnected with the gray colored variety. While this is the case here, the red variety at Corundum Hill is intimately connected with the gray and blue varieties. Generally, the ruby color penetrates a gray stone from a quarter to half an inch from its surface, and then gradually disappears. At the Buck creek locality the color is solid through the whole stone, and I have hope, when the Spring opens to find valuable specimens of it.

I have not discovered any cubic or octohedral minerals at this locality. The law of crystalization prevailing here seems to be the rhomboidal, and I repeat, what I have already said, that there is probably a change going on in the Corundum at this locality and pseudomorphism may prevail here. This is, at least, an open question for scientific investigation

Were I in a position to make a close, practical and systematic investigation of the entire Chrysolite zone, there are strong probabilities that other and valuable discoveries might be made in this rare and interesting mineral. I know of its existence for a distance of one hundred and twenty or thirty miles along the zone, but having passed over the line of out-crops hastily, and not being able at my own expense to investigate the respective localities, I am unable to say whether it occurs in quantity at any other localities than the two I have discussed in this paper. Such examination as I have suggested would perhaps develope gems of Ruby and Sapphire, and Diaspore, another rare and interesting mineral.

I have given a brief outline of the immediate geology along this zone of Chrysolite dikes and a statement of the principal minerals that occur on the Corundum bearing out-crops. I have described as near as practicable the mode of the Corundum's occurence and also the minerals immediately associated with it. I have stated the facts plainly, avoiding technicalities as much as possible, for the benefit of the general reader, and I hope that I have, in this paper, contributed something to the character of the grand old North State for mineral wealth.

C. D. SMITH.

The most striking general feature of the table is the *predominance of westerly winds* in all the divisions, and at nearly all the stations. A little closer inspection discovers that this predominance is most decided in the western region, and very slight in the eastern. It is worthy of note further, that while the winds which make up this result, in the average for the state, are nearly equally distributed to the three octants, S. W., W., and N. W., with a slight plurality of days to the first, in each of the different sub-divisions, it is due to the preponderance of a different octant, viz: of the S. W., in the eastern; N. W., in the middle; and W., in the western section; this preponderance being very marked in the last case. After the westerly winds, it will be observed that the next class in order of frequency is the northerly, except on the immediate sea-coast, where the preponderance passes to the southerly, from the great frequency of the winds from the S. W.; and the most infrequent in all sections and at nearly all the stations, are the easterly winds. And if only the E. octant is considered, it will be seen that in the general average for the State, the prevalence of this wind is limited to about two weeks; and if two stations be omitted, the average would fall to 11 days in the year for all the others. But at Franklin this octant is credited with a number of days only second to that of the W.; and at Wilmington it reaches nearly a month.

If the distribution of the winds be examined in reference to the seasons, it appears that in the State as a whole, the S. W. wind is preponderant in the spring and summer, and in the autumn and winter the N. W. and N. E. octants divide the sway with it almost equally; and the same statement holds for the eastern section with a more decided emphasis on the first of it, while in the middle region the prevalent winds are those from the three westerly octants with the northeastern, the N. W. having the advantage in spring, autumn and winter, the S. W. (slightly) in summer, the N. E. direction being more common in autumn and winter than the S. W., and of almost as frequent occurrence in spring and summer. In the western division the most common wind in all seasons is that from the W., its preponderance being most decided however, in winter and spring.

If the stations be considered individually, the most remarkable local peculiarities are, the prevalence at Boone of winds from the W. fully two-thirds of the year, at Lenoir the predominance of the N. W., at Greensboro of the W., and at Newbern of the S. W. octant; and the occurrence of E. winds for nearly two months at Franklin, while at Oxford this octant is wanting altogether.

These are some of the salient points, obvious on a cursory inspection

the rocks and the mineral deposits found in them. Begining upon the north and coming in regular order towards the Blue Ridge, we have first the Taconic or oldest sedimentary beds. This series enters the State from Georgia and Tennessee, striking through the northwestern part of Clay county, and the central part of Cherokee, continuing through Swain, the northern parts of Jackson and Haywood counties.

The members of this series are quartzite, Limestone (marble) clay slate, and drab colored Talco-micacious slates, with occasionally a solid conglomerate. There is a central belt or zone in this series extending from the Georgia State line through Cherokee county, that has a wonderful grouping of minerals in it. This zone passes from beyond the Notley river in a north-east direction, crossing the Hiwassee at Murphy, and passing up Valley river to its head, and thence through the corner of Macon and into Swain. There is nearly thirty miles along this zone that abounds in Iron beds. The ore is a brown hydrated oxide. It exits in great abundance. The beds are numerous, and the out-crops indicate exhaustless quantities. The ore is rich in metalic iron, and the metal has proved to be of superior quality, well adapted to the manufacture of car wheels, &c. In immediate proximity to the iron ore are beds of Agalmatolite—a superior soapstone for lining blast furnances. It also makes a good lubricator for heavy machinery, as well as superior tips for gass burners. Associated with the iron and soapstone, are numerous and continuous beds of marble. This marble will be valuable as a flux in the reduction of the iron ores. It possesses one advantage as a flux. It is almost pure Lime, being destitute of magnesia. While this is true of the Cherokee marble, the Limestones generally that occur with iron ores in the Silurian and Carboniferous periods are more or less dolomitic, and are therefore more or less refractory in the fire. Hence, in the reduction of the Cherokee ores, with wood coal as fuel and the marble as a flux, the best results must be obtained in the production of pure iron. The marble, besides its value as a flux, cannot fail to be valuable as an ornamental stone. It occurs of great beauty and excellence. The quality, at the respective localities where it crops out, differs materially. At number six, near Murphy, there is a grey marble, susceptible of a high finish. At Marble branch, three miles from Murphy, there is white marble of good quality from which tombstones have been manufactured. At David Taylor's, some twelve miles up the Valley river from Murphy, there was some beautiful white marble raised several years ago by parties who were searching for metalic veins. The other out-crops along the river have not been specially examined, until reaching Mr. J. T. Young's two miles above Valley Town, where there is an out-crop yielding a

well being, and to that variety and productiveness of industries which is most conducive to the collective prosperity of a people.

Sanitary.—And as to salubrity, it must be evident to any one who has considered the topographical features of the State as hereinbefore described, and the prevalent climatic conditions, as developed in the present chapter, that the conditions of insalubrity cannot exist otherwise than locally and exceptionally. And the case becomes still stronger when the underlying geological structure is taken into account, which is almost every where favorable to ready and complete drainage, so that the waters of the most copious rains disappear from the surface in a few hours at most. And the sanitary statistics of the United States census reports show that the death rate for this State for 1870, for example, is much less than the average for the United States,—less than one per cent. against an average of more than one and a quarter, and if the comparison be carried back to include the reports for 1860 and 1850, the rates are still in nearly the same ratio, viz: 1.14 to 1.31; and as has been stated already in another connection, so far as concerns one of the most prevalent and fatal affections, consumption, one of the two small areas of total exemption in the whole United States is found in North Carolina; and if the figures which express the ratio of deaths from this cause to total mortality, for the entire State, be compared with the average for all the states, the contrast will be found not less striking than that of the general averages above given.

BOTANICAL.

It has long been known to botanists that the territory of North Carolina presents one of the finest fields in the United States for collection, on account of the great variety and interest of its vegetable productions. Many plants of northern habit, such as are common in the White Mountains, for example, and along the northern lakes, find their southern geographical limit in the mountains of this State; and quite a number of others spread from the Gulf and the Mississippi Valley to the Cape Fear and even to Pamplico Sound. So that the flora of this State is continental in character and range, combining the botanical features of both extremes as well as of the intermediate regions.

The results of the preceding discussion of the climatology of the State furnish ample explanation of the fact. The close connection between climate and organic life, and the decisive control which meteorological conditions exert over the whole character and range and form of its de-

ence to the development of Manganese. I am opinion, however, that workable quantity of it may be found in that zone.

There is upon the lands of the late Capt. N. S. Jarrett, in the neighborhood of the red marble locality, an interesting locality of Chalcedonic quartz, such as is used in the manufacture of Burr-stones. It has the appearance, in the bluff where it shows itself, of existing in large masses. No excavation has been made, however, to determine whether large blocks of sufficient size can be obtained for the manufacture of solid burrs. It has the appearance, however, of yielding such blocks.

A few weeks ago I saw, for the first time, on Valley river, a fine, well laminated bed of Itacolumite (flexable Sandstone.) The day was too far spent for any extended exploration. It has a lithological relation favorable to the existence of Diamonds. I, however, mention it here as an example of the wonderful grouping of the Valley river zone.

No investigation of the Valley river range has been made further Northeast-ward than the mouth of Nanteyalee. I cannot, therefore, give any reliable information as to the mineral resources Northeast-ward from that point, on that range.

Immediately succeeding these Taconic beds, in descending order, is a range of Aluminous Mica shales. I so name them because they abound in Staurotite and Kyanite, and being rich in Pyrite, are constantly disentagrating and decomposing where they are sufficiently exposed. This decomposition results in a hydrous compound of Iron and Alum. This range of shales passes through Clay, Macon, Jackson and Haywood. In the latter county it, however, pinches or slabs out after crossing the Pigeon river. At this point, and up the Pigeon some five or six miles Southward a duplicate bed sets in rather abruptly and extends on the same direction through Buncombe and a portion of Madison, but slabs out in Yancey. This belt is not rich in Metalic ores, but compensates for this barrenness, in the Alumina it yields to the soil. Much of the fine wheat land of Haywood county owes its superiority to this fact. For while Alumina enters very sparingly into vegetable structure it possesses a well known property of absorbing and retaining moisture, and of giving tenacity to the soil.

Succeeding these beds and overlying them in the inverted order which the rocks here have, set in the great Gneiss beds. About midway between the Aluminous shales and the summit of the Blue Ridge, the character of the Gneiss is marked and peculiar. It abounds in rose colored Garnets. Indeed, I have seen localities where the garnet had replaced the quartz and Feldspar, making a garnetoid rock, composed of black mica and rose garnets. Some of this rock makes handsome cabinet specimens. It is a noteworthy fact that wherever we find this rose colored garnet in the Gneiss, we invariably find sulphurets of Iron and Copper. This rock is evidently the source of the Copper of this belt, because the veins that have been developed are inclosed in it and Syenite, some of which also contains the same variety of Garnet. Following and in the center of this garnetic Gneiss there has been some igneous disturbances, doubtless at an early period after the Gneiss beds were upheaved and turned upon their edges. There is a system of Chrysolite dikes in this particular zone extending from the north-east corner of Mitchell county to Track-rock, in Union county, Georgia, a distance of about hundred and ninety miles. It perhaps continues through Georgia into Alabama. Indeed, I explored a similar system of Chrysolite out-crops in Tallapoosa county, Alabama, holding the same relation to the axis of upheaved and the Taconic beds that they do here. These dikes occupy a narrow zone throughout the entire length. The out-crops, however, while numerous, are at intervals, so that there is no continuous bed of Chrysolite or Serpentine. These Chrysolite dikes bear Corundum at various localities. During the hasty examination which I made of the localities in Mitchell I was unable to find Corundum. I was unable, also, to detect some of the more intimately associated minerals. Through Yancey my explorations had a similar result, with the exception that at one locality where, it was alleged, a handsome piece of blue Corundum had been picked up. There I obtained by panning the sands of the branch some very small fragments and crystals. The general absence of Tourmaline, Hornblend, Margarite, Chalcedony and Ripidolite led me to suspect that but little Corundum would be found on those out-crops I examined.

Passing into Madison county, on the waters of Little Ivey, there exists Corundum on the lands of Wm. Carter, about one mile from Democrat post-office. At this locality it is associated with Margarite, Tourmaline and Ripidolite. I gave instructions to the parties, who held a lease on the property, how to prosecute their search, and have since learned that they succeeded in finding a small vein. There are no out-crops of interest in Buncombe until we reach the valley of New Found creek, on the west side of the French Broad river. There, on the lands of Mrs. Luther, I found a small specimen of the mineral. My examination of other out-crops in the same neighborhood were unsuccessful. At the head of New Found creek the line of dike fissures enters Haywood county and passes down North Hominy creek two or three miles. On the lands of Mr. Enoch Hall I found Corundum in small fragments, having Ripidolite as the associated mineral. The out-crop at this locality is small, covering only a few acres of ground. In Mr. Hall's neighborhood some parties were testing for Mica and found a small vein of Corundum associated with Mica and Albite. This vein, however, is in close proximity to the Chrysolite on Mr. Hall's lands, and constitutes the only instance in which I have found Corundum outside of Chrysolite rock. I have not been advised for over a year as to whether the parties operating upon the property have found it in sufficient quantity to render it an object of commercial interest.

On entering Jackson county, the Chrysolite crops out at several points along the Scott's creek valley, and on the Tuckasegee river, at Webster. At all the localities in this county there exists a good deal of Ripidolite. At one I found Margarite, at two others Bronzite, but at none of them did I find Corundum. My examinations were, however, altogether too hasty to be satisfactory. I am impressed with the belief that this rare and valuable mineral will yet be found in Jackson. Near the dividing line, between the counties of Jackson and Macon, and within Macon, the Chrysolite crops out again. Here a little Corundum has been discovered. There are several out-crops down the Ellijay valley, and at Lyles' mill there has been quite a quantity of fragments and sections of crystals washed out, besides the discovery of some massive Corundum. Gen. Clingman operated upon this property at one time for Sapphire and Ruby gems. I have never understood whether he found any precious stones or not. I think this property is worthy of a more thorough and scientific investigation. Passing from this locality to the Sugar Town valley, we come to the Jenks mine. Here the first discovery of Corundum was made west of the French Broad valley, and inasmuch as much has been said about this discovery, I shall forbear any account of it in this report. The property was purchased by Col. C. W. Jenks, for Capt. E. B. Ward, of Detroit, Michigan. At the time this purchase was made about one thousand pounds of Corundum had been dug out near the surface, and a portion of it sold to Mineralogists for cabinet specimens. Three veins had been cut at a few feet from the surface, and some handsome crystals obtained. The Chrysolite out-crop at this locality is embraced within twenty-five acres of ground. Corundum was found at numerous points over the whole area of out-crop, and masses were obtained weighing as much as forty pounds. Following the digging done by Mr. H. M. Crisp and myself, Col. Jenks' workmen obtained from the vein a crystal weighing three hundred and fifteen pounds. The hexagonal faces were well defined upon it, and while the principal part of it was gray, there were portions of it of sapphire blue and ruby red colors. After the discovery and mining out of this crystal I know scarcely any thing of the operations upon the mine. Col. Jenks enclosed the grounds and allowed no one to go within the enclosure without a written permit from the superintendent. He has kept the results of his operations concealed from the public. I made application to Col. J., through his superintendent, for permission to examine the mine with a view to reporting upon it for the State. He granted permission, with the restriction that the report should be submitted to him for his approval before it should be given to the public. Under such restrictions I declined to examine the mine at all. I, however, have confidence in the value of the mine, based upon my observations previous to the sale of the property. The Corundum at this locality has Ripidolite, Tourmaline, and Margarite as its immediate and most intimate associates; besides these there are Chalcedony, Chromite, Spinel, Actinolite, Asbestus and Anthophyllite upon the mining grounds.

It is unpleasant to be excluded from information which the State is entitled to and the scientific world desire, in regard to this mine, and I am sure public opinion will not approve a policy which has deprived them of it. On three or four different properties in the same neighborhood, Corumdum has been found and a strong probability exists that valuable crystals may be found upon them. The line of out-crops crosses the mountain which divides the Tennessee valley proper from the Sugar Town valley. On reaching the Tennessee valley the disturbing force seems to have scattered and the dikes are therefore scattered. This may be attributed to the configuration of the Blue Ridge at the head of the Tennessee river. Here the ridge forms a considerable curvature around the head of the river, and tending nearly north for eight or ten miles forms a junction with the Nanteyalee chain which is one of the tranverse chains forming one of the peculiarities of our mountain system. Had the axis of disturbance which caused this system of dikes continued upon a direct line as it has done to this point, then it would have entered the central mass of the Blue Ridge beyond the Nanteyalee chain. The disturbing force here conformed to the relation it held to the ridge from Mitchell county to the Tennessee valley, a distance of an hundred and thirty miles, and shifting to the northwestward, reappeared at Buck creek, a tributary of the Nanteyalee, holding its relative distance from the summit of the Blue Ridge.

On reappearing it has produced the grandest mass of Chrysolite rock in the States of this Union—perhaps in the world. The out-crop is a mile and a half in length and covers at least four hundred acres. While all the other out-crops described are inclosed in Gneiss, at Buck creek it is inclosed in a Hornblendic rock. Over the whole area of this Chrysolite bed Corundum has been found, some masses of which will weigh from three to six hundred pounds. One vein has been opened from which a good hand can now raise from three-quarters of a ton to a ton per day. From some tests that have been made, other veins are known to exist. These veins yield principally grey Corundum, having great hardness and toughness. The immediate associates of this grey Corundum are Margarite, Ripidolite, Zoisite, Albite and Hornblend, (the variety Arfvedsonite.) I have obtained specimens containing all these minerals together. It is a noteworthy fact that no Tourmaline has yet been found here. Running through the center of this Chrysolite out-crop there is a green Diorytic rock composed of Smaragdite and Albite, forming a narrow zone. This rock bears a pink or pale red Corundum of great beauty. I have also obtained a few specimens of it of a deep pure ruby color. I have also obtained some specimens of this rock that contained in addition to the red Corundum, a beautiful sky-blue Kyanite. Corundum has been found scattered over the whole area of the out-crop. Actinolite, Ripidolite, Anthophyllite, Vermiculite, Picrolite and Chalcedony (sparingly) exist here in addition to the other minerals mentioned. This locality, when I first discovered Corundum there, was in Macon county, but now lies in Clay, the county line having been changed.

Crossing the mountain to the Southwest Chrysolite crops out again on Licklog and Shooting creeks in the Hiwassee Valley. At Mr. Tipton's on Licklog, Corundum of pink and blue colors occurs wrapt up in a sort of hydrous silicate of Alumina and Magnesia. At Mr. Dodgen's on the same creek a like colored Corundum occurs with Ripidolite. Then in the Shooting creek Valley it occurs on the lands of Mr. James Kirby with Hornblend and Ripidolite, and also on the lands of Amos Ledford, Lucius Ledford, Samuel Hoghead, and H. M. Penland, associated principally with Ripidolite and Tourmaline. Here the zone crosses the Georgia State line, and Corundum occurs at several localities, the associted minerals being Ripidolite, Margarite, Tourmaline and Arfvedsonite.

In the South-eastern corner of Jackson county upon the South side of the Blue Ridge, near the base of Hogback mountain, there exists a Chrysolite out-crop upon the lands of Capt. Thos. D. Johnston, where Corundum has been found. Several hundred pounds were obtained from some excavations made. Amongst this Corundum were some handsome specimens of red and Opalescent colors. It has a remarkable and easy clearage and moles very handsome cabinet specimens. The associated minerals are Margarite, Tourmaline and Ripidolite. When I visited the locality several months ago the excavations were in such condition that I could not see the vein or form any definite opinion of its capacity or character. The out-crop, however, covers several acres of ground.

This discovery of Corundum is not without its value to the arts. Indeed, as an abrasive it has no superior except the Diamond, and its developement and general introduction as an abrasive will enlarge the demand for it. Along the zone of these Chrysolite dikes, it will, I have no doubt be developed in large quantity as the demand for it increases. Besides this general use for it in the arts, I have reason for believing that gems of Sapphire and Ruby of great value will yet be found.

Chromite, or chromate of Iron occurs in the Chrysolite rocks throughout the entire range so far as I have examined it. I have never been upon an out-crop of this rock which did not contain crystals of Chromite imbedded in the rock. At a few localities it has been observed in considerable masses. On the mine fork of Jack's creek in Yancey county, Chrome ore crops out on a Chrysolite ridge, where from the angular character of the blocks there are good reason to suspect that a vein exists. I have obtained specimens at that locality quite free from foreign matter and rich in Chromium. Near the town of Webster, in Jackson county, there also exists Chromite. Many years ago when I first examined the locality, there were masses upon the surface of from one to two hundred pounds weight. It was destroyed for concealment, or used in building a road by the county authorities, so that very little can now be seen upon the surface. During my last examination, however, I found a vein of it exposed in a gulley. This vein is enclosed by Chrysolite. From what I know of the large angular blocks that once lay upon the surface and the character of the small vein I have recently seen, I think that a valuable deposit of this ore exists here. At Col. Jenk's Corundum mine in Macon county, I obtained several masses of Chromite of eight or ten pounds weight previous to the purchase of the property by Col. J. At several other points I have often found small lumps of it from the size of a pea to that of a hen's egg. No special search, however, has been made for it, owing to the remoteness of the localities from railroad transportation. There is one other rare mineral that occurs with the Chrysolite at Webster. I allude to Genthite. This mineral contains a large per cent. of Nickle. It has the appearance of a hydrous silicate, and occurs in seams of serpentine, sometimes a quarter of an inch thick. It also occurs in a very porous Chalcedony. The contrast between the green Genthite and the white Chalcedony makes a rock of rare beauty. There are also specimens of Bronzite at this locality.

There are numerous granite dikes all along the range of Chrysolite dikes, the granite dikes, however, taking a wider range than the Chrysolite dikes. I regard these granite dikes as of the same age of the Chrysolite. They are both due, no doubt, to the same disturbing force. This seems evident from the chrystaline character of the Gneiss enclosing them. The granite dike matter is often well defined, and very distinct from the enclosing wall rock. I observed in the Clarissa Buckhanon mine, in Mitchell,—a mine operated by Capt. J. K. Irby, at the time of my visit in the summer of 1873—that the walling remained, very often unbroken, when the vein matter was blasted out. That mine, when I saw it, was a fine example of a dike fissure filled with a coarse granite. Indeed, true mica mines belong to these granite dikes. I have visited quite a number of workings all along the belt from Mitchell to Georgia, and have not yet seen a good productive mine of mica, only where the evidence was clear as to the dike character of the vein. Nor do these well defined veins invariably make productive mines, for the reason that some fissures are filled with barren matter, while in others the law of crystalization acted on a much larger scale in one than in another. It is worthy of special note, that where, for example, the hexagonal faces of the mica crystals range from one to three inches, this law as to size holds good in that vein. Again, when the prospecter finds mica in his vein, having what the miners call a straight edge, which is only one face of a crystal of mica, say six inches in length, though the remainder of the crystal may be rough and irregular, he may be pretty certain that the vein will yield blocks of good size, and the only remaining question with him is as to quantity and quality. Some dikes seem to have been filled with something like equal proportions of Feldspar, Quarts and Mica, and it sometimes so happens that a large per cent. of the mica in a vein has been very imperfectly crystalized, the plates interlocking, making a sort of gnarled mass, rather than regular transparent plates. These facts should be borne in mind by prospecters for mica mines. A good deal of money has been spent upon large seams of Feldspar, which occasionally occur in Gneiss rock. Some times a few blocks or crystals of glass are obtained of respectable size from these seams. But they being a part of, and incorporated with, the other elements of the Gneiss, are unreliable and in no instance have made valuable mines. Another thing to be considered is the lithological character of the rocks in which the dike veins occur. At some localities the walling is altogether Gneiss, at others one wall is Gneiss and the other Syenite; and again, I have seen the walling a sort of Chlorite shale having Hornblend in its composition. My observations have brought to light an important fact in connection with these respective wallings to regular Mica veins. Wherever one of the walls is Hornblendic rock the Mica is more liable te be specked by Magnetite than if both walls are pure crystaline Gneiss, and it is almost invariably the case that when a vein is walled with the kind of shale just mentioned, the Mica is so much impregnated with Magnetite as to be unfit for the ordinary commercial uses. There is another feature of these granite dikes worthy of note. The Feldspar in some of them has been decomposed and constitutes Kaolin. Where the Feldspar is in this condition, other things being favorable, the Mica is usually well crystalized and of good quality, though other veins, where the vein matter is solid, yield largely of Mica of good size and quality.

The Mitchell county mines when I visited them in the summer of 1873, promised good results. Operations were carried on upon some four or five mines in the neighborhood of Bakersville, perhaps the most important one being the Sinkhole mine, the property of Messrs. Heap & Clap. The vein at this locality is a soft one—the Feldspar being in a decomposed state. Most of the work done upon this vein has been with the pick and without blasting. The yield of mica has been large, and the quality excellent. The vein is perhaps half a mile in length, and at the time of my visit gave no signs of diminishing in depth. If the water can be controled it is valuable property. An interesting feature of this mine is the ancient work done upon it. Large excavations have been made by some ancient race of people of whose history we know nothing. They evidently did the work for mica, because the vein does not bear any metalic ore. Moreover, nothing but fragments of mica have been found in immense dump-heaps, while the vein yields an abundance of large sized mica. The race must have been one possessing a considerable degree of civilization, and certainly attached an economical value to the mica. There is, however, no trace of evidence as to what use they applied it. They were of the race of mound builders, and their occupancy of the country could not have been later than the days of the Toltecs.

I have been informed that other evidence of old workings exists in that section.

I cannot speak in detail of all the mines in Mitchell. That section is evidently rich in mica. Two mines are mentioned in Yancey as profitable for working. The mine of Jos. W. Gibbs on south Toe river, about eight miles south-east of Burnsville, was not fully open at the time of my visit. The vein seemed to be large, some eight or ten feet in thickness, and in proportion to the cubic feet worked out yielded one pound of trimmed mica to every three and three-elevenths cubic feet of the vein worked out. I have recently been informed that Mr. Gibbs is still operating with profit upon the mine.

The Ray mine, situated about four miles south-east from Burnsville, has been extensively worked. At the time of my visit, two companies of hands were operating upon different sections of the vein. I was informed that the yield at that time was from one to one and a half pounds of trimmed mica per day to the hand. This vein is an interesting one. The fissure is a zigzag up the face of the mountain. At least such was the appearance presented by the different openings and driftings upon it. None of the works had been carried to any considerable depth. This mine has, however, been quite a productive and remunerative one, and first and last has yielded a large amount of good merchantable mica. I obtained from the rubbish of the mine some very fair crystals of Beryl, and was informed by the workmen that the owner, Mr. Garrett Ray, had collected quite a number of handsome crystals. Columbite also occurs in this mine. My search, however, through the rubbish was rewarded with obtaining only two small crystals.

My impressions in regard to the Ray mine were that the proprietor ought to have a deep shaft sunk upon the vein. This would settle the question raised in my own mind as to whether the vein bears Tin or not. There are some reasons in my mind for suspecting that Tin may possibly exist at that locality. Where the whole operation has been one of profit, the proprietor could well afford to settle the question in the way suggested.

After leaving Burnsville and following the range South-westward, on reaching Madison the rocks become Chloritic and Slaty, and in and through Buncombe still more so. I have not been able to find any well defined dike fissures filled with granitic matter in these last named rocks, and was not therefore, favorably impressed with Madison and Buncombe as a district likely to prove a good Mica mining section. Nor have I learned that any profitable mine of this mineral has yet been found in either of these counties. A party did make an opening near the head of Swanannoa with flattering prospects, but the last information I had from them they had ceased operations. On reaching Haywood the rocks become more crystaline and the prospects better for granite dikes. A mine has been opened about five miles South of Waynesville and is being operated by Messrs. McCampbell & McLung, of Tennessee. I did not visit the mine but gathered the following facts from Mr. McCampbell. The mine is on lands belonging to the heirs of the late Jas. R. Love of Haywood county. There are two openings upon the vein which he described as being one hundred feet wide and one hundred yards in length. It is a granite vein. The largest sizes of trimed plates of Mica obtained from the mine are 9x11 inches and 6x15 inches. It is but seldom that plates of this size are obtained. This fact speaks well for the mine. Five hands in one month produced five hundred and fifty pounds of trimed, merchantable Mica. This was over four pounds per day to the hand. If similar results can be realized the year around it would certainly make a handsome business. There are other flattering prospects in Haywood county.

Passing into Jackson there are increasing evidences of dike fissures, and the general character of the rocks is more favorable to Mica mines. Several veins have been opened in the county and a good deal of Mica taken out and shipped, but I am sorry that I cannot give any definite information as to the status of operations upon the mines at present. There is, however, strong evidence that Jackson county will prove to be valuable as a mining district for mica. The range passes from Jackson into Macon county. In this county granite dikes are more numerous than in any other county I have visited excepting only Mitchell. There are several openings in this county. The first made and worked is a mine at the head of Cowee creek, now owned and operated by Mr. Brooks, a gentleman from the State of New York. This mine has yielded a large amount of Mica of good quality and of average size. The crystalization of the Mica is firm and its average and color good. The proprietor is not operating a large force upon the mine at present, having divided his forces for the purpose of prospecting upon other properties. This vein, which is called Mica city, is evidently a fisure vein. It is located in Gneiss, and the Gneiss at this place bears copper. Indeed, there is in the quartz and Feldspar that make up the Mica vein, a smaller vein of Pyrite which is magnetic, that bears some Copper and perhaps a little Nickle. In the immediate neighborhood, and on the same range, there is a vein in Gneiss rock that contains Argentiferous Lead, Zinc Blend, Copper Pyrites and Pyrrhotite. I mention this in connection with this Mica vein because it renders that locality unusually interesting.

West of Mica city and on the western side of the Tennessee river, there is another locality where Mr. Brooks is opening for Mica with flattering propects. Near the Watauga gap, and not exceeding a quarter of a mile from the State road, is a locality known as rocky face. Here considerable work has been done and several hundred pounds of merchantable Mica taken out. Within the last year this property changed hands and from some cause unknown to me has not been operated upon since the change was made.

About one and a half miles from Franklin a mica vein has been tested on the lands of Dr. B. W. Moore. The vein is located in Gneiss, and bears the marks of a regular dike. In power it is about six feet with branches. It is Feldspar with a central quartz vein. The Mica usually lies in the Feldspar near—often along side of the quartz. I saw one crystal, usually called block, which weighed upwards of eighty pounds. The glass obtained at this mine is of excellent quality. It promises to be a productive and valuable vein.

West of Franklin, twelve or fifteen miles, there are flattering prospects. Large masses of Mica are seen at the surface of a vein traversing Gneiss rock. There are in the county many other localities that promise favorably, but which have not yet attracted prospecters.

The constantly increasing demand for Mica must lead to a more regular and systematic method of mining for it. This industry is destined to become more general and remunerative in the counties west of the Blue Ridge.

In discussing the question of copper, I must pass over the same zone in which Corundum and Mica are found. The peculiar character of Gneiss, already described as abounding in rose colored garnets constitutes the copper bearing zone with a single exception, which will be pointed out. I have not explored Mitchell county for copper. It may be, however, that it exists in that county. When there last Summer, I passed over a remarkably heavy Trap dike. A few miles from Bakersville, on the road to Jack's-creek, I first saw it and traveled upon it for several miles. I was told by the gentleman, with me, that it constituted the principal rock on the Pumpkin-patch mountain, and extended for several miles north-eastwards. I traveled upon it for several miles south-eastward. I did not see the rock formation on the northwest side of it. It may be that approximating it on the north side copper or magnetic iron will be found. I am not sufficiently familiar with the geology of Madison to say whether there are favorable prospects for copper in that county or not. I once visited a locality, near the head of "Big Ivey," which presented some favorable out-cropping for copper. I am not, however, certain as to whether the locality is in Madison or Buncombe. I know of a point only a few miles from Asheville, on whose lands I am unable to say, where there is an out-crop deserving of exploration for copper. The belt passes into Haywood county, at the head of North Hominy. Here on lands, which at the time of my visit, in 1860, belonged to Geo. Hall, there is an out-crop that is in every way flattering for copper. Some parties did considerable work upon the property, but were misled by an itinerant mining engineer from the North. The gossan is of excellent quality, the vein at the surface large and the walling favorable for a copper mine. The zone passes down North Hominy to Hall's mills with several attractive out-crops between George Hall's and the mill. Eight or ten miles southwestward there are out-crops again in the Massey cove and on the Little mountain, in the direction of Waynesville. At these localities everything seems favorable for copper.

At this point I must leave this zone to discuss a copper locality in Haywood county in an entirely different geology. It is on Wilkin's creek, twenty-five or six miles from Waynesville and down the Pigeon river towards the Tennessee State line. It is lithologically identical with Ducktown, and is in the same geological horizon. When I visited the locality in 1860 a considerable amount of work had been done by Messrs. Hill & McCraken. They first sunk a shaft upon the crest of the hill and found some pockets of black copper. They then abandoned the shaft and drove in a tunnel from the side of the hill. This tunnel penetrated the vein into which they cut some twelve or fifteen feet without reaching the opposite wall. The vein is almost solid Arsenical Pyrite, precisely such as constitutes the veins at Ducktown. I supposed, without analysis, that the vein matter contained about the same per cent. of copper that the same material does at Ducktown at the bottom of the black copper. At least the copper Pyrites distributed through it appears to be about the same. I was assured that the out-crops of gossan extend for four miles North-eastward, and generally as bold as at the locality under consideration. This is the only point outside of Ducktown where I have seen Ducktown duplicated. This locality deserves special exploration; and needs only capital and enterprize to make it a valuable copper mining district.

After passing Waynesville the copper belt widens out, the zone we have been following, passing into Jackson county at the head of Scott's creek. There are several out-crops between this point and the Waychutta mine. Some of these localities have been tested by Messrs. Oram & Davies who are the owners of sixteen thousand acres of land embracing these out-crops. The tests made, developed copper, and I have been informed by reliable gentlemen that the veins are of good size, and the ore, (Chalcopyrite,) of excellent quality.

On the head waters of South Richland, a zone sits in, in which there are out-crops of Gossan. When I examined this section in 1860, I was much pleased with the prospects for Copper. Some work had then been done on the top of the Caney Fork *bald*, a mountain dividing the waters of Pigeon and Tuckasegee. The prospecter had cut a large quartz vein which showed handsome copper ore. Along the spurs of the mountain on the Pigeon or Richland side, I saw two fine Gossan out-crops. Southwestward from this point, on the waters of Caney Fork, there are large exposures of Gossan in Gunstocker Cave. The zone passes down Caney Fork, and crossing the Tuckasegee river, runs into the Cullowhee mountain. In this mountain is the Cullowhee mine. I visited and examined the grounds at this mine in 1860. Having lost the notes of that examination, I must rely upon my memory for the facts I ascertained during that examination. My recollection is that the vein opened by Messrs. Oram & Davies is about six feet in thickness. The ore is a rich yellow copper, (Chalcopyrite.) Capt. Oram reported to me as the average per centum of metalic copper from a box of ore sent to a copper furnace, twenty-seven per cent. I formed the opinion when upon the grounds, that there exists two parallel veins having cross fissures, making a perfect network of veins. This is valuable property, and only needs capital, enterprise and the means of transportation to establish, at that point, a valuable mining industry. Further south-westward is the Wolf creek mine, a property I did not visit after a copper vein was opened upon it. I saw samples of ore from it, however, that made a good showing of yellow copper. This range passes south-westward into Macon county on the waters of Ellajay and Buck creek. I now return to Jackson. The range or zone from the head of Scott's creek passes along the range of the double top mountain, showing the out-crops already alluded to. On reaching Waychutta, there are several out-crops both north-east and south-west of the mine. In 1860 the Waychutta mine showed handsome specmens of green Malachite, copper Pyrites and occasionally some native Copper. I have not been upon the grounds since that date and am unadvised as to the present condition of the mine. Shell ridge, Buck knob and Hornbuckle may all be included in this belt. Buck knob and Shell ridge I examined before any work was done upon either. They have proved to be good copper localities. The Hornbuckle I never visited, but it has good reputation for its out-crop of Gossan.

North-west of the shell ridge is the old Savannah mine. At this point the first discovery of copper was made in Jackson. Here is a good vein several feet in thickness of yellow copper. This property is on a transverse section of rocks. The Gneiss and Syenite strike off to the north-west, and about half a mile from the old Savannah is the new Savannah, which has been opened since the close of the war. Messrs. Higdon and Buckhanon, the owners of the property, drove in a tunnel and cut the vein at twenty-five or thirty feet in depth from the surface. At this point in the vein there is a mixture of gossan, black copper. gangstone and yellow copper. Good specimens cannot now be obtained, owing to the fact that the Pyretous matter of the vein, since its exposure to the atmosphere, is in a state of fermentation. The vein, however, is apparently a large one, being from eight to twelve feet in thickness. The out-crop continues for a quarter of a mile north-westward, and also shows south-eastward on the lands of Messrs. Oram & Davis. This zone passes north-westward, crossing the county line in Bet's gap, and shows copper at the Corner rock on the head of Cowee creek, in Macon county.

The Buck knob zone shows in Macon at the Corbin knob, where some copper has been recently obtained. The belt here is broad. On Tessen tee and Middle creek, in the southern part of Macon, there is a large out-crop of gossan. On Middle creek, near Cabe's mill, two openings were made before 1860, and a large vein cut, but in this instance, as well as all others in this whole copper district, so soon as the prospecters reached the upper part of a vein, they ceased to prosecute the work further. When these works were open, I obtained excellent yellow copper ores. The out-crops extend for the distance of one and a half miles. The principal part of the view belongs to a Cincinnati Company. The Company propose at an early day to erect a furnace for the reduction of these ores. This is no doubt valuable property.

Again, there is a locality on Cortoogajay creek, four miles south-west from Franklin. This is known as the Patton property, and now belongs to the Cincinnatti Company. The vein is in Syenite. It is several feet in thickness, and at the time it was opened, produced very handsome Chalcopyrite. South-westward, at the base of the Nanteyalee mountain, there is another locality knowu as the Waldrope property, where copper occurs, with a fair prospect of a valuable mine.

The whole belt crosses the Nanteyalee mountain and into the south-east corner of Clay county. The section is very mountainous and I have not explored it. The zone, however, shows on the west of the mountains, in Towns county, Georgia, where there are valuable copper properties. In passing over the belt I have only referred to such localities as are known to produce copper. There are quite a number of localities where I have no doubt valuable deposites of copper exist. A noteworthy fact which I have learned is, that the ores on this entire zone in North Carolina are remarkably free from Arsenical impurities. This will certainly add to their value when the time comes for their manipulation in the furnace. The hopes of our people have been so often blasted as to the prospect of railway transportation, that the works at all the copper localities are in a state of dilapidation and it is very rare when a man can be found who will take the trouble to furnish a dozen pounds of ore as samples.

Magnetic iron exists at numerous points in the counties west of the Blue Ridge. Lithologically considered, it is not confined to one class of rocks, but has a wide range in its distribution. My explorations in reference to it have been limited. I have, however, gathered some facts that lead me to believe that valuable deposits of it exist at several points. The first range to be noticed in the order I propose to myself is the Spring creek range. I have not vtsited the Spring creek section, but have seen samples of Magnetite from three or four localities that were highly magnetic. Some parties. were, a year ago, prospecting near the head of Spring Creek, but I have not heard the result. I am also unacquainted with the geological relations of the ore in that section, but have no doubt it is in or at least in close proximity to the quartzite belt that crosses the French Broad river at the Warm Springs. The general strike of this range is in the direction of the head of Spring creek. A few months ago I visited a locality at the head of Fine's creek, not exceeding a half mile from the head of Spring creek. On the western, or Fine's creek side of the mountain, I found Magnetite drifted from toward the crest of the mountain. The specimens picked up were quite angular, and bearing other marks of having been detached from a vein. I also found fragments of Trap rock with the ore. Passing down Fine's creek some two miles, and crossing a spur of the mountain to another fork of the creek, I crossed a large Trap dike where I found some fragments of Magnetic ore. There I learned that at the head of that fork of the creek towards the head of Spring creek there was a fine show of the Magnetite upon the surface. I did not visit this point, the day having been nearly spent, I hastened on to obtain lodgings. In passing down the creek, the windings of the road crossed the Trap dike at several places. I then visited the locality at Mr. Hardy Nolen's. There I obtained specimens of magnetic ore, apparently very pure and strongly magnetic. Trap boulders are scattered over the hill where the ore is obtained. I think that judicious excavations will be very likely to develope a vein of ore at that point.

The Magnetite of Fine's creek evidently has an intimate relation to the Trap dike. No evidence, however sufficiently strong, has been brought to light to determine whether the iron occurs in the Trap or in a soft friable slate, somewhat Chloritish, that exists on the same hill. The most reasonable supposition is, that the ore forms a vein in the slate in immediate proximity to the Trap. I was informed at Mr. Nolen's that the dike appears further on and on the west side of Pigeon river, but I did not pursue my explorations further than Mr. Nolen's.

The second zone passes through Madison a few miles south of Marshall, crossing the French Broad river a short distance above the mouth of Ivy. About three miles up Ivy, from its mouth, there occurs Magnetite on the lands of Mr. Joseph Eller. The prospects are flattering for a large vein at this locality. An excavation, a few feet deep, has been made upon the hill side, and a vien, some two or three feet in thickness, cut. Higher up the hill I observed an out-crop of ore, indicating a much larger vein, and from the manner in which the ore is distributed over the surface, I have but little doubt that it exists in large quantity. It is favorably located for practical operations. The veins are on a steep ridge at considerable elevation above water. At a short distance Ivy creek furnishes umple water power for driving machinery, and the surrounding country for several miles abounds in unbroken forests, capable of furnishing fuel for a number of years to come. The Magnetite at this locality is associated with a Pyroxene like mineral, perhaps, the variety Sahlite. The country rock is principally Gneiss. I did not explore this range in either direction of the strike from Mr. Eller's, and am uninformed as to other out-crops.

The third zone in which Magnetic Iron occurs is in the copper and Corundum belt. In this zone the Magnetite occurs in Syenite and Gneiss, and in some instances with Chlorite at Chrysolite localities. On Elijay creek in Macon county about eight miles Southeast of Franklin on the lands of Messrs. Ward and Moses. A vein is in Gneiss, and at the surface has a power, apparently, of seven or eight feet. The ore is mixed with quartz, but there is a strong probability that at some depth the vein will produce ore comparatively free from foreign matter. This supposition is supported by the fact that in the same neighborhood, on the lands of Mr. David Moses, a shaft was sunk about twenty feet deep in search of a copper vein. At the surface Magnetite and yellow copper were sparcely distributed through a zone of Gneiss some eight or ten feet thick. At a depth of twenty feet the Gneissoid matter was in a good degree absent, and Magnetite with a small amount of copper had taken its place. This is likely to form a valuable vein. Four miles from Franklin in a Southeast direction there exists Specular Iron on the lands of Gen'l Thos. M. Angel. No excavation has been made at this locality. I have observed masses of ore scattered over the surface weighing from one to seventy or eighty pounds. The ore has not been analized, but seems to be very pure. The Iron here occurs with Gneiss. One mile from this locality, there occurs Magnetic Iron on the lands of Mr. Wm. Washburn. The ore has been found in red earth, in masses weighing from one ounce to twenty pounds. The masses are angular and bear marks of having been detached from a vein. The rocks here are Syenite—a large out-crop. Some of the ore obtained at a depth of, perhaps two feet, has a soft slaty Chlorite attached to it. This fact justifies me in determining that the vein is located in Chlorite slate. The ore at this place is solid and highly magnetic.

Taking the Specular and Magnetic ore together they promise a valuable locality for an iron industry. There is a superior water power on Sugar Town river within a mile of these ores, and the country contiguous is heavily timbered.

Near the base of the Nanteyalee mountain at the head of Cortoogajay creek, there is another locality of Magnetic iron on the lands of Mr. W. C. Kinsey. The ore here is found with Syenite. No excavation has been made upon these grounds, but the quantity of ore distributed over the surface indicate a vein of fair dimensions. Should the ore be developed at this locality in sufficient quantity to justify the erection of a furnace, everything else is favorable for manufacturing purposes. There is a splendid water power within one mile of the ore, and the forests are ample for coaling grounds. Here the zone passes across the Nanteyalee mountain into the south-eastern corner of Clay county—a section I have not explored.

There are many points along the whole Blue Ridge range, on the Western slope, where I have observed fragments of Magnetic ore, some of them worthy of careful investigation. There is a probability that numerous veins of this valuable ore may be found at points other than those mentioned.

Plumbago exists along the entire range embracing the Corundum, Copper and Magnetic zones, from Mitchell to Clay. I have occasionally observed fragments the size of a hen's egg of superior quality. I have not, however, made any special explorations in reference to it. There are strong reasons for believing that valuable deposits of it may be found in these ranges.

I ought, perhaps, to have noticed while describing the minerals belonging to the Valley river zone, to have mentioned a bed of black slates on the lands of the late N. S. Jarrett, which are quite fissile, and would, in the hands of skillful workmen, make good roofing tiles.

There is a second Gold belt which passes from Union county, Georgia, into Clay, crossing Brass Town creek, near the State line. This zone lies on the south of the Valley river zone, the gold occurring near the contact of the Taconic series wtth the Metamorphic rocks proper. On Gumlog creek, just on the Georgia side of the line, quartz veins occur in Gneiss aud Mica slate on the south side of the creek, that are rich in gold, while on the opposite side of the creek I have observed Gold in Talco micacious slate without any quartz gang. In this order the zone crosses the State line. On the lands of the Messrs. Brown, Mr. Loyed, Col. Platt, Benjamin Brown and John C. Moore, quartz veins occur. From some of these I have seen very rich gold ones. Upon the property of Mr. John C. Moore, which lies adjoining the Georgia line, works were carried on previous to the commencement of the late war. A stamp mill was erected and some eight or ten thousand pennyweights of Gold obtained. The yield to the ton of ore was good, but the breaking out of the war caused a suspension of operations, and the parties scattered and never returned.

This zone passes in the direction of Fort Hembree, and crossing Hiwassee river, follows up the valley of Tesquittee. Near the head of this creek there exists Gold on the lands of the late Capt. W. B. Tidwell, Capt. W. P. Moore and Mr. Shearer. Some of the ores obtained from this locality I found rich in gold. There is but little gold on any of these ranges upon the eastern side of the Nanteyalee mountains. I know of but two points where attempts have been made to mine for it. One of these is on the range just under consideration. It is on the waters of Briar Town creek, on the eastern side of the Nanteyalee river. It has been said that the quartz at this locality yield a fair per cent. of gold. I have not, however, examined the ore myself, and cannot vouch for the truth of the statement. The other locality referred to is in Macon county, about twelve miles in a southeasterly direction from Franklin, on the waters of Sugar Town river. Many years ago an operation was carried on upon this property and fair wages was realized. Mr. Silas McDowell, the owner of the property, has informed me that the gold obtained was very pure. He states that he had at one time regular octohedral crystals of the metal. This as a gold mine is isolated, having no connection with any system of Gold bearing rocks.

In the Southeastern corner of Macon county in Whitner's Valley and the Horse Cove mining has been done for gold to a considerable extent. The gold along this zone has been obtained from branch and creek deposits. It is not known that veins exists there. Indeed, no systematic search has been made for them. There is apparently a system of trough like vallies or gulches lying immediately along the Southern base of the main ridge, and between it and Buzzard mountain in which these mines exist. In 1856 I observed at one point in these vallies a narrow zone of Talco Micacious slates which led ms to the conclusion that such a zone once existed filling up these narrow gorges or vallies, and by abrazive forces had been carried away, leaving the gold in gravel beds.

This zone continues North-eastward through Casher's Valley and along the Southern base of Hogback mountain which is a section of the main ridge. In the Toxaway, Georgetown and White Water vallies mining has been done similar to that in Horse cove. At one point in Hogback, I have been informed by old miners, that there is a spring breaking out of the rocks which produced daily deposits of gold. Very rich deposits of gold were struck in the ravines just below the spring which were worked up to the spring head. It was found that the sands which daily accumulated just below the spring were rich in gold. Taking the hint the miners excavated a small basin in the rock over which the spring waters ran out. By panning out this basin every morning they would obtain from one to three penny weights of gold. Their eagerness, however, to get at the sources of the gold led them to put a blast into the rock thinking they would immediately develop a vein. The blast no doubt fissured the rock and the result was the gold ceased to flow out with the water. This is a striking exemplification of the old adage of killing the goose that laid the egg. The facts here stated I learned from Col. Henry Platt who operated at this spring, a gentleman every way worthy of a character for truthfulness.

The zone passes from this point through the Blue Ridge into Transylvania county and down Boilston creek, where some gold has been found.

Much remains to be done in a proper exploration of the gold-bearing districts in the trans-montain counties of the State. The probabilities are that mines may be found like that at Gumlog mine, in Union county, Georgia, which, besides the gold, yield zinc blend and argentiferous Galena. The question is worthy, at least, of careful and patient investigation.

In closing this report I deem it eminently proper to remark that the State's resources and her projected system of railways are germain subjects, and that the one cannot be successfully prosecuted to the neglect of the other. The system adopted years ago for the construction of State railways was admirably adapted to the development of her mineral and other resources. Its completion would now add more to her material wealth than all other things combined. In the development of her mineral, agricultural and physical resources west of the Blue Ridge, and their transportation by rail would materially enhance the value of the State stocks in her present road. The development and operation of mines in the west would greatly increase the value of her real estate and proportionately enrich the State. A careful review of all the facts stated in this report will show an immense field for freights which up to the present time has been undeveloped and useless to individual citizens, to the State, and to her railroads. For example, her iron, marble, agalmatolite, burrstone, roofing slates, copper, corundum, chromium, etc.; and add her furniture timbers, timbers for the manufacture of wheel carriages and ship building, locust, lynn, poplar, &c., and there is no district of equal size in the States of this Union that can furnish so large an amount of heavy freights.

It is proper to remark again, that the discussion of the timbers, the agricultural resources, the grazing and dairying business, and the fruit of this transmontain region would have been legitimate in this report, but I have thought proper to pass it over for the present.

The facts stated are humbly submitted to the consideration of the people of the State and to capitalists abroad, with a devout hope that the information may be of future benefit to enterprise and to the State at large.

1
2
3
5
7
8
8
9
10
10
11
12
13
14
15
26
27
28
29
24
23
25
30

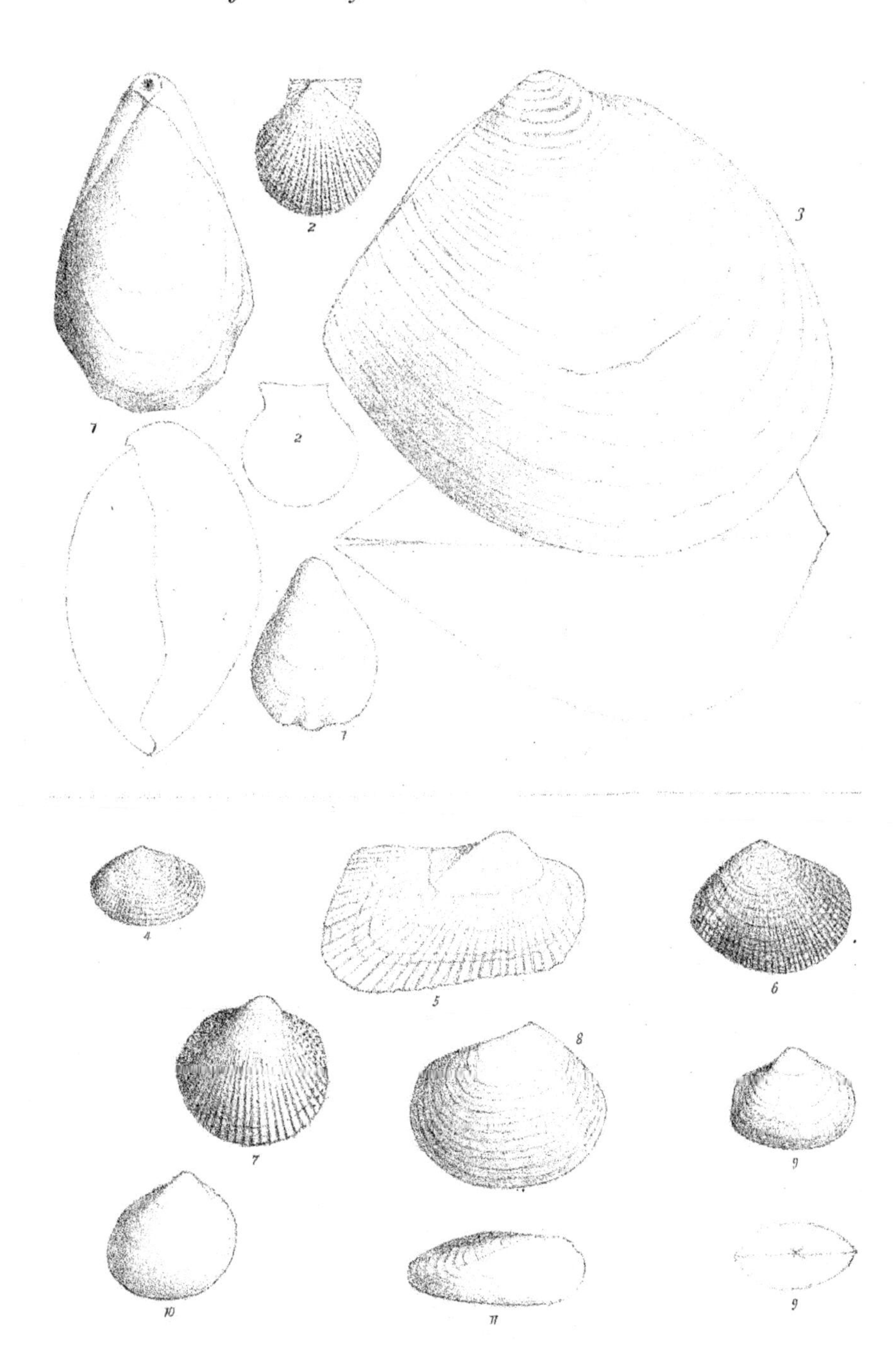
2
3
1
2
1
1
4
5
6
7
8
9
10
11
9

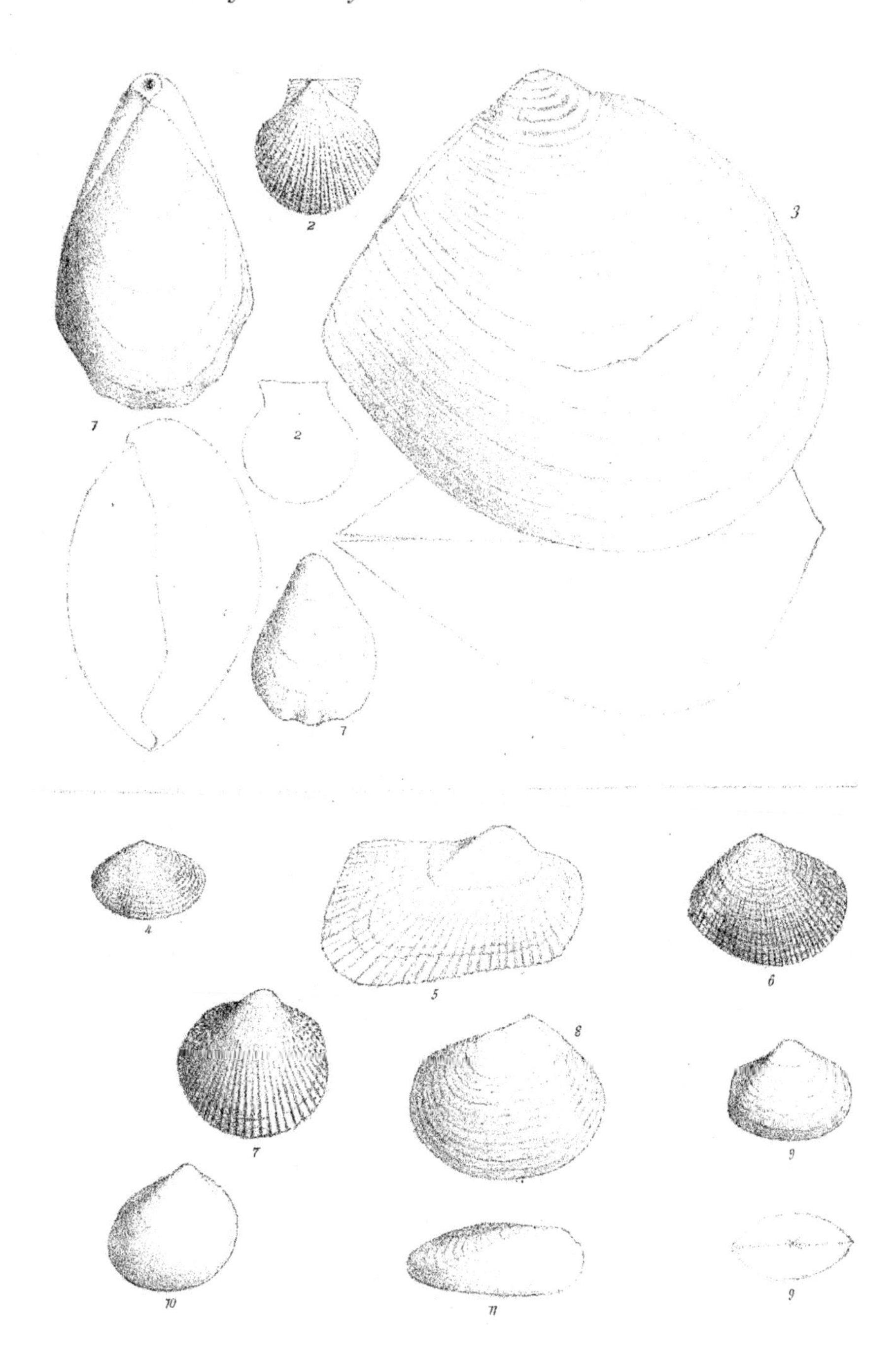
7
2
3
7
2
7
4
5
6
7
8
9
10
11
9

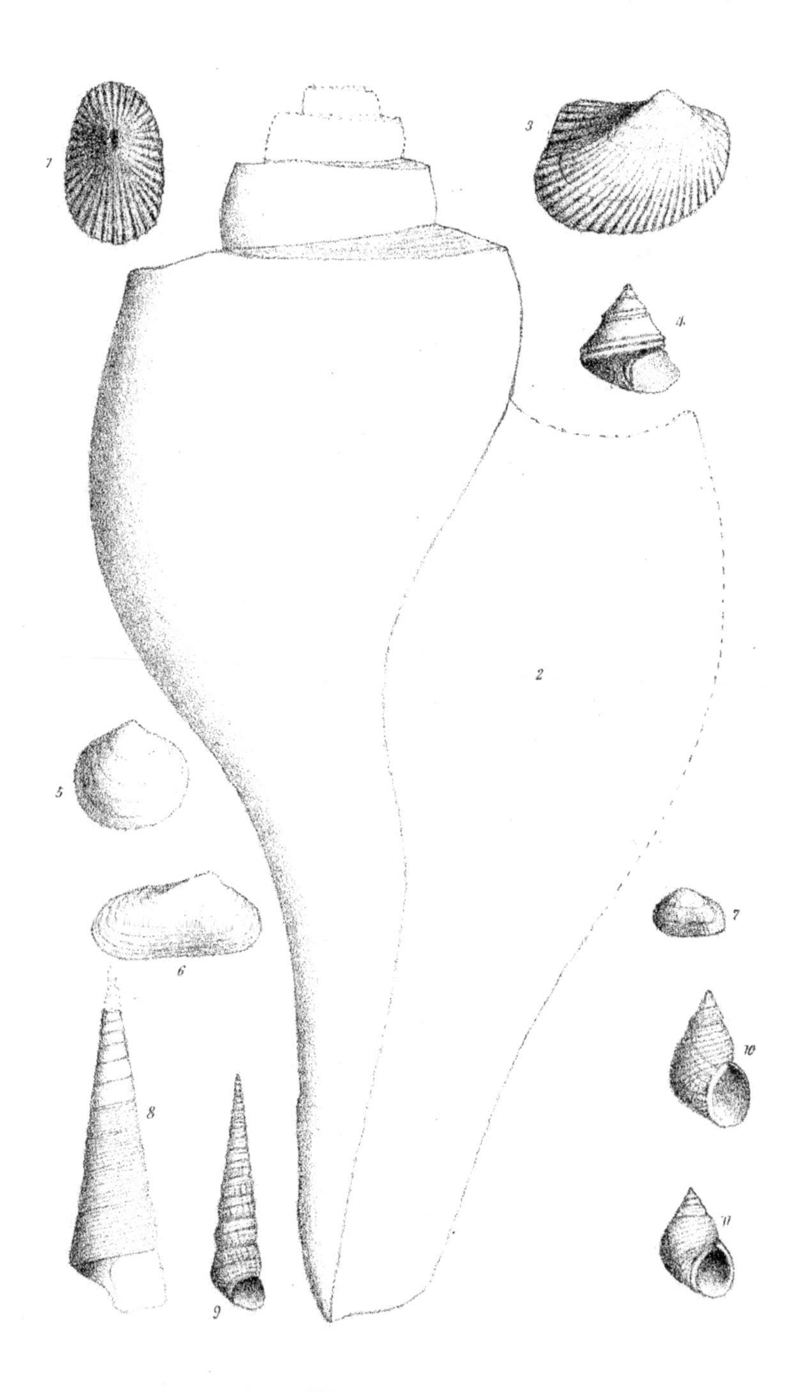
1
2
3
4
5
6
7
8
9
10
11

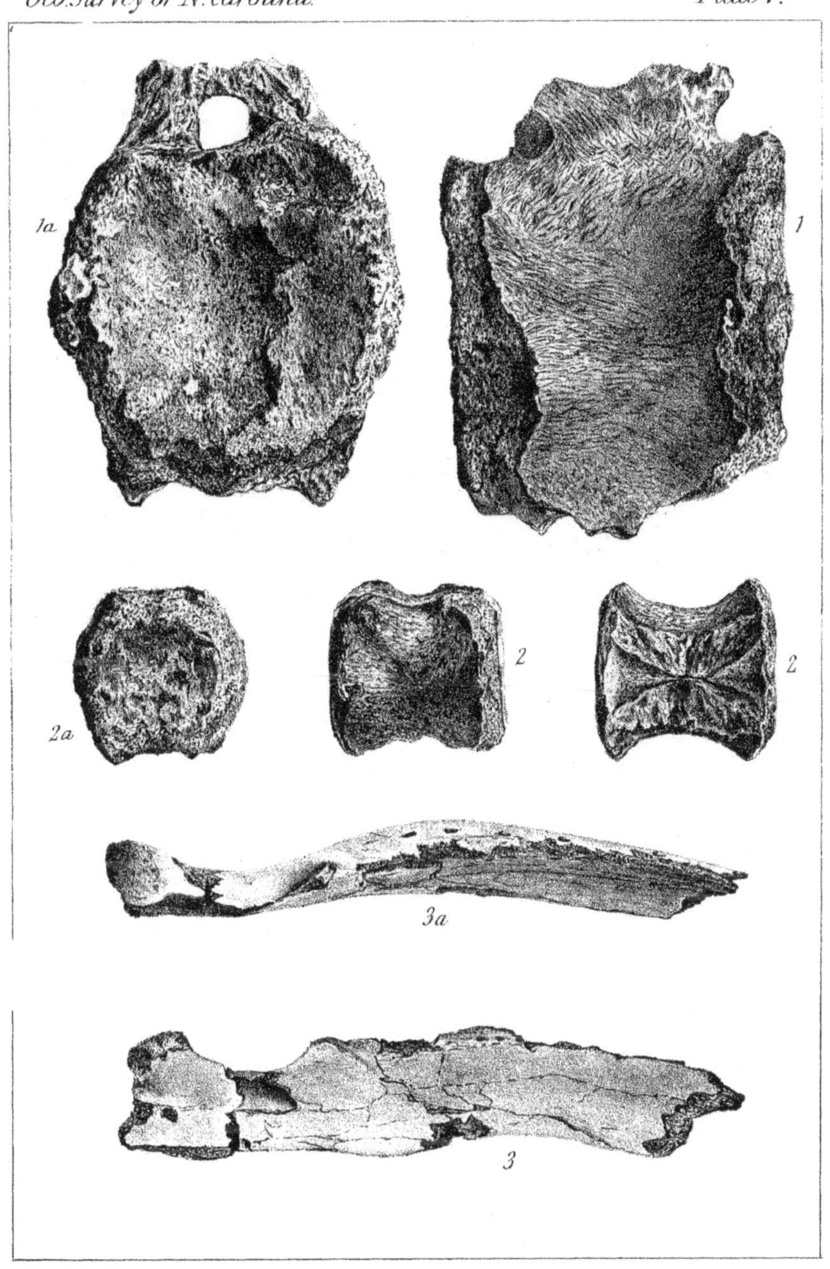

1-2. Hadrosaurus tripos. 3 Eschrichtius polyporus.

GEOL. SURVEY N. CAROLINA

PLATE VI.

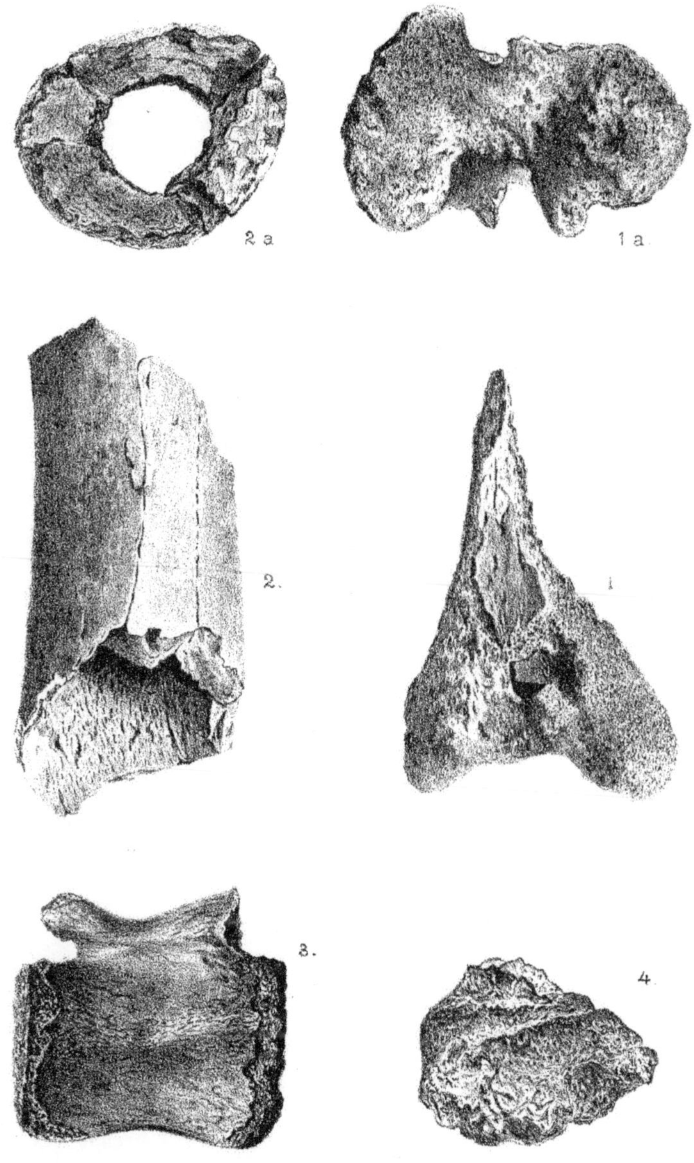

LONGACRE & CO. PHILA.

HYPSIBEMA CRASSICAUDA.

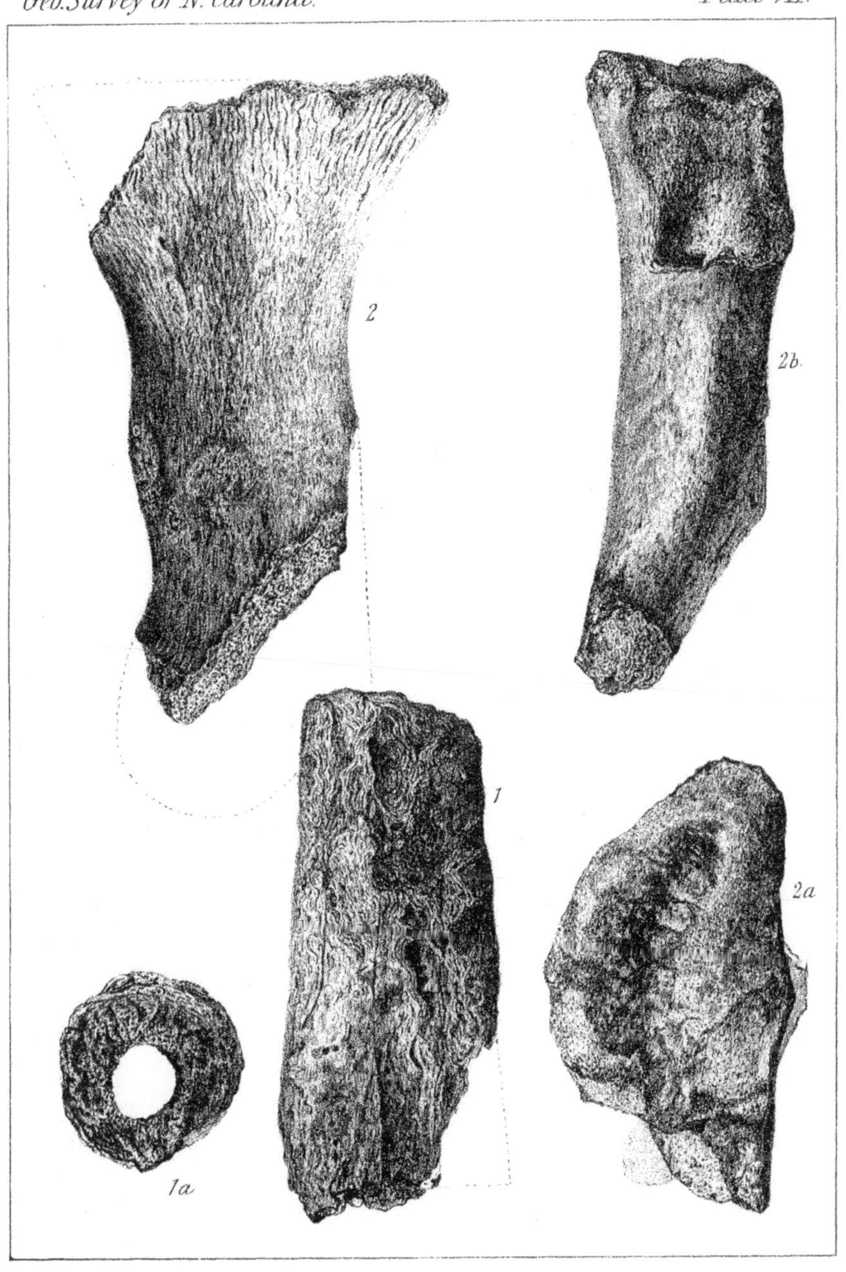

Hypsibema crassicauda.

Milton Keynes UK
Ingram Content Group UK Ltd.
UKHW012151270324
440282UK00003B/24